A2-Level
Mathematics

A2 Maths is seriously tricky — no question about that.
To do well, you're going to need to <u>revise properly</u> and <u>practise hard</u>.

This book has <u>thorough notes</u> on everything in modules C3, C4, S2 and M2.
It'll help you learn the stuff you need and take you <u>step-by-step</u> through loads of examples.

It's got practice questions... lots of them. For <u>every topic</u> there are warm-up and exam-style
questions. Plus there are <u>two full practice exams</u> at the end of each module.

And of course, we've done our best to make the whole thing vaguely entertaining for you.

Complete Revision and Practice
Exam Board: OCR MEI

YORK COLLEGE

163273

Contents

Contents

Contributors:
Andy Ballard, Mary Falkner, Paul Jordin, Sharon Keeley-Holden, Simon Little, Sam Norman, Ali Palin, Andy Park, David Ryan, Lyn Setchell, Caley Simpson, Jane Towle, Chris Worth, Jonathan Wray, Dawn Wright

Proofreaders:
Mona Allen, Alastair Duncombe, Allan Graham, Glenn Rogers

Published by CGP

ISBN: 978 1 84762 587 8

Groovy Website: www.cgpbooks.co.uk

Printed by Elanders Ltd, Newcastle upon Tyne.

Based on the classic CGP style created by Richard Parsons.

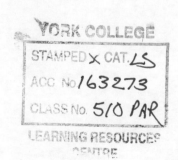

YORK COLLEGE
STAMPED X CAT. LS
ACC No 163273
CLASS No. 510 PAR
LEARNING RESOURCES
CENTRE

Photocopying — it's dull, grey and sometimes a bit naughty. Luckily, it's dead cheap, easy and quick to order more copies of this book from CGP — just call us on 0870 750 1242. Phew!

Text, design, layout and original illustrations © Coordination Group Publications Ltd. (CGP) 2011
All rights reserved.

Functions and Mappings

Welcome to the mystical world of A2 maths. Now let's kick things off right away with mappings and functions...

Values in the **Domain** are **Mapped** to values in the **Range**

1) A <u>mapping</u> is an <u>operation</u> that takes one number (the <u>object</u>) and <u>transforms</u> it into another (the <u>image</u>). E.g. 'multiply by 5', 'square root' and 'divide by 7' are all mappings.

2) The <u>set of numbers</u> you can <u>start</u> with is called the <u>domain</u>, and the <u>set of images</u> (i.e. all the numbers mapped to from numbers in the domain) is called the <u>range</u>. Mappings can be drawn as <u>diagrams</u> like the one to the right or as <u>graphs</u> (see below).

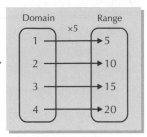

3) The domain and / or range will often be the set of <u>real numbers</u>, $\mathbb{R}$ (a real number is any <u>positive</u> or <u>negative</u> number (or <u>0</u>) including <u>fractions</u>, <u>decimals</u>, <u>surds</u>). If x can take <u>any real value</u>, it's usually written as $x \in \mathbb{R}$.

4) You might have to <u>work out</u> the range of a mapping from the domain you're given. For example, $y = x^2$, $x \in \mathbb{R}$ has the range $y \geq 0$, as the square of any real number is <u>positive</u> (or zero).

> Other common sets include the integers $\mathbb{Z}$, i.e. '...-3, -2, -1, 0, 1, 2, 3...' and the natural numbers $\mathbb{N}$, i.e. '1, 2, 3, ...'

A **Function** is a type of **Mapping**

1) Some mappings take <u>each</u> number in the <u>domain</u> to <u>only one</u> number in the <u>range</u>. These mappings are called <u>functions</u>. If a mapping takes a number from the domain to <u>more than one</u> number in the range (or if it isn't mapped to <u>any</u> number in the range), it's <u>not</u> a function. Functions (e.g. x^2) are usually written as $f(x) = x^2$ or $f : x \rightarrow x^2$.

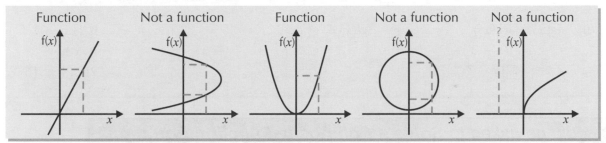

2) For the graphs above, the first and third are <u>functions</u> because each value of x is mapped to a <u>single value</u> of $f(x)$. The second and fourth <u>aren't</u> functions because the values of x are mapped to <u>two different values</u> of $f(x)$. The fifth also <u>isn't</u> a function, this time because $f(x)$ is <u>not defined</u> for $x < 0$.

3) Some mappings that <u>aren't</u> functions can be <u>turned into functions</u> by <u>restricting</u> their <u>domain</u>. For example, the mapping $y = \dfrac{1}{x - 1}$ for $x \in \mathbb{R}$ is not a function, because it's <u>not defined</u> at $x = 1$ (draw the graph if you're not convinced). But if you <u>change</u> the <u>domain</u> to $x > 1$, the mapping is now a function.

4) A function's definition might <u>state</u> the <u>domain</u> and '<u>codomain</u>' like this. ⟹ The codomain is a target set that all mapped elements must fall within. <u>But</u>... the actual range may be smaller, i.e. a subset of the codomain. In the example shown, the codomain is given as $\mathbb{R}$ but the actual range is $f(x) \geq -5$.

$$f : x \rightarrow x^2 - 5, \ f : \mathbb{R} \rightarrow \mathbb{R}$$
'codomain'. 'domain'

Functions can be **One-to-One** or **Many-to-One** and **Even** or **Odd**

1) A <u>one-to-one</u> function maps <u>one</u> element in the <u>domain</u> to <u>one</u> element in the <u>range</u> — e.g. $f(x) = 2x$, $x \in \mathbb{R}$ is one-to-one, as every x is mapped to a <u>unique</u> value in the range (the range is also $\mathbb{R}$). So only 3 in the domain is mapped to 6 in the range.

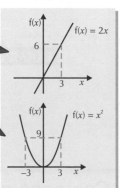

2) A <u>many-to-one</u> function maps <u>more than one</u> element in the <u>domain</u> to <u>one</u> element in the <u>range</u> (remember no element in the domain can map to more than one element in the range, otherwise it wouldn't be a function). $f(x) = x^2$, $x \in \mathbb{R}$ is many-to-one, as <u>two</u> elements in the domain map to the <u>same</u> element in the range — e.g. both 3 and –3 map to 9.

3) Some functions can be '<u>even</u>' or '<u>odd</u>'. <u>Even</u> functions are ones where <u>$f(x) = f(-x)$</u> — they're <u>symmetrical</u> about the <u>y-axis</u>. $\cos x$ and x^n (where n is even) are even functions.

4) For <u>odd</u> functions, <u>$f(x) = -f(-x)$</u> — the graph for $x > 0$ is <u>reflected</u> in the <u>y-axis</u> then <u>reflected again</u> in the <u>x-axis</u> to give the graph for $x < 0$. Odd functions have <u>rotational symmetry</u> about the <u>origin</u>. $\sin x$ and x^n (where n is odd) are examples of odd functions. Both $\sin x$ and $\cos x$ are also <u>periodic</u> — the pattern <u>repeats</u> at <u>regular intervals</u> (for both of these, the interval is 2π or 360°).

Composite Functions

You're not done with functions yet. Oh no. You need to know what happens if you put <u>two (or more) functions</u> together. There's only one way to find out...

Functions can be **Combined** to make a **Composite Function**

1) If you have two functions f and g, you can <u>combine</u> them (do one followed by the other) to make a new function. This is called a <u>composite function</u>.

2) Composite functions are written fg(x) — this means do g first, then f. If it helps, put <u>brackets</u> in until you get used to it, so fg(x) = f(g(x)). The <u>order</u> is really important — usually fg(x) ≠ gf(x).

3) If you get a composite function that's written f²(x), it means ff(x) — you do f <u>twice</u>.

> Composite functions made up of three or more functions work in exactly the same way.

> **EXAMPLE** For the functions $f(x) = 2x^3$ {$x \in \mathbb{R}$} and $g(x) = x - 3$ {$x \in \mathbb{R}$}, find:
>
> a) fg(4)   b) fg(0)   c) gf(0)   d) fg(x)   e) gf(x)   f) f²(x).
>
> a) $fg(4) = f(g(4))$
> $= f(4 - 3) = f(1)$
> $= 2 \times 1^3 = 2$
>
> b) $fg(0) = f(g(0))$
> $= f(0 - 3) = f(-3)$
> $= 2 \times (-3)^3 = 2 \times -27$
> $= -54$
>
> c) $gf(0) = g(f(0))$
> $= g(2 \times 0^3) = g(0)$
> $= 0 - 3 = -3$
>
> From parts b) and c) you can see that fg(x) ≠ gf(x).
>
> d) $fg(x) = f(g(x))$
> $= f(x - 3)$
> $= 2(x - 3)^3$
>
> e) $gf(x) = g(f(x))$
> $= g(2x^3)$
> $= 2x^3 - 3$
>
> f) $f^2(x) = f(f(x))$
> $= f(2x^3)$
> $= 2(2x^3)^3 = 16x^9$

You could be asked to **Solve** a **Composite Function Equation**

If you're asked to <u>solve</u> an equation such as fg(x) = 8, the best way to do it is to <u>work out</u> what fg(x) is, then <u>rearrange</u> fg(x) = 8 to make <u>x</u> the subject.

> **EXAMPLE** For the functions $f(x) = \sqrt{x}$ with domain {$x \geq 0$} and $g(x) = \frac{1}{x - 1}$ with domain {$x > 1$}, solve the equation fg(x) = ½. Also, state the range of fg(x).
>
> First, find fg(x): $fg(x) = f\left(\frac{1}{x - 1}\right) = \sqrt{\frac{1}{x - 1}} = \frac{1}{\sqrt{x - 1}}$
>
> So $\frac{1}{\sqrt{x - 1}} = \frac{1}{2}$
>
> Rearrange this equation to find x:
> $\frac{1}{\sqrt{x - 1}} = \frac{1}{2} \Rightarrow \sqrt{x - 1} = 2 \Rightarrow x - 1 = 4 \Rightarrow x = 5$
>
> To find the range, it's often helpful to draw the graph of fg(x):
>
>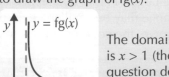
>
> > Be careful with the domains and ranges of composite functions.
>
> The domain of fg(x) is x > 1 (though the question doesn't ask for this) and the range is fg(x) > 0.

> **EXAMPLE** For the functions $f(x) = 2x + 1$ {$x \in \mathbb{R}$} and $g(x) = x^2$ {$x \in \mathbb{R}$}, solve gf(x) = 16.
>
> Find gf(x): $gf(x) = g(2x + 1) = (2x + 1)^2$.
>
> Now solve gf(x) = 16: $(2x + 1)^2 = 16 \Rightarrow 4x^2 + 4x + 1 = 16$
> $\Rightarrow 4x^2 + 4x - 15 = 0$
> $\Rightarrow (2x - 3)(2x + 5) = 0$ so $x = \frac{3}{2}$ or $x = -\frac{5}{2}$

Compose a concerto for f(x) and orchestra...

The most important thing to remember on this page is the order you do the functions in — for fg(x) you always do g first as g is next to x. It's like getting dressed — you wouldn't put your shoes on before your socks, as your socks go next to your feet.

Inverse Functions

Just when you'd got your head around <u>functions</u>, <u>ranges</u>, <u>domains</u> and <u>composite functions</u>, they go and turn it all back to front by introducing <u>inverses</u>.

Only **One-to-One Functions** have **Inverses**

1) An <u>inverse function</u> does the <u>opposite</u> to the function. So if the function was '+ 1', the inverse would be '− 1', if the function was '× 2', the inverse would be '÷ 2' etc. The inverse for a function f(x) is written $f^{-1}(x)$.

2) An inverse function <u>maps</u> an element in the <u>range</u> to an element in the <u>domain</u> — the opposite of a function. This means that only <u>one-to-one functions</u> have inverses, as the inverse of a many-to-one function would be one-to-many, which isn't a function (see p.1).

3) For <u>any</u> inverse $f^{-1}(x)$,

Doing the function and then the inverse... $$f^{-1}f(x) = x = ff^{-1}(x)$$ ...is the same as doing the inverse then doing the function — both just give you x.

4) The <u>domain</u> of the <u>inverse</u> is the <u>range</u> of the <u>function</u>, and the <u>range</u> of the <u>inverse</u> is the <u>domain</u> of the <u>function</u>.

> **EXAMPLE** The function f(x) = x + 7 with domain x ≥ 0 and range f(x) ≥ 7 is one-to-one, so it has an inverse.
>
> The inverse of + 7 is − 7, so $f^{-1}(x) = x - 7$. $f^{-1}(x)$ has domain x ≥ 7 and range $f^{-1}(x)$ ≥ 0.

Work out the **Inverse** using **Algebra**

For <u>simple</u> functions (like the one in the example above), it's easy to work out what the inverse is just by <u>looking</u> at it. But for more <u>complex</u> functions, you need to <u>rearrange</u> the original function to <u>change</u> the <u>subject</u>.

> ### Finding the Inverse
> 1) **Replace f(x) with _y_ to get an equation for _y_ in terms of _x_.**
> 2) **Rearrange the equation to make _x_ the subject.**
> 3) **Replace x with $f^{-1}(x)$ and y with x — this is the inverse function.**
> 4) **Swap round the domain and range of the function.**

> **EXAMPLE** Find the inverse of the function f(x) = 3x² + 2 with domain x ≥ 0, and state its domain and range.
>
> 1) First, replace f(x) with y: y = 3x² + 2.
>
> 2) Rearrange the equation to make x the subject:
> $$y - 2 = 3x^2 \Rightarrow \frac{y-2}{3} = x^2 \Rightarrow \sqrt{\frac{y-2}{3}} = x$$
> x ≥ 0 so you don't need the negative square root.
>
> _It's easier to work with y than f(x)._
>
> 3) Replace x with $f^{-1}(x)$ and y with x:
> $$f^{-1}(x) = \sqrt{\frac{x-2}{3}}$$
>
> 4) Swap the domain and range: the range of f(x) is f(x) ≥ 2, so $f^{-1}(x)$ has domain x ≥ 2 and range $f^{-1}(x)$ ≥ 0.

You might have to **Draw the Graph** of the Inverse

The inverse of a function is its <u>reflection</u> in the line <u>y = x</u>.

> **EXAMPLE** Sketch the graph of the inverse of the function f(x) = x² − 8 with domain x ≥ 0.
>
> It's easy to see what the domains and ranges are from the graph — f(x) has domain x ≥ 0 and range f(x) ≥ −8, and $f^{-1}(x)$ has domain x ≥ −8 and range $f^{-1}(x)$ ≥ 0.
>
> 1. Draw on f(x).
> 2. Then draw y = x.
> 3. Finally, reflect f(x) in y = x to get $f^{-1}(x)$.
> The inverse function is $f^{-1}(x) = \sqrt{x + 8}$.

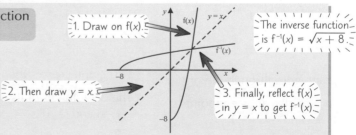

Line y = x on the wall — who is the fairest of them all...

I think I've got the hang of this inverse stuff now — so the inverse of walking to the shops and buying some milk would be taking the money out the till, putting the milk back on the shelf, leaving the shop and walking home backwards. Sorted.

Inverse Trig Functions

Trig functions have inverses too — you need to know what they are, and what their graphs look like...

Arcsin, Arccos and Arctan are the Inverses of Sin, Cos and Tan

On the previous page you saw that some functions have inverses, which reverse the effect of the function. The trig functions have inverses too.

ARCSINE is the inverse of sine. You might see it written as arcsin or sin⁻¹.

ARCCOSINE is the inverse of cosine. You might see it written as arccos or cos⁻¹.

ARCTANGENT is the inverse of tangent. You might see it written as arctan or tan⁻¹.

The inverse trig functions reverse the effect of sin, cos and tan.
For example, sin 30° = 0.5, so arcsin 0.5 = 30°.

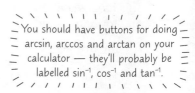
You should have buttons for doing arcsin, arccos and arctan on your calculator — they'll probably be labelled sin⁻¹, cos⁻¹ and tan⁻¹.

To Graph the Inverse Functions you need to Restrict their Domains

1) The functions sine, cosine and tangent are NOT one-to-one mappings (see p.1) — lots of values of x give the same value for sin x, cos x or tan x. For example: cos 0 = cos 2π = cos 4π = 1, and tan 0 = tan π = tan 2π = 0.

2) Only one-to-one functions have inverses, so for the inverse to be a function you have to restrict the domain of the trig function to make it one-to-one (see graphs below). This means that you only plot the graphs between certain x values, so that for each x value, you end up with one y value.

3) As the graphs are inverse functions, they're also reflections of the sin, cos and tan functions in the line $y = x$.

ARCSINE

For arcsin, limit the domain of sin x to $-\frac{\pi}{2} \le x \le \frac{\pi}{2}$ (the range of sin x is still $-1 \le \sin x \le 1$).

This means the domain of arcsin x is $-1 \le x \le 1$ and its range is $-\frac{\pi}{2} \le \arcsin x \le \frac{\pi}{2}$.

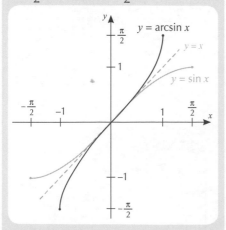

This graph goes through the origin.

The coordinates of its endpoints are $(1, \frac{\pi}{2})$ and $(-1, -\frac{\pi}{2})$.

ARCCOSINE

For arccos, limit the domain of cos x to $0 \le x \le \pi$ (the range of cos x is still $-1 \le \cos x \le 1$).

This means the domain of arccos x is $-1 \le x \le 1$ and its range is $0 \le \arccos x \le \pi$.

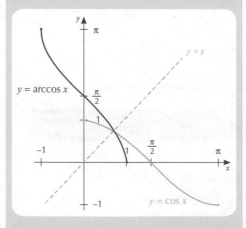

This graph crosses the y-axis at $(0, \frac{\pi}{2})$.

The coordinates of its endpoints are $(-1, \pi)$ and $(1, 0)$.

ARCTANGENT

For arctan, limit the domain of tan x to $-\frac{\pi}{2} < x < \frac{\pi}{2}$ (this doesn't limit the range of tan x).

This means that the domain of arctan x isn't limited, but the range of arctan x is limited to $-\frac{\pi}{2} < \arctan x < \frac{\pi}{2}$.

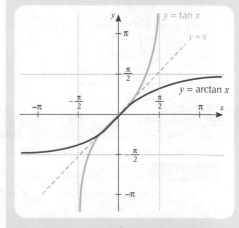

This graph goes through the origin.

It has asymptotes at $y = \frac{\pi}{2}$ and $y = -\frac{\pi}{2}$.

So applying the inverse function reverses everything...

It's really important that you can recognise the graphs of the inverse trig functions — you need to know what shape they are, what restricted domains you need to use to draw them, and any significant points, like where they end or where they cross the axes. You can check the graph by reflecting the curve in the line $y = x$ and seeing if you get the trig function you want.

Modulus

The <u>modulus</u> of a number is really useful if you don't care whether something's positive or negative — like if you were finding the difference between two numbers (e.g. 7 and 12). It doesn't matter which way round you do the subtraction (i.e. 12 − 7 or 7 − 12) — the difference between them is still 5.

Modulus is the Size of a number

1) The <u>modulus</u> of a number is its <u>size</u> — it doesn't matter if it's <u>positive</u> or <u>negative</u>. So for a <u>positive</u> number, the modulus is just the <u>same</u> as the number itself, but for a <u>negative</u> number, the modulus is its <u>positive value</u>. For example, the modulus of 8 is 8, and the modulus of −8 is also 8.

The modulus is sometimes called the absolute value.

2) The modulus of a number, x, is written $|x|$. So the example above would be written $|8| = |-8| = 8$.

3) In <u>general</u> terms, for $x \geq 0$, $|x| = x$ and for $x < 0$, $|x| = -x$.

4) <u>Functions</u> can have a modulus too — the modulus of a function $f(x)$ is its <u>positive value</u>. Suppose $f(x) = -6$, then $|f(x)| = 6$. In general terms,

$$|f(x)| = f(x) \text{ when } f(x) \geq 0 \text{ and}$$
$$|f(x)| = -f(x) \text{ when } f(x) < 0.$$

5) If the modulus is <u>inside</u> the brackets in the form $f(|x|)$, then you make the x-value positive <u>before</u> applying the function. So $f(|-2|) = f(2)$.

You might come across a modulus in an Equation or an Inequality

You'll see how to <u>solve</u> modulus equations on the next page, but first there are some useful <u>relations</u> you should know.

1) If you have $|a| = |b|$, then $a^2 = b^2$ (as $-a$ and a are the <u>same</u> when squared).

$|x| < 5$ means that $x < 5$ and $-x < 5$, and $-x < 5$ is the same as $x > -5$. You put the two inequalities together to get $-5 < x < 5$.

2) <u>Inequalities</u> that have a modulus in them can be really <u>nasty</u> — unfortunately you can't just leave the modulus in there. $|x| < 5$ means that $-5 < x < 5$.

3) Using this, you can <u>rearrange</u> more <u>complicated</u> inequalities like $|x - a| \leq b$. From the method above, this means that $-b \leq x - a \leq b$, so <u>adding a</u> to <u>each bit</u> of the inequality gives $a - b \leq x \leq a + b$.

> **EXAMPLE** Solve $|x - 4| < 7$.
> As $|x - 4| < 7$, this means that $-7 < x - 4 < 7$. Adding 4 to each bit gives $-3 < x < 11$.

The Graphs of |f(x)| and f(|x|) are Different

You'll probably have to draw the <u>graph</u> of a modulus function — and there are <u>two different types</u>.

1) For the graph of $y = |f(x)|$, any <u>negative</u> values of $f(x)$ are made <u>positive</u> by <u>reflecting</u> them in the <u>x-axis</u>. This <u>restricts</u> the <u>range</u> of the modulus function to $|f(x)| \geq 0$ (or some subset <u>within</u> $|f(x)| \geq 0$, e.g. $|f(x)| \geq 1$).

2) For the graph of $y = f(|x|)$, the <u>negative</u> x-values produce the <u>same result</u> as the corresponding <u>positive</u> x-values. So the graph of $f(x)$ for $x \geq 0$ is <u>reflected</u> in the <u>y-axis</u> for the negative x-values.

3) The easiest way to draw these graphs is to draw $f(x)$ (<u>ignoring</u> the modulus for now), then <u>reflect</u> it in the <u>appropriate axis</u>. This will probably make more sense when you've had a look at a couple of <u>examples</u>:

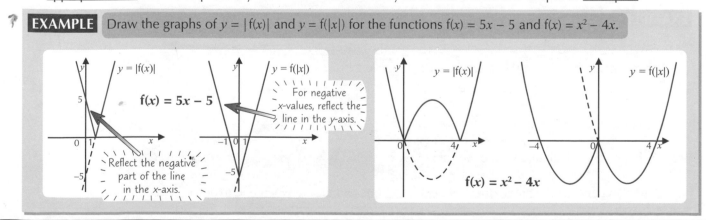

EXAMPLE Draw the graphs of $y = |f(x)|$ and $y = f(|x|)$ for the functions $f(x) = 5x - 5$ and $f(x) = x^2 - 4x$.

Modulus built the city of Mode...

You might have to draw modulus graphs for functions like $f(x) = ax + b$ from scratch. You could be asked for trig graphs and exponentials too. For harder graphs, you'll often be given a graph which you can use as a starting point for the modulus.

Modulus

An exam question might ask you to <u>solve</u> an equation like '$|f(x)| = n$' (for a constant n) or '$|f(x)| = g(x)$' for a function g. I admit, it would be more exciting to solve a <u>crime</u>, but I'm afraid modulus functions must come first...

Solving modulus functions usually produces **More Than One** solution

Here comes the method for solving '$|f(x)| = n$'. Solving '$|f(x)| = g(x)$' is <u>exactly the same</u> — just replace n with g(x).

Solving Modulus Equations of the form $|f(x)| = n$

1) First, <u>sketch</u> the functions $y = |f(x)|$ and $y = n$, on the <u>same axes</u>. ◄——— The <u>solutions</u> you're trying to find are where they <u>intersect</u>.

2) From the graph, work out the <u>ranges of x</u> for which <u>$f(x) \geq 0$</u> and <u>$f(x) < 0$</u>:
   E.g. $f(x) \geq 0$ for $x \leq a$ or $x \geq b$ and $f(x) < 0$ for $a < x < b$ ◄——— These ranges should 'fit together' to cover all possible x values.

3) Use this to write <u>two new equations</u>, one true for each range of x...
   (1) $f(x) = n$ for $x \leq a$ or $x \geq b$ ◄——— The original equation '$|f(x)| = n$' becomes '$f(x) = n$' in the range where $f(x) \geq 0$...
   (2) $-f(x) = n$ for $a < x < b$ ◄——— ...and it becomes '$-f(x) = n$' in the range where $f(x) < 0$.

4) Now just <u>solve each equation</u> and check that any solutions are <u>valid</u>
   — get rid of any solutions <u>outside the range</u> of x you've got for that equation.

5) Look at the graph and <u>check</u> that your solutions look right.

Sketch the Graph to see **How Many Solutions** there are

EXAMPLE   Solve $|x^2 - 9| = 7$.

1) First off, <u>sketch the graphs</u> of $y = |x^2 - 9|$ and $y = 7$. ——————►
   They cross at 4 different points, so there should be <u>4 solutions</u>.

2) Now find out <u>where $f(x) \geq 0$ and $f(x) < 0$</u>:
   $x^2 - 9 \geq 0$ for $x \leq -3$ or $x \geq 3$, and $x^2 - 9 < 0$ for $-3 < x < 3$

   $x^2 - 9 = (x + 3)(x - 3)$, so curve crosses x-axis at 3 and −3.

3) Form two equations for the different ranges of x:
   (1) $x^2 - 9 = 7$ for $x \leq -3$ or $x \geq 3$
   (2) $-(x^2 - 9) = 7$ for $-3 < x < 3$

4) Solving (1) gives: $x^2 = 16 \Rightarrow$ $x = 4, x = -4$
   Check they're valid: $x = -4$ is in '$x \leq -3$' and $x = 4$ is in '$x \geq 3$' — so they're both valid.

   Solving (2) gives: $x^2 - 2 = 0 \Rightarrow x^2 = 2$ so $x = \sqrt{2}, x = -\sqrt{2}$.
   Check they're valid: $x = \sqrt{2}$ and $x = -\sqrt{2}$ are both within $-3 < x < 3$ — so they're also both valid.

5) Check back against <u>the graphs</u> — we've found <u>four solutions</u> and they're <u>in the right places</u>. Nice.

EXAMPLE   Solve $|x^2 - 2x - 3| = 1 - x$.

1) <u>Sketch</u> $y = |x^2 - 2x - 3|$ and $y = 1 - x$. The graphs <u>cross twice</u>. ——————►

2) Looking at <u>where $f(x) \geq 0$</u> and <u>where $f(x) < 0$</u> gives...

   $x^2 - 2x - 3 = (x + 1)(x - 3)$, so it crosses axis at −1 and 3.

3) (1) $x^2 - 2x - 3 = 1 - x$ for $x \leq -1$ or $x \geq 3$
   (2) $-(x^2 - 2x - 3) = 1 - x$ for $-1 < x < 3$.

4) <u>Solving (1)</u> using the quadratic formula gives $x = 2.562$, $x = -1.562$.
   $x \leq -1$ or $x \geq 3$, so this solution is not valid... ➚   ...but this one is.
   <u>Solving (2)</u> using the quadratic formula gives $x = 3.562$, $x = -0.562$.
   $-1 < x < 3$, so this solution is not valid... ➚   ...but this one is.

5) Checking against the <u>graph</u>, there are <u>two solutions</u> and they're <u>where we expected</u>. El coolio.

How very interesting...

So if the effect of the modulus is to make a negative positive, I guess that means that |exam followed by detention followed by getting splashed by a car on the way home| = sleep-in followed by picnic followed by date with Hugh Jackman. I wish.

Transformations of Graphs

Back at AS-level, you came across <u>transformations</u> of graphs — vertical and horizontal <u>translations</u>, <u>stretches</u> and <u>reflections</u>. You also saw the same transformations on <u>trig</u> graphs. As if that wasn't enough for you, you now need to be able to do <u>combinations</u> of transformations — more than one applied to the same graph.

There are **Four** main **Transformations**

The transformations you met in C1 and C2 are <u>translations</u> (adding things — a vertical or horizontal <u>shift</u>), <u>stretches</u> or <u>squeezes</u> (either vertical or horizontal) and <u>reflections</u> in the x- or y- axis. Here's a quick reminder of what each one does:

$y = f(x + c)$

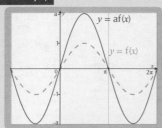

$f(x + c)$ is $f(x)$ <u>translated c units in the $-$ve x-direction</u> (i.e. left), and $f(x - c)$ is $f(x)$ <u>translated c units in the $+$ve x-direction</u> (i.e. right).

$y = f(x) + c$

$f(x) + c$ is $f(x)$ <u>translated c units in the $+$ve y-direction</u> (i.e. upwards), and $f(x) - c$ is $f(x)$ <u>translated c units in the $-$ve y-direction</u> (i.e. downwards).

Translations might be given using a translation vector $\begin{pmatrix} a \\ b \end{pmatrix}$, where a is the horizontal shift and b is the vertical shift.

All these graphs use $f(x) = \sin x$.

$y = af(x)$

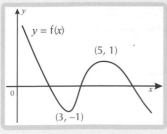

If $a > 1$, the graph of $af(x)$ is $f(x)$ <u>stretched vertically</u> by a factor of a.

If $0 < a < 1$, the graph is <u>squashed</u>.

And if $a < 0$, the graph is also <u>reflected</u> in the x-axis.

$y = f(ax)$

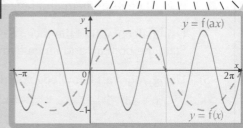

If $a > 1$, the graph of $f(ax)$ is $f(x)$ <u>squashed horizontally</u> by a factor of a.

If $0 < a < 1$, the graph is <u>stretched horizontally</u>.

And if $a < 0$, the graph is also <u>reflected</u> in the y-axis.

Remember that a <u>squash</u> by a factor of a is really a <u>stretch</u> by a factor of $\frac{1}{a}$.

Do **Combinations** of Transformations **One at a Time**

<u>Combinations</u> of transformations can look a bit tricky, but if you take them <u>one step</u> at a time they're not too bad. Don't try and do <u>all</u> the transformations at once — break it up into <u>separate bits</u> (as above) and draw a <u>graph</u> for <u>each stage</u>.

> **EXAMPLE** The graph shows the function $y = f(x)$. Draw the graph of $y = 3f(x + 2)$, showing the coordinates of the turning points.

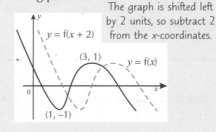

Make sure you do the transformations the right way round — you should do the bit in the brackets first.

Don't try to do everything at once. First draw the graph of $y = f(x + 2)$ and work out the coordinates of the turning points.

The graph is shifted left by 2 units, so subtract 2 from the x-coordinates.

Now use your graph of $y = f(x + 2)$ to draw the graph of $y = 3f(x + 2)$.

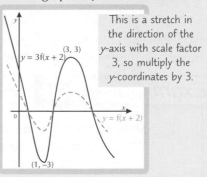

This is a stretch in the direction of the y-axis with scale factor 3, so multiply the y-coordinates by 3.

Tea and cake — the perfect combination...

Working out coordinates can be a bit tricky. The easiest way to do it is to work out what you're doing to the graph, then think about what that does to each point. Have a look at your transformed graph and check that the new coordinates make sense.

C3 Section 1 — Practice Questions

Well, that's the first section over and done with, and what better way to round it off than with some <u>lovely questions</u>. Have a go at these warm-up questions to get you <u>in the mood</u>.

Warm-up Questions

1) For the following mappings, state the range and say whether or not the mapping is a function. If not, explain why, and if so, say whether the function is one-to-one or many-to-one.

   a) $f(x) = x^2 - 16$, $x \geq 0$

   b) $f(x) = x^2 - 7x + 10$, $x \in \mathbb{R}$

   c) $f(x) = \sqrt{x}$, $x \in \mathbb{R}$

   d) $f(x) = \dfrac{1}{x-2}$, $x \in \mathbb{R}$

2) For each pair of functions f and g, find fg(2), gf(1) and fg(x).

   a) $f(x) = \dfrac{3}{x}$, $x > 0$ and $g(x) = 2x + 3$, $x \in \mathbb{R}$

   b) $f(x) = 3x^2$, $x \geq 0$ and $g(x) = x + 4$, $x \in \mathbb{R}$

3) A one-to-one function f has domain $x \in \mathbb{R}$ and range $f(x) \geq 3$. Does this function have an inverse? If so, state its domain and range.

4) Using algebra, find the inverse of the function $f(x) = \sqrt{2x - 4}$, $x \geq 2$. State the domain and range of the inverse.

5) Using your vast knowledge of trig values for common angles, evaluate these (in radians, between 0 and $\frac{\pi}{2}$):

   a) $\sin^{-1}\dfrac{1}{\sqrt{2}}$ b) $\cos^{-1}0$ c) $\tan^{-1}\sqrt{3}$

6) Sketch the graphs of arcsine, arccosine and arctangent. Make sure you show their domains and ranges.

7) For the function $f(x) = 2x - 1$ $\{x \in \mathbb{R}\}$, sketch the graphs of:

   a) $|f(x)|$

   b) $f(|x|)$

8) Use your graph from part 7) a) to help you solve the equation $|2x - 1| = 5$.

9) The function $y = f(x)$ is shown on the graph on the right. Draw the graph of $y = 2f(x) + 1$.

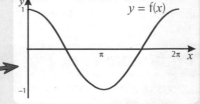

10) For the following functions, say whether they are odd or even and also decide if they're periodic:

   a) $y = x^2$

   b) $y = \tan x$

   c) $y = x^3$

Now that you're in the <u>functions zone</u> (not to be confused with the twilight zone or the phantom zone), I think you're ready to have a go at some <u>exam-style questions</u>.

Exam Questions

1   Show that $f(x) = x\sin x$ is an even function using algebra.
What does this tell you about the graph of $f(x)$?

(3 marks)

2   In words, describe what happens to the curve $y = x^3$ to transform it into the curve $y = 2(x - 1)^3 + 4$.

(6 marks)

C3 Section 1 — Practice Questions

For these questions, arm yourself with a <u>mosquito net</u>, an <u>invisibility cloak</u> and some <u>A2 Maths knowledge</u> and you'll be fine.

3   For the functions f and g, where

$$f(x) = 2^x,\ x \in \mathbb{R} \qquad \text{and} \qquad g(x) = \sqrt{3x - 2},\ x \geq \tfrac{2}{3}, \quad \text{find:}$$

a)   fg(6)

(2 marks)

b)   gf(2)

(2 marks)

c)   (i) $g^{-1}(x)$

(2 marks)

(ii) $fg^{-1}(x)$

(2 marks)

4   The sketch shows the graph of $y = \arccos x$, where y is in radians. *A* and *B* are the end points of the graph.

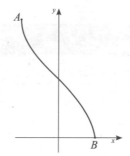

a)   Write down the coordinates of *A* and *B*.

(2 marks)

b)   Express x in terms of y.

(1 mark)

c)   Solve, to 3 significant figures, the equation $\arccos x = 2$ for the interval shown on the graph.

(2 marks)

5   The function $f(x)$ is defined as follows: $f : x \to \dfrac{1}{x + 5}$, domain $x > -5$.

a)   State the range of $f(x)$.

(1 mark)

b)   Find the inverse function, $f^{-1}(x)$, and state its domain and range.

(5 marks)

c)   On the same axes, sketch the graphs of $y = f(x)$ and $y = f^{-1}(x)$.

(3 marks)

6   The graph below shows the curve $y = f(x)$, and the intercepts of the curve with the x- and y-axes.

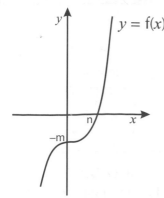

Sketch the graphs of the following transformations on separate axes, clearly labelling the points of intersection with the x- and y-axes in terms of m and n.

a) $y = |f(x)|$

(2 marks)

b) $y = -3f(x)$

(2 marks)

c) $y = f(|x|)$

(2 marks)

e^x, ln x and Graphs

This section is useful 'cos lots of 'real' things increase (or decrease) exponentially — <u>student debts</u>, <u>horrible diseases</u>...
We'll start off with a <u>quick recap</u> of some things from C2, then I'll introduce you to some <u>very special functions</u>...

Graphs of $y = a^x$ and $y = a^{-x}$ show Exponential Growth and Decay

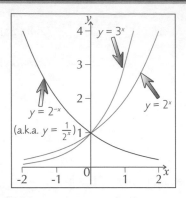

You should be familiar with these graphs from C2.
The main feature of <u>exponential growth / decay</u> is that the <u>rate of increase / decrease</u> of the function is <u>proportional to the function itself</u>.
So if we plotted the <u>gradient</u> of $y = a^x$, it would have the <u>same shape</u> as $y = a^x$.

The main points to remember for <u>$y = a^x$</u> functions (a > 0) are:

1) As $x \to \infty$, $y \to \infty$ (and the gradient also $\to \infty$).

2) As $x \to -\infty$, $y \to 0$ (which means that a^x is <u>always positive</u>).

3) When $x = 0$, $y = 1$ (so they all pass through <u>(0, 1)</u> on the y-axis).

$\to$ means 'tends to'.

The *Gradient* of the *Exponential Function* $y = e^x$ is e^x

There is a value of 'a' for which the <u>gradient</u> of $y = a^x$ is <u>exactly the same as a^x</u>. That value is known as <u>e</u>, an <u>irrational number</u> around <u>2.7183</u> (it's stored in your calculator just like π). Because e is just a number, the graph of <u>$y = e^x$</u> has all the properties of <u>$y = a^x$</u>...

1) <u>$y = e^x$</u> cuts the y-axis at <u>(0, 1)</u>.

2) As $x \to \infty$, $e^x \to \infty$ and as $x \to \underline{-\infty}$, $e^x \to \underline{0}$.

3) $y = e^x$ <u>does not exist</u> for $y \leq 0$ (i.e. e^x <u>can't be zero or –ve</u>).

The <u>disturbingly interesting</u> fact that e^x doesn't change when you differentiate is used lots in the differentiation section — see p.18.

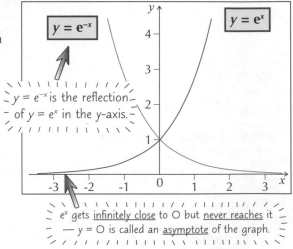

$y = e^{-x}$ is the reflection of $y = e^x$ in the y-axis.

e^x gets <u>infinitely close</u> to O but <u>never reaches</u> it — $y = O$ is called an <u>asymptote</u> of the graph.

ln x is the *Inverse Function* of e^x

<u>ln x</u> (also known as <u>$\log_e x$</u>, or '<u>natural log</u>'*) is the <u>inverse function</u> of <u>e^x</u> (see p.3):

1) $y = \ln x$ is the <u>reflection</u> of $y = e^x$ in the line <u>$y = x$</u>.

2) It cuts the x-axis at <u>(1, 0)</u> (so <u>ln 1 = 0</u>).

3) As $x \to \infty$, $\ln x \to \underline{\infty}$ (but 'slowly'), and as $x \to \underline{0}$, $\ln x \to \underline{-\infty}$.

4) ln x <u>does not exist</u> for $x \leq 0$ (i.e. x <u>can't be zero or negative</u>).

Because ln x is a logarithmic function and the inverse of e^x, we get these juicy <u>formulas</u> and <u>log laws</u>...

$$e^{\ln x} = x$$
$$\ln (e^x) = x$$

i.e. doing one function then the other to x takes you back to x.

$y = \ln x$ has an <u>asymptote</u> at $x = O$.

'Log laws' for ln x

$$\ln x + \ln y = \ln (xy)$$
$$\ln x - \ln y = \ln \left(\frac{x}{y}\right)$$
$$\ln x^k = k \ln x$$

These are the same old log laws you saw in C2, applied to ln x.

These formulas are <u>extremely useful</u> for dealing with <u>equations</u> containing '<u>e^x</u>'s or '<u>ln x</u>'s, as you'll see on the next page...

*Certified organic

'e' is for <u>exponential</u>, but also for <u>easy</u> exam questions — no <u>excuses</u>...

When it comes to logs, I prefer the natural look. Remember the limits of $y = e^x$, $y = e^{-x}$ and $y = \ln x$ from the graphs, and polish up your skills with the log laws from C2, and the rest of the section should be a breeze. Naturally.

Using e^x and ln x — Solving Equations

Now what makes e^x and ln x so clever is that you can use one to <u>cancel out</u> the other, which comes in <u>very handy</u> for <u>solving equations</u>. You'll need all those fruity <u>formulas</u> from the previous page to get through this one...

Use the *Inverse Functions* and *Log Laws* to *Solve Equations*

> **EXAMPLES** a) Solve the equation $2\ln x - \ln 2x = 6$, giving your answer as an <u>exact value</u> of x.
>
> 1) Use the <u>log laws</u> (see previous page) to simplify $2\ln x - \ln 2x = 6$ into:
> $\ln x^2 - \ln 2x = 6 \Rightarrow \ln(x^2 \div 2x) = 6 \Rightarrow \ln(\frac{x}{2}) = 6$.
>
> *Using $e^{\ln x} = x$ from the last page*
>
> 2) Now apply the <u>inverse function</u> e^x to both sides — this will remove the $\ln(\frac{x}{2})$:
> $e^{\ln(\frac{x}{2})} = e^6 \Rightarrow \frac{x}{2} = e^6 \Rightarrow x = 2e^6$. And since we need an <u>exact</u> value, leave it as that.
>
> b) Find the <u>exact solutions</u> of the equation $e^x + 5e^{-x} = 6$.
>
> 1) A big clue here is that you're asked for <u>more than one</u> solution. Think <u>quadratics</u>...
>
> 2) Multiply each part of the equation by e^x to get rid of that e^{-x}:
> $e^x + 5e^{-x} = 6 \Rightarrow e^{2x} + 5 = 6e^x \Rightarrow e^{2x} - 6e^x + 5 = 0$.
>
> *Basic power laws — $(e^x)^2 = e^{2x}$ and $e^{-x} \times e^x = e^0 = 1$.*
>
> 3) It starts to look a bit nicer if you <u>substitute</u> y for e^x: $y^2 - 6y + 5 = 0$.
>
> 4) Since we're asked for exact solutions, it will probably <u>factorise</u>:
> $(y - 1)(y - 5) = 0 \Rightarrow y = 1$ and $y = 5$.
>
> *Using $\ln e^x = x$*
>
> 5) Put e^x back in: $e^x = 1$ and $e^x = 5$.
>
> 6) Take 'ln' of both sides to solve: $\ln e^x = \ln 1 \Rightarrow x = \ln 1 = 0$ and $\ln e^x = \ln 5 \Rightarrow x = \ln 5$.

Real-Life functions look like $y = e^{ax+b} + c$ and $y = \ln(ax + b)$

You should be familiar with the shape of the bog-standard exponential graphs, but most exponential functions will be <u>transformed</u> in some way. You need to know how the <u>key features</u> of the graph change depending on the function.

> **EXAMPLES** Sketch the <u>graphs</u> of the following functions, labelling any <u>key points</u> and stating the value of '<u>a</u>':
> a) $y = e^{-7x+1} - 5$ $(x \in \mathbb{R}, y > a)$ and b) $y = \ln(2x + 4)$ $(x \in \mathbb{R}, x > a)$.
>
> $y = e^{-7x+1} - 5$
>
> 1) 'Key points' usually means where the graph crosses the axes, i.e. where x and y are 0:
> When $x = 0$, $y = e^1 - 5 = \underline{-2.28}$. When $y = 0$, $e^{-7x+1} = 5 \Rightarrow -7x + 1 = \ln 5 \Rightarrow x = \underline{-0.0871}$.
>
>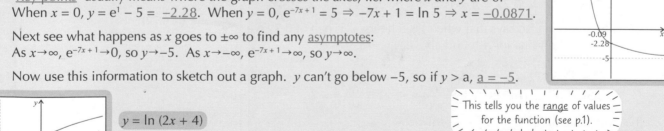
>
> 2) Next see what happens as x goes to $\pm\infty$ to find any <u>asymptotes</u>:
> As $x \to \infty$, $e^{-7x+1} \to 0$, so $y \to -5$. As $x \to -\infty$, $e^{-7x+1} \to \infty$, so $y \to \infty$.
>
> 3) Now use this information to sketch out a graph. y can't go below -5, so if $y > a$, $\underline{a = -5}$.
>
> *This tells you the <u>range</u> of values for the function (see p.1).*
>
>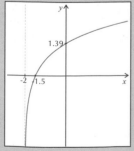
>
> $y = \ln(2x + 4)$
>
> 1) First the intercepts: When $x = 0$, $y = \ln 4 = \underline{1.39}$. When $y = 0$, $2x + 4 = e^0 = 1 \Rightarrow x = \underline{-1.5}$.
>
> 2) As $x \to \infty$, $y \to \infty$ (gradually).
>
> 3) As $x \to -\infty$, y decreases up to the point where $2x + 4 = 0$, at which it can no longer exist (since $\ln x$ can only exist for $x > 0$). This gives an <u>asymptote</u> at $2x + 4 = 0$, i.e. $\underline{x = -2}$.
>
> 4) Sketch the graph using this information. x must be greater than -2, so if $x > a$, $\underline{a = -2}$.
>
> *This tells you the <u>domain</u> (see p.1).*

No problems — only solutions...

All the individual steps to solving these equations are easy — the hard bit is spotting what combination of things to try. A good thing to look for is hidden quadratics, so try and substitute for e^x or $\ln x$ to make things look a bit nicer. The sketches get easier with practice, so you'd best get cracking.

Using e^x and ln x — Solving Equations

This page is all about <u>models</u>. Except they're modelling <u>exponential growth</u> and <u>decay</u> in <u>real-world applications</u> rather than the Chanel Autumn/Winter collection. Sorry.

Use the **Exponential Functions** to **Model** real-life **Growth and Decay**

In the exam you'll usually be given a background story to an exponential equation.
They may then ask you to find some values, work out a missing part of the equation, or even sketch a graph.
There's nothing here you haven't seen before — you just need to know how to deal with all the wordy bits.

EXAMPLE The exponential growth of a colony of bacteria can be modelled by the equation $B = 60e^{0.03t}$, where B is the number of bacteria, and t is the time in hours from the point at which the colony is first monitored ($t \geq 0$). Use the model to predict:

a) the number of bacteria after <u>4 hours</u>.

You need to find B when $t = 4$,
so put the numbers into the equation:

$B = 60 \times e^{(0.03 \times 4)}$
$= 60 \times 1.1274...$
$= 67.6498...$

So $B = 67$ bacteria.

You shouldn't round up here — there are only 67 whole bacteria, not 68.

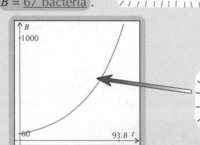

b) the time taken for the colony to grow to <u>1000</u>.

1) You need to find t when B = 1000,
so put the numbers into the equation:
$1000 = 60e^{0.03t}$
$\Rightarrow e^{0.03t} = 1000 \div 60 = 16.6666...$

2) Now take 'ln' of both sides as usual:
$\ln e^{0.03t} = \ln (16.6666...)$
$\Rightarrow 0.03t = 2.8134...$
$\Rightarrow t = 2.8134... \div 0.03 = 93.8$ hours to 3 s.f.

Even if the question doesn't ask for a sketch of the equation, you may still find it useful to do one to give you an idea of what's going on.

EXAMPLE The concentration (C) of a drug in the bloodstream, t hours after taking an initial dose, decreases exponentially according to $C = Ae^{-kt}$, where k is a constant. If the initial concentration is 0.72, and this halves after 5 hours, find the values of A and k and sketch a graph of C against t.

1) The 'initial concentration' is 0.72 when $t = 0$, so put this information in the equation to find the missing constant A:
$0.72 = A \times e^0 \Rightarrow 0.72 = A \times 1 \Rightarrow A = 0.72$.

2) The question also says that when $t = 5$ hours, C is half of 0.72.
So using the value for A found above:
$C = 0.72e^{-kt}$
$0.72 \div 2 = 0.72 \times e^{(-k \times 5)}$
$\Rightarrow 0.36 = 0.72 \times e^{-5k} \Rightarrow 0.36 = \dfrac{0.72}{e^{5k}} \Rightarrow e^{5k} = \dfrac{0.72}{0.36} = 2$.

3) Now take 'ln' of both sides to solve:
$\ln e^{5k} = \ln 2 \Rightarrow 5k = \ln 2$
$\Rightarrow k = \ln 2 \div 5 = 0.139$ to 3 s.f.

4) So the equation is $C = 0.72e^{-0.139t}$.
You still need to do a <u>sketch</u> though, so find the intercepts and asymptotes as you did on the last page:
When $t = 0$, $C = 0.72$. As $t \to \infty$, $e^{-0.139t} \to 0$, so C $\to$ 0.

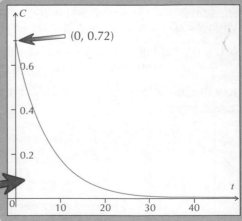

The sketch should make sense for the situation in the question — here t can only be positive as it is the time after an event, so only sketch the graph for $t \geq 0$.

Learn this and watch your knowledge grow exponentially...

For these wordy problems the key is just to extract the relevant information and solve like you did on the last page. The more you practise, the more familiar they'll become — fortunately there's a fair bit of practice at the end of the section.

Proof

The next two pages feature three classic maths ways of <u>proving things</u>, plus a bonus way to <u>disprove</u> stuff...

Some useful **Mini-Proofs**

To warm you up, I've got some nice simple proofs about <u>odd</u> and <u>even numbers</u>.
But first off you need to know these 'proper' definitions for them:

Even numbers = <u>$2a$</u>, odd numbers = <u>$2b + 1$</u> (where a, b are any integers)

Now, take any two odd numbers, $2j + 1$ and $2k + 1$, and two even numbers, $2l$ and $2m$ (j, k, l and m are integers). Then:

Fact 1: <u>odd + odd = even</u>   Proof: $(2j + 1) + (2k + 1) = 2j + 2k + 2 = 2(j + k + 1) = $ even
Fact 2: <u>odd + even = odd</u>   Proof: $(2j + 1) + (2l) = 2j + 2l + 1 = 2(j + l) + 1 = $ odd
Fact 3: <u>even + even = even</u>   Proof: $(2l) + (2m) = 2l + 2m = 2(l + m) = $ even
Fact 4: <u>odd × odd = odd</u>   Proof: $(2j + 1)(2k + 1) = 2j.2k + 2j + 2k + 1 = 2(2jk + j + k) + 1 = $ odd

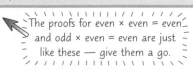
The proofs for even × even = even
and odd × even = even are just
like these — give them a go.

Direct Proof

A <u>direct proof</u> (or 'proof by direct argument') is when you use <u>known facts</u>
to <u>build up</u> your argument and show a statement <u>must</u> be true.

EXAMPLE   A definition of a rational number is 'a number that can be written as a quotient of two integers, where the denominator is non-zero'.

Use this definition to prove that the following statement is true:
"The product of two rational numbers is always a rational number."

Take <u>any two</u> rational numbers, call them <u>a</u> and <u>b</u>.

By the <u>definition</u> of rational numbers you can write them in the form $a = \frac{p}{q}$ and $b = \frac{r}{s}$, where p, q, r and s are all integers, and q and s are non-zero.

The <u>product</u> of a and b is $ab = \frac{p}{q} \times \frac{r}{s} = \frac{pr}{qs}$

pr and qs are the products of integers, so they must also be integers, and because q and s are non-zero, qs must also be non-zero.

We've shown that ab is a quotient of two integers and has a non-zero denominator, so by definition, <u>ab is rational</u>. Hence the original statement is <u>true</u>.

Proof by **Contradiction**

To prove a statement by <u>contradiction</u>, you say 'Suppose the statement <u>isn't true</u>...', then prove that something <u>impossible</u> would have to be true for that to be the case.

EXAMPLE   Prove the following statement: "If x^2 is even, then x must be even."

We can prove the statement by contradiction.

Suppose the statement is <u>not true</u>. Then there must be an <u>odd number</u> x for which x^2 is <u>even</u>.

If x is odd, then you can write x as <u>$2k + 1$</u>, where k is an integer. (This is the definition of an odd number.)

Now, $x^2 = (2k + 1)^2 = 4k^2 + 4k + 1$
$4k^2 + 4k = 2(2k^2 + 2k)$ is <u>even</u> because it is $2\times$ an integer (this is the definition of an even number),
$\Rightarrow 4k^2 + 4k + 1$ is <u>odd</u> (since even + odd = odd).

But this <u>isn't possible</u> if the statement that x^2 is even is true.
We've <u>contradicted</u> the statement that there is an odd number x for which x^2 is even.

So if x^2 is <u>even</u>, then x must be <u>even</u>, hence the original statement is <u>true</u>.

That was proof by contradiction... Oh no it wasn't... Oh yes it was... etc...

One crucial point to remember with proofs is that you have to justify every step of your working. Make sure that you've got a mathematical rule or principle to back up each bit of the proof — you can't take anything for granted.

Proof

And now, part two of our bumper-pack double-bill super-sized prooforama...

Proof by **Exhaustion**

In <u>proof by exhaustion</u> you break things down into two or more <u>cases</u>. You have to make sure that your cases cover <u>all possible situations</u>, then prove <u>separately</u> that the statement is true for <u>each case</u>.

EXAMPLE   Prove the following statement: "For any integer x, the value of $f(x) = x^3 + x + 1$ is an odd integer."

To prove the statement, split the situation into <u>two cases</u>:

       (i) x is an <u>even number</u>,   and   (ii) x is an <u>odd number</u>

(i)   If x is an <u>even integer</u>, then it can be written as <u>$x = 2n$</u>, for some integer n (this is the definition of an even number).

    Substitute $x = 2n$ into the function: $f(2n) = (2n)^3 + 2n + 1 = 8n^3 + 2n + 1 = 2(4n^3 + n) + 1$

    n is an integer $\Rightarrow (4n^3 + n)$ is an integer (as the sum or product of any integers are also integers)

                     $\Rightarrow 2(4n^3 + n)$ is an even integer (because 2× an integer is the definition of an even number)

                     $\Rightarrow 2(4n^3 + n) + 1$ is an <u>odd integer</u> (as even + odd = odd)

> You can use the binomial expansion formula on p.52 to help you find these coefficients.

    So $f(x)$ is <u>odd</u> when x is <u>even</u>.

(ii) If x is an <u>odd integer</u>, then it can be written as <u>$x = 2m + 1$</u>, for some integer m.

    Substitute $x = 2m + 1$ into the function: $f(2m + 1) = (2m + 1)^3 + 2m + 1 + 1 = (8m^3 + 12m^2 + 6m + 1) + 2m + 1 + 1$

                                        $= 8m^3 + 12m^2 + 8m + 3 = 2(4m^3 + 6m^2 + 4m) + 3$

    m is an integer $\Rightarrow (4m^3 + 6m^2 + 4m)$ is an integer

                     $\Rightarrow 2(4m^3 + 6m^2 + 4m)$ is an even integer

                     $\Rightarrow 2(4m^3 + 6m^2 + 4m) + 3$ is an <u>odd integer</u>

    So $f(x)$ is <u>odd</u> when x is <u>odd</u>.

We have shown that $f(x)$ is <u>odd</u> when x is even <u>and</u> when x is odd. As any integer x <u>must</u> be either odd or even, we have therefore shown that $f(x)$ is <u>odd</u> for <u>any</u> integer x.

Disproof by **Counter-example**

<u>Disproof</u> by <u>counter-example</u> is the easiest way to show a mathematical statement is <u>false</u>.
All you have to do is find <u>one case</u> where the statement doesn't hold.

EXAMPLE   Disprove the following statement:
          "For any pair of real numbers x and y, if $x > y$, then $x^2 + x > y^2 + y$."

To <u>disprove</u> the statement, it's enough to find just <u>one example</u> of x and y where $x > y$, but $x^2 + x \leq y^2 + y$.

Let $x = 2$ and $y = -4$.

Then $2 > -4 \Rightarrow x > y$

but $x^2 + x = 2^2 + 2 = 6$ and $y^2 + y = (-4)^2 + (-4) = 12$, so $x^2 + x < y^2 + y$

So when $x = 2$ and $y = -4$, the first part of the statement holds, but the second part of the statement doesn't.

So the statement is <u>not true</u>.

And that's the proof, the whole proof, and nothing but the proof...

When you're trying to disprove something, don't be put off if you can't find a counter-example straight away.
Sometimes you have to just try a few different cases until you find one that doesn't work.

C3 Section 2 — Practice Questions

Well, apart from a surprising U-turn in the middle, there was nothing in that section that was too shocking. While it's all fresh in your mind, have a go at these little questions...

Warm-up Questions

1) Plot the following graphs on the same axes, for $-2 \leq x \leq 2$:
   a) $y = 4e^x$ b) $y = 4e^{-x}$ c) $y = 4 \ln x$ d) $y = \ln 4x$.

2) Find the value of x, to 4 decimal places (where appropriate), when:
   a) $e^{2x} = 6$ b) $\ln (x + 3) = 0.75$ c) $3e^{-4x+1} = 5$ d) $\ln x + \ln 5 = \ln 4$.

3) Solve the following equations, giving your solutions as exact values:
   a) $\ln (2x - 7) + \ln 4 = -3$ b) $2e^{2x} + e^x = 3$.

4) Sketch graphs of the following, labelling key points and asymptotes:
   a) $y = 2 - e^{x+1}$ b) $y = 5e^{0.5x} + 5$ c) $y = \ln (2x) + 1$ d) $y = \ln (x + 5)$

5) The value of a motorbike (£V) varies with age (in t years from new) according to $V = 7500e^{-0.2t}$.
   a) How much did it originally cost?
   b) What is its value after 10 years (to the nearest £)?
   c) After how many years will the motorbike's value have fallen below £500?
   d) Sketch a graph showing how the value of the motorbike varies with age, labelling all key points.

6) Disprove the following statement: "$n^2 - n - 1$ is a prime number, for any integer $n > 2$."

Feeling confident? Thought so.
Let's see how you handle these exam-style problems — they're a wee bit more problematic...

Exam Questions

1   a)   Given that $6e^x = 3$, find the exact value of x.

                                                                      (2 marks)

    b)   Find the exact solutions to the equation:

$$e^{2x} - 8e^x + 7 = 0.$$

                                                                       (4 marks)

    c)   Given that $4 \ln x = 3$, find the exact value of x.

                                                                       (2 marks)

    d)   Solve the equation:

$$\ln x + \frac{24}{\ln x} = 10$$

       giving your answers as exact values of x.

                                                                       (4 marks)

2   The sketch below shows the function $y = e^{ax} + b$, where a and b are constants.

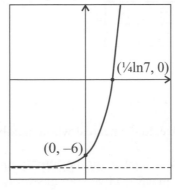

$(\frac{1}{4}\ln 7, 0)$

$(0, -6)$

Find the values of a and b, and the equation of the asymptote shown on the sketch.

                                                                             (5 marks)

C3 Section 2 — Practice Questions

3 A breed of mink is introduced to a new habitat.
   The number of mink, M, after t years in the habitat, is modelled by:
   $$M = 74e^{0.6t} \quad (t \geq 0)$$

   a) State the number of mink that were introduced to the new habitat originally.

   (1 mark)

   b) Predict the number of mink after 3 years in the habitat.

   (2 marks)

   c) Predict the number of complete years it would take for the
       population of mink to exceed 10 000.

   (2 marks)

   d) Sketch a graph to show how the mink population varies with time in the new habitat.

   (2 marks)

4 A curve has the equation $y = \ln(4x - 3)$.

   a) The point A with coordinate $(a, 1)$ lies on the curve. Find a to 2 decimal places.

   (2 marks)

   b) The curve only exists for $x > b$. State the value of b.

   (2 marks)

   c) Sketch the curve, labelling any important points.

   (2 marks)

5 a) Prove the statement below:
       For any integer n, $n^2 - n - 1$ is always odd.

   (3 marks)

   b) Hence prove that $(n^2 - n - 2)^3$ is always even.

   (3 marks)

6 Solve the following equations, giving your answers as exact values of x.

   a) $2e^x + 18e^{-x} = 20$

   (4 marks)

   b) $2 \ln x - \ln 3 = \ln 12$

   (3 marks)

7 A radioactive substance decays exponentially so that its activity, A, can be modelled by
   $$A = Be^{-kt}$$
   where t is the time in days, and $t \geq 0$. Some experimental data is shown below.

t	0	5	10
A	50	42	

   a) State the value of B.

   (1 mark)

   b) Find the value of k, to 3 significant figures.

   (2 marks)

   c) Find the missing value from the table, to the nearest whole number.

   (2 marks)

   d) The half-life of a substance is the time it takes for the activity to halve.
       Find the half-life of this substance, in days. Give your answer to the nearest day.

   (3 marks)

Chain Rule

That's right — our old friend <u>differentiation</u> is back again, this time with some <u>new exciting features</u>. Before you start panicking about how much you've already forgotten, all you need for now is: $\Longrightarrow$ $\boxed{\dfrac{d}{dx}(x^n) = nx^{n-1}}$

The **Chain Rule** is used for **Functions of Functions**

The <u>chain rule</u> is a nifty little tool that allows you to differentiate complicated functions by <u>splitting them up</u> into easier ones. The trick is spotting <u>how</u> to split them up, and choosing the right bit to <u>substitute</u>.

Chain Rule Method

- Pick a suitable function of x for 'u' and rewrite y in terms of u.

- Differentiate u (with respect to x) to get $\dfrac{du}{dx}$, and differentiate y (with respect to u) to get $\dfrac{dy}{du}$.

- Stick it all in the formula.

> If $y = f(u)$ and $u = g(x)$
> then:
> $$\frac{dy}{dx} = \frac{dy}{du} \times \frac{du}{dx}$$

EXAMPLE Find the exact value of $\dfrac{dy}{dx}$ when $x = 1$ for $y = \dfrac{1}{\sqrt{x^2 + 4x}}$.

Write down all the steps — it'll help you avoid small mistakes that could affect your final answer.

1) First, write y in terms of powers to make it easier to differentiate: $y = (x^2 + 4x)^{-\frac{1}{2}}$.

2) Pick a chunk of the equation to call 'u', and rewrite y in terms of u:
   e.g. in this case let $u = x^2 + 4x$, so $y = u^{-\frac{1}{2}}$.

3) Now differentiate both bits separately: $u = x^2 + 4x$, so $\dfrac{du}{dx} = 2x + 4$ and $y = u^{-\frac{1}{2}}$, so $\dfrac{dy}{du} = -\dfrac{1}{2}u^{-\frac{3}{2}}$.

4) Use the chain rule to find $\dfrac{dy}{dx}$: $\dfrac{dy}{dx} = \dfrac{dy}{du} \times \dfrac{du}{dx} = -\dfrac{1}{2}u^{-\frac{3}{2}} \times (2x + 4)$.

5) Substitute in for u and rearrange: $u = x^2 + 4x$, so $\dfrac{dy}{dx} = -\dfrac{1}{2}(x^2 + 4x)^{-\frac{3}{2}}(2x + 4) = -\dfrac{x + 2}{(\sqrt{x^2 + 4x})^3}$.

6) Finally, put in $x = 1$ to answer the question: $\dfrac{dy}{dx} = -\dfrac{1 + 2}{(\sqrt{1^2 + (4 \times 1)})^3} = \dfrac{-3}{5\sqrt{5}} = \dfrac{-3\sqrt{5}}{25}$.

'Exact' means leave in surd form where necessary.

Use **dy/dx = 1 ÷ dx/dy** for **x = f(y)**

> For $x = f(y)$, use
> $$\frac{dy}{dx} = \frac{1}{\left(\dfrac{dx}{dy}\right)}$$

The <u>principle</u> of the chain rule can also be used where <u>x is given in terms of y</u> (i.e. $x = f(y)$). This comes from a bit of mathematical fiddling, but it's quite <u>useful</u>:

$\dfrac{dy}{dx} \times \dfrac{dx}{dy} = \dfrac{dy}{dy} = 1$, so rearranging gives $\dfrac{dy}{dx} = \dfrac{1}{\left(\dfrac{dx}{dy}\right)}$. Here's how to use it...

EXAMPLE A curve has the equation $x = y^3 + 2y - 7$. Find $\dfrac{dy}{dx}$ at the point $(-4, 1)$.

1) Forget that the xs and ys are in the 'wrong' places and differentiate as usual:
   $x = y^3 + 2y - 7$, so $\dfrac{dx}{dy} = 3y^2 + 2$.

2) Use $\dfrac{dy}{dx} = \dfrac{1}{\left(\dfrac{dx}{dy}\right)}$ to find $\dfrac{dy}{dx}$: $\dfrac{dy}{dx} = \dfrac{1}{3y^2 + 2}$.

3) $y = 1$ at the point $(-4, 1)$, so put this in the equation:
   $\dfrac{dy}{dx} = \dfrac{1}{3(1)^2 + 2} = \dfrac{1}{5} = 0.2$, so $\dfrac{dy}{dx} = 0.2$ at the point $(-4, 1)$.

You'll be using this again on the next page so make sure you've learnt it now.

I'm in the middle of a chain rule differentiation...

You know, I'm not sure I've stressed enough just how important differentiation is. It's one of those bits of maths that examiners can tag on to almost any other A-Level topic. It's almost like they have a mantra: 'Give me ANY function and I will ask you to differentiate it, in a multitude of intricate ways'. To which you should respond: 'Bring. It. On.'

Differentiation of e^x and ln x

Remember those special little functions from Section Two? Well you're about to find out just how special they are as we take a look at how to differentiate them. I can tell you're overcome by excitement so I'll not keep you waiting...

The **Gradient** of y = e^x is e^x by **Definition**

$$y = e^x$$
$$\frac{dy}{dx} = e^x$$

OR

$$f(x) = e^x$$
$$f'(x) = e^x$$

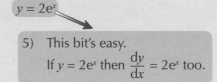
Get used to using both types of function notation. You should remember from C2 that f'(x) means the same as dy/dx.

In the last section (see p.10) we saw that 'e' was just a number for which the gradient of e^x was $\underline{e^x}$. Which makes it pretty simple to differentiate.

EXAMPLE If $f(x) = e^{x^2} + 2e^x$, find $f'(x)$ for $x = 0$.

1) Let's break down the function into its two bits and differentiate them separately:

$$y = e^{x^2} \qquad \text{and} \qquad y = 2e^x$$

2) This is the tricky bit.
   Use the chain rule from the last page:
   $u = x^2$ and $y = e^u$

3) Both u and y are now easy to differentiate:
   $\frac{du}{dx} = 2x$ and $\frac{dy}{du} = e^u$

4) $\frac{dy}{dx} = \frac{du}{dx} \times \frac{dy}{du} = 2x \cdot e^u = 2x \cdot e^{x^2}$

5) This bit's easy.
   If $y = 2e^x$ then $\frac{dy}{dx} = 2e^x$ too.

When $y = kf(x)$ where k is a constant, then dy/dx is just kf'(x).

6) Put the bits back together and you end up with $f'(x) = 2xe^{x^2} + 2e^x$.

7) So when $\underline{x = 0}$, $\underline{f'(x)} = 0 + 2e^0 \underline{= 2}$.

Turn y = ln x into x = e^y to **Differentiate**

$$y = \ln x$$
$$\frac{dy}{dx} = \frac{1}{x}$$

This result you can just learn, but it comes from another bit of mathematical fiddling:

If $y = \ln x$, then $x = e^y$ (see p.10).

Differentiating gives $\frac{dx}{dy} = e^y$, and $\frac{dy}{dx} = \frac{1}{\left(\frac{dx}{dy}\right)} = \frac{1}{e^y} = \frac{1}{x}$ (since $x = e^y$). Nice eh.

EXAMPLE Find $\frac{dy}{dx}$ if $y = \ln (x^2 + 3)$.

1) Use the chain rule again for this one: $y = \ln u$ and $u = x^2 + 3$.

2) $\frac{dy}{du} = \frac{1}{u}$ (from above) and $\frac{du}{dx} = 2x$.

3) So $\frac{dy}{dx} = \frac{dy}{du} \times \frac{du}{dx} = \frac{1}{u} \times 2x = \frac{2x}{x^2 + 3}$.

Look again at your final answer. It comes out to $\frac{f'(x)}{f(x)}$.

This will always be the case for $y = \ln (f(x))$ so you can just learn this result:

$$y = \ln (f(x))$$
$$\frac{dy}{dx} = \frac{f'(x)}{f(x)}$$

These functions pop up everywhere in the e^xams...

There's nothing too tough on this page, so you have no excuse for not getting a good grasp of the basics while you can. The derivatives of e^x and $\ln x$ are just a couple more of those essential little things you've just got to learn. If you don't, you could get stumped by a fairly easy exam question. I know I'd gladly spend every waking hour learning this stuff if I could...

Differentiation of Sin, Cos and Tan

I bet you've always wanted to know how to differentiate trig functions. Well today's your lucky day, 'cos this page tells you how. You see what I did there with the 'cos'? Pun #27 from 'Ye Olde Booke of Maths Punnes'...)

The **Rules** for **dy/dx** of **Sin**, **Cos** and **Tan** only work in **Radians**

For trigonometric functions, where the angle is measured in radians, the following rules apply:

$$\text{If } y = \qquad \frac{dy}{dx} =$$

$$\sin x \longrightarrow \cos x$$
$$\cos x \longrightarrow -\sin x$$
$$\tan x \longrightarrow \frac{1}{\cos^2 x} \text{ or } \sec^2 x$$

$\frac{1}{\cos x}$ is also known as sec x — there's more about this on p.59.

Use the **Chain Rule** with **Sin/Cos/Tan (f(x))**

If you can't follow what's happening here, go back to p.17 and brush up on the chain rule.

EXAMPLE: Differentiate $y = \cos 2x + \sin (x + 1)$ with respect to x.

It's the chain rule (again) for both parts of this equation:

1) Differentiate '$y = \cos 2x$': $y = \cos u$, $u = 2x$,
so $\frac{dy}{du} = -\sin u$ (see above) and $\frac{du}{dx} = 2 \Rightarrow \frac{dy}{dx} = -2\sin 2x$.

2) Differentiate '$y = \sin (x + 1)$': $y = \sin u$, $u = x + 1$,
so $\frac{dy}{du} = \cos u$ (see above) and $\frac{du}{dx} = 1 \Rightarrow \frac{dy}{dx} = \cos (x + 1)$.

3) Put it all together to get $\frac{dy}{dx} = -2\sin 2x + \cos (x + 1)$.

EXAMPLE: Find $\frac{dy}{dx}$ when $x = \tan 3y$.

1) First find $\frac{dx}{dy}$ using the chain rule: $x = \tan u$, $u = 3y$, $\frac{dx}{du} = \frac{1}{\cos^2 u}$, $\frac{du}{dy} = 3$, so $\frac{dx}{dy} = \frac{3}{\cos^2 3y}$.

2) Then use $\frac{dy}{dx} = \frac{1}{\left(\frac{dx}{dy}\right)}$ to get the final answer: $\frac{dy}{dx} = \frac{1}{\left(\frac{3}{\cos^2 3y}\right)} = \frac{1}{3}\cos^2 3y$.

The **Chain Rule** is also useful if the functions are **Squared**

EXAMPLE For $y = 2\cos^2 x + \sin 2x$, show that $\frac{dy}{dx} = 2(\cos 2x - 2\sin x \cos x)$.

1) Writing out the equation in a slightly different way helps with the chain rule: $y = 2(\cos x)^2 + \sin 2x$. Now you can use the chain rule on each bit separately.

2) For the first bit, $y = 2u^2$, $u = \cos x$, so $\frac{dy}{du} = 4u$ and $\frac{du}{dx} = -\sin x$.

For the second bit, $y = \sin u$, $u = 2x$, so $\frac{dy}{du} = \cos u$ and $\frac{du}{dx} = 2$.

3) Putting it all in the chain rule formula gives $\frac{dy}{dx} = -4\sin x \cos x + 2\cos 2x$.

4) Rearranging this gives $\frac{dy}{dx} = 2(\cos 2x - 2\sin x \cos x)$. Et voilà.

I'm having an identity crisis — I can't differentiate between sin and cos...

Don't get tied down by the chain rule (pun #28...). After a bit of practice you'll be able to do it a lot quicker in one step — just say in your working 'using the chain rule...' so the examiner can see how clever you are.

Product Rule

In maths-speak, a 'product' is what you get when you multiply things together. So the 'product rule' is a rule about differentiating things that are multiplied together. And it's yet another rule you have to learn I'm afraid.

Use the **Product Rule** to differentiate **Two Functions Multiplied Together**

This is what it looks like:

$$\text{If } y = uv$$
$$\frac{dy}{dx} = u\frac{dv}{dx} + v\frac{du}{dx}$$

(u and v are functions of x.)

And here's how to use it:

EXAMPLES Differentiate the following with respect to x: a) $x^3 \tan x$ and b) $e^{2x}\sqrt{2x-3}$.

a) $x^3 \tan x$

1) The crucial thing is to write down everything in steps. Start with identifying 'u' and 'v':
$$u = x^3 \text{ and } v = \tan x.$$

2) Now differentiate these two separately, with respect to x:
$$\frac{du}{dx} = 3x^2 \text{ and } \frac{dv}{dx} = \frac{1}{\cos^2 x}.$$

3) Very carefully put all the bits into the formula:
$$\frac{dy}{dx} = u\frac{dv}{dx} + v\frac{du}{dx} = (x^3 \cdot \frac{1}{\cos^2 x}) + (\tan x \cdot 3x^2)$$

4) Finally, rearrange to make it look nicer:
$$\frac{dy}{dx} = \frac{x^3}{\cos^2 x} + 3x^2 \tan x.$$

b) $e^{2x}\sqrt{2x-3}$

1) Again, start with identifying 'u' and 'v':
$$u = e^{2x} \text{ and } v = \sqrt{2x-3}.$$

2) Each of these needs the chain rule to differentiate:
$$\frac{du}{dx} = 2e^{2x} \text{ and } \frac{dv}{dx} = \frac{1}{\sqrt{2x-3}} \text{ (do it in steps if you need to...)}$$

3) Put it all into the product rule formula:
$$\frac{dy}{dx} = u\frac{dv}{dx} + v\frac{du}{dx} = (e^{2x} \cdot \frac{1}{\sqrt{2x-3}}) + (\sqrt{2x-3} \cdot 2e^{2x})$$

4) Rearrange and simplify:
$$\frac{dy}{dx} = e^{2x}\left(\frac{1}{\sqrt{2x-3}} + 2\sqrt{2x-3}\right) = e^{2x}\left(\frac{1+2(2x-3)}{\sqrt{2x-3}}\right)$$
$$= \frac{e^{2x}(4x-5)}{\sqrt{2x-3}}.$$

Use the Rules **Together** to differentiate **Complicated Functions**

In the exam they might tell you which rules to use, but chances are they won't.
And you'll probably have to throw a whole load of rules at any one question.

EXAMPLE Solve the equation $\frac{d}{dx}((x^3 + 3x^2)\ln x) = 2x^2 + 5x$, leaving your answer as an exact value of x.

1) The $\frac{d}{dx}$ just tells you to differentiate the bit in brackets first.

And since $(x^3 + 3x^2)\ln x$ is a product of two functions, use the product rule:
$$u = x^3 + 3x^2 \Rightarrow \frac{du}{dx} = 3x^2 + 6x \qquad \text{and} \qquad v = \ln x \Rightarrow \frac{dv}{dx} = \frac{1}{x} \text{ (see p.18)}$$

So $\frac{d}{dx}((x^3 + 3x^2)\ln x) = [(x^3 + 3x^2) \cdot \frac{1}{x}] + [\ln x \cdot (3x^2 + 6x)] = x^2 + 3x + (3x^2 + 6x)\ln x.$

You should be well up on ln x and e^x after Section 2, but glance back at pages 10-12 if you need to.

2) Now put this into the equation from the question in place of $\frac{d}{dx}((x^3 + 3x^2)\ln x)$:
$$x^2 + 3x + (3x^2 + 6x)\ln x = 2x^2 + 5x$$

You're asked for an exact value so leave in terms of e.

3) Rearrange and solve as follows:
$$(3x^2 + 6x)\ln x = 2x^2 + 5x - x^2 - 3x \Rightarrow (3x^2 + 6x)\ln x = x^2 + 2x \Rightarrow \ln x = \frac{x^2 + 2x}{3(x^2 + 2x)} = \frac{1}{3} \Rightarrow x = e^{\frac{1}{3}}.$$

The first rule of maths club is — you do not talk about maths club...

These rules are supposed to make your life easier when differentiating. Learning them means you don't have to do everything from first principles every time. Try not to get the product rule mixed up with the chain rule. Repeat after me: 'The chain rule is for functions of functions but the product rule is for products of functions'. Snappy, I know...

Quotient Rule

The world is a beautiful, harmonious place full of natural symmetry. So of course, if we have a 'product rule' to differentiate products, we must also have a 'quotient rule' to differentiate... er... quotients. Read on and learn.

Use the **Quotient Rule** for one function **Divided By** another

A quotient is one function divided by another one.
The rule for differentiating quotients looks like this:

$$\text{If } y = \frac{u}{v}$$

$$\frac{dy}{dx} = \frac{v\frac{du}{dx} - u\frac{dv}{dx}}{v^2}$$

You could, if you wanted to, just use the product rule on $y = uv^{-1}$
(try it — you'll get the same answer).
This way is so much quicker and easier though — and it's on the formula sheet.

EXAMPLE: Find the gradient of the tangent to the curve with equation $y = \frac{(2x^2 - 1)}{(3x^2 + 1)}$, at the point (1, 0.25).

1) 'Gradient of tangent' means differentiate.

2) First identify u and v for the quotient rule, and differentiate separately:

This bit's just like the product rule from the last page.

$$u = 2x^2 - 1 \Rightarrow \frac{du}{dx} = 4x \qquad \text{and} \qquad v = 3x^2 + 1 \Rightarrow \frac{dv}{dx} = 6x.$$

3) It's very important that you get things in the right order, so concentrate on what's going where:

Don't try and simplify straight away or you'll get things mixed up.

$$\frac{dy}{dx} = \frac{v\frac{du}{dx} - u\frac{dv}{dx}}{v^2} = \frac{(3x^2 + 1)(4x) - (2x^2 - 1)(6x)}{(3x^2 + 1)^2}$$

4) Now you can simplify things:

$$\frac{dy}{dx} = \frac{12x^3 + 4x - 12x^3 + 6x}{(3x^2 + 1)^2} = \frac{10x}{(3x^2 + 1)^2}.$$

If it's a 'normal' rather than a 'tangent' do $-1 \div$ gradient.

5) Finally, put in $x = 1$ to find the gradient at (1, 0.25): $\frac{dy}{dx} = \frac{10}{(3 + 1)^2} = 0.625$.

EXAMPLE: Use the quotient rule to differentiate $y = \frac{\cos x}{\sin x}$, and hence show that for $y = \frac{1}{\tan x}$, $\frac{dy}{dx} = \frac{-1}{\sin^2 x}$.

1) Start off identifying $u = \cos x$ and $v = \sin x$.

2) Differentiating separately gives: $\frac{du}{dx} = -\sin x$ and $\frac{dv}{dx} = \cos x$ (see p.19).

Don't forget your easy C2 trig identities.

3) Putting everything in the quotient rule formula gives:

$$\frac{dy}{dx} = \frac{(\sin x \times -\sin x) - (\cos x \times \cos x)}{(\sin x)^2} = \frac{-\sin^2 x - \cos^2 x}{\sin^2 x}.$$

4) Use a trig identity to simplify this ($\sin^2 x + \cos^2 x \equiv 1$ should do the trick...):

$$\frac{dy}{dx} = \frac{-(\sin^2 x + \cos^2 x)}{\sin^2 x} = \frac{-1}{\sin^2 x}.$$

5) Linking this back to the question, since $\tan x = \frac{\sin x}{\cos x}$, that means $\frac{1}{\tan x} = \frac{\cos x}{\sin x} = y$.

So $\frac{dy}{dx} = \frac{-1}{\sin^2 x}$. QED*

*Quite Exciting Differentiation

The second rule of maths club is — you do not talk about maths club...

Confused yet? Yes I know, there are three very similar looking rules in this section, all using us and vs and xs and ys all over the shop. You won't remember them by reading them over and over again like some mystical code. You will remember them by using them lots and lots in practice questions. Plain and simple — just how I like my men...

More Differentiation

What?! More differentiation?! Surely not. This page is all about using what you know, and knowing what to use. And if it makes you feel any better, this is the last page in this section.

Finding the *Gradient*, *Tangent*, *dy/dx*, *f'(x)*, *d/dx(f(x))* — all mean '*Differentiate*'

Usually in exams, differentiation will be disguised as something else — either through <u>different notation</u> ($f'(x)$, $\frac{dy}{dx}$ etc.) or by asking for the <u>gradient</u> or <u>rate of change</u> of something.

You could also be asked to find the <u>equation</u> of a <u>tangent</u> or <u>normal</u> to a curve at a given point:

EXAMPLE Find the <u>equation</u> of the <u>tangent</u> to the curve $y = \frac{5x + 2}{3x - 2}$ at the point (1, 7), in the form $y = mx + c$.

1) The gradient of the tangent is just the gradient of the curve at that point. So <u>differentiate</u>...

2) Use the <u>quotient rule</u>: $u = 5x + 2 \Rightarrow \frac{du}{dx} = 5$ and $v = 3x - 2 \Rightarrow \frac{dv}{dx} = 3$.

   So $\frac{dy}{dx} = \frac{5(3x - 2) - 3(5x + 2)}{(3x - 2)^2} = -\frac{16}{(3x - 2)^2}$.

   If you're asked for a 'normal', do $-1 \div$ gradient of tangent here — then the rest is the same.

3) <u>Gradient</u> of tangent at (1, 7) is $\frac{dy}{dx}$ at $x = 1$, which is $-\frac{16}{(3 - 2)^2} = -16$.

4) Use the <u>equation of a straight line</u> $y - y_1 = m(x - x_1)$ with $m = -16$, $y_1 = 7$ and $x_1 = 1$, to give:

   $y - 7 = -16(x - 1) \Rightarrow y = -16x + 23$ is the equation of the tangent.

Differentiate *Again* for *d²y/dx²*, *Turning Points*, *Stationary Points* etc.

Refresh your memory on C2, where you learnt all about <u>maximums</u> and <u>minimums</u>...

EXAMPLE Determine the <u>nature</u> of the <u>stationary point</u> of the curve $y = \frac{\ln x}{x^2}$ $(x > 0)$.

1) First use the <u>quotient rule</u> to find $\frac{dy}{dx}$:

   $u = \ln x \Rightarrow \frac{du}{dx} = \frac{1}{x}$, $v = x^2 \Rightarrow \frac{dv}{dx} = 2x$. So $\frac{dy}{dx} = \frac{x^2\left(\frac{1}{x}\right) - (\ln x)(2x)}{(x^2)^2} = \frac{1 - 2\ln x}{x^3}$.

2) The stationary point occurs where $\frac{dy}{dx} = 0$ (i.e. zero gradient) so this is when:

   $\frac{1 - 2\ln x}{x^3} = 0 \Rightarrow \ln x = \frac{1}{2} \Rightarrow x = e^{\frac{1}{2}}$.

3) To find out whether it's a maximum or minimum, differentiate $\frac{dy}{dx}$ to get $\frac{d^2y}{dx^2}$:

   $u = 1 - 2\ln x \Rightarrow \frac{du}{dx} = -\frac{2}{x}$, $v = x^3 \Rightarrow \frac{dv}{dx} = 3x^2$. So $\frac{d^2y}{dx^2} = \frac{6\ln x - 5}{x^4}$.

   Positive means minimum, negative means maximum — it's all there in C2.

4) When $x = e^{\frac{1}{2}}$, $\frac{d^2y}{dx^2} < 0$ (i.e. <u>negative</u>), which means it's a <u>maximum point</u>.

Parlez vous exam?

It's often noted that mathematics has its own language — you need to make sure you're <u>fluent</u> or all your hard work will go to waste. Become an expert in deciphering exam questions so you do exactly what's expected with the minimum of fuss. Unfortunately, that argument doesn't work the other way round — the examiners need to be able to understand exactly what you've written. They're not prepared to do any deciphering whatsoever, so make sure all your working is clear.

C3 Section 3 — Practice Questions

If you think that was a <u>lot of differentiation</u>, be thankful you didn't live in Ancient Molgarahenia, where differentiation was the only maths permitted. Try these tasty warm-up questions for an <u>authentic taste</u> of Molgarahenian life.

Warm-up Questions

1) <u>Differentiate</u> with respect to x:

   a) $y = \sqrt{x^3 + 2x^2}$ b) $y = \dfrac{1}{\sqrt{x^3 + 2x^2}}$ c) $y = e^{5x^2}$ d) $y = \ln(6 - x^2)$

2) Find $\dfrac{dy}{dx}$ when   a) $x = 2e^y$ b) $x = \ln(2y + 3)$

3) Find $f'(x)$ for the following functions:

   a) $f(x) = \sin^2(x + 2)$ b) $f(x) = 2\cos 3x$ Assume that questions involving trig are using radians unless stated otherwise.

4) Find the value of the <u>gradient</u> for:

   a) $y = e^{2x}(x^2 - 3)$ when $x = 0$ b) $y = \ln x \sin x$ when $x = 1$

5) Find the <u>equation</u> of the <u>tangent</u> to the curve $y = \dfrac{6x^2 + 3}{4x^2 - 1}$ at the point $(1, 3)$.

And finally — a <u>megabeast</u> of a question. You probably won't get anything as involved as this in the exam, but if you think you're hard enough...

6) Find the <u>stationary point</u> on the curve $y = \dfrac{e^x}{\sqrt{x}}$, and say whether it is a <u>maximum or minimum</u>.

It is said that the Great Molgarahenian Plain was carpeted with differentiation <u>as far as the eye could see</u>. The C3 exam won't be <u>quite</u> that bad, but there will be <u>some differentiation</u> in there, so get practising...

Exam Questions

1   Find $\dfrac{dy}{dx}$ for each of the following functions. Simplify your answer where possible.

   a) $y = \ln(3x + 1)\sin(3x + 1)$.

                                                        (4 marks)

   b) $y = \dfrac{\sqrt{x^2 + 3}}{\cos 3x}$.

                                                        (4 marks)

   c) $y = \sin^3(2x^2)$

                                                        (3 marks)

2   Use the quotient rule to show that, for the function $f(x) = \dfrac{1}{\cos x}$:

$$f'(x) = \frac{\tan x}{\cos x}.$$

                                                        (4 marks)

3   The curve shown below has the equation $x = \sqrt{y^2 + 3y}$.

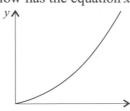

   a)   Find $\dfrac{dy}{dx}$ at the point $(2, 1)$.

                                                        (5 marks)

   b)   Hence find the equation of the tangent to the curve at $(2, 1)$, in the form $y = ax + b$, where a and b are constants.

                                                        (2 marks)

C3 Section 3 — Practice Questions

In 272 BC, the famous Molgarahenian philosopher, <u>Bobby the Wise</u>, was put to death for straying from the path of <u>differentiation</u> and doing some simultaneous equations. Don't be like Bobby, stick with <u>these questions</u> (for now)...

4   Differentiate the following with respect to x.

    a) $\sqrt{(e^x + e^{2x})}$.

(3 marks)

    b) $3e^{2x+1} - \ln(1 - x^2) + 2x^3$.

(3 marks)

5   A curve with equation $y = e^x \sin x$ has 2 turning points in the interval $-\pi \le x \le \pi$.

    a)   Find the value of x at each of these turning points.

(6 marks)

    b)   Determine the nature of each of the turning points.

(5 marks)

6   Find the gradient of the tangent to the curve:

$$y = \sin^2 x - 2\cos 2x$$

at the point where $x = \frac{\pi}{12}$ radians.

(4 marks)

7   Given that $y = \dfrac{e^x + x}{e^x - x}$, find $\dfrac{dy}{dx}$ when $x = 0$.

(3 marks)

8   Find the equation of the normal to the curve $x = \sin 4y$ that passes through the point $\left(0, \frac{\pi}{4}\right)$.

    Give your answer in the form $y = mx + c$, where m and c are constants to be found.

(6 marks)

9   A sketch of the function $f(x) = 4\ln 3x$ is shown in the diagram.

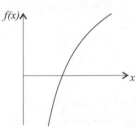

    a)   Find $f'(x)$ at the point where $x = 1$.

(3 marks)

    b)   Find the equation of the tangent to the curve at the point $x = 1$.

(3 marks)

Relating Rates of Change

This is one of those topics where the most awkward bit is getting your head round the information in the question. The actual maths is nothing like as bad as the questions usually make it sound. Honest.

The **Chain Rule** lets you **Connect** different **Rates of Change**

1) Some situations have a number of linked variables, like length, surface area and volume, or distance, speed and acceleration.

2) If you know the rate of change of one of these linked variables, and the equations that connect the variables, you can use the chain rule to help you find the rate of change of the other variables.

EXAMPLE A scientist is testing how a new material expands when it is gradually heated. The diagram shows the sample being tested, which is shaped like a triangular prism. After t minutes, the triangle that forms the base of the prism has base length $7x$ cm and height $4x$ cm, and the height of the prism is also $4x$ cm.

If the sample expands at a constant rate, given by $\frac{dx}{dt} = 0.05$ cm min^{-1}, find an expression in terms of x for $\frac{dV}{dt}$, where V is the volume of the prism.

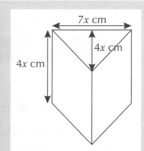

The best way to start this kind of question is to write down what you know. We've got enough information to write an expression for the volume of the prism:

$$V = (\tfrac{1}{2} \times 7x \times 4x) \times 4x = 56x^3 \text{ cm}^3$$

Differentiate this with respect to x: $\quad \dfrac{dV}{dx} = 168x^2$

We know that $\frac{dx}{dt} = 0.05$. So we can use the chain rule to find $\frac{dV}{dt}$: $\quad \dfrac{dV}{dt} = \dfrac{dV}{dx} \times \dfrac{dx}{dt} = 168x^2 \times 0.05 = 8.4x^2$

Watch out for **Slightly Trickier** questions

1) There are a couple of sneaky tricks in this type of question that could catch you out if you're not prepared for them.

2) In this next example, you have to spot that there's a hidden derivative described in words.

3) You also need to remember the rule $\dfrac{dy}{dx} = \dfrac{1}{\left(\frac{dx}{dy}\right)}$ (see p17).

EXAMPLE A giant metal cube from space is cooling after entering the Earth's atmosphere. As it cools, the surface area of the cube decreases at a constant rate of 0.027 m^2 s^{-1}. If the side length of the cube after t seconds is x m, find $\frac{dx}{dt}$ at the point when $x = 15$ m.

Start with what you know:

The cube has side length x m, so the surface area of the cube is $\quad A = 6x^2 \quad \Rightarrow \quad \dfrac{dA}{dx} = 12x$

> We use $\frac{d}{dt}$ because it's a rate of time.

A decreases at a constant rate of 0.027 m^2 s^{-1} — we can write this as $\dfrac{dA}{dt} = -0.027$

> This value is negative because A is decreasing.

Now use the chain rule to find $\frac{dx}{dt}$: $\quad \dfrac{dx}{dt} = \dfrac{dx}{dA} \times \dfrac{dA}{dt} = \dfrac{1}{\left(\frac{dA}{dx}\right)} \times \dfrac{dA}{dt} = \dfrac{1}{12x} \times -0.027 = -\dfrac{0.00225}{x}$

So when $x = 15$, $\dfrac{dx}{dt} = -\dfrac{0.00225}{x} = -\dfrac{0.00225}{15} = -0.00015$ m s^{-1}

I'd rate this page 10 out of 10 — if I do say so myself...

If you get stuck on a question like this, don't panic. Somewhere in the question there'll be enough information to write at least one equation linking some of the variables. If in doubt, write down any equations you can make, differentiate them all, and then see which of the resulting expressions you can link using the chain rule to make the thing you're looking for.

Implicit Differentiation

This really isn't as complicated as it looks... in fact, I think you'll find that if something's implicit between x and y, it can be ximplicity itself. No, that's not a typo, it's a hilarious joke... 'implicit' between 'x' and 'y'... do you see?...

You need **Implicit Differentiation** if you can't write the **Equation** as $y = f(x)$

1) An '<u>implicit relation</u>' is the maths name for any equation in x and y that's written in the form $f(x, y) = g(x, y)$ instead of $y = f(x)$. ◄ $f(x, y)$ and $g(x, y)$ don't actually both have to include x and y — one of them could even be a constant.

2) Some implicit relations are either awkward or impossible to rewrite in the form <u>$y = f(x)$</u>. This can happen, for example, if the equation contains a number of <u>different powers of y</u>, or terms where <u>x is multiplied by y</u>.

3) This can make implicit relations tricky to <u>differentiate</u> — the solution is <u>implicit differentiation</u>:

Implicit Differentiation

To find $\dfrac{dy}{dx}$ for an implicit relation between x and y:

1) **Differentiate terms involving x only (and constant terms) with respect to x, as normal.**

2) **Use the <u>chain rule</u> to differentiate terms involving y only:**
$$\frac{d}{dx}f(y) = \frac{d}{dy}f(y)\frac{dy}{dx}$$
◄ In other words, 'differentiate with respect to y, and stick a $\dfrac{dy}{dx}$ on the end'.

3) **Use the <u>product rule</u> to differentiate terms in <u>both</u> x and y:**
$$\frac{d}{dx}u(x)v(y) = u(x)\frac{d}{dx}v(y) + v(y)\frac{d}{dx}u(x)$$
This version of the product rule is slightly different from the one on p20 — it's got v(y) instead of v(x).

4) **Rearrange the resulting equation in x, y and $\dfrac{dy}{dx}$ to make $\dfrac{dy}{dx}$ the subject.**

EXAMPLE Use implicit differentiation to find $\dfrac{dy}{dx}$ if $2x^2y + y^3 = 6x^2 + 5$.

We need to <u>differentiate each term</u> of the equation with respect to x.

Start by sticking '$\dfrac{d}{dx}$' in front of each term:
$$\frac{d}{dx}2x^2y + \frac{d}{dx}y^3 = \frac{d}{dx}6x^2 + \frac{d}{dx}5$$

First, deal with the <u>terms in x</u> and <u>constant terms</u> — in this case that's the two terms on the RHS:
$$\Rightarrow \frac{d}{dx}2x^2y + \frac{d}{dx}y^3 = 12x + 0$$

Now use the <u>chain rule</u> on the <u>term in y</u>:
$$\Rightarrow \frac{d}{dx}2x^2y + 3y^2\frac{dy}{dx} = 12x + 0$$
Using the chain rule from the box above, f(y) = y³.
Leave this $\dfrac{dy}{dx}$ where it is for now.

And use the <u>product rule</u> on the term in <u>x and y</u>:
$$\Rightarrow 2x^2\frac{d}{dx}(y) + y\frac{d}{dx}(2x^2) + 3y^2\frac{dy}{dx} = 12x + 0$$
$$\Rightarrow 2x^2\frac{dy}{dx} + y4x + 3y^2\frac{dy}{dx} = 12x + 0$$
So in terms of the box above, u(x) = 2x² and v(y) = y.

You get a $\dfrac{dy}{dx}$ term here too (from the '$\dfrac{d}{dx}$v(y)' bit).

Finally, <u>rearrange</u> to make $\dfrac{dy}{dx}$ the subject:
$$\Rightarrow \frac{dy}{dx}(2x^2 + 3y^2) = 12x - 4xy$$
$$\Rightarrow \frac{dy}{dx} = \frac{12x - 4xy}{2x^2 + 3y^2}$$

If an imp asks to try your ice lolly, don't let the imp lick it...

Learn the versions of the chain rule and product rule from the box above. All the different bits of the method for implicit differentiation can make it confusing — read the example carefully and make sure you understand every little bit of it.

Implicit Differentiation

If you've gone to all the hard work of <u>differentiating</u> an <u>implicit relation</u>, it would be a shame not to use it. It'd be like a <u>shiny toy</u> that's been kept in its box and never played with. Don't make the maths sad — <u>play with it</u>.

Implicit Differentiation still gives you an expression for the Gradient

Most <u>implicit differentiation</u> questions aren't really that different at heart to any other <u>differentiation question</u>. Once you've got an expression for the <u>gradient</u>, you'll have to <u>use it</u> to do the sort of stuff you'd normally expect.

EXAMPLE

Curve A has the equation $x^2 + 2xy - y^2 = 10x + 4y - 21$

a) Show that when $\frac{dy}{dx} = 0$, $y = 5 - x$.

b) Find the coordinates of the stationary points of A.

For starters, we're going to need to find $\frac{dy}{dx}$ by <u>implicit differentiation</u>:

a)
$$\frac{d}{dx}x^2 + \frac{d}{dx}2xy - \frac{d}{dx}y^2 = \frac{d}{dx}10x + \frac{d}{dx}4y - \frac{d}{dx}21$$

$$\Rightarrow 2x + \frac{d}{dx}2xy - \frac{d}{dx}y^2 = 10 + \frac{d}{dx}4y - 0$$

Differentiate x², 10x and 21 with respect to x.

$$\Rightarrow 2x + \frac{d}{dx}2xy - 2y\frac{dy}{dx} = 10 + 4\frac{dy}{dx}$$

Use the chain rule to differentiate y² and 4y.

$$\Rightarrow 2x + 2x\frac{dy}{dx} + y\frac{d}{dx}2x - 2y\frac{dy}{dx} = 10 + 4\frac{dy}{dx}$$

Use the product rule to differentiate 2xy.

$$\Rightarrow 2x + 2x\frac{dy}{dx} + 2y - 2y\frac{dy}{dx} = 10 + 4\frac{dy}{dx}$$

$$\Rightarrow 2x\frac{dy}{dx} - 2y\frac{dy}{dx} - 4\frac{dy}{dx} = 10 - 2x - 2y$$

Collect '$\frac{dy}{dx}$' terms on one side, and everything else on the other side.

$$\Rightarrow \frac{dy}{dx} = \frac{10 - 2x - 2y}{2x - 2y - 4}$$

So when $\frac{dy}{dx} = 0$, $\quad \frac{10 - 2x - 2y}{2x - 2y - 4} = 0 \quad \Rightarrow \quad 10 - 2x - 2y = 0 \quad \Rightarrow \quad y = 5 - x$

Now we can <u>use</u> the answer to part a) in the equation of the <u>curve</u> to find the points where $\frac{dy}{dx} = 0$.

b) When $\frac{dy}{dx} = 0$, $y = 5 - x$. So at the stationary points,

$$x^2 + 2xy - y^2 = 10x + 4y - 21$$

$$\Rightarrow x^2 + 2x(5 - x) - (5 - x)^2 = 10x + 4(5 - x) - 21$$

Substitute y = 5 − x into the original equation to find the values of x at the stationary points.

$$\Rightarrow x^2 + 10x - 2x^2 - 25 + 10x - x^2 = 10x + 20 - 4x - 21$$

$$\Rightarrow -2x^2 + 20x - 25 = 6x - 1$$

$$\Rightarrow -2x^2 + 14x - 24 = 0$$

$$\Rightarrow x^2 - 7x + 12 = 0$$

$$\Rightarrow (x - 3)(x - 4) = 0$$

$$\Rightarrow x = 3 \text{ or } x = 4$$

$x = 3 \Rightarrow y = 5 - 3 = 2 \qquad x = 4 \Rightarrow y = 5 - 4 = 1$

So the stationary points of A are (3, 2) and (4, 1).

Pah, differentiation? They should have called it same-iation...

...you know, cos all the questions basically end up asking for the same thing. Other familiar faces that are likely to show up in implicit differentiation questions include finding tangents and normals to implicitly defined curves. All these differentiation questions set off in different ways to end up asking you the same thing, so make sure you know the basics.

C3 Section 4 — Practice Questions

Like me, that section was <u>short and sweet</u>. There's only one page of practice questions, so make the most of them.

Warm-up Questions

1) Use <u>implicit differentiation</u> to find $\dfrac{dy}{dx}$ for each of the following equations:

   a) $4x^2 - 2y^2 = 7x^2y$ (b) $3x^4 - 2xy^2 = y$ (c) $\cos x \sin y = xy$ *Assume that questions involving trig are using radians unless stated otherwise.*

2) Using your answers to question 1, find:
   a)   the <u>gradient</u> of the <u>tangent</u> to the graph of $4x^2 - 2y^2 = 7x^2y$ at $(1, -4)$,
   b)   the <u>gradient</u> of the <u>normal</u> to the graph of $3x^4 - 2xy^2 = y$ at $(1, 1)$.

3) A cuboid has length x cm, width $2x$ cm and height $3x$ cm.
   The cuboid is expanding, for some unexplained reason.
   If A is the <u>surface area</u> of the cuboid and V is its <u>volume</u>, find $\dfrac{dA}{dx}$ and $\dfrac{dV}{dx}$,
   and use them to show that if $\dfrac{dV}{dt} = 3$ cm³s⁻¹, then $\dfrac{dA}{dt} = \dfrac{22}{3x}$ cm²s⁻¹.

Be warned — in the exam, <u>rates of change</u> questions can be a bit <u>monstrous</u> (again, like me).

Exam Questions

1   The curve C has the equation $3e^x + 6y = 2x^2y$.

   a)   (i)   Use implicit differentiation to find an expression for $\dfrac{dy}{dx}$.
                                   (3 marks)

         (ii)   Show that at the stationary points of C, $y = \dfrac{3e^x}{4x}$.
                                     (2 marks)

   b)   Hence find the exact coordinates of the two stationary points of C.
                                     (4 marks)

2   The equation of curve C is $6x^2y - 7 = 5x - 4y^2 - x^2$.

   a)   The line T has the equation $y = c$ and passes through a point on C where $x = 2$.
      Find c, given that $c > 0$.
                                     (3 marks)

   b) T also crosses C at point Q.
      (i)   Find the coordinates of Q.
                                     (3 marks)

      (ii)   Find the gradient of C at Q.
                                     (6 marks)

3

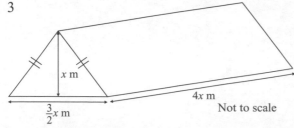

x m $4x$ m $\dfrac{3}{2}x$ m   Not to scale

The triangular prism shown in the diagram is expanding. The dimensions of the prism after t seconds are given in terms of x.
The prism is $4x$ m long, and its cross-section is an isosceles triangle with base $\dfrac{3}{2}x$ m and height x m.

   a)   Show that, if the surface area of the prism after t seconds is A m², then $A = \dfrac{35}{2}x^2$.
                                     (3 marks)

   The surface area of the prism is increasing at a constant rate of 0.07 m² s⁻¹.

   b)   Find $\dfrac{dx}{dt}$ when $x = 0.5$.
                                     (3 marks)

   c)   If the volume of the prism is V m³, find the rate of change of V when $x = 1.2$.
                                     (4 marks)

Integration of e^x and 1/x

Although it was many moons ago that you last encountered <u>integration</u>, way back at AS level, it's an integral part of C3 (and pops up again later in C4). It does the <u>opposite</u> of <u>differentiation</u>, so some of this stuff should look familiar to you.

e^x integrates to give e^x (+ C)

As e^x <u>differentiates</u> to give e^x (see p.18), it makes sense that

$$\int e^x dx = e^x + C$$

Don't forget the constant of integration.

Once you're happy with that, you can use it to solve lots of integrations that have an e^x term in them.
If the <u>coefficient</u> of x isn't 1, you need to <u>divide</u> by that coefficient when you <u>integrate</u> — so $\int e^{kx} dx = \frac{1}{k} e^{kx} + C$

EXAMPLES Integrate the following: a) e^{7x} b) 2e^{4-3x} c) e$^{\frac{x}{2}}$.

a) $\int e^{7x} dx = \boxed{\frac{1}{7} e^{7x} + C}$
If you differentiated e^{7x} using the chain rule, you'd get $7e^{7x}$. So when you integrate, you need to <u>divide by 7</u> (the coefficient of x). This is so that if you differentiated your answer you'd get back to e^{7x}.

b) $\int 2e^{4-3x} dx = \boxed{-\frac{2}{3} e^{4-3x} + C}$
This one isn't as bad as it looks — if you differentiated $2e^{4-3x}$, you'd get $-6e^{4-3x}$, so you need to <u>divide by -3</u> (the coefficient of x) when you integrate. Differentiating your answer gives you $2e^{4-3x}$.

c) $\int e^{\frac{x}{2}} dx = \int e^{\frac{1}{2}x} dx = \boxed{2e^{\frac{x}{2}} + C}$
If you differentiated this one using the chain rule, you'd get $\frac{1}{2}e^{\frac{x}{2}}$, so you need to <u>multiply by 2</u> when you integrate.

Whenever you integrate,

ALWAYS DIFFERENTIATE YOUR ANSWER TO CHECK IT WORKS

— you should end up with the thing you <u>integrated</u> in the first place. It's the best way to check that you <u>divided</u> or <u>multiplied</u> by the right number.

1/x integrates to ln |x| (+ C)

When you first came across integration in C2, you couldn't integrate $\frac{1}{x} (= x^{-1})$ by <u>increasing</u> the <u>power</u> by 1 and <u>dividing</u> by it, as you ended up <u>dividing by 0</u> (which is baaaaad).

However, on p.18, you saw that ln x <u>differentiates</u> to give $\frac{1}{x}$, so

$$\int \frac{1}{x} dx = \ln|x| + C$$

Don't worry about where the modulus sign (see p.5) comes from — using |x| just means that there isn't a problem when x is negative.

EXAMPLES Integrate the following: a) $\frac{5}{x}$ b) $\frac{1}{3x}$ c) $\frac{1}{4x+5}$.

a) $\int \frac{5}{x} dx = 5 \int \frac{1}{x} dx = \boxed{5 \ln|x| + C}$
5 is a constant coefficient — you can take it outside the integral if you want.
You could also write 5ln|x| as ln|x⁵|.

b) $\int \frac{1}{3x} dx = \frac{1}{3} \int \frac{1}{x} dx = \boxed{\frac{1}{3} \ln|x| + C}$
Be careful with ones like this — 1/3 is just the coefficient, so it goes outside ln |x|. Don't make the mistake of putting ln |3x| — this would differentiate to give 1/x (as ln 3x = ln 3 + ln x, so when you differentiate, ln 3 disappears).

c) $\int \frac{1}{4x+5} dx = \boxed{\frac{1}{4} \ln|4x+5| + C}$
However, for this one you have to leave the coefficient (4) inside ln because it's part of the function $4x + 5$. You still have to <u>divide by 4</u> though (again, try differentiating it to see why).

Integration feels pretty constant to me...

These integrations are pretty easy — the only thing you have to worry about is if x has a coefficient that isn't 1. When this happens, work out what you think the answer will look like (e.g. e^x, ln|x|, etc.), then differentiate to see what you get. Then you might have to adjust your answer, usually by dividing or multiplying by the coefficient, to get back to what you started with.

Integrating Other Useful Things

Sometimes you get integrals that look really nasty — like trig functions and fractions. However, there are a couple of clever tricks that can make them easy to integrate.

Sin and Cos are Easy to integrate

From Section 3, you know that sin x differentiates to give cos x and cos x differentiates to give $-\sin x$ (where the angle x is in radians). So it's pretty obvious that:

$$\int \sin x \, dx = -\cos x + C$$
$$\int \cos x \, dx = \sin x + C$$

Integrating tan x is a bit different — see below.

If x has a coefficient that isn't 1 (e.g. sin $3x$), you just divide by the coefficient when you integrate — just like on the previous page.

EXAMPLE Find $\int \cos 4x - 2\sin 2x \, dx$.

Integrate each term separately using the results from above:

$\int \cos 4x \, dx = \frac{1}{4}\sin 4x$ $\int -2\sin 2x \, dx = -2\left(-\frac{1}{2}\cos 2x\right) = \cos 2x$

Putting these terms together and adding the constant gives:

$$\int \cos 4x - 2\sin 2x \, dx = \frac{1}{4}\sin 4x + \cos 2x + C$$

Some Fractions integrate to In

If you have a fraction that has a function of x on the numerator and a different function of x on the denominator (e.g. $\frac{x-2}{x^3+1}$), you'll probably struggle to integrate it. However, if you have a fraction where the numerator is the derivative of the denominator (e.g. $\frac{3x^2}{x^3+1}$), it integrates to give ln of whatever the denominator is (in this case, $x^3 + 1$).

In general terms, this is written as:

$$\int \frac{f'(x)}{f(x)} \, dx = \ln|f(x)| + C$$

This is another one that comes from the chain rule (p.17) — if you differentiated ln .|f(x)|, you'd end up with the fraction on the left.

The hardest bit about questions like this is recognising that the denominator differentiates to give the numerator. Once you've spotted that, it's dead easy. They might make the numerator a multiple of the derivative of the denominator just to confuse things, so watch out for that.

EXAMPLES

Find   a) $\int \frac{8x^3 - 4}{x^4 - 2x} \, dx$ and   b) $\int \frac{3\sin 3x}{\cos 3x + 2} \, dx$.

a) $\frac{d}{dx}(x^4 - 2x) = 4x^3 - 2$

and $8x^3 - 4 = 2(4x^3 - 2)$

The numerator is 2 × the derivative of the denominator, so

$\int \frac{8x^3 - 4}{x^4 - 2x} \, dx = 2\ln|x^4 - 2x| + C$

b) $\frac{d}{dx}(\cos 3x + 2) = -3\sin 3x$

The numerator is minus the derivative of the denominator, so

$\int \frac{3\sin 3x}{\cos 3x + 2} \, dx = -\ln|\cos 3x + 2| + C$

$= -\ln|\cos 3x + 2| - \ln k = -\ln|k(\cos 3x + 2)|$

Using $C = -\ln k$, you can combine all the terms into one using the laws of logs. ln k is just a constant.

You might have noticed from part (b) above that you can work out the integral of tan x using this method:

$\tan x = \frac{\sin x}{\cos x}$,   The numerator is minus the derivative of the denominator, so

and $\frac{d}{dx}(\cos x) = -\sin x$ $\int \tan x \, dx = \int \frac{\sin x}{\cos x} \, dx = -\ln|\cos x| + C$

2 pages in and I've run out of jokes on integration. Please help...

If you come across an integration question with a fraction that doesn't seem to integrate easily, have a quick look and see if one bit is the derivative of the other. If it is, use the rule above and you'll be as happy as Larry (and Larry's always happy).

Integration Using the Chain Rule Backwards

Most integrations aren't as bad as they look — on the previous page, you saw how to integrate special <u>fractions</u>, and now it's time for certain <u>products</u>. There are some things you can look out for when you're integrating...

You can use the *Chain Rule* in *Reverse*

You came across the <u>chain rule</u> in Section 3 (back on p.17) — it's where you write the thing you're differentiating in terms of u (and u is a <u>function</u> of x). You end up with the <u>product</u> of <u>two derivatives</u> ($\frac{dy}{du}$ and $\frac{du}{dx}$).

When it comes to integrating, if you spot that your integral is a <u>product</u> where one bit is the <u>derivative</u> of part of the other bit, you can use this rule:

$$\int \frac{du}{dx} f'(u)\, dx = f(u) + C \qquad \text{where } u \text{ is a function of } x.$$

EXAMPLE

Find   a) $\int 6x^5 e^{x^6}\, dx$ and   b) $\int e^{\sin x} \cos x\, dx$.

a) $\int 6x^5 e^{x^6}\, dx = e^{x^6} + C$ If you differentiated $y = e^{x^6}$ using the chain rule, you'd get $6x^5 e^{x^6}$.
This is the function you had to integrate.

b) $\int e^{\sin x} \cos x\, dx = e^{\sin x} + C$ If you differentiated $y = e^{\sin x}$ using the chain rule, you'd get $e^{\sin x} \cos x$.
This is the function you had to integrate.

Some *Products* are made up of a *Function* and its *Derivative*

Similarly, if you spot that part of a <u>product</u> is the <u>derivative</u> of the other part of it (which is raised to a <u>power</u>), you can integrate it using this <u>rule</u>:

$$\int (n+1) f'(x) [f(x)]^n\, dx = [f(x)]^{n+1} + C$$

Remember that the <u>derivative</u> will be a <u>multiple</u> of $n+1$ (not n) — watch out for any other multiples too. This will probably make more sense if you have a look at an <u>example</u>:

EXAMPLE

Find $\int 12x^3 (2x^4 - 5)^2\, dx$.

Here, $f(x) = 2x^4 - 5$, so differentiating gives $f'(x) = 8x^3$. $n = 2$, so $n + 1 = 3$.

Putting all this into the rule above gives:

$$\int 3(8x^3)(2x^4 - 5)^2\, dx = \int 24x^3 (2x^4 - 5)^2\, dx = (2x^4 - 5)^3 + C$$

Divide everything by 2 to match the original integral:

$$\int 12x^3 (2x^4 - 5)^2\, dx = \tfrac{1}{2}(2x^4 - 5)^3 + C.$$

To get rid of hiccups, drink a glass of water backwards...

It seems to me that most of this section is about reversing the things you learnt in Section 3. I don't know why they ask you to differentiate stuff if you're just going to have to integrate it again and end up where you started. At least it keeps you busy.

Integration by Substitution

Just a little bit more integration to go now — and there are two exciting new types. Integration by substitution is covered on this page, but you'll have to wait till the next page for integration by parts. Ooo, the suspense.

Use **Integration by Substitution** on **Products** of **Two Functions**

Integration by substitution is a clever method that lets you integrate functions of functions by simplifying the integral. It's a bit like the method on the previous page, but more general — you don't have to have a function and its derivative for it to work. Like the chain rule, you have to write part of the function in terms of u, where u is some function of x.

Integration by Substitution

1) You'll be given an integral that's made up of two functions of x (one is sometimes just x) — e.g. $x(3x + 2)^3$.

2) Substitute u for one of the functions of x (to give a function that's easier to integrate) — e.g. $u = 3x + 2$.

   You'll be told what substitution to use (unless it's a really easy one).

3) Next, find $\dfrac{du}{dx}$, and rewrite it so that dx is on its own — e.g. $\dfrac{du}{dx} = 3$, so $dx = \dfrac{1}{3}du$.

   $\dfrac{du}{dx}$ isn't really a fraction, but you can treat it as one for this bit.

4) Rewrite the original integral in terms of u and du — e.g. $\int x(3x + 2)^3\, dx$ becomes $\int \left(\dfrac{u-2}{3}\right)u^3 \dfrac{1}{3}du = \int \dfrac{u^4 - 2u^3}{9}\, du$.

5) You should now be left with something that's easier to integrate — just integrate as normal, then at the last step replace u with the original substitution (so for this one, replace u with $3x + 2$).

EXAMPLE

Use the substitution $u = x^2 - 2$ to find $\int 4x^3(x^2 - 2)^4\, dx$.

As $u = x^2 - 2$, $\dfrac{du}{dx} = 2x$, so $dx = \dfrac{1}{2x}du$.

Substituting gives $\int 4x^3(x^2 - 2)^4\, dx = \int 4x^3 u^4 \dfrac{1}{2x}du = \int 2x^2 u^4 du$.

You've still got an x^2 in there which you need to get rid of. As $u = x^2 - 2$, $x^2 = u + 2$, so the integral becomes $\int 2(u + 2)u^4 du = \int 2u^5 + 4u^4 du$.

You could simplify this more if you wanted.

Integrate... $\int 2u^5 + 4u^4 du = \dfrac{1}{3}u^6 + \dfrac{4}{5}u^5 + C$ ...and substitute x back in: $= \dfrac{1}{3}(x^2 - 2)^6 + \dfrac{4}{5}(x^2 - 2)^5 + C$.

For **Definite Integrals**, you have to **Change** the **Limits**

If you're given a definite integral, it's really important that you remember to change the limits to u. Doing it this way means you don't have to put x back in at the last step — just put the numbers into the integration for u.

EXAMPLE

Use the substitution $u = \cos x$ to find $\displaystyle\int_{\frac{\pi}{2}}^{2\pi} -12\sin x \cos^3 x\, dx$.

As $u = \cos x$, $\dfrac{du}{dx} = -\sin x$, so $dx = -\dfrac{1}{\sin x}du$.

Find the limits of u:

when $x = \dfrac{\pi}{2}$, $u = \cos\dfrac{\pi}{2} = 0$,

when $x = 2\pi$, $u = \cos 2\pi = 1$.

So the limits of u are 0 and 1.

Substituting all this gives:

$$\int_{\frac{\pi}{2}}^{2\pi} -12\sin x \cos^3 x\, dx = \int_0^1 -12\sin x\, u^3 \dfrac{-1}{\sin x}du = \int_0^1 12u^3 du$$

Integrating and putting in the values of the limits gives:

$$[3u^4]_0^1 = [3(1)^4] - [3(0)^4] = 3$$

You could also have solved this one using the method on p.31.

Never substitute salt for sugar...

Life is full of limits — age limits, time limits, height limits, limits of how many times I can gaze at my Hugh Jackman poster while still getting my work done... But at least limits of integration will get you exam marks, so it's worth practising them.

Integration by Parts

Just like you can <u>differentiate products</u> using the <u>product rule</u> (see p.20), you can <u>integrate products</u> using the... er... <u>integration by parts</u>. Not quite as catchy I know, but just as thrilling.

Integration by Parts is the *Reverse* of the *Product Rule*

If you have to integrate a <u>product</u> but can't use integration by substitution (see previous page), you might be able to use <u>integration by parts</u>. The <u>formula</u> for integrating by parts is:

$$\int u\frac{dv}{dx}\,dx = uv - \int v\frac{du}{dx}\,dx$$

where u and v are both functions of x.

The hardest thing about integration by parts is <u>deciding</u> which bit of your product should be <u>u</u> and which bit should be $\frac{dv}{dx}$. There's no set rule for this — you just have to look at both parts and see which one <u>differentiates</u> to give something <u>nice</u>, then set that one as u. For example, if you have a product that has a <u>single x</u> as one part of it, choose this to be u. It differentiates to <u>1</u>, which makes <u>integrating</u> $v\frac{du}{dx}$ dead easy.

EXAMPLE Find $\int 2xe^x\,dx$.

Let $u = 2x$ and let $\frac{dv}{dx} = e^x$. Then u differentiates to give $\frac{du}{dx} = 2$ and $\frac{dv}{dx}$ integrates to give $v = e^x$.

Putting these into the formula gives: $\int 2xe^x\,dx = 2xe^x - \int 2e^x\,dx$

$$= 2xe^x - 2e^x + C$$

If you have a product that has ln x as one of its factors, let u = ln x, as ln x is easy to differentiate but quite tricky to integrate (see below).

EXAMPLE Find $\int x\sin x\,dx$.

Let $u = x$ and let $\frac{dv}{dx} = \sin x$.

Then u differentiates to give $\frac{du}{dx} = 1$ and $\frac{dv}{dx}$ integrates to give $v = -\cos x$.

Putting these into the formula gives: $\int x\sin x\,dx = -x\cos x - \int -\cos x\,dx$

$$= -x\cos x + \int \cos x\,dx$$
$$= \sin x - x\cos x + C$$

You can integrate *ln x* using *Integration by Parts*

Up till now, you haven't been able to integrate <u>ln x</u>, but all that is about to change. There's a little trick you can use — write ln x as $1\cdot$ln x then <u>integrate by parts</u>.

To find $\int \ln x\,dx$, write ln $x = 1\cdot$ln x.

Let $u = \ln x$ and let $\frac{dv}{dx} = 1$. Then u differentiates to give $\frac{du}{dx} = \frac{1}{x}$ and $\frac{dv}{dx}$ integrates to give $v = x$.

Putting these into the formula gives:

$$\int \ln x\,dx = x\ln x - \int x\frac{1}{x}\,dx = x\ln x - \int 1\,dx = x\ln x - x + C$$

Every now and then I fall apart...

After you've had a go at some examples, you'll probably realise that integrals with e^x, $\sin x$ or $\cos x$ in them are actually quite easy, as all three are really easy to integrate and differentiate. Fingers crossed you get one of them in the exam.

C3 Section 5 — Practice Questions

That was a whistlestop tour of the <u>magical world of integration</u> —
and to test your powers, here are some questions for you to have a go at.

Warm-up Questions

1) Find $\int 4e^{2x}\,dx$.

2) Find $\int e^{3x-5}\,dx$.

3) Find $\int \frac{2}{3x}\,dx$.

4) Find $\int \frac{2}{2x+1}\,dx$.

5) Find $\int \cos 4x\,dx$.

6) Integrate $\int \frac{\cos x}{\sin x}\,dx$.

7) Integrate $\int 3x^2 e^{x^3}\,dx$.

8) Integrate $\int \frac{20x^4 + 12x^2 - 12}{x^5 + x^3 - 3x}\,dx$.

9) Use the <u>substitution</u> $u = e^x - 1$ to find $\int e^x(e^x + 1)(e^x - 1)^2\,dx$.

10) Use <u>integration by parts</u> to find $\int 3x^2 \ln x\,dx$.

11) Use <u>integration by parts</u> to find $\int 4x \cos 4x\,dx$.

The examiners might try and <u>disguise</u> integration questions by asking you to <u>find an area</u> under a curve.
Crafty little beggars. Don't be fooled — just remember the things you learnt in this section.

Exam Questions

1   Find $\int 3e^{(5-6x)}\,dx$.

(2 marks)

2   **Figure 1** shows the graph of $y = x \sin x$. The region R is bounded by the curve and the x-axis ($0 \le x \le \pi$).

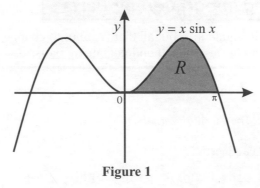

Figure 1

Find the exact area of R using integration by parts.

(4 marks)

3   Find the value of $\int_1^2 \frac{8}{x}(\ln x + 2)^3\,dx$ using the substitution $u = \ln x$. Give your answer to 4 s.f.

(6 marks)

Location of Roots

Although it's not in your exam, you have to do a piece of coursework about finding <u>approximations of roots</u>. This section covers the <u>background knowledge</u> you'll need for the coursework task.

A *Change of Sign* from *f(a)* to *f(b)* means a *Root Between a and b*

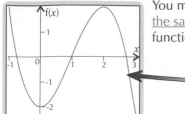

You might have to '<u>solve</u>' or '<u>find the roots of</u>' an equation (where <u>f(x) = 0</u>). This is <u>exactly the same</u> as finding the <u>value of x</u> where the graph <u>crosses the x-axis</u>. The <u>graph</u> of the function gives you a rough idea <u>how many</u> roots there are (<u>if any</u>) and <u>where</u>.

E.g. the function $f(x) = 3x^2 - x^3 - 2$ (shown here) has <u>3 roots</u> in the interval $-1 < x < 3$, since it crosses the x-axis <u>three times</u> (i.e. there are 3 solutions to the equation $3x^2 - x^3 - 2 = 0$). You can also see from the graph that <u>x = 1</u> is a root, and the other roots are <u>close to x = -1 and x = 3</u>.

> The interval $-1 < x < 3$ can also be written (1, 3).

Look at the graph above at the root $x = 1$. For x-values <u>just before</u> the root, f(x) is <u>negative</u>, and <u>just after</u> the root, f(x) is <u>positive</u>. It's the other way around for the other two roots, but either way:

> f(x) changes sign as it passes through a root.

This is only true for <u>continuous functions</u> — ones that are <u>joined up</u> all the way along with no 'jumps' or gaps.

> To show that a root lies in the <u>interval</u> between <u>two values</u> 'a' and 'b':
>
> 1) Find <u>f(a)</u> and <u>f(b)</u>.
>
> 2) If the two answers have <u>different signs</u>, and the function is <u>continuous</u>, there's a root somewhere between 'em.

> $f(x) = \tan x$ is an example of a non-continuous function — it has gaps where f(x) changes sign even though there's no root.

EXAMPLE   Show that $x^4 + 3x - 5 = 0$ has a root in the interval $1.1 < x < 1.2$.

1) Put both 1.1 and 1.2 into the expression:
   $f(1.1) = (1.1)^4 + (3 \times 1.1) - 5 = \underline{-0.2359}$. $f(1.2) = (1.2)^4 + (3 \times 1.2) - 5 = \underline{0.6736}$.

2) f(1.1) and f(1.2) have <u>different signs</u>, and f(x) is <u>continuous</u>, so there's a root in the interval $1.1 < x < 1.2$.

You can find a *Root* using a *Decimal Search*

A <u>decimal search</u> is a pretty easy way to <u>approximate</u> a root — all you have to do is work out the <u>value of the function</u> at <u>different values of x</u>, narrowing your interval whenever there's a <u>sign change</u>. You just keep going until you've reached the number of decimal places (i.e. the <u>accuracy</u>) you want.

EXAMPLE   Use a decimal search to find a root of $x^5 - 4x - 6 = 0$, correct to 1 d.p.

1) Let $f(x) = x^5 - 4x - 6$. Start working out f(x) for different values of x. It's a good idea to put your results in a table.

x	f(x)
-1	-3
0	-6
1	-9
2	18

> There's a sign change here, so you don't need to go any further. A root lies between 1 and 2.

2) Now work out the values of f(x) in the interval (1, 2).

> Remember — this means 1 < x < 2.

x	f(x)
1.1	-8.78949
1.2	-8.31168
1.3	-7.48707
1.4	-6.22176
1.5	-4.40625
1.6	-1.91424
1.7	1.39857

3) The root lies between 1.6 and 1.7, so work out f(x) for values in the interval (1.6, 1.7).

x	f(x)
1.61	-1.6224...
1.62	-1.3222...
1.63	-1.0136...
1.64	-0.6963...
1.65	-0.3701...
1.66	-0.0350...
1.67	0.3091...

4) From this table, you can see that the root lies between 1.66 and 1.67 — so x = 1.7 to 1 d.p.

> If you'd wanted the root to 2 d.p., you'd have to work out values in the interval (1.66, 1.67).

Location of Roots

Methods like the <u>decimal search</u> on the previous page are known as <u>systematic</u> searching methods.
There are <u>two more</u> like this you need to know, then you can move on to the thrill-a-minute <u>iteration formulas</u>.

Bisection divides the interval In Half

The <u>bisection method</u> is a bit like the decimal search — you find an <u>interval</u> that contains the root, then keep <u>narrowing</u> the interval down until you get the accuracy you want. However, at each stage, you divide the interval in <u>half</u>, and pick the half that has the <u>sign change</u> in it — which saves you having to work out f(x) for every number on the way.

EXAMPLE   Use interval bisection to find a root of $x^5 - 4x - 6 = 0$ in the interval (1, 2), correct to 1 d.p.

1) Let f(x) = $x^5 - 4x - 6$. 1.5 bisects the interval (1, 2), so work out f(1.5).
   f(1.5) = −4.40625 (and f(1) = −9 and f(2) = 18), so the root lies between 1.5 and 2.

   Yes, I know this is the same question you did before. I did it on purpose.

2) Now you want to bisect the interval (1.5, 2) — so use 1.75. f(1.75) = 3.4130...
   As f(1.5) was negative, the root lies between 1.5 and 1.75.

   At each stage, the interval gets smaller.

3) Next bisect (1.5, 1.75): f(1.625) = −1.1690... so the root is in the interval (1.625, 1.75).

4) 1.6875 bisects this interval, and f(1.6875) = 0.9341... The root is in the interval (1.625, 1.6875).

5) Continuing like this, you'll find that the root lies in the interval (1.65625, 1.6875), both of which round to 1.7.
   So x = 1.7 to 1 d.p.

Linear Interpolation is a bit harder

<u>Linear interpolation</u> finds a value that divides up the interval in such a way that one end of the interval <u>closes in</u> on the root. You do this by finding where the <u>straight line</u> between f(a) and f(b) for the interval (a, b) <u>crosses the x-axis</u>, then use this value as one of the end points of your new interval. <u>Repeat</u> this method until you find a value (say c) for which f(c) is <u>close to 0</u> (e.g. |f(c)| < 0.001), and take c as your root.

EXAMPLE   Use linear interpolation to find a root of $x^5 - 4x - 6 = 0$ in the interval (1, 2), correct to 1 d.p.

You want to work out where the chord between (1, f(1)) and (2, f(2)) crosses the x-axis.

You can do this using the formula $x = \dfrac{a|f(b)| + b|f(a)|}{|f(a)| + |f(b)|}$.

You could work out the equation of the line in the form $y = mx + c$ (using the points you know) then solving to find x when $y = 0$.

As f(1) = −9 and f(2) = 18, this gives $x = \dfrac{1(|18|) + 2(|-9|)}{|(-9)| + |(18)|} = \dfrac{36}{27} = \dfrac{4}{3} (= 1.3333...)$.

Now work out the value of f(1.3333...) = −7.1193..., so the root lies in the interval (1.3333..., 2).
Continuing with this process, you'll eventually get to a root between 1.65 and 1.7 for which f(c) is just less than 0.
By checking that f(1.75) > 0, you can show that the root is 1.7 to 1 d.p.

Iteration is a more Effective way to find roots

The rest of the section is about the <u>iteration method</u> — put an approximate value of a root x into an <u>iteration formula</u>, and out pops a slightly more accurate value. <u>Repeat</u> as necessary until you have an <u>accurate enough</u> answer.

EXAMPLE   Use the <u>iteration formula</u> $x_{n+1} = \sqrt[3]{x_n + 4}$ to solve f(x) = 0, where f(x) = $x^3 - 4 - x$, to 2 d.p.
            Start with $x_0 = 2$.

1) The notation x_n just means the approximation of x at the nth iteration.
   So putting x_0 in the formula for x_n, gives you x_{n+1}, which is x_1, the first iteration.

2) $x_0 = 2$, so $x_1 = \sqrt[3]{x_0 + 4} = \sqrt[3]{2 + 4} = 1.8171...$

   Leave this in your calculator for accuracy.

3) This value now gets put back into the formula to find x_2:
   $x_1 = 1.8171...$, so $x_2 = \sqrt[3]{x_1 + 4} = \sqrt[3]{1.8171... + 4} = 1.7984...$

   You should now just be able to type '$\sqrt[3]{(ANS + 4)}$' in your calculator and keep pressing enter for each iteration.

4) Carry on until you get answers that are the same when rounded to 2 d.p:
   $x_2 = 1.7984...$, so $x_3 = \sqrt[3]{x_2 + 4} = \sqrt[3]{1.7984... + 4} = 1.7965...$

5) x_2, x_3, and all further iterations are the same when rounded to 2 d.p., so the root is x = 1.80 to 2 d.p.

To check your root, work out the <u>error bounds</u> — values <u>either side</u> of the root (so that <u>all</u> values in the range would be rounded to the root) that have a <u>sign change</u> in between them. Here, the error bounds are <u>1.795</u> and <u>1.805</u> (all values within the range would round to 1.80). f(1.795) = −0.011 and f(1.805) = 0.076. There's a sign change so x = 1.80 to 2 d.p.

Iterative Methods

Now we come to the trickier bits. It's all well and good being able to plug numbers into a formula, but where do those formulas come from? And why don't they always work? Read on to find out...

Rearrange the Equation to get the Iteration Formula

The iteration formula is just a rearrangement of the equation, leaving a single 'x' on one side.

There are often several different ways to rearrange the equation — different arrangements may find different roots of the equation, or no roots at all...

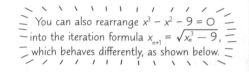

You can also rearrange $x^3 - x^2 - 9 = 0$ into the iteration formula $x_{n+1} = \sqrt{x_n^3 - 9}$, which behaves differently, as shown below.

EXAMPLE Show that $x^3 - x^2 - 9 = 0$ can be rearranged into $x = \sqrt{\dfrac{9}{x-1}}$.

1) The '9' is on its own in the fraction so try:
$$x^3 - x^2 - 9 = 0 \Rightarrow x^3 - x^2 = 9$$

2) The LHS can be factorised now: $x^2(x-1) = 9$

3) Get the x^2 on its own by dividing by $x-1$: $x^2 = \dfrac{9}{x-1}$

4) Finally, take the square root of both sides: $x = \sqrt{\dfrac{9}{x-1}}$

You can now use the iteration formula $x_{n+1} = \sqrt{\dfrac{9}{x_n - 1}}$ to find approximations of the roots.

Sometimes an iteration formula just will not find a root. In these cases, no matter how close to the root you have x_0, the iteration sequence diverges — the numbers get further and further apart. The iteration also might stop working — e.g. if you have to take the square root of a negative number. In your coursework, you have to give an example of an iterative formula failing and explain why it fails — a good way of doing this is to draw a graph (see next page).

EXAMPLE The equation $x^3 - x^2 - 9 = 0$ has a root close to $x = 2.5$.
What is the result of using $x_{n+1} = \sqrt{x_n^3 - 9}$ with $x_0 = 2.5$ to find this root?

1) Start with $x_1 = \sqrt{2.5^3 - 9} = 2.5739...$ (seems okay so far...)

2) Subsequent iterations give: $x_2 = 2.8376...$, $x_3 = 3.7214...$, $x_4 = 6.5221...$ — so the sequence diverges.

The Newton-Raphson Method uses Differentiation

There's another method you can use to find a root — it's called the Newton-Raphson method. To find roots of an equation in the form f(x) = 0, find f'(x) then use this formula:

$$x_{n+1} = x_n - \frac{f(x_n)}{f'(x_n)}$$

You don't need to worry about where this formula comes from for C3.

EXAMPLE Find a root of the equation $x^2 \ln x = 5$ to 5 s.f., using $x_0 = 2$.

1) First, rearrange the equation so it's in the form f(x) = 0: $x^2 \ln x - 5 = 0$.

2) Next, find f'(x): using the product rule (see p.20), let $u = x^2$, so $\dfrac{du}{dx} = 2x$. Let $v = \ln x$, so $\dfrac{dv}{dx} = \dfrac{1}{x}$.
Putting this into the product rule formula gives: $\dfrac{dy}{dx} = x(1 + 2\ln x)$.

3) The formula for the Newton-Raphson method is $x_{n+1} = x_n - \dfrac{x_n^2 \ln x_n - 5}{x_n(1 + 2\ln x_n)}$.

4) Starting with $x_0 = 2$, this gives $x_1 = 2 - \dfrac{2^2 \ln 2 - 5}{2(1 + 2\ln 2)} = 2.466709...$

5) Further iterations give: $x_2 = 2.395369...$
$x_3 = 2.393518...$
$x_4 = 2.393517...$
$x_5 = 2.393517...$ So a root of $x^2 \ln x = 5$ is 2.3935 (5 s.f.).

I feel like stopping working sometimes...

Like the other methods, the Newton-Raphson method might fail if you start too far away from the root. Other than that, it's a pretty good way of finding a root — as long as you have a function you can differentiate (see Section 3 for a recap).

Iterative Methods

Whilst iterations are pretty thrilling on their own, put them into a <u>diagram</u> and the world's your lobster. Well, that might be a bit of an exaggeration, but you can show <u>convergence</u> or <u>divergence</u> easily on a diagram. And it looks pretty.

You can show **Iterations** on a **Diagram**

Once you've calculated a <u>sequence of iterations</u> using $x_{n+1} = f(x_n)$, you can plot the points on a <u>diagram</u> and use it to show whether your sequence <u>converges</u> or <u>diverges</u>.

> ### Sketching Iterations
>
> 1) First, sketch the graphs of <u>$y = x$</u> and <u>$y = f(x)$</u> (where f(x) is the <u>iterative formula</u>). The point where the two graphs <u>meet</u> is the <u>root</u> you're aiming for.
>
> 2) Draw a <u>vertical line</u> from the x-value of your <u>starting point</u> (x_0) until it meets the <u>curve</u> $y = f(x)$.
>
> 3) Now draw a <u>horizontal line</u> from this point to the <u>line</u> $y = x$. At this point, the x-value is x_1, the value of your <u>first iteration</u>. This is one <u>step</u>.
>
> 4) Draw <u>another step</u> — a <u>vertical line</u> from this point to the curve, and a <u>horizontal line</u> joining it to the line $y = x$.
>
> 5) Repeat step 4) for <u>each</u> of your <u>iterations</u>.
>
> 6) If your steps are getting <u>closer and closer</u> to the root, the sequence of iterations is <u>converging</u>. If the steps are moving <u>further and further away</u> from the root, the sequence is <u>diverging</u>.

This method produces two different types of diagrams — cobweb diagrams and staircase diagrams.

Convergent iterations **Home In** on the **Root**

It's probably easiest to follow the method by looking at a few <u>examples</u>:

EXAMPLES

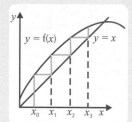

This is an example of a <u>convergent staircase diagram</u>. Starting at x_0, the next iterations x_1, x_2 and x_3 are getting <u>closer</u> to the point where the two graphs intersect (the root).

This is an example of a <u>convergent cobweb diagram</u>. In this case, the iterations <u>alternate</u> between being <u>below</u> the root and <u>above</u> the root, but are still getting <u>closer</u> each time.

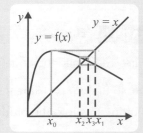

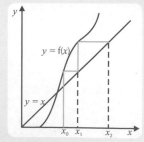

This is an example of a <u>divergent staircase diagram</u>. Starting at x_0, the iterations x_1 and x_2 are getting <u>further away</u> from the root.

In each case, the diagram will look different depending on where your starting point is.

There are cobwebs on my staircase...

Drawing diagrams isn't too bad — it's mainly just a case of drawing straight lines. If your iterative function is a bit nasty (which it probably will be), you can get computer programs that'll sketch the graph (and even draw on the iterations) for you.

Iterative Methods

So now that you know all you need to know to be able to tackle the coursework, let's have a look at how it all fits together in a <u>worked example</u>. Brace yourself...

Your **Coursework** will combine all the **Different Methods**

In your coursework, you'll have to use <u>different methods</u> to find roots — like in this giant worked example.

EXAMPLE   The graph below shows both roots of the continuous function $f(x) = 6x - x^2 + 13$.
   a)   Show that the positive root, α, of $f(x) = 0$ lies in the interval $7 < x < 8$.
   b)   Show that $6x - x^2 + 13 = 0$ can be rearranged into the formula: $x = \sqrt{6x + 13}$.
   c)   Use the iteration formula $x_{n+1} = \sqrt{6x_n + 13}$ and $x_0 = 7$ to find α to 1 d.p.
   d)   Sketch a diagram to show the convergence of the sequence for x_1, x_2 and x_3.
   e)   Use the Newton-Raphson method to find the negative root, β, to 5 s.f.
         Start with $x_0 = -1$. Find error bounds to check your root.

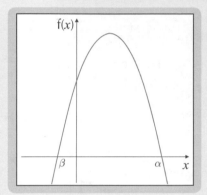

a) $f(x)$ is a <u>continuous function</u>, so if $f(7)$ and $f(8)$ have <u>different signs</u> then there is a root in the interval $7 < x < 8$:

$$f(7) = (6 \times 7) - 7^2 + 13 = 6.$$
$$f(8) = (6 \times 8) - 8^2 + 13 = -3.$$

There is a <u>change of sign</u> so $7 < \alpha < 8$.

b)   Get the x^2 on its own to make: $6x + 13 = x^2$

Now take the (positive) square root to leave: $x = \sqrt{6x + 13}$.

c)   Using $x_{n+1} = \sqrt{6x_n + 13}$ with $x_0 = 7$, gives $x_1 = \sqrt{6 \times 7 + 13} = 7.4161...$

Continuing the iterations:
$x_2 = \sqrt{6 \times 7.4161... + 13} = 7.5826...$ $x_3 = \sqrt{6 \times 7.5826... + 13} = 7.6482...$
$x_4 = \sqrt{6 \times 7.6482... + 13} = 7.6739...$ $x_5 = \sqrt{6 \times 7.6739... + 13} = 7.6839...$
$x_6 = \sqrt{6 \times 7.6839... + 13} = 7.6879...$ $x_7 = \sqrt{6 \times 7.6879... + 13} = 7.6894...$

The list of results from each iteration x_1, x_2, x_3... is called the iteration <u>sequence</u>.

x_4 to x_7 all round to 7.7 to 1 d.p., so to 1 d.p. $\alpha = 7.7$.

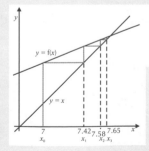

d)   Sketch $y = \sqrt{6x + 13}$ and $y = x$ on the same axes, and mark on the position of x_0. All you have to do is draw on the <u>lines</u> and label the <u>values</u> of x_1, x_2 and x_3. You can see from the diagram that the sequence is a <u>convergent staircase</u>.

e)   Find $f'(x)$: $f'(x) = 6 - 2x$. Putting this into the <u>Newton-Raphson formula</u> gives:

$$x_{n+1} = x_n - \frac{6x_n - x_n^2 + 13}{6 - 2x_n}$$

Starting with $x_0 = -1$, this gives $x_1 = -1 - \dfrac{6(-1) - (-1)^2 + 13}{6 - 2(-1)} = -1.75$.
Further iterations give $x_2 = -1.690789...$
                                     $x_3 = -1.690415...$
                                     $x_4 = -1.690415...$ So $\beta = -1.6904$ to 5 s.f.

The <u>error bounds</u> for this are -1.69035 and -1.69045, and $f(-1.69035) = 0.0006$, $f(-1.69045) = -0.0003$. There is a <u>sign change</u> so the root is accurate to 5 s.f.

You might have to <u>compare</u> the different iteration methods — to do this, all you have to do is use <u>each method</u> to find the <u>same root</u>, then think about which one was the easiest to use, which was the quickest (i.e. took the <u>fewest iterations</u>) etc.

Trouble finding a root? Try sat-nav...

And that's your lot — wasn't so bad, was it? All done and dusted, except for some practice questions to prepare you for the coursework. So calculators at the ready, grab your lucky pen and prepare to iterate your heart out...

C3 Section 6 — Practice Questions

Oh happy day, there's light at the end of the C3 tunnel. You won't be asked any questions on iteration in your exam, but here are some practice questions to prepare you for your coursework. Aren't I nice?

Practice Questions

1) The graph shows the function $f(x) = e^x - x^3$ for $0 \leq x \leq 5$.
   How many roots does the equation $e^x - x^3 = 0$ have in the interval $0 \leq x \leq 5$?

   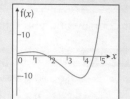

2) Show that there is a root in the interval:
   a) $3 < x < 4$ for $\sin(2x) = 0$,   *Don't forget to use radians when you're given trig functions.*
   b) $2.1 < x < 2.2$ for $\ln(x - 2) + 2 = 0$,
   c) $4.3 < x < 4.5$ for $x^3 - 4x^2 = 7$.

3) The equation $x^4 - x^5 + 3 = 0$ has a root in the interval (1, 2). Find this root to 1 d.p. using
   a) decimal search,
   b) bisection.
   c) Find the first 4 iterations using linear interpolation.

4) Find error bounds to show that, to 1 d.p, $x = 1.2$ is a root of the equation $x^3 + x - 3 = 0$.

5) Use the formula $x_{n+1} = -\frac{1}{2}\cos x_n$, with $x_0 = -1$, to find a root of $\cos x + 2x = 0$ to 2 d.p.

6) Use the formula $x_{n+1} = \sqrt{\ln x_n + 4}$, with $x_0 = 2$, to find a root of $x^2 - \ln x - 4 = 0$ to 3 d.p.

7) a) Show that the equation $2x^2 - x^3 + 1 = 0$ can be written in the form:

   (i) $x = \sqrt{\dfrac{-1}{2-x}}$ (ii) $x = \sqrt[3]{2x^2 + 1}$ (iii) $x = \sqrt{\dfrac{x^3 - 1}{2}}$

   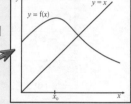

   b) Use iteration formulas based on each of the above rearrangements with $x_0 = 2.3$ to find a root of $2x^2 - x^3 + 1 = 0$ to 2 d.p. Which of the three formulas converge to a root?

8) Using the position of x_0 as given on the graph, draw a staircase or cobweb diagram showing how the sequence converges. Label x_1 and x_2 on the diagram.

9) Use the Newton-Raphson method to find a root of $x^4 - 2x^3 = 5$ to 5 s.f., starting with $x_0 = 2.5$.

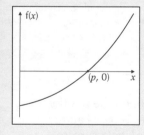

10) The sketch on the left shows part of the graph of the function $f(x) = 2xe^x - 3$.
    The curve crosses the x-axis at the point P $(p, 0)$, as shown, so p is a root of the equation $f(x) = 0$.
    a) Show that $0.7 < p < 0.8$.
    b) Show that $f(x) = 0$ can be rewritten as: $x = \frac{3}{2}e^{-x}$.
    c) Starting with $x_0 = 0.7$, use the iteration $x_{n+1} = \frac{3}{2}e^{-x_n}$ to find x_1, x_2, x_3 and x_4 to 4 d.p.
    d) By finding error bounds, show that $p = 0.726$, to 3 d.p.

11) The graph of the function $y = \sin 3x + 3x$, $0 < x < \pi$, meets the line $y = 1$ when $x = a$.
    a) Show that $0.1 < a < 0.2$.
    b) Show that the equation $\sin 3x + 3x = 1$ can be written as $x = \frac{1}{3}(1 - \sin 3x)$.
    c) Starting with $x_0 = 0.2$, use the iteration $x_{n+1} = \frac{1}{3}(1 - \sin 3x_n)$ to find x_4, to 3 d.p.
    d) Use the Newton-Raphson method to find the same root, starting with $x_0 = 0.2$ again.
       Comment on which method was more effective.

12) The sequence given by $x_{n+1} = \sqrt[3]{x_n^2 - 4}$, $x_0 = -1$, converges to a number 'b'.
    a) Find the values of x_1, x_2, x_3 and x_4 correct to 4 decimal places.
    b) Show that $x = b$ is a root of the equation $x^3 - x^2 + 4 = 0$.
    c) Find error bounds to show that $b = -1.315$ to 3 decimal places.

13) The equation $f(x) = 0$, where $f(x) = \ln(x + 3) - x + 2$, $x > -3$, has a root at $x = m$.
    a) Show that m lies between 3 and 4.
    b) Find, using iteration, the value of m correct to 2 decimal places.
       Use the iteration formula $x_{n+1} = \ln(x_n + 3) + 2$, with $x_0 = 3$.
    c) Find error bounds to verify that your answer to part b) is correct to 2 decimal places.

General Certificate of Education
Advanced Subsidiary (AS) and Advanced Level

Core Mathematics C3 — Practice Exam One

Time Allowed: 1 hour 30 min

Graphical calculators may be used for this exam.

Give any non-exact numerical answers to an appropriate degree of accuracy.

There are 72 marks available for this paper.

Section A (36 marks)

1 For the function:

$$f(x) = 3 \ln x - \ln 3x, \qquad x > 0$$

find:

a) the exact value of x when $f(x) = 0$.

(2 marks)

b) $f^{-1}(x)$.

(2 marks)

2 For the functions $g(x) = \sqrt{2x + 3}$, $x \geq -1.5$, and $h(x) = \dfrac{6}{x^2 - 4}$, $x > 2$, find:

a) gh(4)

(2 marks)

b) hg(3)

(2 marks)

c) hg(x)

(3 marks)

3 a) Sketch the graph of $f(x) = |5x - 4|$, showing clearly where it touches the coordinate axes.

(2 marks)

b) Hence or otherwise solve the equation $|5x - 4| = 2$.

(3 marks)

4   The graph below shows the function $y = f(x)$, $x \in \mathbb{R}$, with turning points $A(-1, -2)$ and $B(3, 2)$.

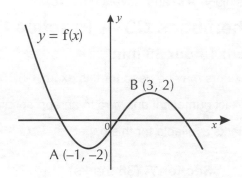

On separate axes, sketch the graphs of the following, clearly showing the coordinates of A and B where possible.

a) $y = f(|x|)$.

(3 marks)

b) $y = 3f(x + 2)$.

(3 marks)

5   A curve has the equation $x = \dfrac{e^y + 2y}{e^y - 2y}$.

a)   Find $\dfrac{dy}{dx}$.

(3 marks)

b)   Find an equation of the normal to the curve at the point $(1, 0)$ in the form $y = ax + b$.

(3 marks)

6   The UK population, P, of an endangered species of bird has been modelled over time, t years, by the function:

$$P = 5700e^{-0.15t} \quad (t \geq 0)$$

The time $t = 0$ is set as the beginning of the year 2010.

a)   State the UK population of the species at the start of 2010.

(1 mark)

b)   Predict the UK population of the species at the start of 2020.

(2 marks)

c)   Predict the year that the population will drop to below 1000.

(2 marks)

d)   Sketch a graph to show the predicted UK population of the species between 2010 and 2025.

(3 marks)

Section B (36 marks)

7   The graph below shows the curve $y = \dfrac{3\ln x}{x^2}$, $x \geq 0$. The shaded region R is bounded by the curve, the x-axis and the line $x = 3$.

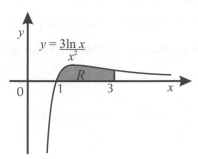

a)   Find the value of the integral $\displaystyle\int_1^3 \dfrac{3\ln x}{x^2}\,dx$ using integration by parts. Give your answer to 5 decimal places.

(5 marks)

b)   (i)   Find $\dfrac{dy}{dx}$.

(4 marks)

(ii)   Hence find the gradient of the curve at the point $x = 1$.

(2 marks)

c)   A different curve is given by the equation $y = \dfrac{x}{1 - x^2}$.

Find the exact value of $\displaystyle\int_0^{\frac{1}{2}} \dfrac{x}{1 - x^2}\,dx$ using the substitution $u = 1 - x^2$.

(7 marks)

8   A curve C_1 has the equation $x^3 + x^2 y = y^2 - 1$.

a)   Use implicit differentiation to find an expression for $\dfrac{dy}{dx}$.

(4 marks)

The points P and Q lie on C_1. P has coordinates $(1, a)$ and Q has coordinates $(1, b)$.

b)   (i)   Find the values of a and b, given that $a > b$.

(2 marks)

(ii)   Find the equation of the normal to C_1 at Q.

(3 marks)

The curve C_2 given by the equation $y = \dfrac{4}{3 - x^2}$ also passes through the point P.

c)   (i)   Using algebra, show that $\dfrac{4}{3 - x^2}$ is an even function.
What does this tell you about the graph of the curve C_2?

(3 marks)

(ii)   Find $\dfrac{dy}{dx}$ for the curve C_2.

(3 marks)

(iii)   Find the gradient of C_2 at P.

(2 marks)

(iv)   Verify that C_2 has a turning point at R, which has coordinates $(0, \tfrac{4}{3})$.

(1 mark)

General Certificate of Education
Advanced Subsidiary (AS) and Advanced Level

Core Mathematics C3 — Practice Exam Two

Time Allowed: 1 hour 30 min

Graphical calculators may be used for this exam.

Give any non-exact numerical answers to an appropriate degree of accuracy.

There are 72 marks available for this paper.

Section A (36 marks)

1   The functions f and g are defined as follows:

$$f(x) = \frac{1}{x^2}, \quad x \in \mathbb{R}, \ x \neq 0$$
$$g(x) = x^2 - 9, \quad x \in \mathbb{R}$$

a)   State the range of g.

(1 mark)

b)   Neither f nor g have an inverse. Explain why.

(1 mark)

c)   Find
    (i)   fg(4)

(2 marks)

    (ii)   gf(1)

(2 marks)

2   Use integration by parts to find $\int 4xe^{-2x}\,dx$.

(4 marks)

3   a)   Prove the following statement:

For all integers n, $n^3 - n$ is always even.

(2 marks)

b)   Disprove the following statement:

For integers p and q, if $p > q$, then $p^2 > q^2$.

(2 marks)

4   For the function:
$$f(x) = (\sqrt{x+2})\ln(x+2) \quad (x > -2)$$

a)   Show that $f(x) = 6\ln 3$ when $x = 7$.

(2 marks)

b)   Show that $f'(x) = \frac{1}{3}(1 + \ln 3)$ when $x = 7$.

(4 marks)

c)   Hence show that the equation of the tangent to the curve:
$$y = (\sqrt{x+2})\ln(x+2).$$
at the point $x = 7$ can be written as:
$$3y = x + x\ln 3 + 11\ln 3 - 7.$$

(2 marks)

5   Find $\int_{1}^{2}\left(\frac{\ln x}{\sqrt{x}}\right)^{2} dx$, using the substitution $u = \ln x$. Give your answer to 3 significant figures.

(5 marks)

6   A curve is given by the implicit equation $\sin \pi x - \cos\left(\frac{\pi y}{2}\right) = 0.5$, for $0 \le x \le 2, 0 \le y \le 2$.

a)   Show that $\frac{dy}{dx} = -\frac{2\cos \pi x}{\sin\frac{\pi y}{2}}$.

(2 marks)

b)   Hence find:
     (i)   the coordinates of the stationary point of the curve,

(4 marks)

     (ii) the equation of the tangent to the curve when $x = \frac{1}{6}$.

(3 marks)

Section B (36 marks)

7   a)   A curve has the equation $y = e^{2x} - 5e^x + 3x$.

   (i)   Find $\dfrac{dy}{dx}$.

(2 marks)

   (ii)   Find $\dfrac{d^2y}{dx^2}$.

(2 marks)

   (iii)   Show that the stationary points on the curve occur when $x = 0$ and $x = \ln \frac{3}{2}$.

(4 marks)

   (iv)   Determine the nature of each of the stationary points.

(4 marks)

   b)   A different curve has the equation $f(x) = e^{x^2 - 4}$, $x \geq 0$.

   (i)   Find the inverse, $f^{-1}(x)$.

(3 marks)

   (ii)   Describe in words the geometrical transformations that would turn the curve $f(x) = e^{x^2 - 4}$ into the curve $f(x) = -3e^{x^2 - 4} + 5$.

(3 marks)

8   The diagram shows a container in the shape of a hollow regular tetrahedron, which is inverted so that the vertex P is at the bottom. The container is being filled with water.

   After t minutes, the distance from P to the surface of the water is x cm, and the volume of water in the container is V cm^3.

   A regular tetrahedron with edge length a and vertical height h has volume $\dfrac{\sqrt{2}}{12}a^3$, and $h = \sqrt{\dfrac{2}{3}}\,a$.

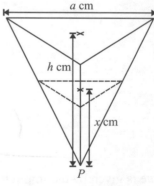

   a)   Given that the water in the container forms a smaller tetrahedron similar to the container, find expressions in terms of x for:

   (i)   The edge length of this smaller tetrahedron after t minutes,

(2 marks)

   (ii)   The volume of water in the container after t minutes, V.

(3 marks)

   Water is being poured into the container at a constant rate of 240 cm^3 min^{-1}.

   b)   Find $\dfrac{dx}{dt}$ when the depth of the water in the container is 8 cm.

(6 marks)

   The value of $\dfrac{dx}{dt}$ is measured when $x = 12$, and found to be $\dfrac{32}{9\sqrt{3}}$.

   This is less than the value expected if $\dfrac{dV}{dt} = 240$ cm^3 min^{-1}.

   It is discovered that water has been flowing out of the container through a leak at P at a constant rate of r cm^3 min^{-1} since the container first started being filled.

   c)   (i)   Find $\dfrac{dV}{dt}$ if $\dfrac{dx}{dt} = \dfrac{32}{9\sqrt{3}}$ when $x = 12$.

(4 marks)

   (ii)   Hence find r.

(3 marks)

Simplifying Expressions

What a lovely way to start C4 — a page on <u>algebraic fractions</u>. Still, at least they're over with early on, so if they pop up later on you'll know what to do. No, not run away and cower in a corner — use the things you learnt on this page.

Simplify algebraic fractions by Factorising and Cancelling Factors

<u>Algebraic fractions</u> are a lot like normal fractions — and you can treat them in the <u>same way</u>, whether you're <u>multiplying</u>, <u>dividing</u>, <u>adding</u> or <u>subtracting</u> them. All fractions are much <u>easier</u> to deal with when they're in their <u>simplest form</u>, so the first thing to do with algebraic fractions is to <u>simplify</u> them as much as possible.

1) Look for <u>common factors</u> in the <u>numerator</u> and <u>denominator</u> — <u>factorise</u> top and bottom and see if there's anything you can <u>cancel</u>.

2) If there's a <u>fraction</u> in the numerator or denominator (e.g. $\frac{1}{x}$), <u>multiply</u> the <u>whole thing</u> (i.e. top and bottom) by the same factor to get rid of it (for $\frac{1}{x}$, you'd multiply through by x).

EXAMPLES Simplify the following:

a) $\dfrac{3x+6}{x^2-4} = \dfrac{3(x+2)}{(x+2)(x-2)} = \dfrac{3}{x-2}$

Watch out for the difference of two squares — see C1.

b) $\dfrac{2+\frac{1}{2x}}{4x^2+x} = \dfrac{\left(2+\frac{1}{2x}\right) \times 2x}{x(4x+1) \times 2x} = \dfrac{4x+1}{2x^2(4x+1)} = \dfrac{1}{2x^2}$

3) You <u>multiply</u> algebraic fractions in exactly the same way as normal fractions — multiply the <u>numerators</u> together, then multiply the <u>denominators</u>. It's a good idea to <u>cancel</u> any <u>common factors</u> before you multiply.

4) To <u>divide</u> by an algebraic fraction, you just <u>multiply</u> by its <u>reciprocal</u> (the reciprocal is 1 ÷ the original thing — for fractions you just turn the fraction <u>upside down</u>).

EXAMPLES Simplify the following:

a) $\dfrac{x^2-2x-15}{2x+8} \times \dfrac{x^2-16}{x^2+3x} = \dfrac{(x+3)(x-5)}{2(x+4)} \times \dfrac{(x+4)(x-4)}{x(x+3)}$

Factorise both fractions.

$= \dfrac{(x-5)(x-4)}{2x} \left(= \dfrac{x^2-9x+20}{2x} \right)$

b) $\dfrac{3x}{5} \div \dfrac{3x^2-9x}{20} = \dfrac{3x}{5} \times \dfrac{20}{3x(x-3)}$

Turn the second fraction upside down.

$= \dfrac{4}{x-3}$

Add and Subtract fractions by finding a Common Denominator

You'll have come across <u>adding</u> and <u>subtracting fractions</u> before, so here's a little reminder of how to do it:

EXAMPLE Simplify:

$\dfrac{2y}{x(x+3)} + \dfrac{1}{y^2(x+3)} - \dfrac{x}{y}$

① Find the Common Denominator

Take all the individual 'bits' from the bottom lines and multiply them together. Only use each bit once unless something on the bottom line is raised to a power.

The individual 'bits' here are x, (x + 3) and y...

$xy^2(x+3)$

...but you need to use y^2 because there's a y^2 in the second fraction's denominator.

The common denominator is the lowest common multiple (LCM) of all the denominators.

② Put Each Fraction over the Common Denominator

Make the denominator of each fraction into the common denominator.

$\dfrac{y^2 \times 2y}{y^2x(x+3)} + \dfrac{x \times 1}{xy^2(x+3)} - \dfrac{xy(x+3) \times x}{xy(x+3)y}$

Multiply the top and bottom lines of each fraction by whatever makes the bottom line the same as the common denominator.

③ Combine into One Fraction

Once everything's over the common denominator you can just add the top lines together.

All the bottom lines are the same — so you can just add the top lines.

$= \dfrac{2y^3 + x - x^2y(x+3)}{xy^2(x+3)}$

$= \dfrac{2y^3 + x - x^3y - 3x^2y}{xy^2(x+3)}$

Who are you calling common...

Nothing on this page should be a big shock to you — it's all stuff you've done before. You've been using normal fractions for years, and algebraic fractions work in just the same way. They look a bit scary, but they're all warm and fuzzy inside.

Algebraic Division

I'll be honest with you, <u>algebraic division</u> is a bit tricky. But as long as you take it <u>slowly</u> and don't rush, it'll all fall into place. And it's really quick and easy to <u>check your answer</u> if you're not sure. What more could you want?

There are some **Terms** you need to **Know**

There are a few words that keep popping up in <u>algebraic division</u>, so make sure you know what they all mean.

1) <u>DEGREE</u> — the highest power of x in the polynomial (e.g. the degree of $4x^5 + 6x^2 - 3x - 1$ is 5).

2) <u>DIVISOR</u> — this is the thing you're dividing by (e.g. if you divide $x^2 + 4x - 3$ by $x + 2$, the divisor is $x + 2$).

3) <u>QUOTIENT</u> — the bit that you get when you divide by the divisor (not including the remainder — see p.49).

Method 1 — **Divide** by **Subtracting Multiples** of the **Divisor**

Back in C1, you learnt how to do <u>algebraic division</u> by <u>subtracting</u> chunks of the <u>divisor</u>.
Here's a quick reminder of how to divide a polynomial by $x - k$:

Algebraic Division

1) <u>Subtract</u> a multiple of $(x - k)$ to get rid of the highest power of x.

2) <u>Repeat</u> step 1 until you've got rid of all the powers of x.

3) <u>Work out</u> how many lumps of $(x - k)$, you've subtracted, and read off the <u>remainder</u>.

Have a look back at your C1 notes if you can't remember how to do this.

EXAMPLE Divide $2x^3 - 3x^2 - 3x + 7$ by $x - 2$.

① Start with $2x^3 - 3x^2 - 3x + 7$, and <u>subtract</u> $2x^2$ lots of $(x - 2)$ to get rid of the x^3 term. $\longrightarrow (2x^3 - 3x^2 - 3x + 7) - 2x^2(x - 2) = x^2 - 3x + 7$

② Now <u>start again</u> with $x^2 - 3x + 7$. The highest power of x is the x^2 term, so <u>subtract</u> x lots of $(x - 2)$ to get rid of that. $\longrightarrow (x^2 - 3x + 7) - x(x - 2) = -x + 7$

③ All that's left now is $-x + 7$. Get rid of $-x$ by <u>subtracting</u> $-1 \times (x - 2)$. $\Longrightarrow (-x + 7) - (-1(x - 2)) = 5$

So $(2x^3 - 3x^2 - 3x + 7) \div (x - 2) = 2x^2 + x - 1$ remainder 5.

Method 2 — use **Algebraic Long Division**

To divide two <u>algebraic</u> expressions, you can use <u>long division</u> (using the same method you'd use for numbers).

EXAMPLE Divide $2x^3 - 7x^2 - 16x + 11$ by $x - 5$.

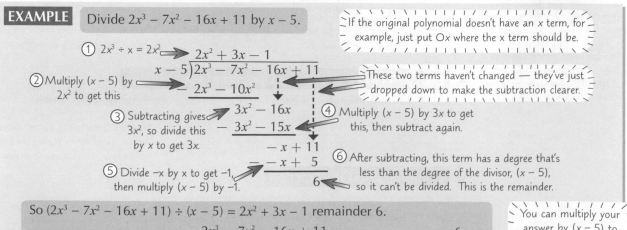

If the original polynomial doesn't have an x term, for example, just put $0x$ where the x term should be.

① $2x^3 \div x = 2x^2$

② Multiply $(x - 5)$ by $2x^2$ to get this

These two terms haven't changed — they've just dropped down to make the subtraction clearer.

③ Subtracting gives $3x^2$, so divide this by x to get $3x$.

④ Multiply $(x - 5)$ by $3x$ to get this, then subtract again.

⑤ Divide $-x$ by x to get -1, then multiply $(x - 5)$ by -1.

⑥ After subtracting, this term has a degree that's less than the degree of the divisor, $(x - 5)$, so it can't be divided. This is the remainder.

So $(2x^3 - 7x^2 - 16x + 11) \div (x - 5) = 2x^2 + 3x - 1$ remainder 6.

This could also be written as $\dfrac{2x^3 - 7x^2 - 16x + 11}{x - 5} = 2x^2 + 3x - 1 + \dfrac{6}{x - 5}$.

You can multiply your answer by $(x - 5)$ to check you've got it right.

Just keep repeating — divide and conquer, divide and conquer...

For algebraic division to work, the degree of the divisor has to be less than (or equal to) the degree of the original polynomial (for example, you couldn't divide $x^2 + 2x + 3$ by $x^3 + 4$ as $3 > 2$, but you could do it the other way around). If you don't like either of these methods, you'll be pleased to know there's another way to divide coming up on the next page.

Algebraic Division

I really spoil you — as if <u>two different methods</u> for doing <u>algebraic division</u> weren't enough, I'm going to give you a <u>third</u>. If you're not sure about any of the <u>terms</u>, look back at the <u>definitions</u> on p.48.

Method 3 — use the Formula f(x) ≡ q(x)d(x) + r(x)

There's a handy <u>formula</u> you can use to do <u>algebraic division</u>. It looks like this:

> A polynomial $f(x)$ can be written in the form $f(x) \equiv q(x)d(x) + r(x)$, where $q(x)$ is the quotient, $d(x)$ is the divisor and $r(x)$ is the remainder.

This comes from the Remainder Theorem that you met in C1. It's a good method for when you're dividing by a quadratic — long division can get a bit tricky when the divisor has 3 terms.

You'll be given $f(x)$ and $d(x)$ in the <u>question</u>, and it's down to you to <u>work out</u> $q(x)$ and $r(x)$. Here's how you do it:

Using the Formula

1) First, you have to work out the <u>degrees</u> of the <u>quotient</u> and <u>remainder</u>, which depend on the degrees of the <u>polynomial</u> and the <u>divisor</u>. The degree of the quotient is $\deg f(x) - \deg d(x)$, and the degree of the remainder has to be <u>less</u> than the degree of the <u>divisor</u>.

2) Write out the division using the <u>formula</u> above, but replace $q(x)$ and $r(x)$ with <u>general polynomials</u> (i.e. a general polynomial of degree 2 is $Ax^2 + Bx + C$, and a general polynomial of degree 1 is $Ax + B$, where A, B, C, etc. are <u>constants</u> to be found).

3) The next step is to work out the <u>values</u> of the constants — you do this by <u>substituting</u> in values for x to make bits <u>disappear</u>, and by <u>equating coefficients</u>.

Equating coefficients means comparing the coefficients of each power of x on the LHS and the RHS.

4) It's best to start with the <u>constant term</u> and <u>work backwards</u> from there.

5) Finally, write out the division again, <u>replacing</u> A, B, C, etc. with the values you've <u>found</u>.

The method looks a bit <u>intense</u>, but follow through the <u>examples</u> below to see how it works.

Start with the Remainder and Work Backwards

When you're using this method, you might have to use <u>simultaneous equations</u> to work out some of the coefficients. Have a look back at your C1 notes for a reminder of how to do this if you need to.

EXAMPLE   Divide $x^4 - 3x^3 - 3x^2 + 10x + 5$ by $x^2 - 5x + 6$.

$f(x)$ has degree 4 and $d(x)$ has degree 2, which means that $q(x)$ has degree $4 - 2 = 2$. The remainder has degree 1 or 0 — put in $Dx + E$, as D can always be 0.

① First, write out the division in the form $f(x) \equiv q(x)d(x) + r(x)$:

$x^4 - 3x^3 - 3x^2 + 10x + 5 \equiv (Ax^2 + Bx + C)(x^2 - 5x + 6) + Dx + E$

$\equiv (Ax^2 + Bx + C)(x - 2)(x - 3) + Dx + E$.

$d(x)$ factorises to give $(x - 2)(x - 3)$.

② <u>Substitute $x = 2$ and $x = 3$</u> into the identity to make the $q(x)d(x)$ bit disappear. This gives the equations $5 = 2D + E$ and $8 = 3D + E$. Solving these <u>simultaneously</u> gives $D = 3$ and $E = -1$, so the <u>remainder</u> is $3x - 1$.

③ Now, using these values of D & E and putting <u>$x = 0$</u> into the identity gives the equation $5 = 6C + E$, so $C = 1$.

④ Using the values of C, D and E and <u>equating the coefficients</u> of x^4 and x^3 gives: $1 = A$ and $-3 = -5A + B$, so $B = 2$. Putting these values into the original identity gives:

$x^4 - 3x^3 - 3x^2 + 10x + 5 \equiv (x^2 + 2x + 1)(x^2 - 5x + 6) + 3x - 1$.

EXAMPLE   Divide $x^3 + 5x^2 - 18x - 10$ by $x - 3$.

$f(x)$ has degree 3 and $d(x)$ has degree 1, which means that $q(x)$ has degree $3 - 1 = 2$. The remainder has degree 0.

First, write out the division in the form $f(x) \equiv q(x)d(x) + r(x)$: $x^3 + 5x^2 - 18x - 10 \equiv (Ax^2 + Bx + C)(x - 3) + D$. Putting $x = 3$ into the identity gives $D = 8$. Now, setting $x = 0$ gives the equation $-3C + D = -10$, so $C = 6$. Equating the coefficients of x^3 and x^2 gives $A = 1$ and $-3A + B = 5$, so $B = 8$.

So $x^3 + 5x^2 - 18x - 10 \equiv (x^2 + 8x + 6)(x - 3) + 8$.

A reminder about remainders...

The degree of the remainder has to be less than the degree of the divisor, otherwise it would be included in the quotient. E.g. if $r(x) = (x + 1)$ and $d(x) = (x - 3)$, then $r(x)$ can be divided by $d(x)$, giving a remainder of 4 (so $(x + 1)$ wasn't the remainder).

50

Partial Fractions

Wait, wait — come back. You're not done with fractions yet. Not by a long way (well, 2 pages).

'Expressing in Partial Fractions' is the Opposite of Adding Fractions (sort of)

1) You can split a fraction with more than one linear factor in the denominator into partial fractions.

$\dfrac{7x - 7}{(2x + 1)(x - 3)}$ can be written as partial fractions of the form $\dfrac{A}{(2x + 1)} + \dfrac{B}{(x - 3)}$.

$\dfrac{9x^2 + x + 16}{(x + 2)(2x - 1)(x - 3)}$ can be written as partial fractions of the form $\dfrac{A}{(x + 2)} + \dfrac{B}{(2x - 1)} + \dfrac{C}{(x - 3)}$.

$\dfrac{x^2 + 17x + 16}{(x + 2)^2(3x - 1)}$ can be written as partial fractions of the form $\dfrac{A}{(x + 2)^2} + \dfrac{B}{(x + 2)} + \dfrac{C}{(3x - 1)}$. ⟵ Watch out here — this one doesn't quite follow the pattern.

2) The tricky bit is figuring out what A, B and C are.
You can use the substitution method or the equating coefficients method:

EXAMPLE Express $\dfrac{9x^2 + x + 16}{(x + 2)(2x - 1)(x - 3)}$ in partial fractions.

You know that $\dfrac{9x^2 + x + 16}{(x + 2)(2x - 1)(x - 3)} \equiv \dfrac{A}{(x + 2)} + \dfrac{B}{(2x - 1)} + \dfrac{C}{(x - 3)}$. Now to work out A, B and C.

1 Add the partial fractions and cancel the denominators from both sides

$\dfrac{A}{(x + 2)} + \dfrac{B}{(2x - 1)} + \dfrac{C}{(x - 3)} \equiv \dfrac{A(2x - 1)(x - 3) + B(x + 2)(x - 3) + C(2x - 1)(x + 2)}{(x + 2)(2x - 1)(x - 3)}$

So the numerators are equal: $9x^2 + x + 16 \equiv A(2x - 1)(x - 3) + B(x + 2)(x - 3) + C(2x - 1)(x + 2)$

2 Substitute x for values which get rid of all but one of A, B and C...

Substituting $x = 3$ gets rid of A and B: $(9 \times 3^2) + 3 + 16 = 0 + 0 + C((2 \times 3) - 1)(3 + 2)$
$100 = 25C \Rightarrow \underline{C = 4}$

Substituting $x = -2$ gets rid of B and C: $(9 \times (-2)^2) + (-2) + 16 = A((2 \times -2) - 1)(-2 - 3) + 0 + 0$
$50 = 25A \Rightarrow \underline{A = 2}$

Substituting $x = 0.5$ gets rid of A and C: $(9 \times (0.5^2)) + 0.5 + 16 = 0 + B(0.5 + 2)(0.5 - 3) + 0$
$18.75 = -6.25B \Rightarrow \underline{B = -3}$

...OR compare coefficients in the numerators

$9x^2 + x + 16 \equiv A(2x - 1)(x - 3) + B(x + 2)(x - 3) + C(2x - 1)(x + 2)$

x^2 coefficients: $9 = 2A + B + 2C$
x coefficients: $1 = -7A - B + 3C$
constant terms: $16 = 3A - 6B - 2C$

Solving these equations simultaneously gives $A = 2$, $B = -3$ and $C = 4$ — the same as the substitution method.

3 Write out the solution $\dfrac{9x^2 + x + 16}{(x + 2)(2x - 1)(x - 3)} \equiv \dfrac{2}{(x + 2)} - \dfrac{3}{(2x - 1)} + \dfrac{4}{(x - 3)}$

Watch out for Difference of Two Squares Denominators

Just for added meanness, they might give you an expression like $\dfrac{4}{x^2 - 1}$ and tell you to express it as partial fractions.

You have to recognise that the denominator is a difference of two squares, write it as two linear factors, and then carry on as normal. E.g. $\dfrac{21x - 2}{9x^2 - 4} \equiv \dfrac{21x - 2}{(3x - 2)(3x + 2)} \equiv \dfrac{A}{(3x - 2)} + \dfrac{B}{(3x + 2)}$

Not all coefficients are created equal — but some are...

It's worth getting to grips with both methods for step 2. Sometimes one's easier to use than the other, and sometimes you might want to mix and match. It's just another crucial step on the path to going down in history as a mathematical great.

C4 Section 1 — Algebra

Partial Fractions

Now things are hotting up in the partial fractions department — here's an example involving a <u>repeated factor</u>.

Sometimes it's best to use Substitution AND Equate Coefficients

EXAMPLE

Express $\dfrac{x^2 + 17x + 16}{(x + 2)^2(3x - 1)}$ in partial fractions.

You know that $\dfrac{x^2 + 17x + 16}{(x + 2)^2(3x - 1)} \equiv \dfrac{A}{(x + 2)^2} + \dfrac{B}{(x + 2)} + \dfrac{C}{(3x - 1)}$. Now to work out A, B and C.

1 Add the partial fractions

$$\dfrac{A}{(x + 2)^2} + \dfrac{B}{(x + 2)} + \dfrac{C}{(3x - 1)} \equiv \dfrac{A(3x - 1) + B(x + 2)(3x - 1) + C(x + 2)^2}{(x + 2)^2(3x - 1)}$$

Cancel the denominators from both sides $x^2 + 17x + 16 \equiv A(3x - 1) + B(x + 2)(3x - 1) + C(x + 2)^2$

2 Substitute x for values which get rid of all but one of A, B and C

Substituting $x = -2$ gets rid of B and C: $(-2)^2 + (17 \times -2) + 16 = A((3 \times -2) - 1) + 0 + 0$

$$-14 = -7A \quad \Rightarrow \underline{A = 2}$$

Substituting $x = \frac{1}{3}$ gets rid of A and B: $\left(\frac{1}{3}\right)^2 + \left(17 \times \frac{1}{3}\right) + 16 = 0 + 0 + C\left(\frac{1}{3} + 2\right)^2$

$$\dfrac{196}{9} = \dfrac{49}{9}C \quad \Rightarrow \underline{C = 4}$$

The trouble is, there's <u>no value of x</u> you can substitute to get rid of A and C to just leave <u>B</u>.
So: Equate coefficients of x^2

From $x^2 + 17x + 16 \equiv A(3x - 1) + B(x + 2)(3x - 1) + C(x + 2)^2$

Coefficients of x^2 are: $1 = 3B + C$

You know $C = 4$, so: $1 = 3B + 4 \quad \Rightarrow \underline{B = -1}$

3 Write out the solution You now know A, B and C, so: $\dfrac{x^2 + 17x + 16}{(x + 2)^2(3x - 1)} \equiv \dfrac{2}{(x + 2)^2} - \dfrac{1}{(x + 2)} + \dfrac{4}{(3x - 1)}$

You can integrate Partial Fractions

Once you've <u>broken down</u> a scary-looking <u>algebraic fraction</u> into <u>partial fractions</u>, you can <u>integrate</u> it, using the methods from C3 Section 5.

EXAMPLE

Find $\displaystyle\int \dfrac{9x^2 + x + 16}{(x + 2)(2x - 1)(x - 3)}\, dx$.

This is the example from p.50, and you've just seen that it can be written as partial fractions like this:

$$\dfrac{2}{(x + 2)} - \dfrac{3}{(2x - 1)} + \dfrac{4}{(x - 3)}$$

Don't forget the coefficients here. Have a look back at p.29 if you can't remember how to do this.

Integrating the partial fractions is much easier:

$$\int \dfrac{2}{(x + 2)} - \dfrac{3}{(2x - 1)} + \dfrac{4}{(x - 3)}\, dx = 2\ln|x + 2| - \frac{3}{2}\ln|2x - 1| + 4\ln|x - 3| + C$$

$$= \ln\left|\dfrac{(x + 2)^2(x - 3)^4}{(2x - 1)^{\frac{3}{2}}}\right| + C$$

I'm partial to a cup of tea...

Partial fractions quite often pop up in a two-part question — for the first part, you'll have to write a tricky fraction in partial fractions, and in the second part you'll have to integrate it. That's a big clue that you're not supposed to try and integrate the scary-looking fraction, you're supposed to integrate the nice easy partial fractions instead. Don't say I didn't warn you...

The Binomial Expansion

Yeah, I know the <u>binomial expansion</u>. We spent some time together back in C1. Thought I'd never see it again. And then, of all the sections in all the maths books in all the world, the binomial expansion walks into mine...

The **Binomial Expansion Formula** is pretty useful

The <u>binomial expansion</u> is a way to raise a given expression to <u>any power</u>.

For simpler cases it's basically a fancy way of <u>multiplying out brackets</u>.

This is the <u>general formula</u> for <u>binomial expansions</u>:

$$(1 + x)^n = 1 + nx + \frac{n(n-1)}{1 \times 2}x^2 + \dots + \frac{n(n-1)\dots(n-r+1)}{1 \times 2 \times \dots \times r}x^r + \dots$$

The **Binomial Expansion** sometimes gives a **Finite Expression**

From the general formula, it looks like the expansion always goes on forever.
But if n is a <u>positive integer</u>, the binomial expansion is <u>finite</u>.

EXAMPLE Give the binomial expansion of $(1 + x)^5$.

You can use the <u>general formula</u> and plug in <u>$n = 5$</u>:

$n(n-1)$

$$(1 + x)^5 = 1 + 5x + \frac{5(5-1)}{1 \times 2}x^2 + \frac{5(5-1)(5-2)}{1 \times 2 \times 3}x^3 + \frac{5(5-1)(5-2)(5-3)}{1 \times 2 \times 3 \times 4}x^4$$

$n = 5$

$$+ \frac{5(5-1)(5-2)(5-3)(5-4)}{1 \times 2 \times 3 \times 4 \times 5}x^5 + \frac{5(5-1)(5-2)(5-3)(5-4)(5-5)}{1 \times 2 \times 3 \times 4 \times 5 \times 6}x^6 + \dots$$

$$= 1 + 5x + \frac{5 \times 4}{1 \times 2}x^2 + \frac{5 \times 4 \times 3}{1 \times 2 \times 3}x^3 + \frac{5 \times 4 \times 3 \times 2}{1 \times 2 \times 3 \times 4}x^4$$

$$+ \frac{5 \times 4 \times 3 \times 2 \times 1}{1 \times 2 \times 3 \times 4 \times 5}x^5 + \frac{5 \times 4 \times 3 \times 2 \times 1 \times 0}{1 \times 2 \times 3 \times 4 \times 5 \times 6}x^6 + \dots$$

You can stop here — all the terms after this one are zero

$$= 1 + 5x + \frac{20}{2}x^2 + \frac{60}{6}x^3 + \frac{120}{24}x^4 + \frac{120}{120}x^5 + \frac{0}{720}x^6 + \dots$$

$$= 1 + 5x + 10x^2 + 10x^3 + 5x^4 + x^5$$

The formula still works if the coefficient of x isn't 1.

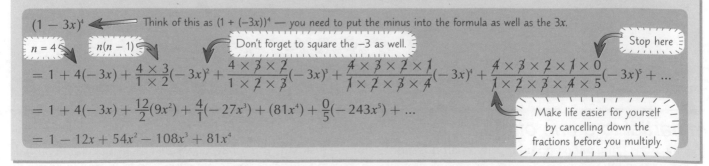

EXAMPLE Give the binomial expansion of $(1 - 3x)^4$.

This time $n = 4$, but you also have to <u>replace every x</u> in the formula with <u>$-3x$</u>:

$(1 - 3x)^4$ ← Think of this as $(1 + (-3x))^4$ — you need to put the minus into the formula as well as the 3x.

$n = 4$ $n(n-1)$ Don't forget to square the −3 as well.   Stop here

$$= 1 + 4(-3x) + \frac{4 \times 3}{1 \times 2}(-3x)^2 + \frac{4 \times 3 \times 2}{1 \times 2 \times 3}(-3x)^3 + \frac{4 \times 3 \times 2 \times 1}{1 \times 2 \times 3 \times 4}(-3x)^4 + \frac{4 \times 3 \times 2 \times 1 \times 0}{1 \times 2 \times 3 \times 4 \times 5}(-3x)^5 + \dots$$

$$= 1 + 4(-3x) + \frac{12}{2}(9x^2) + \frac{4}{1}(-27x^3) + (81x^4) + \frac{0}{5}(-243x^5) + \dots$$

Make life easier for yourself by cancelling down the fractions before you multiply.

$$= 1 - 12x + 54x^2 - 108x^3 + 81x^4$$

The Binomial Expansion

Unfortunately, you only get a nice, neat, <u>finite expansion</u> when you've got a <u>positive integer n</u>. But that pesky n sometimes likes to be a <u>negative number</u> or a <u>fraction</u>. n for nuisance. n for naughty.

If n is **Negative** the expansion gets more complicated...

EXAMPLE   Find the binomial expansion of $\dfrac{1}{(1+x)^2}$ up to and including the term in x^3.

This is where things start to get a bit more interesting.

First, <u>rewrite the expression</u>: $\dfrac{1}{(1+x)^2} = (1+x)^{-2}$.

You can still use the <u>general formula</u>. This time $\underline{n = -2}$:

$$n = -2 \qquad n(n-1)$$

$$(1+x)^{-2} = 1 + (-2)x + \frac{(-2)\times(-2-1)}{1\times 2}x^2 + \frac{(-2)\times(-2-1)\times(-2-2)}{1\times 2\times 3}x^3 + ...$$

$$= 1 + (-2)x + \frac{(-2)\times(-3)}{1\times 2}x^2 + \frac{(-2)\times(-3)\times(-4)}{1\times 2\times 3}x^3 + ...$$

$$= 1 + (-2)x + \frac{3}{1}x^2 + \frac{-4}{1}x^3 + ...$$

$$= 1 - 2x + 3x^2 - 4x^3 + ...$$

> With a negative n, you'll never get zero as a coefficient. If the question hadn't told you to stop, the expansion could go on forever.

> Again, you can cancel down before you multiply — but be careful with those minus signs.

We've left out all the terms after $-4x^3$, so the cubic equation you've ended up with is an <u>approximation</u> to the original expression. You could also write the answer like this:

$$\frac{1}{(1+x)^2} \approx 1 - 2x + 3x^2 - 4x^3$$

... and if n is a **Fraction** things can be tricky too

The binomial expansion formula doesn't just work for integer values of n.

EXAMPLE   Find the binomial expansion of $\sqrt[3]{1+2x}$ up to and including the term in x^3.

This time we've got a <u>fractional power</u>: $\sqrt[3]{1+2x} = (1+2x)^{\frac{1}{3}}$

So this time $n = \frac{1}{3}$, and you also need to replace x with $2x$:

$$n = \frac{1}{3} \qquad n(n-1)$$

$$(1+2x)^{\frac{1}{3}} = 1 + \frac{1}{3}(2x) + \frac{\frac{1}{3}\times(\frac{1}{3}-1)}{1\times 2}(2x)^2 + \frac{\frac{1}{3}\times(\frac{1}{3}-1)\times(\frac{1}{3}-2)}{1\times 2\times 3}(2x)^3 + ...$$

$$= 1 + \frac{2}{3}x + \frac{\frac{1}{3}\times(-\frac{2}{3})}{1\times 2}4x^2 + \frac{\frac{1}{3}\times(-\frac{2}{3})\times(-\frac{5}{3})}{1\times 2\times 3}8x^3 + ...$$

$$= 1 + \frac{2}{3}x + \frac{(-\frac{2}{9})}{2}4x^2 + \frac{(\frac{10}{27})}{6}8x^3 + ...$$

$$= 1 + \frac{2}{3}x + \left(-\frac{2}{9}\times\frac{1}{2}\right)4x^2 + \left(\frac{10}{27}\times\frac{1}{6}\right)8x^3 + ...$$

$$= 1 + \frac{2}{3}x - \frac{4}{9}x^2 + \frac{40}{81}x^3 + ...$$

> Cancelling down is much trickier with this type of expansion — it's usually safer to multiply everything out fully.

> Exam questions often ask for the coefficients as simplified fractions.

The Binomial Expansion

More binomial goodness... this page is so jam-packed with the stuff, there's only room for a one-line intro...

If the **Constant** *in the brackets isn't* **1**, *you have to* **Factorise** *first*

So the general binomial expansion of $(1 + x)^n$ works fine for any n, and you can replace the x with other x-terms, but that 1 has to be a 1 before you can expand. That means you sometimes need to start with a sneaky bit of factorisation.

EXAMPLE   Give the binomial expansion of $(3 - x)^4$.

To use the <u>general formula</u>, you need the <u>constant term</u> in the brackets to be <u>1</u>.
You can take the 3 outside the brackets by <u>factorising</u>:

> The aim here is to get an expression in the form $c(1 + dx)^n$, where c and d are constants.

$$3 - x = 3(1 - \tfrac{1}{3}x)$$
$$\text{so} \quad (3 - x)^4 = [3(1 - \tfrac{1}{3}x)]^4$$
$$= 3^4(1 - \tfrac{1}{3}x)^4$$
$$= 81(1 - \tfrac{1}{3}x)^4$$

Now we can use the general formula, with $n = 4$, and $-\tfrac{1}{3}x$ instead of x:

$$\left(1 - \tfrac{1}{3}x\right)^4 = 1 + 4\left(-\tfrac{1}{3}x\right) + \tfrac{4 \times 3}{1 \times 2}\left(-\tfrac{1}{3}x\right)^2 + \tfrac{4 \times 3 \times 2}{1 \times 2 \times 3}\left(-\tfrac{1}{3}x\right)^3 + \tfrac{4 \times 3 \times 2 \times 1}{1 \times 2 \times 3 \times 4}\left(-\tfrac{1}{3}x\right)^4$$
$$= 1 - \tfrac{4}{3}x + 6\left(\tfrac{1}{9}x^2\right) + 4\left(-\tfrac{1}{27}x^3\right) + \tfrac{1}{81}x^4$$
$$= 1 - \tfrac{4x}{3} + \tfrac{2x^2}{3} - \tfrac{4x^3}{27} + \tfrac{x^4}{81}$$

So now we can expand the original expression:

$$(3 - x)^4 = 81\left(1 - \tfrac{1}{3}x\right)^4$$
$$= 81\left(1 - \tfrac{4x}{3} + \tfrac{2x^2}{3} - \tfrac{4x^3}{27} + \tfrac{x^4}{81}\right)$$
$$= 81 - 108x + 54x^2 - 12x^3 + x^4$$

Some **Binomial Expansions** *are only* **Valid** *for* **Certain Values** *of* x

When you find a binomial expansion, you usually have to state which values of x the expansion is valid for.

> If n is a <u>positive integer</u>, the binomial expansion of $(p + qx)^n$ is valid for <u>all values of x</u>.

If n is <u>not</u> a positive integer, the expansion would be <u>infinite</u>. Because you only write out a few terms, the binomial expansion you get is just an <u>approximation</u>. But the approximation is only valid if the sequence <u>converges</u> — this only happens if x is <u>small enough</u> (for larger values of x, the sequence will diverge)...

> If n is a <u>negative integer</u> or a <u>fraction</u>, the binomial expansion of $(p + qx)^n$ is valid when $\left|\dfrac{qx}{p}\right| < 1$.

> You can rewrite this as $|x| < \left|\dfrac{p}{q}\right|$ — just use the version you find easiest to remember.

This means there's a little bit more to do for the two examples on the previous page:

> $(1 + x)^{-2} = 1 - 2x + 3x^2 - 4x^3 + ...$ This expansion is valid for $|x| < 1$.

> $(1 + 2x)^{\frac{1}{3}} = 1 + \tfrac{2}{3}x - \tfrac{4}{9}x^2 + \tfrac{40}{81}x^3 + ...$
>
> This expansion is valid if $|2x| < 1 \Rightarrow 2|x| < 1 \Rightarrow |x| < \tfrac{1}{2}$.

> You might already know the rules $|ab| = |a||b|$ and $\left|\dfrac{a}{b}\right| = \dfrac{|a|}{|b|}$. If you don't, then get to know them — they're handy for rearranging these limits.

Lose weight and save money — buy no meals...

Two facts: 1) You can pretty much guarantee that there'll be a binomial expansion question on your C4 exam, and 2) any binomial expansion question they can throw at you will feature some combination of these adaptations of the general formula.

Binomial Expansions and Partial Fractions

Binomial expansions on their own are pretty nifty, but when you combine them with <u>partial fractions</u> (see p.50-51) they become all-powerful. I'm sure there's some sort of message about friendship or something in there...

Split functions into Partial Fractions, then add the Expansions

You can find the binomial expansion of even more complicated functions by splitting them into partial fractions first.

EXAMPLE

$$f(x) = \frac{x-1}{(3+x)(1-5x)}$$

a) f(x) can be expressed in the form $\frac{A}{(3+x)} + \frac{B}{(1-5x)}$. Find the values of A and B.

b) Use your answer to part a) to find the binomial expansion of f(x) up to and including the term in x^2.

c) Find the range of values of x for which your answer to part b) is valid.

a) Convert f(x) into <u>partial fractions</u>:

$$\frac{x-1}{(3+x)(1-5x)} \equiv \frac{A}{(3+x)} + \frac{B}{(1-5x)} \Rightarrow x-1 \equiv A(1-5x) + B(3+x)$$

Let $x = -3$, then $-3 - 1 = A(1-(-15)) \Rightarrow -4 = 16A \Rightarrow A = -\frac{1}{4}$

Let $x = \frac{1}{5}$, then $\frac{1}{5} - 1 = B\left(3 + \frac{1}{5}\right) \Rightarrow -\frac{4}{5} = \frac{16}{5}B \Rightarrow B = -\frac{1}{4}$

b) Start by <u>rewriting</u> the partial fractions in $(a+bx)^n$ form:

$$f(x) = -\frac{1}{4}(3+x)^{-1} - \frac{1}{4}(1-5x)^{-1}$$

Now do the two <u>binomial expansions</u>:

$$(3+x)^{-1} = \left(3\left(1+\frac{1}{3}x\right)\right)^{-1}$$
$$= \frac{1}{3}\left(1+\frac{1}{3}x\right)^{-1}$$
$$= \frac{1}{3}\left(1 + (-1)\left(\frac{1}{3}x\right) + \frac{(-1)(-2)}{2}\left(\frac{1}{3}x\right)^2 + ...\right)$$
$$= \frac{1}{3}\left(1 - \frac{1}{3}x + \frac{1}{9}x^2 + ...\right)$$
$$= \frac{1}{3} - \frac{1}{9}x + \frac{1}{27}x^2 + ...$$

$$(1-5x)^{-1} = 1 + (-1)(-5x) + \frac{(-1)(-2)}{2}(-5x)^2 + ...$$
$$= 1 + 5x + 25x^2 + ...$$

And put <u>everything together</u>:

$$f(x) = -\frac{1}{4}(3+x)^{-1} - \frac{1}{4}(1-5x)^{-1} \approx -\frac{1}{4}\left(\frac{1}{3} - \frac{1}{9}x + \frac{1}{27}x^2\right) - \frac{1}{4}(1 + 5x + 25x^2)$$
$$= -\frac{1}{12} + \frac{1}{36}x - \frac{1}{108}x^2 - \frac{1}{4} - \frac{5}{4}x - \frac{25}{4}x^2$$
$$= -\frac{1}{3} - \frac{11}{9}x - \frac{169}{27}x^2$$

c) Each of the two expansions from part b) is valid for different values of x.
The combined expansion of f(x) is valid where these two ranges <u>overlap</u>, i.e. over the <u>narrower of the two ranges</u>.

The expansion of $(3+x)^{-1}$ is valid when $\left|\frac{x}{3}\right| < 1 \Rightarrow \frac{|x|}{|3|} < 1 \Rightarrow |x| < 3$.

The expansion of $(1-5x)^{-1}$ is valid when $|-5x| < 1 \Rightarrow |-5||x| < 1 \Rightarrow |x| < \frac{1}{5}$.

Remember — the expansion of $(p+qx)^n$ is valid when $\left|\frac{qx}{p}\right| < 1$.

The expansion of f(x) is valid for values of x in both ranges, so the expansion of f(x) is valid for $|x| < \frac{1}{5}$.

Don't mess with me — I'm a partial arts expert...

Here's where it all comes together. This example looks pretty impressive, but if you know your stuff you'll sail through questions like this. I think that's all I've got to say for this page... hmm, looks like I've still got another line to fill... So, going anywhere nice on your holidays this year? Read any good books lately? (Answer: Yes, this one.)

C4 Section 1 — Practice Questions

Ah, here we are on another of these <u>soothing green</u> pages. Relax... this is your <u>happy place</u>... nothing to worry about here... enjoy this tranquil blue pool of shimmering <u>warm-up questions</u>.

Warm-up Questions

1) Simplify the following:

   a) $\dfrac{4x^2 - 25}{6x - 15}$

   b) $\dfrac{2x + 3}{x - 2} \times \dfrac{4x - 8}{2x^2 - 3x - 9}$

   c) $\dfrac{x^2 - 3x}{x + 1} \div \dfrac{x}{2}$

2) Write the following as a single fraction:

   a) $\dfrac{x}{2x + 1} + \dfrac{3}{x^2} + \dfrac{1}{x}$

   b) $\dfrac{2}{x^2 - 1} - \dfrac{3x}{x - 1} + \dfrac{x}{x + 1}$

3) Use algebraic long division to divide $x^3 + 2x^2 - x + 19$ by $x + 4$.

4) Write $2x^3 + 8x^2 + 7x + 8$ in the form $(Ax^2 + Bx + C)(x + 3) + D$. Using your answer, state the result when $2x^3 + 8x^2 + 7x + 8$ is divided by $(x + 3)$.

> ⸜ You have to factorise the denominator in Q5 parts d, e and g, and in Q6, part d. ⸝

5) Express the following as <u>partial fractions</u>.

   a) $\dfrac{4x + 5}{(x + 4)(2x - 3)}$

   b) $\dfrac{-7x - 7}{(3x + 1)(x - 2)}$

   c) $\dfrac{x - 18}{(x + 4)(3x - 4)}$

   d) $\dfrac{5x}{x^2 + x - 6}$

   e) $\dfrac{6 + 4y}{9 - y^2}$

   f) $\dfrac{10x^2 + 32x + 16}{(x + 3)(2x + 4)(x - 2)}$

   g) $\dfrac{4x^2 + 12x + 6}{x^3 + 3x^2 + 2x}$

   h) $\dfrac{-11x^2 + 6x + 11}{(2x + 1)(3 - x)(x + 2)}$

6) Express the following as partial fractions — watch out for the <u>repeated factors</u>.

   a) $\dfrac{2x + 2}{(x + 3)^2}$

   b) $\dfrac{6x^2 + 17x + 5}{x(x + 2)^2}$

   c) $\dfrac{-18x + 14}{(2x - 1)^2(x + 2)}$

   d) $\dfrac{8x^2 - x - 5}{x^3 - x^2}$

7) Use $\dfrac{3x + 10}{(2x + 3)(x - 4)} \equiv \dfrac{A}{2x + 3} + \dfrac{B}{x - 4}$ to find $\displaystyle\int \dfrac{3x + 10}{(2x + 3)(x - 4)}\, dx$.

8) Give the <u>binomial expansion</u> of:

   a) $(1 + 2x)^3$

   b) $(1 - x)^4$

   c) $(1 - 4x)^4$

9) For <u>what values of n</u> does the binomial expansion of $(1 + x)^n$ result in a <u>finite expression</u>?

10) Find the <u>binomial expansion</u> of each of the following, up to and including the term in x^3:

   a) $\dfrac{1}{(1 + x)^4}$

   b) $\dfrac{1}{(1 - 3x)^3}$

   c) $\sqrt{1 - 5x}$

11) a) If the full binomial expansion of $(c + dx)^n$ is an <u>infinite series</u>, what values of x is the expansion <u>valid</u> for?

    b) What values of x are the expansions from question 10 valid for?

12) Give the <u>binomial expansions</u> of the following, up to and including the term in x^2. State which values of x each expansion is valid for.

    a) $\dfrac{1}{(3 + 2x)^2}$

    b) $\sqrt[3]{8 - x}$

C4 Section 1 — Practice Questions

By now all your cares should have <u>floated away</u> on the <u>algebraic breeze</u>.
Time for a bracing dip in an ice-cool bath of <u>exam questions</u>.

Exam Questions

1   Given that, for $x \neq -\frac{1}{3}$, $\dfrac{5 + 9x}{(1 + 3x)^2} \equiv \dfrac{A}{(1 + 3x)^2} + \dfrac{B}{(1 + 3x)}$, where A and B are integers,
     find the values of A and B.

(3 marks)

2   Write $\dfrac{2x^2 - 9x - 35}{x^2 - 49}$ as a fraction in its simplest form.

(3 marks)

3   Find the binomial expansion of $(16 + 3x)^{\frac{1}{4}}$, for $|x| < \frac{16}{3}$, up to and including the term in x^2.

(5 marks)

4   a)   Find the binomial expansion of $\left(1 - \frac{4}{3}x\right)^{-\frac{1}{2}}$, up to and including the term in x^3.

(4 marks)

     b)   Hence find the values of integer constants a, b and c, such that

$$\sqrt{\frac{27}{(3 - 4x)}} \approx a + bx + cx^2,$$

          and state the range of values of x for which this approximation is valid.

(3 marks)

5   a)   Show that $\sqrt{\dfrac{1 + 2x}{1 - 3x}} \approx 1 + \frac{5}{2}x + \frac{35}{8}x^2$.

(5 marks)

     b)   For what values of x is your expansion valid?

(2 marks)

C4 Section 1 — Practice Questions

Congratulations, you've almost achieved <u>C4 Algebra nirvana</u>. Just a few more <u>exam question</u> steps and you'll be there...

6          $f(x) = \dfrac{36x^2 + 3x - 10}{(4 + 3x)(1 - 3x)^2}$

   a)   Given that f(x) can be expressed in the form

$$f(x) = \frac{A}{(4 + 3x)} + \frac{B}{(1 - 3x)} + \frac{C}{(1 - 3x)^2}$$

       find the values of A, B and C.

(4 marks)

   b)   Find the binomial expansion of f(x), up to and including the term in x^2.

(6 marks)

   c)   Find the range of values of x for which the binomial expansion of f(x) is valid.

(2 marks)

7   Write $x^3 + 15x^2 + 43x - 30$ in the form $(Ax^2 + Bx + C)(x + 6) + D$,
where A, B, C and D are constants to be found.

(3 marks)

8   a)   Find the values of A and B such that $\dfrac{13x - 17}{(5 - 3x)(2x - 1)} \equiv \dfrac{A}{(5 - 3x)} + \dfrac{B}{(2x - 1)}$.

(3 marks)

   b) (i)   Find the binomial expansion of $(2x - 1)^{-1}$, up to and including the term in x^2.

(2 marks)

       (ii)   Show that $\dfrac{1}{(5 - 3x)} \approx \dfrac{1}{5} + \dfrac{3}{25}x + \dfrac{9}{125}x^2$, for $|x| < \dfrac{5}{3}$.

(5 marks)

   c)   Using your answers to parts (a) and (b), find the first three terms
of the binomial expansion of $\dfrac{13x - 17}{(5 - 3x)(2x - 1)}$.

(2 marks)

9    $f(x) = \dfrac{5x^2 + 3x + 6}{(3 - x)(2x - 1)^2}$

   Given that f(x) can be expressed in the form $f(x) = \dfrac{A}{(3 - x)} + \dfrac{B}{(2x - 1)^2} + \dfrac{C}{(2x - 1)}$,

   find the values of A and B and C.

(4 marks)

10         $f(x) = \dfrac{1}{\sqrt{(9 - 4x)}}$, for $|x| < \dfrac{9}{4}$.

   a)   Find the binomial expansion of f(x) up to and including the term in x^3.

(5 marks)

   b)   Hence find the first three terms in the expansion of $\dfrac{2 - x}{\sqrt{(9 - 4x)}}$.

(4 marks)

Secant, Cosecant and Cotangent

After a guest appearance in C3, trigonometry returns in its own feature-length section. First up, three new functions. These ones are pretty important — they'll come in really handy when you're solving trig equations.

Cosec, Sec and Cot are the Reciprocals of Sin, Cos and Tan

When you take the reciprocal of the three main trig functions, sin, cos and tan, you get three new trig functions — cosecant (or cosec), secant (or sec) and cotangent (or cot).

$$\operatorname{cosec} \theta \equiv \frac{1}{\sin \theta}$$

$$\sec \theta \equiv \frac{1}{\cos \theta}$$

$$\cot \theta \equiv \frac{1}{\tan \theta}$$

*The trick for remembering which is which is to look at the third letter — co**sec** (1/**sin**), **sec** (1/**cos**) and co**t** (1/**tan**).*

Since $\tan \theta = \frac{\sin \theta}{\cos \theta}$, you can also think of cot θ as being $\frac{\cos \theta}{\sin \theta}$.

Graphing Cosec, Sec and Cot

COSEC   This is the graph of $y = \operatorname{cosec} x$.

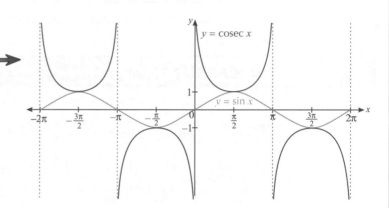

1) Since $\operatorname{cosec} x = \frac{1}{\sin x}$, $y = \operatorname{cosec} x$ is underlined at any point where $\sin x = 0$. So cosec x has asymptotes at $x = n\pi$ (where n is any integer).

2) The graph of cosec x has minimum points at $y = 1$ (wherever the graph of sin x has a maximum).

3) It has maximum points at $y = -1$ (wherever sin x has a minimum).

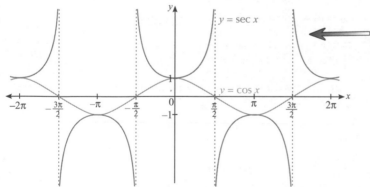

SEC   This is the graph of $y = \sec x$.

1) As $\sec x = \frac{1}{\cos x}$, $y = \sec x$ is underlined at any point where $\cos x = 0$. So sec x has asymptotes at $x = \left(n\pi + \frac{\pi}{2}\right)$ (where n is any integer).

2) The graph of sec x has minimum points at $y = 1$ (wherever the graph of cos x has a maximum).

3) It has maximum points at $y = -1$ (wherever cos x has a minimum).

COT   This is the graph of $y = \cot x$.

1) Since $\cot x = \frac{1}{\tan x}$, $y = \cot x$ is undefined at any point where $\tan x = 0$. So cot x has asymptotes at $x = n\pi$ (where n is any integer).

2) $y = \cot x$ crosses the x-axis at every place where the graph of tan x has an asymptote — this is any point with the coordinates $\left(\left(n\pi + \frac{\pi}{2}\right), 0\right)$.

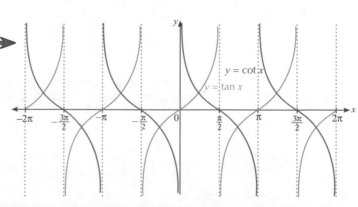

Why did I multiply cot x by sin x? Just 'cos...

Remember to look at the third letter to work out which trig function it's the reciprocal of. I'm afraid you do need to be able to sketch the three graphs from memory. Someone in examiner world clearly has a bit of a graph-sketching obsession. You might have to transform a trig graph too — you use the same method as you would for other graphs (see p.7).

Using Trigonometric Identities

Ahh, <u>trig identities</u>. More useful than a monkey wrench, and more fun than rice pudding. Probably.

Learn these **Three Trig Identities**

Hopefully you remember using this handy little <u>trig identity</u> before:

IDENTITY 1:

$$\cos^2\theta + \sin^2\theta \equiv 1$$

> The ≡ sign tells you that this is true for all values of θ, rather than just certain values.

You can use it to produce a couple of other identities that you need to know about...

IDENTITY 2:

$$\sec^2\theta \equiv 1 + \tan^2\theta$$

To get this, you just take everything in Identity 1, and <u>divide</u> it by $\cos^2\theta$:

$$\frac{\cos^2\theta}{\cos^2\theta} + \frac{\sin^2\theta}{\cos^2\theta} \equiv \frac{1}{\cos^2\theta}$$
$$1 + \tan^2\theta \equiv \sec^2\theta$$

> Remember that $\cos^2\theta = (\cos\theta)^2$.

IDENTITY 3:

$$\csc^2\theta \equiv 1 + \cot^2\theta$$

You get this one by <u>dividing</u> everything in Identity 1 by $\sin^2\theta$:

$$\frac{\cos^2\theta}{\sin^2\theta} + \frac{\sin^2\theta}{\sin^2\theta} \equiv \frac{1}{\sin^2\theta}$$
$$\cot^2\theta + 1 \equiv \csc^2\theta$$

Use the **Trig Identities** to **Simplify Equations**...

You can use identities to get rid of any trig functions that are making an equation difficult to solve.

> **EXAMPLE** Solve the equation $\cot^2 x + 5 = 4 \csc x$ in the interval $0° \le x \le 360°$.
>
> You can't solve this while it has both cot and cosec in it, so use Identity 3 to swap $\cot^2 x$ for $\csc^2 x - 1$.
>
> $$\csc^2 x - 1 + 5 = 4 \csc x$$
>
> Now rearranging the equation gives: $\csc^2 x + 4 = 4 \csc x \implies \csc^2 x - 4 \csc x + 4 = 0$
>
> So you've got a quadratic in cosec x — factorise it like you would any other quadratic equation.
>
> $$\csc^2 x - 4 \csc x + 4 = 0$$
> $$(\csc x - 2)(\csc x - 2) = 0$$
>
> > If it helps, think of this as $y^2 - 4y + 4 = 0$. Factorise it, and then replace the y with cosec x.
>
> One of the brackets must be equal to zero — here they're both the same, so you only get one equation:
>
> $$(\csc x - 2) = 0 \implies \csc x = 2$$
>
> Now you can convert this into sin x, and solve it easily:
>
> $$\csc x = 2 \implies \sin x = \tfrac{1}{2}$$
> $$x = 30° \text{ or } x = 150°$$
>
> To find the other values of x, draw a quick sketch of the sin curve: From the graph, you can see that sin x takes the value of ½ twice in the given interval, once at $x = 30°$ and once at $x = 180 - 30 = 150°$.
>
>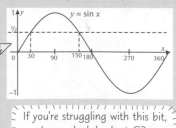
>
> > If you're struggling with this bit, have a look back at C2.

...or to **Prove** that two things are **The Same**

You can also use <u>identities</u> to prove that two <u>trig expressions</u> are <u>the same</u>, like this:

> **EXAMPLE** Show that $\dfrac{\tan^2 x}{\sec x} \equiv \sec x - \cos x$.
>
> You need to take one side of the identity and play about with it until you get the other side. $\implies$ Left-hand side: $\dfrac{\tan^2 x}{\sec x}$.
>
> Try replacing $\tan^2 x$ with $\sec^2 x - 1$: $\equiv \dfrac{\sec^2 x - 1}{\sec x} \equiv \dfrac{\sec^2 x}{\sec x} - \dfrac{1}{\sec x} \equiv \sec x - \cos x$ ...which is the <u>right-hand side</u>.

The Addition Formulas

You might have noticed that there are quite a lot of formulas lurking in this here trigonometry jungle. There are some more coming up on this page I'm afraid, so brace yourself — they're all about <u>adding</u> and <u>subtracting</u> angles...

You can use the **Addition Formulas** to find **Sums of Angles**

You can use the <u>addition formulas</u> to find the sin, cos or tan of the <u>sum</u> or <u>difference</u> of two angles.

When you have an expression like $\sin(x + 60°)$ or $\cos(n - \frac{\pi}{2})$, you can use these formulas to <u>expand the brackets</u>.

$$\sin(A \pm B) \equiv \sin A \cos B \pm \cos A \sin B$$

$$\cos(A \pm B) \equiv \cos A \cos B \mp \sin A \sin B$$

$$\tan(A \pm B) \equiv \frac{\tan A \pm \tan B}{1 \mp \tan A \tan B}$$

These formulas are given to you on the formula sheet.

Watch out for the $\pm$ and $\mp$ signs in the formulas — especially for cos and tan. If you use the sign on the top on the RHS, you have to use the sign on the top on the left-hand side too — so $\cos(A + B) = \cos A \cos B - \sin A \sin B$.

Use the **Formulas** to find the **Exact Value** of trig expressions

1) You should know the value of sin, cos and tan for <u>common angles</u> (in <u>degrees</u> and <u>radians</u>). These values come from using <u>Pythagoras</u> on <u>right-angled triangles</u> — you did it in C2.

2) In the exam you might be asked to calculate the <u>exact value</u> of sin, cos or tan for another angle using your knowledge of those angles and the <u>addition formulas</u>.

3) Find a <u>pair of angles</u> from the table which <u>add or subtract</u> to give the angle you're after. Then plug them into the <u>addition formula</u>, and work it through.

	0°	30°	45°	60°	90°
	0	$\frac{\pi}{6}$	$\frac{\pi}{4}$	$\frac{\pi}{3}$	$\frac{\pi}{2}$
sin	0	$\frac{1}{2}$	$\frac{1}{\sqrt{2}}$	$\frac{\sqrt{3}}{2}$	1
cos	1	$\frac{\sqrt{3}}{2}$	$\frac{1}{\sqrt{2}}$	$\frac{1}{2}$	0
tan	0	$\frac{1}{\sqrt{3}}$	1	$\sqrt{3}$	n/a

EXAMPLE Using the addition formula for tangent, show that $\tan 15° = 2 - \sqrt{3}$.

Pick two angles that <u>add or subtract to give 15°</u>, and put them into the tan addition formula. It's easiest to use <u>tan 60°</u> and <u>tan 45°</u> here, since neither of them are <u>fractions</u>.

$$\tan 15° = \tan(60° - 45°) = \frac{\tan 60° - \tan 45°}{1 + \tan 60° \tan 45°}$$

Using $\tan(A - B) = \frac{\tan A - \tan B}{1 + \tan A \tan B}$

Substitute the values for tan 60° and tan 45° into the equation:

$$= \frac{\sqrt{3} - 1}{1 + (\sqrt{3} \times 1)} = \frac{\sqrt{3} - 1}{\sqrt{3} + 1}$$

Now rationalise the denominator of the fraction to get rid of the $\sqrt{3}$.

$$\frac{\sqrt{3} - 1}{\sqrt{3} + 1} \times \frac{\sqrt{3} - 1}{\sqrt{3} - 1} = \frac{3 - 2\sqrt{3} + 1}{3 - \sqrt{3} + \sqrt{3} - 1}$$

If you can't remember how to rationalise the denominator have a peek at your C1 notes.

Simplify the expression... $$= \frac{4 - 2\sqrt{3}}{2} = 2 - \sqrt{3}$$ ...and there's the <u>right-hand side</u>.

You can use these formulas to **Prove Identities** too

You might be asked to use the addition formulas to <u>prove an identity</u>. All you need to do is put the <u>numbers</u> and <u>variables</u> from one side into the <u>addition formulas</u> and simplify until you get the expression you're after.

EXAMPLE Prove that $\cos(a + 60°) + \sin(a + 30°) \equiv \cos a$

Be careful with the + and − signs here.

Put the numbers from the question into the addition formulas:

$$\cos(a + 60°) + \sin(a + 30°) \equiv (\cos a \cos 60° - \sin a \sin 60°) + (\sin a \cos 30° + \cos a \sin 30°)$$

Now substitute in any sin and cos values that you know...

$$= \frac{1}{2}\cos a - \frac{\sqrt{3}}{2}\sin a + \frac{\sqrt{3}}{2}\sin a + \frac{1}{2}\cos a$$

..and simplify: $$= \frac{1}{2}\cos a + \frac{1}{2}\cos a = \cos a$$

This section's got more identities than Clark Kent...

I was devastated when my secret identity was revealed — I'd been masquerading as a mysterious caped criminal mastermind with an army of minions and a hidden underground lair. It was great fun, but I had to give it all up and write about trig.

The Double Angle Formulas

Whenever you see a trig expression with an <u>even</u> multiple of x in it, like sin $2x$, you can use one of the <u>double angle formulas</u> to prune it back to an expression just in terms of a single x.

There's a **Double Angle Formula** for **Each Trig Function**

<u>Double angle formulas</u> are just a slightly different kind of <u>identity</u>. They're called "double angle" formulas because they turn any <u>tricky 2x</u> type terms in trig equations back into <u>plain x terms</u>.

You need to know the double angle formulas for <u>sin</u>, <u>cos</u> and <u>tan</u>:

$$\sin 2A \equiv 2 \sin A \cos A$$

$$\cos 2A \equiv \cos^2 A - \sin^2 A$$
$$\text{or} \qquad \equiv 2\cos^2 A - 1$$
$$\text{or} \qquad \equiv 1 - 2\sin^2 A$$

$$\tan 2A \equiv \frac{2 \tan A}{1 - \tan^2 A}$$

You can use the identity $\cos^2 A + \sin^2 A \equiv 1$ to get the other versions of the cos 2A formula.

You get these formulas by writing $2A$ as $A + A$ and using the addition formulas from the previous page.

Use the **Double Angle Formulas** to **Simplify** and **Solve Equations**

If an equation has a <u>mixture</u> of <u>sin x</u> and <u>sin 2x</u> terms in it, there's not much that you can do with it. So that you can <u>simplify</u> it, and then <u>solve</u> it, you have to use one of the <u>double angle formulas</u>.

EXAMPLE Solve the equation $\cos 2x - 5 \cos x = 2$ in the interval $0 \le x \le 2\pi$.

First use the double angle formula $\cos 2A \equiv 2 \cos^2 A - 1$ to get rid of cos $2x$ (use this version so that you don't end up with a mix of sin and cos terms).

$$2 \cos^2 x - 1 - 5 \cos x = 2$$

Simplify so you have zero on one side...
...then factorise and solve the quadratic that you've made:

$$2 \cos^2 x - 5 \cos x - 3 = 0$$
$$(2 \cos x + 1)(\cos x - 3) = 0$$
$$\text{So } (2 \cos x + 1) = 0 \text{ or } (\cos x - 3) = 0$$

The second bracket gives you $\cos x = 3$, which has no solutions since $-1 \le \cos x \le 1$.

So all that's left is to solve the first bracket to find x:

$$2 \cos x + 1 = 0$$
$$\cos x = -\tfrac{1}{2} \implies x = \tfrac{2}{3}\pi \text{ or } x = \tfrac{4}{3}\pi.$$

Sketch the graph of cos x to find all values of x in the given interval: $\cos x = -\frac{1}{2}$ twice, once at $\frac{2}{3}\pi$ and once at $2\pi - \frac{2}{3}\pi = \frac{4}{3}\pi$.

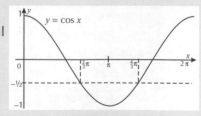

You can use a **Double Angle Formula** even when the x term **Isn't 2x**

Whenever you have an expression that contains any angle that's <u>twice the size</u> of another, you can use the double angle formulas — whether it's sin x and sin $2x$, cos $2x$ and cos $4x$ or tan x and tan $\frac{x}{2}$.

EXAMPLE Prove that $2 \cot \frac{x}{2}(1 - \cos^2 \frac{x}{2}) \equiv \sin x$

Use the identity $\sin^2 \theta + \cos^2 \theta \equiv 1$ to replace $1 - \cos^2 \frac{x}{2}$ on the left-hand side:

Left-hand side: $2 \cot \frac{x}{2} \sin^2 \frac{x}{2}$

Now write cot θ as $\frac{\cos \theta}{\sin \theta}$:

$$2 \frac{\cos \frac{x}{2}}{\sin \frac{x}{2}} \sin^2 \frac{x}{2} \equiv 2 \cos \frac{x}{2} \sin \frac{x}{2}$$

Now you can use the sin $2A$ double angle formula to write $\sin x \equiv 2 \sin \frac{x}{2} \cos \frac{x}{2}$ (using $A = \frac{x}{2}$).

So using the sin double angle formula... $\equiv \sin x$ ...you get the <u>right-hand side</u>.

You can work out <u>half-angle formulas</u> for <u>cos</u> and <u>tan</u> from the double angle formulas. This example uses the one for <u>sin</u>.

Double the angles, double the fun...

You definitely need to know the double angle formulas off by heart, because they won't be on the exam formula sheet. So it's a case of the old "learn 'em, write 'em out, and keep going until you can do all three perfectly" strategy. And don't forget to be on the lookout for sneaky questions that want you to use a double angle formula but don't contain a "2x" bit.

The R Addition Formulas

A different kind of addition formula this time — one that lets you go from an <u>expanded expression</u> to one with <u>brackets</u>...

Use the **R Formulas** when you've got a **Mix** of **Sin** and **Cos**

If you're solving an equation that contains <u>both</u> $\sin \theta$ and $\cos \theta$ terms, e.g. $3\sin \theta + 4\cos \theta = 1$, you need to <u>rewrite</u> it so that it only contains <u>one</u> trig function. The formulas that you use to do that are known as the <u>R formulas</u>:

One set for sine:
$$a\sin \theta \pm b\cos \theta \equiv R\sin (\theta \pm \alpha)$$

And one set for cosine:
$$a\cos \theta \pm b\sin \theta \equiv R\cos (\theta \mp \alpha)$$

where a and b are <u>positive</u>. Again, you need to be careful with the + and − signs here — see p.61.

Using the R Formulas

1) You'll start with an identity like $2\sin x + 5\cos x \equiv R\sin (x + \alpha)$, where <u>$R$ and α need to be found</u>.

2) First, <u>expand the RHS</u> using the <u>addition formulas</u> (see p.61): $2\sin x + 5\cos x \equiv R\sin x \cos \alpha + R\cos x \sin \alpha$.

This is because $\dfrac{R\sin \alpha}{R\cos \alpha} = \tan \alpha$.

3) <u>Equate the coefficients</u> of $\sin x$ and $\cos x$. You'll get <u>two equations</u>: ① $R\cos \alpha = 2$ and ② $R\sin \alpha = 5$.

$(R\sin \alpha)^2 + (R\cos \alpha)^2$ $\equiv R^2(\sin^2\alpha + \cos^2\alpha)$ $\equiv R^2$ (using the identity $\sin^2\alpha + \cos^2\alpha \equiv 1$).

4) To find α, <u>divide</u> equation ② by equation ①, then take <u>$\tan^{-1}$</u> of the result.

5) To find R, <u>square</u> equations ① and ② and <u>add</u> them together, then take the <u>square root</u> of the answer.

This method looks a bit scary, but follow the example below through and it should make more sense.

Solve the equation in **Stages**

You'll almost always be asked to solve equations like this in <u>different stages</u> — first <u>writing out</u> the equation in the form of one of the R formulas, then <u>solving</u> it. You might also have to find the <u>maximum</u> or <u>minimum</u> value.

EXAMPLE (Part 1): Express $2\sin x - 3\cos x$ in the form $R\sin (x - \alpha)$, given that $R > 0$ and $0 \le \alpha \le 90°$.

$2\sin x - 3\cos x \equiv R\sin (x - \alpha)$, so expand the RHS to get $2\sin x - 3\cos x \equiv R(\sin x \cos \alpha - \cos x \sin \alpha)$.

Equating coefficients gives the equations $R\cos \alpha = 2$ and $R\sin \alpha = 3$.

Solving for α: $\dfrac{R\sin \alpha}{R\cos \alpha} = \dfrac{3}{2} = \tan \alpha$

$\alpha = \tan^{-1} 1.5 = 56.31°$

This value fits into the correct range so you can leave it as it is.

Look at the coefficients of $\sin x$ on each side of the equation — on the LHS it's 2 and on the RHS it's $R\cos \alpha$, so $2 = R\cos \alpha$. You find the coefficient of $\cos x$ in the same way.

Solving for R: $(R\cos \alpha)^2 + (R\sin \alpha)^2 = 2^2 + 3^2 = R^2$

$R = \sqrt{2^2 + 3^2} = \sqrt{13}$

So $2\sin x - 3\cos x = \sqrt{13} \sin (x - 56.31°)$

EXAMPLE (Part 2): Hence solve $2\sin x - 3\cos x = 1$ in the interval $0 \le x \le 360°$.

If $2\sin x - 3\cos x = 1$, that means $\sqrt{13} \sin (x - 56.31°) = 1$, so $\sin (x - 56.31°) = \dfrac{1}{\sqrt{13}}$.

$0 \le x \le 360°$, so $-56.31° \le x - 56.31° \le 303.69°$.

Careful — you're looking for solutions between $-56.31°$ and $303.69°$ here.

Solve the equation using arcsin:

$x - 56.31° = \sin^{-1}\left(\dfrac{1}{\sqrt{13}}\right) = 16.10°$ <u>or</u> $180 - 16.10 = 163.90°$.

So $x = 16.10 + 56.31 = \boxed{72.4°}$ <u>or</u> $x = 163.90 + 56.31 = \boxed{220.2°}$

EXAMPLE (Part 3): What are the max and min values of $2\sin x - 3\cos x$?

The maximum and minimum values of sin (and cos) are ± 1, so the maximum and minimum values of $R\sin (x - \alpha)$ are $\pm R$.

As $2\sin x - 3\cos x = \sqrt{13} \sin (x - 56.31°)$, $R = \sqrt{13}$, so the maximum and minimum values are $\boxed{\pm \sqrt{13}}$.

Once you've rewritten your equation using the R formulas, you can sketch the graph (using the methods on p.7), where R is the scale factor for the stretch and α is the horizontal shift.

A pirate's favourite trigonometry formula...

The R formulas might look a bit scary, but they're OK really — just do lots of examples until you're happy with the method. Careful with the <u>adjusting the interval</u> bit that came up in part 2 above — it's pretty fiddly and easy to get muddled over.

More Trigonometry Stuff

And here we have the final trig page... a collection of random bits that didn't really fit on the other pages. That's one of the scary things about trig questions — you never know what you're going to get.

The Factor Formulas come from the Addition Formulas

As if there weren't enough trig formulas already, here come a few more. Don't worry though — these ones are given to you on the exam formula sheet so you don't need to learn them off by heart.

$$\sin A + \sin B \equiv 2\sin\left(\frac{A+B}{2}\right)\cos\left(\frac{A-B}{2}\right)$$

$$\sin A - \sin B \equiv 2\cos\left(\frac{A+B}{2}\right)\sin\left(\frac{A-B}{2}\right)$$

$$\cos A + \cos B \equiv 2\cos\left(\frac{A+B}{2}\right)\cos\left(\frac{A-B}{2}\right)$$

$$\cos A - \cos B \equiv -2\sin\left(\frac{A+B}{2}\right)\sin\left(\frac{A-B}{2}\right)$$

These are the factor formulas, and they come from the addition formulas (see below). They come in handy for some integrations — it's a bit tricky to integrate $2\cos 3\theta \cos\theta$, but integrating $\cos 4\theta + \cos 2\theta$ is much easier.

EXAMPLE Use the addition formulas to show that $\cos A + \cos B \equiv 2\cos\left(\frac{A+B}{2}\right)\cos\left(\frac{A-B}{2}\right)$

You can derive the other formulas using the same method.

Use the cos addition formulas: $\cos(x + y) \equiv \cos x \cos y - \sin x \sin y$
and $\cos(x - y) \equiv \cos x \cos y + \sin x \sin y$.
Add them together to get: $\cos(x + y) + \cos(x - y) \equiv \cos x \cos y - \sin x \sin y + \cos x \cos y + \sin x \sin y$
$$\equiv 2\cos x \cos y.$$
Now substitute in $A = x + y$ and $B = x - y$.
Subtracting these gives $A - B = x + y - (x - y) = 2y$, so $y = \frac{A-B}{2}$.
Adding gives $A + B = x + y + (x - y) = 2x$, so $x = \frac{A+B}{2}$.

So $\cos A + \cos B \equiv 2\cos\left(\frac{A+B}{2}\right)\cos\left(\frac{A-B}{2}\right)$.

You might have to use Different Bits of Trig in the Same Question

Some exam questions might try and catch you out by making you use more than one identity to show that two things are equal...

EXAMPLE Show that $\cos 3\theta \equiv 4\cos^3\theta - 3\cos\theta$.

First, write $\cos 3\theta$ as $\cos(2\theta + \theta)$, then you can use the cos addition formula:
$\cos(3\theta) \equiv \cos(2\theta + \theta) \equiv \cos 2\theta \cos\theta - \sin 2\theta \sin\theta$.

You have to use both the addition formula and the double angle formulas in this question.

Now you can use the cos and sin double angle formulas to get rid of the 2θ:
$\cos 2\theta \cos\theta - \sin 2\theta \sin\theta \equiv (2\cos^2\theta - 1)\cos\theta - (2\sin\theta\cos\theta)\sin\theta$

This uses the identity $\sin^2\theta + \cos^2\theta \equiv 1$ in the form $\sin^2\theta \equiv 1 - \cos^2\theta$.

$\equiv 2\cos^3\theta - \cos\theta - 2\sin^2\theta\cos\theta \equiv 2\cos^3\theta - \cos\theta - 2(1 - \cos^2\theta)\cos\theta$

$\equiv 2\cos^3\theta - \cos\theta - 2\cos\theta + 2\cos^3\theta \equiv \boxed{4\cos^3\theta - 3\cos\theta}$.

...or even drag up trig knowledge from C2 or even GCSE. This question looks short and sweet, but it's actually pretty nasty — you need to know a sneaky conversion between sin and cos.

EXAMPLE If $y = \arcsin x$ for $-1 \le x \le 1$ and $-\frac{\pi}{2} \le y \le \frac{\pi}{2}$, show that $\arccos x = \frac{\pi}{2} - y$.

$y = \arcsin x$, so $x = \sin y$ (as arcsin is the inverse of sin).

Now the next bit isn't obvious — you need to use an identity to switch from sin to cos. This gives... $x = \cos\left(\frac{\pi}{2} - y\right)$.

Now, taking inverses gives $\arccos x = \arccos\left(\cos\left(\frac{\pi}{2} - y\right)\right)$, so $\boxed{\arccos x = \frac{\pi}{2} - y}$.

Converting Sin to Cos (and back):
$\sin t \equiv \cos\left(\frac{\pi}{2} - t\right)$
and $\cos t \equiv \sin\left(\frac{\pi}{2} - t\right)$.
Remember sin is just cos shifted by $\frac{\pi}{2}$ and vice versa.

Trig is like a box of chocolates...

You'll be pleased to know that you've seen all the trig formulas you need for C4. I know there are about 1000 of them (N.B. exaggerations like this may lose you marks in the exam), but any of them could pop up. Examiners particularly like it when you have to use one identity or formula to prove or derive another, so get practising. Then go off and have a nice cup of tea.

C4 Section 2 — Practice Questions

There are a <u>lot of formulas</u> in this section — try writing them all out and <u>sticking them somewhere</u> so you can learn them. The best way to get to grips with them is to <u>practise using them</u> — so here are some questions for you to have a go at.

Warm-up Questions

1) For $\theta = 30°$, find the exact values of:
   a) $\operatorname{cosec} \theta$
   b) $\sec \theta$
   c) $\cot \theta$

2) Sketch the graphs of cosecant, secant and cotangent for $-2\pi \le x \le 2\pi$.

3) Use the identity $\cos^2\theta + \sin^2\theta \equiv 1$ to produce the identity $\sec^2\theta \equiv 1 + \tan^2\theta$.

4) Use the trig identities to show that $\cot^2\theta + \sin^2\theta \equiv \operatorname{cosec}^2\theta - \cos^2\theta$.

5) State the three different versions of the double angle formula for cos.

6) Use the double angle formula to solve the equation: $\sin 2\theta = -\sqrt{3}\sin\theta$, $0 \le \theta \le 360°$.

7) Using the addition formula for cos, find the exact value of $\cos\frac{\pi}{12}$.

8) Find the exact value of $\sin(A + B)$, given that $\sin A = \frac{4}{5}$ and $\sin B = \frac{7}{25}$.
   You might find these triangles useful: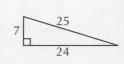

9) Which two R formulas could you use to write $a\cos\theta + b\sin\theta$ $(a, b > 0)$ in terms of just sin or just cos?

10) Write $5\sin\theta - 6\cos\theta$ in the form $R\sin(\theta - \alpha)$, where $R > 0$ and $0 \le \alpha \le 90°$.

11) Use the addition formulas to show that $\sin A - \sin B \equiv 2\cos\left(\frac{A+B}{2}\right)\sin\left(\frac{A-B}{2}\right)$.

12) Show that $\frac{\cos\theta}{\sin\theta} + \frac{\sin\theta}{\cos\theta} \equiv 2\operatorname{cosec}2\theta$.

Here is a selection of the <u>finest trigonometry exam questions</u> available, matured for 21 days and served with a delicious peppercorn sauce.

Exam Questions

1 a) Sketch the graph of $y = \operatorname{cosec} x$ for $-\pi \le x \le \pi$.

Don't forget to put your calculator in RAD mode when you're using radians (and DEG mode when you're using degrees)...

(3 marks)

b) Solve the equation $\operatorname{cosec} x = \frac{5}{4}$ for $-\pi \le x \le \pi$.
   Give your answers correct to 3 significant figures.

(3 marks)

c) Solve the equation $\operatorname{cosec} x = 3\sec x$ for $-\pi \le x \le \pi$.
   Give your answers correct to 3 significant figures.

(3 marks)

C4 Section 2 — Practice Questions

Take a <u>deep breath</u> and get ready to dive in again — here come some more <u>lovely trig questions</u>...

2   a)   Write $9\sin\theta + 12\cos\theta$ in the form $R\sin(\theta + \alpha)$, where $R > 0$ and $0 \le \alpha \le \frac{\pi}{2}$.

(3 marks)

      b)   Using the result from part (a) solve $9\sin\theta + 12\cos\theta = 3$,
giving all solutions for θ in the range $0 \le \theta \le 2\pi$.

(5 marks)

3   Using the double angle and addition identities for sin and cos,
find an expression for $\sin 3x$ in terms of $\sin x$ only.

(4 marks)

4   a)   Show that $\dfrac{2\sin x}{1 - \cos x} - \dfrac{2\cos x}{\sin x} \equiv 2\operatorname{cosec} x$

(4 marks)

      b)   Use this result to find all the solutions for which

$$\frac{2\sin x}{1 - \cos x} - \frac{2\cos x}{\sin x} = 4 \qquad 0 < x < 2\pi.$$

(3 marks)

5   a)   Write $5\cos\theta + 12\sin\theta$ in the form $R\cos(\theta - \alpha)$, where $R > 0$ and $0 \le \alpha \le 90°$.

(4 marks)

      b)   Hence solve $5\cos\theta + 12\sin\theta = 2$ for $0 \le \theta \le 360°$, giving your answers to 2 decimal places.

(5 marks)

      c)   Use your results from part a) above to find the minimum value of $(5\cos\theta + 12\sin\theta)^3$.

(2 marks)

6   a)   (i)   Using an appropriate identity, show that $3\tan^2\theta - 2\sec\theta = 5$
can be written as $3\sec^2\theta - 2\sec\theta - 8 = 0$.

(2 marks)

          (ii)   Hence or otherwise show that $\cos\theta = -\frac{3}{4}$ or $\cos\theta = \frac{1}{2}$.

(3 marks)

      b)   Use your results from part a) above to solve the equation $3\tan^2 2x - 2\sec 2x = 5$
for $0 \le x \le 180°$. Give your answers to 2 decimal places.

(3 marks)

Parametric Equations of Curves

Parametric equations seem kinda weirdy to start with, but they're actually pretty clever. You can use them to replace <u>one</u> horrifically complicated equation with <u>two</u> relatively normal-looking ones. I bet that's just what you always wanted...

Parametric Equations split up x and y into Separate Equations

1) Normally, graphs in the (x, y) plane are described using a <u>Cartesian equation</u> — a single equation linking x and y.

2) Sometimes, particularly for more <u>complicated</u> graphs, it's easier to have two linked equations, called <u>parametric equations</u>.

3) In parametric equations x and y are each <u>defined separately</u> in terms of a <u>third variable</u>, called a <u>parameter</u>. The parameter is usually either t or θ.

EXAMPLE

This graph is given by the parametric equations $y = t^2 - 1$ and $x = t + 1$:

This point corresponds to $t = -3$.
So $x = -3 + 1 = -2$,
$y = (-3)^2 - 1 = 8$.

Here $t = 2$.
So $x = 2 + 1 = 3$,
$y = 2^2 - 1 = 3$.

When $t = 0$,
$x = 0 + 1 = 1$,
$y = 0^2 - 1 = -1$.

You can use the parametric equations of a graph to find <u>coordinates</u> of points on the graph, and to find the value of the <u>parameter</u> for given <u>x- or y-coordinates</u>.

EXAMPLE

A curve is defined by the parametric equations $y = \dfrac{1}{3t}$ and $x = 2t - 3$, $t \neq 0$.

a) Find the x- and y- values of the point the curve passes through when $t = 4$.
b) What value of t corresponds to the point where $y = 9$?
c) What is the value of y when $x = -15$?

Nothing to this question — just sub the right values into the right equations and you're away:

a) When $t = 4$, $x = 8 - 3 = 5$, and $y = \dfrac{1}{12}$

b) $9 = \dfrac{1}{3t} \Rightarrow t = \dfrac{1}{27}$

c) $-15 = 2t - 3 \Rightarrow t = -6 \Rightarrow y = -\dfrac{1}{18}$

> Use the equation for x to find t first, then use that value of t in the other equation to find y.

Circles can be given by Parametric Equations too

You saw the <u>Cartesian equations</u> of <u>circles</u> way back at AS-level, but now you get to use their <u>parametric equations</u>.

A circle with <u>centre (0, 0)</u> and <u>radius r</u> is defined by the parametric equations $x = r \cos \theta$ and $y = r \sin \theta$...

...and a circle with <u>centre (a, b)</u> and <u>radius r</u> is defined by the parametric equations $x = r \cos \theta + a$ and $y = r \sin \theta + b$.

EXAMPLES

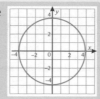

This is the circle given by the equations $x = 4 \cos \theta$ and $y = 4 \sin \theta$. It has radius 4 and centre (0, 0).

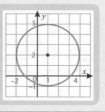

And this is the circle given by the equations $x = 3 \cos \theta + 1$ and $y = 3 \sin \theta + 2$. It has radius 3 and centre (1, 2).

If the values of r are <u>different</u> in each equation (e.g. $x = 2 \cos \theta$ and $y = 3 \sin \theta$), you'll get an <u>ellipse</u> instead of a circle. For this example, the ellipse will be 4 units wide and 6 units tall.

Using Parametric Equations

There's plenty of <u>tinkering around</u> with equations to be done in this topic, so get your <u>rearranging</u> hat on. My rearranging hat is a jaunty straw boater.

Use **Parametric Equations** to find where graphs **Intersect**

A lot of parametric equations questions involve identifying points on the curve defined by the equations.

EXAMPLE

The curve shown in this sketch has the parametric equations $y = t^3 - t$ and $x = 4t^2 - 1$.

Find the coordinates of the points where the graph crosses:
a) the x-axis,
b) the y-axis,
c) the line $8y = 3x + 3$.

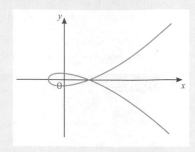

Part a) is pretty straightforward. You've got the <u>y-coordinates</u> already:

a) On the x-axis, $y = 0$.

Use the <u>parametric equation for y</u> to find the <u>values of t</u> where the graph crosses the x-axis:

So $0 = t^3 - t \implies t(t^2 - 1) = 0 \implies t(t + 1)(t - 1) = 0 \implies t = 0, t = -1, t = 1$

t = −1 and t = 1 give the same coordinates — that's where the curve crosses over itself.

Now use those values to find the <u>x-coordinates</u>:

$t = 0 \implies x = 4(0)^2 - 1 = -1 \qquad t = -1 \implies x = 4(-1)^2 - 1 = 3 \qquad t = 1 \implies x = 4(1)^2 - 1 = 3$

So the graph crosses the x-axis at the points $(-1, 0)$ and $(3, 0)$.

The sketch shows there are two points where the graph crosses each axis.

And b) is <u>very similar</u>:

b) On the y-axis, $x = 0$.

So $0 = 4t^2 - 1 \implies t^2 = \frac{1}{4} \implies t = \pm\frac{1}{2}$

$t = \frac{1}{2} \implies y = \left(\frac{1}{2}\right)^3 - \frac{1}{2} = -\frac{3}{8} \qquad\qquad t = -\frac{1}{2} \implies y = \left(-\frac{1}{2}\right)^3 - \left(-\frac{1}{2}\right) = \frac{3}{8}$

So the graph crosses the y-axis at the points $(0, -\frac{3}{8})$ and $(0, \frac{3}{8})$.

Part c) is just a little trickier. First, <u>sub the parametric equations into $8y = 3x + 3$</u>:

c) $8y = 3x + 3 \implies 8(t^3 - t) = 3(4t^2 - 1) + 3$

<u>Rearrange</u> and <u>factorise</u> to find the values of t you need:

$\implies 8t^3 - 8t = 12t^2 \implies 8t^3 - 12t^2 - 8t = 0 \implies t(2t + 1)(t - 2) = 0 \implies t = 0, t = -\frac{1}{2}, t = 2$

Go back to the <u>parametric equations</u> to find the x- and y-coordinates:

$t = 0 \implies x = -1, y = 0$
$t = -\frac{1}{2} \implies x = 4(\frac{1}{4}) - 1 = 0, y = (-\frac{1}{2})^3 + \frac{1}{2} = \frac{3}{8}$
$t = 2 \implies x = 4(4) - 1 = 15, y = 2^3 - 2 = 6$

You can check the answers by sticking these values back into $8y = 3x + 3$.

So the graph crosses the line $4y = 3x + 3$ at the points $(-1, 0)$, $(0, \frac{3}{8})$, $(15, 6)$.

y-coordinates? y not...

You quite often get given a sketch of the curve that the parametric equations define. Don't forget that the sketch can be useful for checking your answers — if the curve crosses the x-axis twice, and you've only found one x-coordinate for when $y = 0$, you know something's gone a bit pear-shaped and you should go back and sort it out, sunshine.

Parametric and Cartesian Equations

If you've been dying for θ to put in an appearance since I mentioned it on page 67, then I've got good news. If, on the other hand, you're bored of parametric equations already... I'm sorry.

Rearrange *Parametric Equations to get the* **Cartesian Equation**

Some parametric equations can be converted into Cartesian equations. There are two main ways to do this:

To convert Parametric Equations to a Cartesian Equation:

① Rearrange one of the equations to make the parameter the subject, then substitute the result into the other equation.

or

② If your equations involve trig functions, use trig identities (see C4 Section 2) to eliminate the parameter.

You can use the first method to combine the parametrics used in the examples on p67:

EXAMPLE Give the Cartesian equations, in the form $y = f(x)$, of the curves represented by the following pairs of parametric equations:

a) $y = t^2 - 1$ and $x = t + 1$, b) $y = \dfrac{1}{3t}$ and $x = 2t - 3$, $t \neq 0$.

You want the answer in the form $y = f(x)$, so leave y alone for now, and rearrange the equation for x to make t the subject:

a) $x = t + 1 \Rightarrow t = x - 1$

Now you can eliminate t from the equation for y:

$y = t^2 - 1 \quad \Rightarrow \quad y = (x - 1)^2 - 1 = x^2 - 2x + 1 - 1$
$\Rightarrow \quad y = x^2 - 2x$

b) $x = 2t - 3 \Rightarrow t = \dfrac{x + 3}{2}$

So $y = \dfrac{1}{3t} \Rightarrow y = \dfrac{1}{3\left(\frac{x+3}{2}\right)} \quad \Rightarrow \quad y = \dfrac{1}{\frac{3(x+3)}{2}} \quad \Rightarrow \quad y = \dfrac{2}{3x + 9}$

If there are **Trig Functions**... use **Trig Identities**

Things get a little trickier when the likes of sin and cos decide to put in an appearance:

EXAMPLE A curve has parametric equations

$$x = 1 + \sin\theta, \quad y = 1 - \cos 2\theta$$

Give the Cartesian equation of the curve in the form $y = f(x)$.

If you try to make θ the subject of these equations, things will just get messy. The trick is to find a way to get both x and y in terms of the same trig function.

You can get $\sin\theta$ into the equation for y using the identity $\cos 2\theta = 1 - 2\sin^2\theta$:

$$y = 1 - \cos 2\theta = 1 - (1 - 2\sin^2\theta) = 2\sin^2\theta$$

If one of the parametric equations includes $\cos 2\theta$ or $\sin 2\theta$, that's probably the one you need to substitute — so make sure you know the double angle formulas.

Rearranging the equation for x gives:

$$\sin\theta = x - 1, \quad \text{so} \quad y = 2\sin^2\theta$$
$$\Rightarrow y = 2(x - 1)^2 = 2x^2 - 4x + 2$$

Cartesy peasy, lemon squeezy...

Sometimes you'll get a nasty question where it's really difficult to get the parameter on its own — in that case you might have to do something clever like think about multiplying x and y or dividing y by x. If something like that comes up in an exam, they'll usually give you a hint — but be aware that you might need to think outside the box.

Differentiation of Parametric Equations

You'll probably be sad to hear that this is the <u>last page</u> on parametric equations. Try to contain your disappointment. Still, it does see the appearance of an old friend — <u>differentiation</u>.

Differentiating Parametric Equations is a lot Simpler than you might expect

Just suppose you've got a <u>curve</u> defined by two <u>parametric equations</u>, with the parameter t: $y = f(t)$ and $x = g(t)$.

If you can't find the <u>Cartesian equation</u>, it seems like it would be a bit tricky to find the gradient, $\dfrac{dy}{dx}$.

Luckily the chain rule (see p17) is on hand to help out:

$$\frac{dy}{dx} = \frac{dy}{dt} \div \frac{dx}{dt}$$

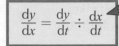 This is exactly the same as on p17, except we've replaced '$\times \frac{dt}{dx}$' with '$\div \frac{dx}{dt}$'

EXAMPLE The curve C is defined by the parametric equations $y = t^3 - 2t + 4$ and $x = t^2 - 1$.

Find: a) $\dfrac{dy}{dx}$ in terms of t,   b)   the gradient of C when $t = -1$.

Start by <u>differentiating</u> the two parametric equations <u>with respect to t</u>:

a) $\dfrac{dy}{dt} = 3t^2 - 2, \dfrac{dx}{dt} = 2t$

Now use the <u>chain rule</u> to combine them:

$$\frac{dy}{dx} = \frac{dy}{dt} \div \frac{dx}{dt} = \frac{3t^2 - 2}{2t}$$

Use the answer to a) to find the <u>gradient</u> for a <u>specific value</u> of t:

b)   When $t = -1$, $\dfrac{dy}{dx} = \dfrac{3(-1)^2 - 2}{2(-1)} = \dfrac{3 - 2}{-2} = -\dfrac{1}{2}$

Use the Gradient to find Tangents and Normals

Of course, it's rarely as straightforward as just finding the gradient. A lot of the time, you'll then have to use it in the equation of a <u>tangent</u> or <u>normal</u> to the parametric curve.

EXAMPLE For the curve C in the example above, find:
   a)   the equation of the tangent to the curve when $t = 2$,
   b)   the equation of the normal to the curve when $t = 2$.

First you need the <u>coordinates</u> of the point where <u>$t = 2$</u>:

a)   When $t = 2$, $x = (2)^2 - 1 = 3$ and $y = (2)^3 - 2(2) + 4 = 8 - 4 + 4 = 8$.

You also need the <u>gradient</u> at that point:

When $t = 2$, $\dfrac{dy}{dx} = \dfrac{3(2)^2 - 2}{2(2)} = \dfrac{10}{4} = \dfrac{5}{2}$

Now use that information to find the equation of the <u>tangent</u>:

The tangent to C at $(3, 8)$ has an equation of the form $y = mx + c$.

So $8 = \dfrac{5}{2}(3) + c \Rightarrow c = \dfrac{1}{2}$.

The tangent to curve C when $t = 2$ is $y = \dfrac{5}{2}x + \dfrac{1}{2}$.

You could also use $y - y_1 = m(x - x_1)$ to get the equation.

You can find the <u>normal</u> in a similar way:

b)   The normal to C at $(3, 8)$ has gradient $-\dfrac{1}{\left(\frac{5}{2}\right)} = -\dfrac{2}{5}$.

So $8 = -\dfrac{2}{5}(3) + c \Rightarrow c = \dfrac{46}{5}$.

The normal to curve C when $t = 2$ is $y = -\dfrac{2}{5}x + \dfrac{46}{5}$.

If you're not quite following all this tangents and normals business, take a look back at C2 to refresh your memory.

And now, yet another chocolate biscuit reference...

To an examiner, adding a 'find the tangent' or 'find the normal' part to a parametric equations question is like adding chocolate to a digestive biscuit — it makes it at least 4 times better. In other words: this is very likely to show up in your C4 exam, so be ready for it. And in case you were wondering, tangent = milk chocolate, normal = dark chocolate.

C4 Section 3 — Practice Questions

Before it became famous in the world of maths, the word 'parametric' had several other jobs. For example, it once starred as the last name of a <u>Bond villain</u> from the <u>former Yugoslavia</u>. Here are some <u>questions</u>. Enjoy.

Warm-up Questions

1) For the following circles, write down the radius and the coordinates of the centre:
   a) The circle given by the parametric equations $x = 7 \cos \theta$ and $y = 7 \sin \theta$.
   b) The circle given by the parametric equations $x = 5 \cos \theta + 2$ and $y = 5 \sin \theta - 1$.

2) A curve is defined by the parametric equations $y = 2t^2 + t + 4$ and $x = \dfrac{6 - t}{2}$.
   a) Find the values of x and y when $t = 0, 1, 2$ and 3.
   b) What are the values of t when: (i) $x = -7$ (ii) $y = 19$?
   c) Find the Cartesian equation of the curve, in the form $y = f(x)$.

3) The parametric equations of a curve are $x = 2\sin\theta$ and $y = \cos^2\theta + 4$, $-\dfrac{\pi}{2} \leq \theta \leq \dfrac{\pi}{2}$.
   a) What are the coordinates of the points where: (i) $\theta = \dfrac{\pi}{4}$ (ii) $\theta = \dfrac{\pi}{6}$
   b) What is the Cartesian equation of the curve?
   c) What restrictions are there on the values of x for this curve?

4) The curve C is defined by the parametric equations $x = \dfrac{\sin \theta}{3}$ and $y = 3 + 2\cos2\theta$.
   Find the Cartesian equation of C.

5) A curve has parametric equations $y = 4 + \dfrac{3}{t}$ and $x = t^2 - 1$.
   What are the coordinates of the points where this curve crosses
   a) the y-axis b) the line $x + 2y = 14$?

6) A curve is defined by the parametric equations $x = t^2$, $y = 3t^3 - 4t$.
   a) Find $\dfrac{dy}{dx}$ for this curve.
   b) Find the coordinates of the stationary points of the curve.

Former career of the word '<u>parametric</u>' #2 — stand-in for the word '<u>hallelujah</u>' in an early draft of <u>Handel's Messiah</u>. Meanwhile, back at the <u>practice questions</u>...

Exam Questions

1   The curve C is defined by the parametric equations
$$x = 1 - \tan\theta, \quad y = \tfrac{1}{2}\sin2\theta, \quad -\tfrac{\pi}{2} < \theta < \tfrac{\pi}{2}.$$
   a) P is the point on curve C where $\theta = \dfrac{\pi}{3}$. Find the exact coordinates of P.
   (2 marks)

   b) Point Q on curve C has coordinates $(2, -\tfrac{1}{2})$. Find the value of θ at Q.
   (2 marks)

   c) Using the identity $\sin2\theta \equiv \dfrac{2\tan\theta}{1 + \tan^2\theta}$, show that the Cartesian equation of C is $y = \dfrac{1 - x}{x^2 - 2x + 2}$.
   (3 marks)

2   The circle on the right is given by the parametric equations
   $x = 5 \cos \theta + a$ and $y = 5 \sin \theta + b$.
   Work out the values of a and b.
   (2 marks)

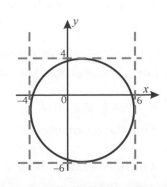

C4 Section 3 — Practice Questions

Former career of the word 'parametric' #3 — proposed name for the next ocean to be discovered.
Unfortunately it turned out all the oceans have already been discovered. Ooh look, more questions...

3

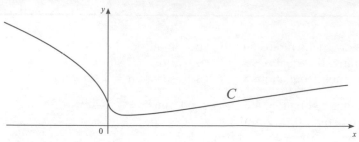

Curve C has parametric equations $x = t^3 + t$, $y = t^2 - 2t + 2$.

a) K is a point on C, and has the coordinates $(a, 1)$. Find the value of a.

(2 marks)

b) The line $8y = x + 6$ passes through C at points K, L and M.
Find the coordinates of L and M, given that the x-coordinate of M is greater than the x-coordinate of L.

(6 marks)

4   The curve C is defined by the parametric equations $x = 3\theta - \cos3\theta$, $y = 2\sin\theta$, $-\pi \le \theta \le \pi$.

a) Find an expression for $\dfrac{dy}{dx}$.

(3 marks)

b) (i) Show that the gradient of C at the point $(\pi + 1, \sqrt{3})$ is $\dfrac{1}{3}$.

(3 marks)

(ii) Find the equation of the normal to C when $\theta = \dfrac{\pi}{6}$.

(4 marks)

5   The curve C, shown on the diagram below, is given by the parametric equations:

$$x = \tan\theta, \qquad y = \sin\theta, \qquad 0 < \theta < \dfrac{\pi}{2}.$$

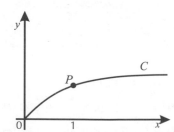

The point P has coordinates $(1, \dfrac{1}{\sqrt{2}})$.

a) Find an expression for $\dfrac{dy}{dx}$, giving your answer in terms of θ, and hence find
the exact value of the gradient at the point P.

(5 marks)

b) Find the equation of the normal to the curve at P.

(3 marks)

6   A curve, C, has parametric equations $x = t^2 + 2t - 3$, $y = 2 - t^3$.

a) The line L is the tangent to C at $y = -6$. Show that the equation of L is $y = -2x + 4$.

(4 marks)

b) L also meets C at point P.

(i) Find the coordinates of P.

(4 marks)

(ii) Find the equation of the normal to the curve at P.

(3 marks)

Numerical Integration

OK, this page is called <u>numerical integration</u>, but it doesn't really involve that much actual integration. Most of it's putting <u>numbers</u> into a <u>formula</u>, which is dead easy.

Estimate the area using the *Trapezium Rule*

Here's a quick reminder of the <u>Trapezium Rule</u> — look back over your C2 notes if you can't remember how to do it.

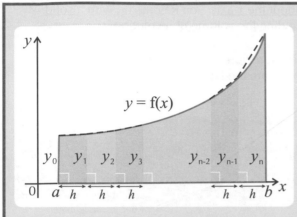

The area of each trapezium is $A_n = \frac{h}{2}(y_n + y_{n+1})$

The area represented by $\int_a^b y \, dx$ is approximately:

$$\int_a^b y \, dx \approx \frac{h}{2}[y_0 + 2(y_1 + y_2 + \dots + y_{n-1}) + y_n]$$

Remember that 5 ordinates is the same as 4 strips.

where n is the number of strips or intervals and h is the width of each strip.

You can find the width of each strip using $h = \frac{(b-a)}{n}$

$y_0, y_1, y_2, \dots, y_n$ are the heights of the sides of the trapeziums — you get these by putting the x-values into the equation of the curve.

Use *More Strips* to get a *More Accurate* answer

Using <u>more strips</u> (i.e. <u>increasing n</u>) gives you a <u>more accurate</u> approximation. You can <u>check</u> how accurate your answer is by working out the <u>percentage error</u> (see below).

EXAMPLE Use the Trapezium Rule to approximate the area of $\int_0^4 \frac{6x^2}{x^3+2} \, dx$, using a) $n = 2$ and b) $n = 4$.

a) For 2 strips, the width of each strip is $h = \frac{4-0}{2} = 2$, so the x-values are 0, 2 and 4.

x	$y = \frac{6x^2}{x^3+2}$
$x_0 = 0$	$y_0 = 0$
$x_1 = 2$	$y_1 = 2.4$
$x_2 = 4$	$y_2 = 1.455$

(3 d.p.)

Putting these values into the formula gives:

$\int_0^4 \frac{6x^2}{x^3+2} \, dx$

$\approx \frac{2}{2}[0 + 2(2.4) + 1.455]$

$= [4.8 + 1.455] = \boxed{6.255}$

(3 d.p.)

b) For 4 strips, the width of each strip is $h = \frac{4-0}{4} = 1$, so the x-values are 0, 1, 2, 3 and 4.

x	$y = \frac{6x^2}{x^3+2}$
$x_0 = 0$	$y_0 = 0$
$x_1 = 1$	$y_1 = 2$
$x_2 = 2$	$y_2 = 2.4$
$x_3 = 3$	$y_3 = 1.862$
$x_4 = 4$	$y_4 = 1.455$

(3 d.p.)

Putting these values into the formula gives:

$\int_0^4 \frac{6x^2}{x^3+2} \, dx$

$\approx \frac{1}{2}[0 + 2(2 + 2.4 + 1.862) + 1.455]$

$= \frac{1}{2}[12.524 + 1.455] = \boxed{6.990}$ (3 d.p.)

You need the *Exact Answer* to work out the *Percentage Error*

To work out the <u>percentage error</u>, calculate or use the <u>exact value</u> of the integral, then use this <u>formula</u>:

$$\% \text{ Error} = \frac{\text{exact value} - \text{approximate value}}{\text{exact value}} \times 100$$

EXAMPLE Calculate the percentage error for a) and b) above to 2 d.p.

This was calculated using the formula on p.30.

First, work out the exact value of the integral: $\int_0^4 \frac{6x^2}{x^3+2} \, dx = [2\ln|x^3 + 2|]_0^4 = [2\ln 66] - [2\ln 2] = 6.993 \, (3 \, d.p.)$

For part a), the percentage error is $\frac{6.993 - 6.255}{6.993} \times 100 = \boxed{10.55\%}$, and for part b), $\frac{6.993 - 6.990}{6.993} \times 100 = \boxed{0.04\%}$.

The approximation with <u>more strips</u> has a <u>lower percentage error</u> — so it's a <u>more accurate</u> approximation.

I lost my notes in the Bermuda Trapezium...

The key thing to remember about the Trapezium Rule (well, apart from the rule itself) is that the more strips you have, the more accurate your answer (and so the lower the % error). More strips = more accurate = smaller % error. Got it?

Volumes of Revolution

Volumes of revolution is a really exciting title for a fairly exciting subject. Sadly, it isn't to do with plotting your own revolution, but it does let you calculate the volumes of weird-shaped things.

You have to find the **Volume** of an area **Rotated About the X-Axis**...

If you're given a definite integral, the solution you come up with is the area under the graph between the two limits (you did this back in C2). If you now rotate that area 2π radians about the x-axis, you'll come up with a solid — and this is what you want to find the volume of. The formula for finding the volume of revolution is:

$$V = \pi \int_{x=x_1}^{x=x_2} y^2 \, dx$$

where y is a function of x (i.e. $y = f(x)$) and x_1 and x_2 are the limits of x.

EXAMPLE

Find the volume, V, of the solid formed when R, the area enclosed by the curve $y = \sqrt{6x^2 - 3x + 2}$, the x-axis and the lines $x = 1$ and $x = 2$, is rotated 2π radians about the x-axis.

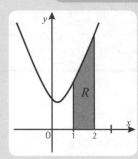

If $y = \sqrt{6x^2 - 3x + 2}$, then $y^2 = 6x^2 - 3x + 2$.

Putting this into the formula gives:

> Don't forget to square y — you might think it's obvious, but it's easily done.

$$V = \pi \int_1^2 6x^2 - 3x + 2 \, dx = \pi \left[2x^3 - \frac{3}{2}x^2 + 2x\right]_1^2$$

$$= \pi\left(\left[2(2)^3 - \frac{3}{2}(2)^2 + 2(2)\right] - \left[2(1)^3 - \frac{3}{2}(1)^2 + 2(1)\right]\right)$$

$$= \pi\left([16 - 6 + 4] - \left[2 - \frac{3}{2} + 2\right]\right) = \pi\left(14 - 2\frac{1}{2}\right) = \boxed{11\frac{1}{2}\pi}$$

...or the **Volume** of an area **Rotated About the Y-Axis**

Instead of rotation about the x-axis, you might be asked to find the volume when an area is rotated about the y-axis instead. You do this using this formula:

$$V = \pi \int_{y=y_1}^{y=y_2} x^2 \, dy$$

This time, you need to rearrange the equations to get x^2 on its own (you'll often be given a function that already has x^2 in it). The limits are horizontal lines, e.g. $y = 1$ and $y = 2$.

EXAMPLE

Find the volume, V, of the solid formed when R, the area enclosed by the curve $y = \sqrt{x^2 + 5}$, the y-axis and the lines $y = 3$ and $y = 6$, is rotated 2π radians about the y-axis.

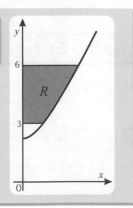

First, rearrange the equation to get x^2 on its own:

$$y = \sqrt{x^2 + 5} \Rightarrow y^2 = x^2 + 5 \quad \text{so } x^2 = y^2 - 5.$$

Now integrate: $V = \pi \int_3^6 y^2 - 5 \, dy = \pi\left[\frac{1}{3}y^3 - 5y\right]_3^6$

$$= \pi\left(\left[\frac{1}{3}(6)^3 - 5(6)\right] - \left[\frac{1}{3}(3)^3 - 5(3)\right]\right)$$

$$= \pi(42 - (-6)) = \boxed{48\pi}$$

Come the revolution, I will have to kill you all...

Not to be confused with the French Revolution, the Industrial Revolution or the lesser-known CGP Revolution, volumes of revolution is part of A2 Maths. So don't go getting any ideas about overthrowing your teachers and not letting them eat cake.

Differential Equations

Differential equations are tricky little devils that have a lot to do with <u>differentiation</u> as well as <u>integration</u>. They're often about <u>rates of change</u>, so the variable t pops up quite a lot.

Differential Equations have a dy/dx Term
(or $\frac{dP}{dt}, \frac{ds}{dt}, \frac{dV}{dr}$, etc. — depending on the variables)

1) A <u>differential equation</u> is an equation that includes a <u>derivative term</u> (such as $\frac{dy}{dx}$), as well as <u>other variables</u> (like x and y).

2) Before you even think (or worry) about <u>solving</u> them, you have to be able to <u>set up</u> ('<u>formulate</u>') differential equations.

3) Differential equations tend to involve a <u>rate of change</u> (giving a derivative term) and a <u>proportion relation</u>. Remember — if $a \propto b$, then $a = kb$ for some <u>constant</u> k.

> **EXAMPLE** The number of bacteria in a petri dish is increasing over time, t, at a rate directly proportional to the number of bacteria, b, at a given time. Formulate a differential equation that shows this information.
>
> The rate of change, $\frac{db}{dt}$, is proportional to b, so $\frac{db}{dt} \propto b$. This means that $\frac{db}{dt} = kb$ for some constant k, $k > 0$.

> **EXAMPLE** The volume of interdimensional space jelly, V, in a container is decreasing over time, t, at a rate directly proportional to the square of its volume. Show this as a differential equation.
>
> The rate of change, $\frac{dV}{dt}$, is proportional to V^2, so $\frac{dV}{dt} \propto V^2$. $\frac{dV}{dt} = -kV^2$ for some constant k, $k > 0$.
>
> *V is decreasing, so don't forget the $-$.*

Solve differential equations by Integrating

Now comes the really juicy bit — <u>solving</u> differential equations. It's not as bad as it looks (honest).

Solving Differential Equations

1) **In C4, you only have to <u>solve</u> differential equations if they have <u>separable variables</u> — where x and y can be <u>separated</u> into <u>functions</u> f(x) and g(y).**

   Remember — it might not be in terms of x and y.

2) **<u>Write</u> the differential equation in the form $\frac{dy}{dx} = f(x)g(y)$.**

3) **Then <u>rearrange</u> the equation to get all the terms with y on the <u>LHS</u> and all the terms with x on the <u>RHS</u>. It'll look something like this: $\frac{1}{g(y)}dy = f(x)dx$.**

   Like in integration by substitution, you can treat dy/dx as a fraction here.

4) **Now <u>integrate both sides</u>: $\int \frac{1}{g(y)}dy = \int f(x)dx$.**

5) **<u>Rearrange</u> your answer to get it in a nice form — you might be asked to find it in the form $y = h(x)$. Don't forget the <u>constant</u> of integration (you only need one — not one on each side). It might be useful to write the constant as $\ln k$ rather than C (see p.30).**

6) **If you're asked for a <u>general solution</u>, leave C (or k) in your answer. If they want a <u>particular solution</u>, they'll give you x and y values for a <u>certain point</u>. All you do is put these values into your equation and use them to <u>find C</u> (or k).**

> **EXAMPLE** Find the particular solution of $\frac{dy}{dx} = 2y(1 + x)^2$ when $x = -1$ and $y = 4$.
>
> This equation has separable variables: f(x) = $2(1 + x)^2$ and g(y) = y.
>
> Rearranging this equation gives: $\frac{1}{y}dy = 2(1 + x)^2dx$
>
> And integrating: $\int \frac{1}{y}dy = \int 2(1 + x)^2dx$
>
> $\Rightarrow \ln|y| = \frac{2}{3}(1 + x)^3 + C$
>
> *If you were asked for a general solution, you could just leave it in this form.*
>
> Now put in the values of x and y to find the value of C:
>
> $\ln 4 = \frac{2}{3}(1 + (-1))^3 + C \Rightarrow \ln 4 = C$
>
> so $\ln|y| = \frac{2}{3}(1 + x)^3 + \ln 4$

I will formulate a plan to take over the world...

...starting with Cumbria. I've always liked Cumbria. You're welcome to join my army of minions, but first you'll have to become an expert on solving differential equations. Do that, and I'll give you Grasmere — or name a mountain after you.

Differential Equations

One of the most exciting things about differential equations is that you can apply them to real-life situations. Well, I say exciting, but perhaps I should say 'mildly interesting', or maybe just 'more stuff for you to learn'.

You might be given Extra Information

1) In the exam, you might be given a question that takes a real-life problem and uses differential equations to model it.

2) Population questions come up quite often — the population might be increasing or decreasing, and you have to find and solve differential equations to show it. In cases like this, one of your variables will usually be t, time.

3) You might be given a starting condition — e.g. the initial population. The important thing to remember is that:

> the starting condition occurs when $t = 0$.

This is pretty obvious, but it's really important.

4) You might also be given extra information — e.g. the population after a certain number of years (where you have to figure out what t is), or the number of years it takes to reach a certain population (where you have to work out what the population will be). Make sure you always link the numbers you get back to the situation.

Exam Questions are often Broken Down into lots of Parts

Questions like the one below can be a bit overwhelming, but follow it through step by step and it shouldn't be too bad.

EXAMPLE

The population of rabbits in a park is decreasing as winter approaches.
The rate of decrease is directly proportional to the current number of rabbits (P).

a) Formulate a differential equation to model the rate of decrease in terms of the variables P, t (time in days) and k, a positive constant.

b) If the initial population is P_0, solve your differential equation to find P in terms of P_0, k and t.

c) Given that $k = 0.1$, find the time at which the population of rabbits will have halved, to the nearest day.

a) If the rate of decrease is proportional to the number of rabbits, then $\frac{dP}{dt} = -kP$ (it's negative because the population is decreasing).

b) First, solve the differential equation to find the general solution: $\frac{dP}{dt} = -kP \Rightarrow \frac{1}{P} dP = -k\, dt$

Integrating this gives: $\int \frac{1}{P} dP = \int -k\, dt$

$\Rightarrow \ln P = -kt + C$

You don't need modulus signs for $\ln P$ as $P \geq 0$ — you can't have a negative population.

At $t = 0$, $P = P_0$. Putting these values into the equation gives: $\ln P_0 = -k(0) + C$

$\Rightarrow \ln P_0 = C$

So the differential equation becomes: $\ln P = -kt + \ln P_0$

$\Rightarrow P = e^{(-kt + \ln P_0)} = e^{-kt} e^{\ln P_0}$

$\Rightarrow P = P_0 e^{-kt}$

Remember that $e^{\ln x} = x = \ln e^x$.

c) When the population of rabbits has halved, $P = \frac{1}{2}P_0$. You've been told that $k = 0.1$, so substitute these values into the equation above and solve for t:

$\frac{1}{2}P_0 = P_0 e^{-0.1t}$

$\frac{1}{2} = e^{-0.1t}$

$\ln \frac{1}{2} = -0.1t$

$-0.6931 = -0.1t \Rightarrow t = 6.931$

So, to the nearest day, $t = 7$. This means that it will take 7 days for the population of rabbits to halve.

At t = 10, we kill all the bunnies...

These questions can get a bit morbid — just how I like them. They might look a bit scary, as they throw a lot of information at you in one go, but once you know how to solve them, they're a walk in the park. Rabbit traps optional.

C4 Section 4 — Practice Questions

Phew, that was a bit of a tricky section. I bet you could do with a break. Well, hold on just a minute — here are some practice questions to do first to check you know your stuff. Let's start with a gentle warm-up.

Warm-up Questions

1) Use the Trapezium Rule to estimate the value of $\int_0^6 (6x - 12)(x^2 - 4x + 3)^2 dx$, first using 4 strips and then again with 6 strips. Calculate the percentage error for each answer.

2) Find the volume of the solid formed when the area bounded by the curve $y = \frac{1}{x}$, the x-axis and the lines $x = 2$ and $x = 4$ is rotated 2π radians about the x-axis.

3) Find the volume of the solid formed when the area bounded by the curve $y = x^2 + 1$, the y-axis and the lines $y = 1$ and $y = 3$ is rotated 2π radians about the y-axis.

4) Find the general solution to the differential equation $\frac{dy}{dx} = \frac{1}{y}\cos x$. Give your answer in the form $y^2 = f(x)$.

5) The population of squirrels is increasing suspiciously quickly. The rate of increase is directly proportional to the current number of squirrels, S.

   a) Formulate a differential equation to model the rate of increase in terms of S, t (time in weeks) and k, a positive constant.

   b) The squirrels need a population of 150 to successfully take over the forest. If the initial population is 30 and the value of k is 0.2, how long (to the nearest week) will it take before they can overthrow the evil hedgehogs?

Unfortunately the exam questions are less likely to be about rebel squirrels, as the examiners tend to be on the hedgehogs' side. If you ever meet an examiner, look closely to make sure he's not a hedgehog in disguise.

Exam Questions

1   Find the volume of the solid formed when the region R, bounded by the curve $y = \cos x$, the x-axis and the lines $x = \frac{\pi}{4}$ and $x = \frac{\pi}{3}$, is rotated 2π radians about the x-axis.
Give your answer to 3 decimal places.

(4 marks)

2   The graph below shows the curve of $y = \frac{1}{x^2}$ for $x > 0$.

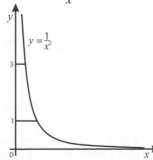

The region bounded by the curve, the y-axis and the lines $y = 1$ and $y = 3$ is rotated 2π radians about the y-axis. Calculate the exact volume of the solid formed.

(5 marks)

C4 Section 4 — Practice Questions

One more page of questions, then you're onto the <u>final section</u> of C4. That's right, the <u>last one</u>.

3   **Figure 1** shows the graph of $y = x \sin x$. The region R is bounded by the curve and the x-axis ($0 \leq x \leq \pi$).

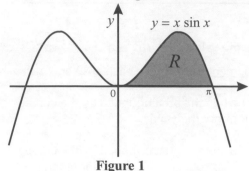

Figure 1

a)   Fill in the missing values of y in the table below. Give your answers to 4 decimal places.

x	0	$\frac{\pi}{4}$	$\frac{\pi}{2}$	$\frac{3\pi}{4}$	π
y	0	0.5554			0

(2 marks)

b)   Hence find an approximation for the area of R, using the Trapezium Rule.
     Give your answer to 3 decimal places.

(4 marks)

c)   Find the exact area of R using integration by parts.

(4 marks)

d)   Hence find the percentage error of the approximation.

(2 marks)

4   a)   Find the general solution to the differential equation

$$\frac{dy}{dx} = \frac{\cos x \cos^2 y}{\sin x}.$$

(4 marks)

b)   Given that $y = \pi$ when $x = \frac{\pi}{6}$, solve the differential equation above.

(2 marks)

5   A company sets up an advertising campaign to increase sales of margarine. After the campaign, the number of tubs of margarine sold each week, m, increases over time, t weeks, at a rate that is directly proportional to the square root of the number of tubs sold.

a)   Formulate a differential equation in terms of t, m and a constant k.

(2 marks)

b)   At the start of the campaign, the company was selling 900 tubs of margarine a week.
     Use this information to solve the differential equation, giving m in terms of k and t.

(4 marks)

c)   Hence calculate the number of tubs sold in the fifth week after the campaign, given that $k = 2$.

(3 marks)

Vectors

If you did M1, then you've probably seen some of this vector stuff before. If not, you've got lots to look forward to. In any case, we're going to start with the basics — like what vectors are.

Vectors have Magnitude and Direction — Scalars Don't

1) Vectors have both size and direction — e.g. a velocity of 2 m/s on a bearing of 050°, or a displacement of 3 m north. Scalars are just quantities without a direction, e.g. a speed of 2 m/s, a distance of 3 m.

2) Vectors are drawn as lines with arrowheads on them.

- The length of the line represents the magnitude (size) of the vector (e.g. the speed component of velocity). Sometimes vectors are drawn to scale.

- The direction of the arrowhead shows the direction of the vector.

There are two ways of writing vectors:
1) Using a lower case, bold letter.

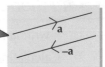

When you're handwriting a vector like this, you should underline the letter, i.e. <u>a</u>.

2) Putting an arrow over the endpoints.

Find the Resultant by Drawing Vectors Nose to Tail

You can add vectors together by drawing the arrows nose to tail.
The single vector that goes from the start to the end of the vectors is called the resultant vector.

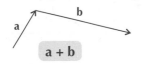

a + b

Resultant: r = a + b

a + b = b + a

Resultant: r = a + b + c

Subtracting a Vector is the Same as Adding a Negative Vector

1) The vector **–a** is in the opposite direction to the vector **a**. They're both exactly the same size.

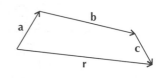

2) So subtracting a vector is the same as adding the negative vector:

$$b - a = b + (-a)$$

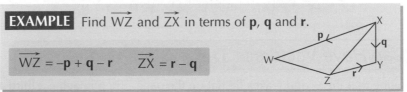

$$b - a \qquad b + (-a)$$

3) You can use the adding and subtracting rules to find a vector in terms of other vectors.

EXAMPLE Find $\overrightarrow{WZ}$ and $\overrightarrow{ZX}$ in terms of **p**, **q** and **r**.

$$\overrightarrow{WZ} = -p + q - r \qquad \overrightarrow{ZX} = r - q$$

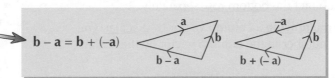

Vectors a, 2a and 3a are all Parallel

You can multiply a vector by a scalar (just a number, remember) — the length changes but the direction stays the same.

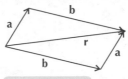 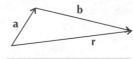

a   × 3   3a   × –1   –3a

Multiplying a vector by a non-zero scalar always produces a parallel vector.

This is $\frac{2}{3}(9a + 15b)$.

This is $\frac{1}{3}(9a + 15b)$.

All these vectors are parallel: | 9a + 15b | 18a + 30b | 6a + 10b | 3a + 5b |

This is 2(9**a** + 15**b**).

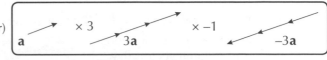

Eating pasta = buying anti-pasta?...

If an exam question asks you to show that two lines are parallel, you just have to show that one vector's a multiple of the other. By the way — exam papers often use λ and μ as scalars in vector questions (so you don't confuse them with vectors).

Vectors

There are a few more ways of representing vectors that you need to know about. Then it's off to the third dimension...

Position Vectors Describe Where a Point Lies

You can use a vector to describe the position of a point, in relation to the origin, O.

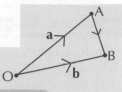

> The position vector of point A is $\overrightarrow{OA}$. It's usually called vector **a**.
> The position vector of point B is $\overrightarrow{OB}$. It's usually called vector **b**.

You can write other vectors in terms of position vectors:
$$\overrightarrow{AB} = -\overrightarrow{OA} + \overrightarrow{OB} = \overrightarrow{OB} - \overrightarrow{OA}$$
$$= -\mathbf{a} + \mathbf{b} = \mathbf{b} - \mathbf{a}$$

Vectors can be described using i + j Units

1) A unit vector is any vector with a magnitude of 1 unit.

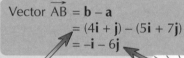

There's more on unit vectors on the next page.

2) The vectors **i** and **j** are standard unit vectors. **i** is in the direction of the x-axis, and **j** is in the direction of the y-axis. They each have a magnitude of 1 unit, of course.

3) They're a dead handy way of describing any vector. You use them to say how far horizontally and vertically you have to go to get from the start of the vector to the end.

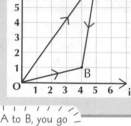

The position vector of point A = **a** = 5**i** + 7**j**
The position vector of point B = **b** = 4**i** + **j**

This tells you that point B lies 4 units to the right and 1 unit above the origin — it's just like coordinates.

Vector $\overrightarrow{AB}$ = **b** − **a**
$= (4\mathbf{i} + \mathbf{j}) - (5\mathbf{i} + 7\mathbf{j})$
$= -\mathbf{i} - 6\mathbf{j}$

Add/subtract the **i** and **j** components separately.

To go from A to B, you go 1 unit left and 6 units down. It's just like a translation.

And then there are Column Vectors

1) If writing **i**'s and **j**'s gets a bit much for your wrists, you can use column vectors instead. $x\mathbf{i} + y\mathbf{j} = \begin{pmatrix} x \\ y \end{pmatrix}$

2) Calculating with them is a breeze. Just add or subtract the top row, then add or subtract the bottom row separately.

3) When you're multiplying a column vector by a scalar, you multiply each number in the column vector by the scalar.

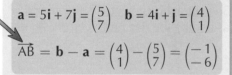

$\mathbf{a} = 5\mathbf{i} + 7\mathbf{j} = \begin{pmatrix} 5 \\ 7 \end{pmatrix}$ $\mathbf{b} = 4\mathbf{i} + \mathbf{j} = \begin{pmatrix} 4 \\ 1 \end{pmatrix}$

$\overrightarrow{AB} = \mathbf{b} - \mathbf{a} = \begin{pmatrix} 4 \\ 1 \end{pmatrix} - \begin{pmatrix} 5 \\ 7 \end{pmatrix} = \begin{pmatrix} -1 \\ -6 \end{pmatrix}$

$2\mathbf{b} - 3\mathbf{a} = 2\begin{pmatrix} 4 \\ 1 \end{pmatrix} - 3\begin{pmatrix} 5 \\ 7 \end{pmatrix} = \begin{pmatrix} 8 \\ 2 \end{pmatrix} - \begin{pmatrix} 15 \\ 21 \end{pmatrix} = \begin{pmatrix} -7 \\ -19 \end{pmatrix}$

You Can Have Vectors in Three Dimensions Too

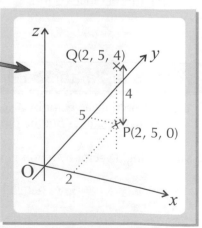

1) Imagine that the x- and y-axes lie flat on the page. Then imagine a third axis sticking straight through the page at right angles to it — this is the z-axis.

2) The points in three dimensions are given (x, y, z) coordinates.

3) When you're talking vectors, **k** is the unit vector in the direction of the z-axis.

4) You can write three-dimensional vectors as column vectors like this: $x\mathbf{i} + y\mathbf{j} + z\mathbf{k} = \begin{pmatrix} x \\ y \\ z \end{pmatrix}$

5) So the position vector of point Q is: $2\mathbf{i} + 5\mathbf{j} + 4\mathbf{k} = \begin{pmatrix} 2 \\ 5 \\ 4 \end{pmatrix}$

I've got B + Q units in my kitchen...

Three dimensions doesn't really make things much more difficult — it just gives you an extra number to calculate with. You add, subtract and multiply 3D column vectors in the same way as 2D ones — you just have three rows to deal with.

Vectors

Pythagoras pops up all over the place, and here he is again. Fascinating fact — Pythagoras refused to say words containing the Greek equivalent of the letter c. I read it on the internet, so it has to be true.

Use **Pythagoras' Theorem** to Find Vector **Magnitudes**

1) The <u>magnitude</u> of vector **a** is written as $|\mathbf{a}|$, and the magnitude of $\overrightarrow{AB}$ is written as $|\overrightarrow{AB}|$.

A vector's magnitude is sometimes called its modulus.

2) The **i** and **j** components of a vector form a convenient <u>right-angled triangle</u>, so just bung them into the <u>Pythagoras formula</u> to find the vector's magnitude.

3) You might be asked to find a <u>unit vector</u> in the direction of a particular vector. Remember — a unit vector has a <u>magnitude of 1</u> (see the previous page).

A unit vector in the direction of vector $\mathbf{a} = \dfrac{\mathbf{a}}{|\mathbf{a}|}$

EXAMPLE

$\mathbf{a} = 5\mathbf{i} + 3\mathbf{j}$

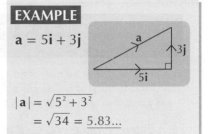

$$|\mathbf{a}| = \sqrt{5^2 + 3^2}$$
$$= \sqrt{34} = \underline{5.83\ldots}$$

EXAMPLE If vector **p** has a magnitude of 12 units, find a unit vector parallel to **p**.

$$\frac{\mathbf{p}}{|\mathbf{p}|} = \frac{\mathbf{p}}{12} = \frac{1}{12}\mathbf{p}$$

You Can Use **Pythagoras** in **Three Dimensions** Too

1) You can use a variation of <u>Pythagoras' theorem</u> to find the distance of any point in 3 dimensions from the origin, O.

The distance of point (x, y, z) from the origin is $\sqrt{x^2 + y^2 + z^2}$

EXAMPLE 1

Find $|\overrightarrow{OQ}|$.

$$|\overrightarrow{OQ}| = \sqrt{x^2 + y^2 + z^2}$$
$$= \sqrt{2^2 + 5^2 + 4^2}$$
$$= \sqrt{45}$$
$$= 6.7 \text{ units}$$

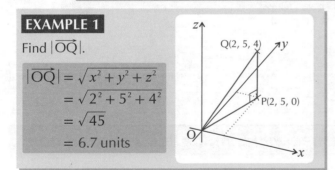

Here's where this formula comes from:
$$OP = \sqrt{x^2 + y^2}$$
$$OP^2 = x^2 + y^2$$
$$OQ = \sqrt{OP^2 + z^2}$$
$$OQ = \sqrt{x^2 + y^2 + z^2}$$

EXAMPLE 2 Find the magnitude of the vector $\mathbf{r} = 5\mathbf{i} + 7\mathbf{j} + 3\mathbf{k}$.

$$|\mathbf{r}| = \sqrt{5^2 + 7^2 + 3^2}$$
$$= \sqrt{83} = 9.1 \text{ units}$$

2) There's also a Pythagoras-based formula for finding <u>the distance between any two points</u>.

The distance between points (x_1, y_1, z_1) and (x_2, y_2, z_2) is $\sqrt{(x_1 - x_2)^2 + (y_1 - y_2)^2 + (z_1 - z_2)^2}$

EXAMPLE

The position vector of point A is $3\mathbf{i} + 2\mathbf{j} + 4\mathbf{k}$, and the position vector of point B is $2\mathbf{i} + 6\mathbf{j} - 5\mathbf{k}$. Find $|\overrightarrow{AB}|$.

A has the coordinates $(3, 2, 4)$, B has the coordinates $(2, 6, -5)$.

$$|\overrightarrow{AB}| = \sqrt{(x_1 - x_2)^2 + (y_1 - y_2)^2 + (z_1 - z_2)^2}$$
$$= \sqrt{(3 - 2)^2 + (2 - 6)^2 + (4 - (-5))^2}$$
$$= \sqrt{1 + 16 + 81} = 9.9 \text{ units}$$

You can play Battleships with 3D coordinates too — but you don't have to...

The magnitude is just a <u>scalar</u>, so it doesn't have a direction — the magnitude of $\overrightarrow{AB}$ is the same as the magnitude of $\overrightarrow{BA}$. Squaring the numbers in the formulas gets rid of any minus signs, so you don't have to worry about which way round you subtract the coordinates (phew). There's not a lot new on this page, in fact, it's mostly just good old Pythagoras.

Vector Equations of Lines

At first glance, <u>vector equations of straight lines</u> don't look much like normal straight-line equations. But they're pretty similar if you look closely. In any case, just learn the formulas <u>really well</u> and you'll be fine.

Learn the Equation of the Line Through a Point and Parallel to Another Vector

A straight line which goes through point A, and is parallel to vector **b**, has the vector equation: **r** = **a** + _t_**b**

a = position vector of point A
r = position vector of a point on the line, and _t_ = a scalar.

A is a fixed point.

This is pretty much a 3D version of the old $y = mx + c$ equation. **b** is similar to the gradient, m, and **a** gives a point that the line passes through, just like c gives the y-axis intercept.

In Cartesian form, the equation is
$$\frac{x - a_1}{b_1} = \frac{y - a_2}{b_2} = \frac{z - a_3}{b_3} (= t).$$

Each different value you stick in for _t_ in the vector equation gives you the <u>position vector, **r**</u>, of a different point on the line.

Alternative ways of writing this are:
$\mathbf{r} = (3 + t)\mathbf{i} + (2 + 3t)\mathbf{j} + (6 - 2t)\mathbf{k}$,
$$\mathbf{r} = \begin{pmatrix} 3 \\ 2 \\ 6 \end{pmatrix} + t\begin{pmatrix} 1 \\ 3 \\ -2 \end{pmatrix} \text{ and } \mathbf{r} = \begin{pmatrix} 3 + t \\ 2 + 3t \\ 6 - 2t \end{pmatrix}$$

EXAMPLE A straight line is parallel to the vector $\mathbf{i} + 3\mathbf{j} - 2\mathbf{k}$. It passes through a point with the position vector $3\mathbf{i} + 2\mathbf{j} + 6\mathbf{k}$. Find its vector equation.

$$\mathbf{r} = \mathbf{a} + t\mathbf{b} = (3\mathbf{i} + 2\mathbf{j} + 6\mathbf{k}) + t(\mathbf{i} + 3\mathbf{j} - 2\mathbf{k})$$

And the Equation of the Line Passing Through Two Known Points

A straight line through points C and D, with position vectors **c** and **d**, has the vector equation:

$$\mathbf{r} = \mathbf{c} + t(\mathbf{d} - \mathbf{c})$$

r = position vector of a point on the line, _t_ = a scalar.

This is basically the same as the vector equation above. You just have to find a vector in the direction of CD first (i.e. **d** − **c**).

EXAMPLE
A line passes through points with the coordinates (3, 2, 4) and (–1, 3, 0). Find a vector equation for this line.

If $\mathbf{c} = \begin{pmatrix} 3 \\ 2 \\ 4 \end{pmatrix}$, and $\mathbf{d} = \begin{pmatrix} -1 \\ 3 \\ 0 \end{pmatrix}$, then $\mathbf{r} = \begin{pmatrix} 3 \\ 2 \\ 4 \end{pmatrix} + t\left(\begin{pmatrix} -1 \\ 3 \\ 0 \end{pmatrix} - \begin{pmatrix} 3 \\ 2 \\ 4 \end{pmatrix}\right)$ $\Rightarrow \mathbf{r} = \begin{pmatrix} 3 \\ 2 \\ 4 \end{pmatrix} + t\begin{pmatrix} -4 \\ 1 \\ -4 \end{pmatrix}$

Find the Point of Intersection of two Lines with Simultaneous Equations

If Line 1, $\mathbf{r} = \begin{pmatrix} 5 \\ 2 \\ -1 \end{pmatrix} + \mu\begin{pmatrix} 1 \\ -2 \\ -3 \end{pmatrix}$, and Line 2, $\mathbf{r} = \begin{pmatrix} 2 \\ 0 \\ 4 \end{pmatrix} + \lambda\begin{pmatrix} 1 \\ 2 \\ -1 \end{pmatrix}$, <u>intersect</u>, there'll be a value for μ and a value for λ

that result in <u>the same point for both lines</u>. This is the <u>point of intersection</u>.

EXAMPLE Determine whether Line 1 and Line 2 (above) intersect. If they do, find the point of intersection.

At the point of intersection, $\begin{pmatrix} 5 \\ 2 \\ -1 \end{pmatrix} + \mu\begin{pmatrix} 1 \\ -2 \\ -3 \end{pmatrix} = \begin{pmatrix} 2 \\ 0 \\ 4 \end{pmatrix} + \lambda\begin{pmatrix} 1 \\ 2 \\ -1 \end{pmatrix}$. You can get 3 equations from this:
① $5 + \mu = 2 + \lambda$
② $2 - 2\mu = 0 + 2\lambda$
③ $-1 - 3\mu = 4 - \lambda$

Solve the first two <u>simultaneously</u>: $2 × ①: 10 + 2\mu = 4 + 2\lambda$ ④
④ − ②: $8 + 4\mu = 4 \Rightarrow \mu = -1$
sub. in ②: $2 - 2(-1) = 0 + 2\lambda \Rightarrow \lambda = 2$

Substitute the values for μ and λ into equation ③. If they make the equation <u>true</u>, then the lines <u>do</u> intersect:
$-1 - (3 × -1) = 4 - 2 \Rightarrow 2 = 2$ — True, so they do intersect.

Now find the <u>intersection point</u>: $\mathbf{r} = \begin{pmatrix} 5 \\ 2 \\ -1 \end{pmatrix} + \mu\begin{pmatrix} 1 \\ -2 \\ -3 \end{pmatrix} = \begin{pmatrix} 5 \\ 2 \\ -1 \end{pmatrix} - 1\begin{pmatrix} 1 \\ -2 \\ -3 \end{pmatrix} \Rightarrow \mathbf{r} = \begin{pmatrix} 4 \\ 4 \\ 2 \end{pmatrix} = 4\mathbf{i} + 4\mathbf{j} + 2\mathbf{k}$

This is the <u>position vector</u> of the intersection point. The coordinates are (4, 4, 2).

Stardate 45283.5, position vector $20076\mathbf{i} + 23485\mathbf{j} + 48267\mathbf{k}$...
You might be given vector equations in **i**, **j**, **k** form or in column form, so practise these examples using each vector form.

Scalar Product

The <u>scalar product of two vectors</u> is kind of what it says on the tin — two vectors multiplied together to give a <u>scalar result</u>. But this is A2, so it's going to be <u>trickier than simple multiplying</u>. It even involves a bit of cos-ing.

Learn the Definition of the **Scalar Product of Two Vectors**

<u>Scalar Product of Two Vectors</u>

$$\mathbf{a.b} = |\mathbf{a}||\mathbf{b}|\cos\theta$$

θ is the angle <u>between</u> position vectors $\mathbf{a}$ and $\mathbf{b}$.

<u>Both</u> vectors have to be <u>directed away</u> from the intersection point.

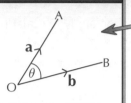

Watch out — the correct angle might not always be obvious.

θ is the angle in the definition.

Here you have to continue $\mathbf{b}$ on so that it's also directed away from the intersection point.

1) The scalar product of two vectors is always a <u>scalar quantity</u> — it's <u>never</u> a vector.

2) The <u>scalar product</u> can be used to calculate the <u>angle</u> between two lines (see the next page):

$\mathbf{a.b} = |\mathbf{a}||\mathbf{b}|\cos\theta$ rearranges to $\cos\theta = \dfrac{\mathbf{a.b}}{|\mathbf{a}||\mathbf{b}|}$.

3) The scalar product $\mathbf{a.b}$ is read '<u>a dot b</u>'. It's really, really important to put the dot in, as it shows you mean the <u>scalar product</u> (rather than a different sort of vector product that you don't have to worry about in C4).

A **Zero Scalar Product** *Means the Vectors are* **Perpendicular**

1) If the two vectors are <u>perpendicular</u>, they're at <u>90°</u> to each other.

2) <u>Cos 90° = 0</u>, so the scalar product of the two vectors is <u>0</u>.

Scalar Product of Two Perpendicular Vectors

$$\mathbf{a.b} = |\mathbf{a}||\mathbf{b}|\cos 90° = 0$$

3) The unit vectors $\mathbf{i}$, $\mathbf{j}$ and $\mathbf{k}$ are all <u>perpendicular</u> to each other.

So, $\mathbf{i.j} = 1 \times 1 \times 0 = 0$ and $3\mathbf{j.4k} = 3 \times 4 \times 0 = 0$

4) This all assumes that the vectors are <u>non-zero</u>. Because if either vector was 0, you'd always get a scalar product of <u>0</u>, regardless of the angle between them.

The Scalar Product of **Parallel Vectors** *is just the* **Product of the Magnitudes**

1) If two vectors are <u>parallel</u>, the angle between them is <u>0°</u>. And <u>cos 0° = 1</u>, so...

Scalar Product of Two Parallel Vectors

$$\mathbf{a.b} = |\mathbf{a}||\mathbf{b}|\cos 0° = |\mathbf{a}||\mathbf{b}|$$

2) Two $\mathbf{i}$ unit vectors are <u>parallel</u> to each other (as are two $\mathbf{j}$s or two $\mathbf{k}$s).

So, $\mathbf{j.j} = 1 \times 1 \times 1 = 1$ and $3\mathbf{k.4k} = 3 \times 4 \times 1 = 12$

3) Again, this all assumes that the vectors are <u>non-zero</u>.

Scaly product — a lizard-skin handbag...

The fact that two perpendicular vectors have a zero scalar product is the key to loads of vector exam questions.
E.g. you might be asked to show two vectors are perpendicular, or told that two vectors are perpendicular and asked to find a missing vector. Whatever they ask, you'll definitely have to multiply the two vectors — and you're about to learn how.

Scalar Product

Finding the scalar product of two vectors is super quick and easy once you know how to do it.

Learn This Result for the Scalar Product

1) You can use this result to find the <u>scalar product</u> of two known vectors:

> If $\mathbf{a} = a_1\mathbf{i} + a_2\mathbf{j} + a_3\mathbf{k}$, and $\mathbf{b} = b_1\mathbf{i} + b_2\mathbf{j} + b_3\mathbf{k}$, then $\mathbf{a.b} = a_1b_1 + a_2b_2 + a_3b_3$

2) The <u>normal laws</u> of multiplication apply to scalar products too — e.g. the <u>commutative law</u> ($\mathbf{a.b} = \mathbf{b.a}$) and the <u>distributive law</u> ($\mathbf{a.(b + c)} = \mathbf{a.b} + \mathbf{a.c}$).

3) By applying these laws, you can derive the result above...

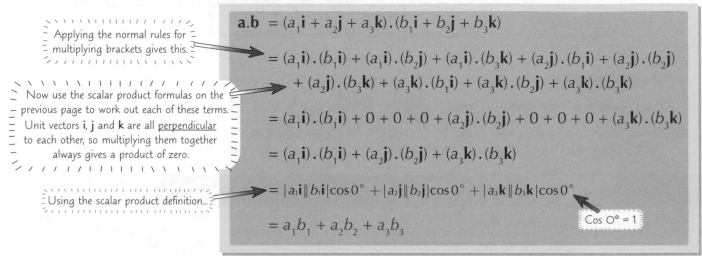

Applying the normal rules for multiplying brackets gives this.

$$\mathbf{a.b} = (a_1\mathbf{i} + a_2\mathbf{j} + a_3\mathbf{k}).(b_1\mathbf{i} + b_2\mathbf{j} + b_3\mathbf{k})$$

$$= (a_1\mathbf{i}).(b_1\mathbf{i}) + (a_1\mathbf{i}).(b_2\mathbf{j}) + (a_1\mathbf{i}).(b_3\mathbf{k}) + (a_2\mathbf{j}).(b_1\mathbf{i}) + (a_2\mathbf{j}).(b_2\mathbf{j})$$
$$+ (a_2\mathbf{j}).(b_3\mathbf{k}) + (a_3\mathbf{k}).(b_1\mathbf{i}) + (a_3\mathbf{k}).(b_2\mathbf{j}) + (a_3\mathbf{k}).(b_3\mathbf{k})$$

Now use the scalar product formulas on the previous page to work out each of these terms. Unit vectors $\mathbf{i}$, $\mathbf{j}$ and $\mathbf{k}$ are all <u>perpendicular</u> to each other, so multiplying them together always gives a product of zero.

$$= (a_1\mathbf{i}).(b_1\mathbf{i}) + 0 + 0 + 0 + (a_2\mathbf{j}).(b_2\mathbf{j}) + 0 + 0 + 0 + (a_3\mathbf{k}).(b_3\mathbf{k})$$

$$= (a_1\mathbf{i}).(b_1\mathbf{i}) + (a_2\mathbf{j}).(b_2\mathbf{j}) + (a_3\mathbf{k}).(b_3\mathbf{k})$$

Using the scalar product definition...

$$= |a_1\mathbf{i}\| b_1\mathbf{i}|\cos 0° + |a_2\mathbf{j}\| b_2\mathbf{j}|\cos 0° + |a_3\mathbf{k}\| b_3\mathbf{k}|\cos 0°$$

Cos 0° = 1

$$= a_1b_1 + a_2b_2 + a_3b_3$$

Use the Scalar Product to Find the Angle Between Two Vectors

Finding the <u>angle</u> between two vectors often crops up in vector exam questions.
It's just a matter of using the above result to find the <u>scalar product</u> of the two vectors,
then popping it into the <u>scalar product definition</u>, $\cos\theta = \dfrac{\mathbf{a.b}}{|\mathbf{a}\|\mathbf{b}|}$, to find the <u>angle</u>.

EXAMPLE Find the angle between the vectors $-\mathbf{i} - 6\mathbf{j}$ and $4\mathbf{i} + 2\mathbf{j} + 8\mathbf{k}$.

$\cos\theta = \dfrac{\mathbf{a.b}}{|\mathbf{a}\|\mathbf{b}|}$. Let $\mathbf{a} = -\mathbf{i} - 6\mathbf{j}$ and $\mathbf{b} = 4\mathbf{i} + 2\mathbf{j} + 8\mathbf{k}$.

1) Find the <u>scalar product</u> of the vectors.

$$\mathbf{a.b} = (-1 \times 4) + (-6 \times 2) + (0 \times 8) = -4 - 12 + 0 = -16$$

This uses the result above.

2) Find the <u>magnitude</u> of each vector (see page 81).

$$|\mathbf{a}| = \sqrt{(-1)^2 + (-6)^2 + (0)^2} = \sqrt{37} \qquad |\mathbf{b}| = \sqrt{(4)^2 + (2)^2 + (8)^2} = \sqrt{84}$$

3) Now plug these values into the equation and find the <u>angle</u>.

$$\cos\theta = \frac{\mathbf{a.b}}{|\mathbf{a}\|\mathbf{b}|} = \frac{-16}{\sqrt{37}\sqrt{84}} \Rightarrow \theta = \underline{106.7°}$$

Scalar product — Ooops. I best stop eating chips every day...

So when you scalar multiply two vectors, you basically multiply the $\mathbf{i}$ components together, multiply the $\mathbf{j}$ components together, multiply the $\mathbf{k}$ components together, then add up all the products. You end up with <u>just a number</u>, with no $\mathbf{i}$s, $\mathbf{j}$s or $\mathbf{k}$s attached to it. You'll see this more in the examples on the next page, so don't worry if it seems a bit strange at the mo.

Scalar Product

Right, you've learnt the definitions and the facts. Now it's time to put them to good use.

You Might have to Find the Angle from *Vector Equations* or from *Two Points*

1) If you're given the <u>vector equations</u> for lines that you're finding the angle between, it's important to use the correct bits of the vector equations.

2) You use the **b** bit in **r** = **a** + t**b** (the '<u>parallel to</u>' or the '<u>direction</u>' bit).

EXAMPLE Line l has the equation $\mathbf{r} = \begin{pmatrix} 2 \\ 0 \\ 4 \end{pmatrix} + \lambda \begin{pmatrix} 1 \\ 2 \\ -1 \end{pmatrix}$.

Point A and point B have the coordinates (4, 4, 2) and (1, 0, 3) respectively. Point A lies on l. Find the acute angle between l and line segment AB.

1) First draw a <u>diagram</u> — it'll make everything clearer.

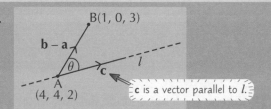

c is a vector parallel to l.

2) Find the vectors that you want to <u>know the angle</u> between.

$$\vec{AB} = \mathbf{b} - \mathbf{a} = \begin{pmatrix} 1 \\ 0 \\ 3 \end{pmatrix} - \begin{pmatrix} 4 \\ 4 \\ 2 \end{pmatrix} = \begin{pmatrix} -3 \\ -4 \\ 1 \end{pmatrix}$$ and the 'parallel to' bit of l (which we've called **c**): $\mathbf{c} = \begin{pmatrix} 1 \\ 2 \\ -1 \end{pmatrix}$

3) Find the <u>scalar product</u> of these vectors. $\vec{AB} \cdot \mathbf{c} = (-3 \times 1) + (-4 \times 2) + (1 \times -1) = -3 - 8 - 1 = -12$

4) Find the <u>magnitude</u> of each vector.

$$|\vec{AB}| = \sqrt{(-3)^2 + (-4)^2 + (1)^2} = \sqrt{26} \qquad |\mathbf{c}| = \sqrt{(1)^2 + (2)^2 + (-1)^2} = \sqrt{6}$$

5) Now plug these values into the equation and find the angle.

$$\cos\theta = \frac{\vec{AB} \cdot \mathbf{c}}{|\vec{AB}||\mathbf{c}|} = \frac{-12}{\sqrt{26}\sqrt{6}} \Rightarrow \theta = 164° \text{ (3 s.f.)}$$

6) Whoops. The formula gives the <u>non-acute angle</u> — the situation must have been more like this:

Remember — the vectors diverge on each side of the angle given by the formula.

Don't panic — just <u>subtract this angle from 180°</u> to get the acute angle, x, between the lines.

$$180° - 164° = 16°$$

Prove Lines are *Perpendicular* by Showing that the *Scalar Product = 0*

EXAMPLE Show that the lines $\mathbf{r}_1 = (\mathbf{i} + 6\mathbf{j} + 2\mathbf{k}) + \lambda(\mathbf{i} + 2\mathbf{j} + 2\mathbf{k})$ and $\mathbf{r}_2 = (3\mathbf{i} - \mathbf{j} + \mathbf{k}) + \mu(4\mathbf{i} - 3\mathbf{j} + \mathbf{k})$ are perpendicular.

1) Make sure you've got the right bit of each vector equation — it's the <u>direction</u> you're interested in, so it's **b** in **r** = **a** + t**b**. $\qquad \mathbf{i} + 2\mathbf{j} + 2\mathbf{k}$ and $4\mathbf{i} - 3\mathbf{j} + \mathbf{k}$

2) Find the <u>scalar product</u> of the vectors. $\qquad (\mathbf{i} + 2\mathbf{j} + 2\mathbf{k}).(4\mathbf{i} - 3\mathbf{j} + \mathbf{k}) = 4 - 6 + 2 = 0$

3) Draw the correct <u>conclusion</u>. $\qquad$ The scalar product is 0, so the vectors are <u>perpendicular</u>.

P...P...P... — prove perpendicularity using products...

They'll word these questions in a zillion different ways. Drawing a diagram can often help you figure out what's what.

Equations of Planes

Planes might seem a bit complicated at first glance — but most of the maths you need to do with them is surprisingly similar to stuff you've already seen with lines. Plus, the word 'plane' offers almost endless potential for dodgy puns.

Learn how to find Equations of Planes

1) A plane is a flat 2D surface. You can define a plane with a Cartesian equation in three coordinates (normally x, y and z) or using a vector equation.

2) The Cartesian equation of a plane will be in the form $ax + by + cz + d = 0$. The vector equation of a plane will be in the form $\mathbf{r} = \mathbf{a} + \lambda\mathbf{b} + \mu\mathbf{c}$.

3) A normal to a plane is a line or vector that's perpendicular to the plane — so it meets the plane at a right angle.

Finding the Cartesian Equation from a Point and a Normal is Easy

If $\mathbf{n}$ is a normal vector to a plane, and $\mathbf{a}$ is the position vector of a point on the plane, then the Cartesian equation of the plane is $n_1 x + n_2 y + n_3 z + d = 0$, where $d = -\mathbf{a} \cdot \mathbf{n}$.

$\mathbf{n} = \begin{pmatrix} n_1 \\ n_2 \\ n_3 \end{pmatrix}$

EXAMPLE The point A has coordinates (10, –5, 1) and lies on a plane, P. The vector $3\mathbf{i} + 2\mathbf{j} - \mathbf{k}$ is perpendicular to P. Find the Cartesian equation of P.

Remember, if a vector's perpendicular to a plane (or line), that means it's a normal.

The position vector of A is $10\mathbf{i} - 5\mathbf{j} + \mathbf{k}$.

So the constant term d is: $d = -\mathbf{a} \cdot \mathbf{n} = -[a_1 n_1 + a_2 n_2 + a_3 n_3] = -[(10 \times 3) + (-5 \times 2) + (1 \times -1)] = -19$

So the Cartesian equation of P is $3x + 2y - z - 19 = 0$.

You might have to prove that your normal is actually a normal before you find the equation of the plane. A vector is a normal to a plane if it's perpendicular to any two non-parallel vectors on the plane — so to prove it, get two non-parallel vectors on the plane (e.g. by finding the vectors joining given points on the plane) and show their scalar products with the normal are both 0 (see p83).

You can find the Vector Equation from a Point and Two Vectors

The vector equation of a plane is $\mathbf{r} = \mathbf{a} + \lambda\mathbf{b} + \mu\mathbf{c}$, where $\mathbf{a}$ is the position vector of a point on the plane, and $\mathbf{b}$ and $\mathbf{c}$ are two non-parallel vectors that lie on the plane.

EXAMPLE Find the vector equation of the plane passing through A = (2, 9, 2), B = (0, 6, 3) and C = (8, 4, 1).

The vectors $\overrightarrow{AB}$ and $\overrightarrow{AC}$ lie on the plane we're looking for, and they're pretty much guaranteed not to be parallel, so we can use the position vector of A as $\mathbf{a}$, the vector $\overrightarrow{AB}$ as $\mathbf{b}$ and the vector $\overrightarrow{AC}$ as $\mathbf{c}$:

$$\mathbf{a} = \begin{pmatrix} 2 \\ 9 \\ 2 \end{pmatrix}, \quad \mathbf{b} = \overrightarrow{AB} = -\begin{pmatrix} 2 \\ 9 \\ 2 \end{pmatrix} + \begin{pmatrix} 0 \\ 6 \\ 3 \end{pmatrix} = \begin{pmatrix} -2 \\ -3 \\ 1 \end{pmatrix}, \quad \mathbf{c} = \overrightarrow{AC} = -\begin{pmatrix} 2 \\ 9 \\ 2 \end{pmatrix} + \begin{pmatrix} 8 \\ 4 \\ 1 \end{pmatrix} = \begin{pmatrix} 6 \\ -5 \\ -1 \end{pmatrix}$$

So the vector equation of the plane is $\mathbf{r} = \mathbf{a} + \lambda\mathbf{b} + \mu\mathbf{c} = \begin{pmatrix} 2 \\ 9 \\ 2 \end{pmatrix} + \lambda\begin{pmatrix} -2 \\ -3 \\ 1 \end{pmatrix} + \mu\begin{pmatrix} 6 \\ -5 \\ -1 \end{pmatrix}$

Time for some plane speaking...

Check out how similar the second example on this page is to the examples for finding the vector equation of a line on p82. I told you this stuff with planes was really similar to the stuff with lines... I reckon this page has been plane sailing...

Lines and Planes

It should be as plane as the nose on your face that there's more to planes than just finding their equations. The next thrill that awaits is the intersection of lines and planes.

You can find the Point where a Plane meets a Line

Finding the point of intersection between a line and a plane is, unsurprisingly, pretty similar to finding the point of intersection between two lines. In fact, when you've got the Cartesian equation of the plane, it's easier.

EXAMPLE Find the point where the line $\mathbf{r} = \begin{pmatrix} 6 \\ 0 \\ 1 \end{pmatrix} + t\begin{pmatrix} 3 \\ 1 \\ 10 \end{pmatrix}$ meets the plane $3x + 5y - z - 5 = 0$.

Write the components of the vector equation of the line as three equations:
$$x = 6 + 3t, \quad y = t, \quad z = 1 + 10t$$

Now stick those into the equation of the plane and solve for t:
$$3x + 5y - z - 5 = 0$$
$$\Rightarrow \quad 3(6 + 3t) + 5(t) - (1 + 10t) - 5 = 0$$
$$\Rightarrow \quad 18 + 9t + 5t - 1 - 10t - 5 = 0$$
$$\Rightarrow \quad 12 + 4t = 0$$
$$\Rightarrow \quad t = -3$$

So at the point where the line and plane meet, $t = -3$.
Put $t = -3$ back into the equation of the line to get the coordinates of this point:

$$\mathbf{r} = \begin{pmatrix} 6 \\ 0 \\ 1 \end{pmatrix} + t\begin{pmatrix} 3 \\ 1 \\ 10 \end{pmatrix} = \begin{pmatrix} 6 \\ 0 \\ 1 \end{pmatrix} - 3\begin{pmatrix} 3 \\ 1 \\ 10 \end{pmatrix} = \begin{pmatrix} 6 - 9 \\ 0 - 3 \\ 1 - 30 \end{pmatrix} = \begin{pmatrix} -3 \\ -3 \\ -29 \end{pmatrix}$$

So the line and plane meet at $(-3, -3, -29)$.

Use Normal Vectors to find the Angle Between Two Planes

The angle between two planes is the same as the angle between their normals.

To find a normal to a plane from its Cartesian equation, use the coefficients of x, y and z (when they're all on the same side of the equation) as the components of the normal vector.

This is almost the reverse of the method for finding the Cartesian equation from the previous page.

When you've got your two normals, you can use the scalar product to find the angle between them (see p84).

EXAMPLE Find the angle between the planes $5x + 2y + 3z = 9$ and $x - 3y + z = 7$.

Use the coefficients of x, y and z in the equations to find a normal to each plane:

$\mathbf{n_1} = \begin{pmatrix} 5 \\ 2 \\ 3 \end{pmatrix}$ is a normal to $5x + 2y + 3z = 9$ and $\mathbf{n_2} = \begin{pmatrix} 1 \\ -3 \\ 1 \end{pmatrix}$ is a normal to $x - 3y + z = 7$.

The angle between the planes is equal to the angle between the normals, so

$$\cos\theta = \frac{\mathbf{n_1}.\mathbf{n_2}}{|\mathbf{n_1}||\mathbf{n_2}|} = \frac{(5 \times 1) + (2 \times -3) + (3 \times 1)}{\sqrt{5^2 + 2^2 + 3^2}\sqrt{1^2 + (-3)^2 + 1^2}} = \frac{2}{\sqrt{38}\sqrt{11}} = 0.0978$$
$$\Rightarrow \theta = \cos^{-1} 0.0978 = 84.4°$$

I hope that ex-planes everything...

Most exam questions about planes will be a combination of the examples on the last two pages, with some bits from the rest of this section thrown in for good measure. Make sure you practise lots of exam-style questions so you can see how all this vector stuff fits together. And if that gives you a headache, take a couple of planekillers... ho ho... ... ...I'll get my coat.

C4 Section 5 — Practice Questions

Vectors might cause some mild vexation. It's not the simplest of topics, but <u>practising</u> does help.
Try these warm-up questions and see if you can remember what you've just read.

Warm-up Questions

1) Give two vectors that are <u>parallel</u> to each of the following: a) $2\mathbf{a}$ b) $3\mathbf{i} + 4\mathbf{j} - 2\mathbf{k}$ c) $\begin{pmatrix} 1 \\ 2 \\ -1 \end{pmatrix}$

2) Find these vectors in terms of vectors $\mathbf{a}$, $\mathbf{b}$ and $\mathbf{c}$.

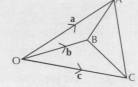

   a) $\overrightarrow{AB}$ b) $\overrightarrow{BA}$ c) $\overrightarrow{CB}$ d) $\overrightarrow{AC}$

3) Give the <u>position vector</u> of point P,
   which has the coordinates $(2, -4, 5)$.
   Give your answer in <u>unit vector</u> form.

4) Find the <u>magnitudes</u> of these vectors:

   a) $3\mathbf{i} + 4\mathbf{j} - 2\mathbf{k}$ b) $\begin{pmatrix} 1 \\ 2 \\ -1 \end{pmatrix}$

5) If A$(1, 2, 3)$ and B$(3, -1, -2)$, find: a) $|\overrightarrow{AB}|$ b) $|\overrightarrow{OA}|$ c) $|\overrightarrow{OB}|$

6) Find <u>vector equations</u> for the following <u>lines</u>.
   Give your answer in $\mathbf{i}$, $\mathbf{j}$, $\mathbf{k}$ form and in <u>column vector</u> form.

   a)   a straight line through $(4, 1, 2)$, parallel to vector $3\mathbf{i} + \mathbf{j} - \mathbf{k}$.
   b)   a straight line through $(2, -1, 1)$ and $(0, 2, 3)$.

7) Find <u>three points</u> that lie on the line with <u>vector equation</u> $\mathbf{r} = \begin{pmatrix} 3 \\ 2 \\ 4 \end{pmatrix} + t\begin{pmatrix} -1 \\ 3 \\ 0 \end{pmatrix}$.

8) Find $\mathbf{a} . \mathbf{b}$ if: a) $\mathbf{a} = 3\mathbf{i} + 4\mathbf{j}$ and $\mathbf{b} = \mathbf{i} - 2\mathbf{j} + 3\mathbf{k}$ b) $\mathbf{a} = \begin{pmatrix} 4 \\ 2 \\ 1 \end{pmatrix}$ and $\mathbf{b} = \begin{pmatrix} 3 \\ -4 \\ -3 \end{pmatrix}$

9) $\mathbf{r}_1 = \begin{pmatrix} 2 \\ -1 \\ 2 \end{pmatrix} + t\begin{pmatrix} -4 \\ 6 \\ -2 \end{pmatrix}$ and $\mathbf{r}_2 = \begin{pmatrix} 3 \\ 2 \\ 4 \end{pmatrix} + u\begin{pmatrix} -1 \\ 3 \\ 0 \end{pmatrix}$

   a)   Show that these lines <u>intersect</u> and find the <u>position vector</u> of their <u>intersection point</u>.
   b)   Find the <u>angle</u> between these lines.

10) Find a vector that is <u>perpendicular</u> to $3\mathbf{i} + 4\mathbf{j} - 2\mathbf{k}$.

11) Find a Cartesian equation of the plane perpendicular to $\mathbf{i} + 3\mathbf{j} - 3\mathbf{k}$ which contains the point $(2, 2, 4)$.

12) Find a vector equation for the plane containing the points $(1, -2, 5)$, $(6, 2, -3)$ and $(4, 0, 2)$.

You might look at an exam question and think that it's complete <u>gobbledegook</u>.
But chances are, when you look at it carefully, you can <u>use what you know</u> to solve it.

Exam Questions

1   The quadrilateral ABCD has vertices A$(1, 5, 9)$, B$(3, 2, 1)$, C$(-2, 4, 3)$ and D$(5, -1, -7)$.

   a)   Find the vector $\overrightarrow{AB}$.

   (2 marks)

   b)   C and D lie on line l_1. Using the parameter μ, find a vector equation for l_1.

   (2 marks)

   c)   Find the coordinates of the intersection point of l_1 and the line that passes through AB.

   (5 marks)

   d)   (i)   Find the acute angle between l_1 and AB. Give your answer to 1 decimal place.

   (4 marks)

   (ii)   Find the shortest distance from point A to l_1.

   (4 marks)

C4 Section 5 — Practice Questions

And there's more, as Jimmy Cricket (not to be confused with Jiminy Cricket) used to say.

2   The lines l_1 and l_2 are given by the vector equations:

     l_1 : $\mathbf{r} = (3\mathbf{i} - 3\mathbf{j} - 2\mathbf{k}) + \mu(\mathbf{i} - 4\mathbf{j} + 2\mathbf{k})$

     l_2 : $\mathbf{r} = (10\mathbf{i} - 21\mathbf{j} + 11\mathbf{k}) + \lambda(-3\mathbf{i} + 12\mathbf{j} - 6\mathbf{k})$

   a)   Show that l_1 and l_2 are parallel.

(1 mark)

   b)   Show that point A(2, 1, –4) lies on l_1.

(2 marks)

   c)   Point B lies on l_2 and is such that the line segment AB is perpendicular to l_1 and l_2.
       Find the position vector of point B.

(6 marks)

   d)   Find $|\overrightarrow{AB}|$.

(2 marks)

3   The lines l_1 and l_2 are given by the equations: $l_1 : \mathbf{r} = \begin{pmatrix} 3 \\ 0 \\ -2 \end{pmatrix} + \lambda \begin{pmatrix} 1 \\ 3 \\ -2 \end{pmatrix}$ $l_2 : \mathbf{r} = \begin{pmatrix} 0 \\ 2 \\ 1 \end{pmatrix} + \mu \begin{pmatrix} 2 \\ -5 \\ -3 \end{pmatrix}$

   a)   Show that l_1 and l_2 do not intersect.

(4 marks)

   b)   Point P has position vector $\begin{pmatrix} 5 \\ 8 \\ -3 \end{pmatrix}$. Point Q is the image of point P after reflection in line l_1.

       Point P and Q both lie on the line with equation $\mathbf{r} = \begin{pmatrix} 5 \\ 4 \\ -9 \end{pmatrix} + t \begin{pmatrix} 0 \\ 2 \\ 3 \end{pmatrix}$.

     (i)   Find the intersection point of line segment PQ and line l_1.

(4 marks)

     (ii)   Show that the line segment PQ and line l_1 are perpendicular.

(2 marks)

     (iii)   Find the position vector of point Q.

(3 marks)

4   Point A has the position vector $3\mathbf{i} + 2\mathbf{j} + \mathbf{k}$ and point B has position vector $3\mathbf{i} - 4\mathbf{j} - \mathbf{k}$.

   a)   Show that AOB is a right-angled triangle.

(3 marks)

   b)   Find angle ABO in the triangle using the scalar product definition.

(5 marks)

   c)   (i)   Point C has the position vector $3\mathbf{i} - \mathbf{j}$. Show that triangle OAC is isosceles.

(3 marks)

       (ii)   Calculate the area of triangle OAC.

(4 marks)

   d)   (i)   Find a vector equation for line l, which passes through points A and B.

(2 marks)

       (ii)   The point D lies on line l and has the position vector $a\mathbf{i} + b\mathbf{j} + \mathbf{k}$. Find a and b.

(3 marks)

5   The equation of plane A is $3x + 4y + 2z = 1$. The equation of plane B is $x - y + 6z = -5$.

   a)   Write down normal vectors to each plane.

(1 mark)

   b)   The acute angle between planes A and B measures $\theta°$. Find the value of θ.

(3 marks)

   c)   Find the coordinates of the point of intersection between the line $\mathbf{r} = \begin{pmatrix} 5 \\ 1 \\ 3 \end{pmatrix} + \lambda \begin{pmatrix} -3 \\ 2 \\ 0 \end{pmatrix}$ and plane A.

(4 marks)

General Certificate of Education
Advanced Subsidiary (AS) and Advanced Level

Core Mathematics C4 — Practice Exam One

Time Allowed: 1 hour 30 min

Graphical calculators may be used for this exam.

Give any non-exact numerical answers to an appropriate degree of accuracy.

There are 72 marks available for this paper.

Section A (36 marks)

1   The graph below shows the curve $y = \dfrac{3\ln x}{x^2}$, $x \geq 0$. The shaded region R is bounded by the curve, the x-axis and the line $x = 3$.

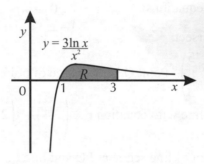

    a)   Complete the table for the missing y-values. Give your answers to 5 decimal places.

x	1	1.5	2	2.5	3
y	0		0.51986	0.43982	

(2 marks)

    b)   Find an approximation for the area of R, using the Trapezium Rule and all the values in the table.

(3 marks)

2   a)   Express $\dfrac{(x^2 - 9)(3x^2 - 10x - 8)}{(6x + 4)(x^2 - 7x + 12)}$ as a fraction in its simplest form.

(2 marks)

    b)   Divide $2x^3 - x^2 - 16x + 3$ by $x^2 - 3x - 1$, stating the quotient and remainder.

(4 marks)

3   a)   Express $\dfrac{5x^2 + 10x - 13}{(2 - x)^2(1 + 4x)}$ in partial fractions of the form $\dfrac{A}{(2 - x)} + \dfrac{B}{(2 - x)^2} + \dfrac{C}{(1 + 4x)}$,

   where A, B and C are constants to be found.

   (5 marks)

   b)   Hence find $\displaystyle\int \dfrac{5x^2 + 10x - 13}{(2 - x)^2(1 + 4x)}\, dx$.

   (4 marks)

4   The curve $y = \ln(x^2 - 1)$, $(x > 1)$ is shown on the graph below.

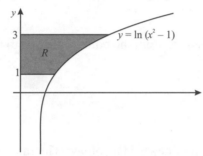

   The shaded region R is bounded by the curve, the y-axis and the lines $y = 1$ and $y = 3$.

   Find the volume formed when this region is rotated 2π radians about the y-axis.

   Give your answer to 4 significant figures.

   (4 marks)

5   a)   Find the binomial expansion of $(1 - x)^{-\frac{1}{2}}$, up to and including the term in x^3.

   (2 marks)

   b)   (i)   Hence show that $(25 - 4x)^{-\frac{1}{2}} \approx \dfrac{1}{5} + \dfrac{2}{125}x + \dfrac{6}{3125}x^2 + \dfrac{4}{15625}x^3$ for small values of x.

   (4 marks)

   (ii)   State the range of values of x for which the expansion from part (i) is valid.

   (1 mark)

6   By writing $\sin 2\theta$ in terms of $\sin \theta$ and $\cos \theta$, solve the equation

$$3 \sin 2\theta \tan \theta = 5, \qquad \text{for } 0 \le \theta \le 2\pi.$$

   Give your answers to 3 significant figures.

   (5 marks)

Section B (36 marks)

7   Line L_1 has vector equation: $\mathbf{r} = \begin{pmatrix} -1 \\ 0 \\ 3 \end{pmatrix} + \lambda \begin{pmatrix} 2 \\ 2 \\ 1 \end{pmatrix}$.

   a)   Show that the line passing through points $P(-2, -2, -1)$ and $Q(-5, -4, 1)$
        intersects with L_1 and find the point at which they meet.

        (5 marks)

   b)   Given that $\overrightarrow{OT} = 3\overrightarrow{OP}$, show that the distance between Q and T is $\sqrt{21}$.

        (3 marks)

   c) $\overrightarrow{PV}$ is perpendicular to L_1. If the coordinates of V are $(0, f, g)$, show that $2f + g = -9$.

        (3 marks)

   d)   The line L_2 passes through Q and is parallel to the vector $\begin{pmatrix} 1 \\ 1 \\ 1 \end{pmatrix}$.
        Find the acute angle between L_1 and L_2.

        (4 marks)

   e)   Hence or otherwise, find the shortest distance from the point $(-1, 0, 3)$ to the line L_2.

        (3 marks)

8   a)   An ecologist is monitoring the population of newts in a colony. The rate of increase of the
         population is directly proportional to the square root of the current number of newts in the colony.
         When there were 36 newts in the colony, the rate of change was calculated to be 0.36 newts per week.

         Formulate a differential equation to model the rate of change, in terms of the variables
         N (number of newts) and t (time in weeks).

         (4 marks)

   b)   After more research, the ecologist decides that the differential equation
        $$\frac{dN}{dt} = \frac{kN}{\sqrt{t}},$$
        for a positive constant k, is a better model for the population.
        When the ecologist began the survey, the initial population of newts in the colony was 25.

        (i)   Solve the differential equation, leaving your answer in terms of k and t.

              (3 marks)

        (ii) Given that the value of k is 0.05, calculate how long (to the nearest week) it will take for the
              population to double.

              (2 marks)

   c)   The population of ducks (x) and water boatmen insects (y) on a river vary over time, t weeks.
        The populations are modelled by the curve C, given by the parametric equations
        $$x = 10\sin t + 50, \qquad y = 300\cos 2t + 600.$$

        (i)   Find an expression for $\frac{dy}{dx}$ in terms of t.

              (2 marks)

        (ii) Verify that C has a stationary point where $t = \pi$. State the number of ducks and the
              number of water boatmen at this point.

              (3 marks)

        (iii) Find a Cartesian equation for C in the form $y = f(x)$.

              (3 marks)

        (iv) Using your answer to (iii), work out how many water boatmen there will be when there are
              45 ducks on the river.

              (1 mark)

General Certificate of Education
Advanced Subsidiary (AS) and Advanced Level

Core Mathematics C4 — Practice Exam Two

Time Allowed: 1 hour 30 min

Graphical calculators may be used for this exam.

Give any non-exact numerical answers to an appropriate degree of accuracy.

There are 72 marks available for this paper.

Section A (36 marks)

1   a)   Express $\dfrac{x^2 + 5x - 14}{2x^2 - 4x}$ as a fraction in its simplest form.

(2 marks)

    b)   Using your answer to part a) or otherwise, write $\dfrac{x^2 + 5x - 14}{2x^2 - 4x} + \dfrac{14}{x(x - 4)}$
         as a single fraction, simplifying your answer as much as possible.

(3 marks)

2   a)   Write $\sqrt{2}\cos\theta - 3\sin\theta$ in the form $R\cos(\theta + \alpha)$, where $R > 0$ and $0 \le \alpha \le \frac{\pi}{2}$.

(3 marks)

    b)   Hence, or otherwise, solve the equation $\sqrt{2}\cos\theta - 3\sin\theta = 3$ for $0 \le \theta \le 2\pi$.
         Give your answers to 3 significant figures.

(3 marks)

    c)   Find the maximum and minimum values of $(\sqrt{2}\cos\theta - 3\sin\theta)^4$, and state where the
         maximum and minimum points occur in the interval $0 \le \theta \le 2\pi$.

(4 marks)

3   Vector **x** is perpendicular to both vector **y** and vector **z**.

$\mathbf{x} = p\mathbf{i} + \frac{3}{5}\mathbf{j} + q\mathbf{k}$

$\mathbf{y} = 15\mathbf{i} - 20\mathbf{j} + 3\mathbf{k}$

$\mathbf{z} = \frac{3}{2}\mathbf{i} - 2\mathbf{j} + 4\mathbf{k}$

    a)   (i)   Find the values of p and q.

(3 marks)

         (ii) Find a unit vector in the direction of **y**.

(2 marks)

    b)   Given that the scalar product of **y** and **z** is 74.5, show that the angle
         between these vectors is 51° to the nearest degree.

(3 marks)

4   a)   Find integers A and B, such that $\dfrac{5x+4}{(2-x)(1+3x)} \equiv \dfrac{A}{(2-x)} + \dfrac{B}{(1+3x)}$.

(3 marks)

b)   Hence find the binomial expansion of $\dfrac{5x+4}{(2-x)(1+3x)}$, up to and including the term in x^3.

(4 marks)

c)   Find the range of values for which your answer to part b) is valid.

(1 mark)

5   a)   Using the Trapezium Rule with 4 strips, approximate the area of $\displaystyle\int_0^1 e^x \cos x \, dx$, where x is a measure in radians. Give your answer to 3 significant figures.

(4 marks)

b)   How could you improve your approximation?

(1 mark)

Section B (36 marks)

6

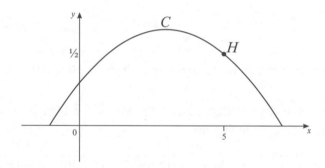

A novelty lemon-shaped lemonade bottle is modelled by rotating the curve C above 2π radians about the x-axis. The parametric equations of curve C are $x = 3 + 4\sin\theta$, $y = \dfrac{1+\cos 2\theta}{3}$, $-\dfrac{\pi}{2} \le \theta \le \dfrac{\pi}{2}$.

Point H on C has coordinates $(5, \frac{1}{2})$, where the units on the axes are in inches.

a)   Find the value of θ at point H.

(2 marks)

b)   Show that the Cartesian equation of C can be written $y = \dfrac{-x^2 + 6x + 7}{24}$.

(5 marks)

c)   Show that the domain of values of x for the curve C is $-1 \le x \le 7$.

(2 marks)

d)   Find an expression for y^2 in terms of x.

(3 marks)

e)   Hence find the volume of the bottle (using the domain of x as the limits).

(6 marks)

7   a)   The spread of an infection within a community of puffins is increasing exponentially. It is modelled by the differential equation given below, where t is the time in weeks and P is the number of infected puffins. Find the general solution to the differential equation.

$$\frac{e^{2t} + t^2}{e^{2t} + t}\frac{dP}{dt} = 2P, \quad t, P \geq 0.$$

(7 marks)

b)   (i)   Given that $P = 3$ when $t = 0$, find the particular solution to the differential equation above.   *(2 marks)*

(ii)   Hence estimate the number of infected puffins (to the nearest 10) after 3 weeks.

(2 marks)

It is discovered that the spread of the infection can be temporarily slowed down by the introduction of antibiotics. However, this only works for a short period of time (approximately 3 weeks) before the bacteria become immune.

The likelihood of a puffin becoming infected can be modelled by the equation $y = \cos^2\frac{x}{2}$, where y is the probability of infection, and x is the time in weeks, $0 \leq x \leq 2\pi$.
This is shown on the graph below:

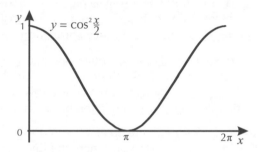

c)   Use the double angle formula for cos to show that

$$\cos^2\frac{x}{2} \equiv \frac{1 + \cos x}{2}.$$

(3 marks)

d)   Hence find the exact range of values of x for which the probability of infection is less than 0.75.   *(4 marks)*

C4 Comprehension Paper

For C4, you also have to do a comprehension paper. You have to read an argument or description of a mathematical technique, then answer questions to show that you've understood it. You'll have an hour to do it, and it's worth 18 marks. It probably won't be anything you've come across before, so don't panic if it doesn't look familiar. Just read it through carefully a couple of times, then have a go at the questions.

Correlation

Welcome to the <u>Statistics</u> part of the book. First thing on the agenda is <u>correlation</u>.
<u>Correlation</u> is all about how closely two quantities are <u>associated</u> (linked). And it can involve a fairly hefty formula.

Draw a **Scatter Diagram** to see **Patterns** in Data

Sometimes variables are measured in <u>pairs</u> — maybe because you want to find out <u>how closely</u> they're <u>linked</u>.
These pairs of variables might be things like: — '<u>my age</u>' and '<u>length of my feet</u>', or
                                                  — '<u>temperature</u>' and '<u>number of accidents on a stretch of road</u>'.

You can plot readings from a pair of variables on a <u>scatter diagram</u> — this'll tell you something about the data.

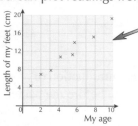

The variables 'my age' and 'length of my feet' seem linked
— all the points lie <u>close</u> to a <u>line</u>. As I got older, my feet got
bigger and bigger (though I stopped measuring when I was 10).

It's a lot harder to see any connection between the
variables 'temperature' and 'number of accidents'
— the data seems <u>scattered</u> pretty much everywhere.

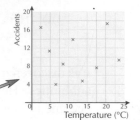

Correlation is a measure of **How Closely** variables are **Linked**

1) Sometimes, as one variable gets <u>bigger</u>, the other one also gets <u>bigger</u> — then the scatter diagram
   might look like the one on the right. Here, a line of best fit would have a <u>positive gradient</u>.
   The two variables are <u>positively correlated</u> (or there's a <u>positive correlation</u> between them).

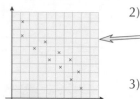

2) But if one variable gets <u>smaller</u> as the other one gets <u>bigger</u>, then
   the scatter diagram might look like this one — and the line of best
   fit would have a <u>negative gradient</u>. The two variables are <u>negatively
   correlated</u> (or there's a <u>negative correlation</u> between them).

3) And if the two variables <u>aren't</u> linked at all, you'd expect a <u>random</u>
   scattering of points — it's hard to say where the line of best fit
   would be. The variables <u>aren't correlated</u> (or there's <u>no correlation</u>).

WARNING

A strong correlation doesn't necessarily mean that one factor <u>causes</u> the other.
The number of televisions sold in Japan and the number of cars sold in America may well be
correlated, but that doesn't mean that high TV sales in Japan <u>cause</u> high car sales in the US.
More likely, some <u>other</u> factor (e.g. a global economic boom) <u>causes both</u>.

The **Product-Moment Correlation Coefficient (r)** measures Correlation

1) The <u>Product-Moment Correlation Coefficient</u> (<u>PMCC</u>, or <u>r</u>, for short)
   measures how close to a <u>straight line</u> the points on a scatter graph lie.

   *In reality, you're unlikely to get a PMCC of +1
   or −1 — your data points might lie <u>close</u> to a
   straight line, but it's unlikely they'd all be <u>on</u> it.*

2) The PMCC is always <u>between +1 and −1</u>.
   If all your points lie <u>exactly</u> on a <u>straight line</u> with a <u>positive gradient</u> (perfect positive correlation), <u>r = +1</u>.
   If all your points lie <u>exactly</u> on a <u>straight line</u> with a <u>negative gradient</u> (perfect negative correlation), <u>r = −1</u>.

3) If r = 0 (or more likely, <u>pretty close</u> to 0), that would mean the variables <u>aren't correlated</u>.

4) The formula for the PMCC is a <u>real stinker</u>. But some calculators can work it out if you type in the pairs of readings,
   which makes life easier. Otherwise, just take it nice and slow.

$$r = \frac{S_{xy}}{\sqrt{S_{xx}S_{yy}}} = \frac{\sum[x-\bar{x}][y-\bar{y}]}{\sqrt{(\sum[x-\bar{x}]^2)(\sum[y-\bar{y}]^2)}} = \frac{\sum xy - \frac{[\sum x][\sum y]}{n}}{\sqrt{\left(\sum x^2 - \frac{[\sum x]^2}{n}\right)\left(\sum y^2 - \frac{[\sum y]^2}{n}\right)}}$$

*This version is the easiest to
use, but it's still a bit hefty.*

*See page 99 for more
about S_{xy} and S_{xx}.*

WARNING   The PMCC is only a measure of a <u>linear</u> relationship between two variables (i.e. how
close they'd be to a <u>straight line</u> if you plotted a scatter diagram). In this diagram,
the PMCC would be <u>low</u>, but the two variables definitely look <u>linked</u> ('associated').
It looks like the points lie on a <u>parabola</u> (the shape of an x^2 curve) — not a straight line.

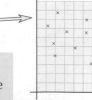

Correlation and Hypothesis Tests

You usually find a correlation coefficient using data from a <u>sample</u>, but it's the <u>population</u> that you're really interested in. A <u>hypothesis test</u> can check whether your sample correlation coefficient means anything for the population.

EXAMPLE A researcher selects a random sample of fleas to investigate whether longer fleas tend to jump further. Her data recording the length of fleas (x mm) and the average distance they jump (y cm) is below.

Find the product-moment correlation coefficient (r) between the variables x and y.

x	1.6	2.0	2.1	2.1	2.5	2.8	2.9	3.3	3.4	3.8	4.1	4.4
y	11.4	11.8	11.5	12.2	12.5	12.0	12.9	13.4	12.8	13.4	14.2	14.3

1) There are <u>12</u> pairs of readings, so <u>$n = 12$</u>.

2) It's best to add a few <u>extra rows</u> to your table to work out the sums you need...

x	1.6	2	2.1	2.1	2.5	2.8	2.9	3.3	3.4	3.8	4.1	4.4	$35 = \Sigma x$
y	11.4	11.8	11.5	12.2	12.5	12	12.9	13.4	12.8	13.4	14.2	14.3	$152.4 = \Sigma y$
x^2	2.56	4	4.41	4.41	6.25	7.84	8.41	10.89	11.56	14.44	16.81	19.36	$110.94 = \Sigma x^2$
y^2	129.96	139.24	132.25	148.84	156.25	144	166.41	179.56	163.84	179.56	201.64	204.49	$1946.04 = \Sigma y^2$
xy	18.24	23.6	24.15	25.62	31.25	33.6	37.41	44.22	43.52	50.92	58.22	62.92	$453.67 = \Sigma xy$

Stick all these in the formula to get:
$$r = \frac{\left[453.67 - \frac{35 \times 152.4}{12}\right]}{\sqrt{\left[110.94 - \frac{35^2}{12}\right] \times \left[1946.04 - \frac{152.4^2}{12}\right]}} = \frac{9.17}{\sqrt{8.857 \times 10.56}} = \underline{0.948}$$ (to 3 s.f.)

This value of r looks <u>pretty high</u>. But before you can conclude whether this is evidence of x and y being <u>correlated</u> in the whole <u>population</u>, you need to test whether r differs from 0 in a <u>statistically significant</u> way.

Use **Tables** to find **Critical Values** of r

1) To test your value of r, you need the population to be '<u>bivariate normal</u>'.

2) As long as the following <u>two conditions</u> are satisfied, everything is probably <u>fine</u>:
   i) Your data should come from a <u>random sample</u>.
   ii) The <u>bulk</u> of the data should form an <u>ellipse</u> (roughly) on a <u>scatter diagram</u>.

3) However, if one or both of your variables is <u>skewed</u> (i.e. asymmetrical) or <u>bimodal</u> (i.e. data points occur in <u>two groups</u>), then this test could give a <u>false</u> result.

4) The <u>null hypothesis</u> and the <u>alternative hypothesis</u> for the test are as follows:

   For a <u>one-tailed</u> test: $H_0: r = 0$ and $H_1: r < 0$ or $H_1: r > 0$
   For a <u>two-tailed</u> test: $H_0: r = 0$ and $H_1: r \neq 0$

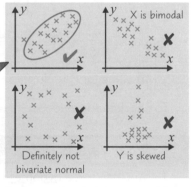

5) Then as long as you know n and the <u>significance level</u> of your test, you can look up the <u>critical value</u> for r in tables.

EXAMPLE For the data in the above example, carry out a hypothesis test at the 5% significance level to investigate whether x and y are positively correlated in the flea population.

- Before carrying out the test, check you can draw a fairly neat <u>ellipse</u> around your points. Here, it looks safe to assume that the data is from a <u>bivariate normal</u> population.

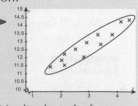

- This is a <u>one-tailed test</u>, because you want to test whether you have evidence for r being <u>positive</u> in the population. Use hypotheses $H_0: r = 0$ and $H_1: r > 0$.

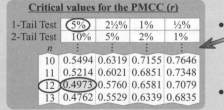

Critical values for the PMCC (r)			
1-Tail Test	5%	2½%	1%	½%
2-Tail Test	10%	5%	2%	1%
n				
10	0.5494	0.6319	0.7155	0.7646
11	0.5214	0.6021	0.6851	0.7348
12	0.4973	0.5760	0.6581	0.7079
13	0.4762	0.5529	0.6339	0.6835

Your formula booklet will contain a table showing critical values of r for n between 3 and 60.

- From <u>tables</u> (see p138 for more) the one-tail <u>critical value</u> of r for $n = 12$ at a significance level of 5% is <u>0.4973</u>. This means that under H_0, there is a probability of just 5% that r will be <u>greater than</u> 0.4973 (or <u>less than</u> –0.4973 if your alternative hypothesis is $H_1: r < 0$).

- In this example, the value of r was 0.948. This is above the critical value, so you can <u>reject H_0</u>. This means there is evidence at the 5% significance level that x and y are <u>positively correlated</u>.

What's a statistician's favourite soap — Correlation Street... (Boom boom)

Let me make one thing perfectly clear... this hypothesis test involving the PMCC will <u>only</u> be reliable if your data has come from a bivariate normal population, and so you <u>must</u> do that check of the scatter diagram. I hope that's perfectly clear.

Rank Correlation

Spearman's Rank Correlation Coefficient (SRCC or r_s) works with Ranks

You can use Spearman's Rank Correlation Coefficient (SRCC or r_s for short) when your data is a set of ranks. Ranks are the positions of the values when you put them in order — e.g. from biggest to smallest, or from best to worst, etc.

EXAMPLE At a dog show, two judges ranked 8 of the labradors (A-H) in the following order. Calculate the SRCC (r_s) between the sets of ranks, and comment on your result.

Position	1st	2nd	3rd	4th	5th	6th	7th	8th
Judge 1:	B	C	E	A	D	F	G	H
Judge 2:	C	B	E	D	F	A	G	H

First, make a table of the ranks of the 8 labradors — i.e. for each dog, write down where it came in the show.

Dog	A	B	C	D	E	F	G	H
Rank from Judge 1:	4	1	2	5	3	6	7	8
Rank from Judge 2:	6	2	1	4	3	5	7	8

Now for each dog, work out the difference (d) between the ranks from the two judges — you can ignore minus signs.

Dog	A	B	C	D	E	F	G	H
d	2	1	1	1	0	1	0	0

Take a deep breath, and add another row to your table — this time for d^2:

Dog	A	B	C	D	E	F	G	H	Total = Σd^2
d^2	4	1	1	1	0	1	0	0	8

Then the SRCC is:
$$r_s = 1 - \frac{6\sum d^2}{n(n^2-1)}$$

You can ignore minus signs when you work out d, since only d^2 is used to work out the SRCC.

So here, $r_s = 1 - \dfrac{6 \times 8}{8 \times (8^2 - 1)} = 1 - \dfrac{48}{504} = 0.905$ (to 3 sig. fig.).

Interpret r_s in the same way as you'd interpret the PMCC (see p96).

This value for r_s is close to +1, so it appears the judges ranked the dogs in a pretty similar way.

To check this is evidence that the judges mark in a similar way more generally, perform a hypothesis test.

Critical Values of r_s are in Tables

There's no need to check anything about the distributions with this test.

1) You can use a hypothesis test to check whether a value of r_s is different from 0 in a statistically significant way. The process is very similar to the test on the previous page, but you need to use a different table of critical values.

2) The null and alternative hypotheses are:
   For a one-tailed test — H_0: No association and H_1: Positive association or H_1: Negative association
   For a two-tailed test — H_0: No association and H_1: Some association

3) As with the test described on p97, if your value of r_s is greater than the critical value (or less than the negative of the critical value), then you can reject H_0 and say that you have statistically significant evidence of an association.

EXAMPLE Test whether your value of r_s for the dog-show judges shows an association at the 1% significance level.

- Use a two-tailed test — you're testing for a positive or negative association.
- Your hypotheses are — H_0: No association and H_1: Some association.
- The two-tail critical value for $n = 8$ at the 1% significance level is 0.8810. Since r_s is greater than the critical value, you can reject H_0 and conclude that you have evidence at the 1% significance level that there is some association between the judges' ranks.

Critical values for SRCC (r_s)			
1-Tail Test 5%	2½%	1%	½%
2-Tail Test 10%	5%	2%	1%
n			
7	0.7143	0.7857	0.8929	0.9286
8	0.6429	0.7381	0.8333	0.8810
9	0.6000	0.7000	0.7833	0.8333
10	0.5636	0.6485	0.7455	0.7939

Your formula booklet will contain a table showing critical values of r_s for n between 4 and 60.

A bigger version of this table is on p138.

Spearman's correlation coefficient isn't rank — in fact, it's pretty cool...

You can also use the SRCC with 'normal' numerical data (like the flea data on p97), since it can sometimes recognise a 'non-linear association' between the variables much better than the PMCC. E.g. with the data on the right, Spearman would give a clearer result of an association than the PMCC.

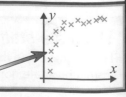

Linear Regression

Linear regression is just fancy stats-speak for 'finding lines of best fit'. Not so scary now, eh...

Decide which is the **Independent Variable** and which is the **Dependent**

EXAMPLE   The data below shows the load on a lorry, x (in tonnes), and the fuel efficiency, y (in km per litre).

x	5.1	5.6	5.9	6.3	6.8	7.4	7.8	8.5	9.1	9.8
y	9.6	9.5	8.6	8.0	7.8	6.8	6.7	6	5.4	5.4

1) On a graph, the variable along the x-axis is the explanatory or independent variable — it's the variable you can control, or the one that you think is affecting the other. The variable 'load' goes along the x-axis here.

2) The variable up the y-axis is the response or dependent variable — it's the variable you think is being affected. In this example, this is the fuel efficiency.

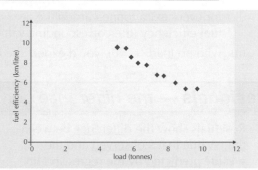

The **Regression Line** (Line of Best Fit) is in the form **y = a + bx**

To find the line of best fit for the above data you need to work out some sums.
Then it's quite easy to work out the equation of the line. If your line of best fit is $y = a + bx$, this is what you do...

(1) First work out these four sums — a table is probably the best way: $\sum x$, $\sum y$, $\sum x^2$, $\sum xy$.

x	5.1	5.6	5.9	6.3	6.8	7.4	7.8	8.5	9.1	9.8	$72.3 = \sum x$
y	9.6	9.5	8.6	8	7.8	6.8	6.7	6	5.4	5.4	$73.8 = \sum y$
x^2	26.01	31.36	34.81	39.69	46.24	54.76	60.84	72.25	82.81	96.04	$544.81 = \sum x^2$
xy	48.96	53.2	50.74	50.4	53.04	50.32	52.26	51	49.14	52.92	$511.98 = \sum xy$

(2) Then work out S_{xy}, given by: $S_{xy} = \sum (x - \overline{x})(y - \overline{y}) = \sum xy - \dfrac{(\sum x)(\sum y)}{n}$

and S_{xx}, given by: $S_{xx} = \sum (x - \overline{x})^2 = \sum x^2 - \dfrac{(\sum x)^2}{n}$

These are the same as the terms used to work out the PMCC (see p96).

A regression line always goes through the point $(\overline{x}, \overline{y})$. Once you know 'b', you can use this fact to help you work out the value of 'a' in two different ways...

(3) The gradient (b) of your regression line is given by: $b = \dfrac{S_{xy}}{S_{xx}}$

(4) And the intercept (a) is given by: $a = \overline{y} - b\overline{x}$.

(i) $\overline{x}$ and $\overline{y}$ must satisfy the line's equation — i.e. $\overline{y} = a + b\overline{x}$.
(ii) You can use the point $(\overline{x}, \overline{y})$ as the 'known point' (x_1, y_1) in the line equation $y - y_1 = b(x - x_1)$ — this gives $y - \overline{y} = b(x - \overline{x})$. Rearrange this to get $y = bx + (\overline{y} - b\overline{x})$, meaning $a = \overline{y} - b\overline{x}$.

(5) Then the regression line is just: $y = a + bx$.

EXAMPLE   Find the equation of the regression line of y on x for the data above.

The 'regression line of y on x' means that x is the independent variable, and y is the dependent variable.

1) Work out the sums: $\sum x = 72.3$, $\sum y = 73.8$, $\sum x^2 = 544.81$, $\sum xy = 511.98$.

2) Then work out S_{xy} and S_{xx}: $S_{xy} = 511.98 - \dfrac{72.3 \times 73.8}{10} = -21.594$, $S_{xx} = 544.81 - \dfrac{72.3^2}{10} = 22.081$

3) So the gradient of the regression line is: $b = \dfrac{-21.594}{22.081} = -0.978$ (to 3 sig. fig.)

Remember: $\overline{x} = \dfrac{\sum x}{n}$

4) And the intercept is: $a = \dfrac{\sum y}{n} - b\dfrac{\sum x}{n} = \dfrac{73.8}{10} - (-0.978) \times \dfrac{72.3}{10} = 14.451 = 14.5$ (to 3 sig. fig.)

5) This all means that your regression line is: $y = 14.5 - 0.978x$

Loads of calculators will work out regression lines for you — but you still need to know this method, since they might give you just the sums from Step 1.

Linear Regression

So you've worked through the formulas and found a regression line. Now you need to know:
(i) what it means, (ii) if it's any good, and (iii) the dangers of using regression lines without due care and attention.

You should be able to Interpret your Regression Coefficients

On the previous page, you found the regression line of y (fuel efficiency in km per litre) on x (load in tonnes) was:

$$y = 14.5 - 0.978x$$

This tells you:

(i) for every extra tonne carried (i.e. as x increases by 1 unit), you'd expect the lorry's fuel efficiency (the corresponding value of y) to fall by 0.978 km per litre,

(ii) with no load ($x = 0$), you'd expect the lorry to do 14.5 km per litre of fuel.

Assuming the trend continues down to $x = 0$.

Residuals — the difference between Practice and Theory

1) Residuals show the difference between the y-value that's observed and the y-value predicted by the regression line.

> Residual = Observed y-value – Estimated y-value

2) Residuals are shown by a vertical line from the actual point to the regression line.

3) Ideally, you'd like your residuals to be small — this would show your regression line fits the data well. If they're large (i.e. a high percentage of the dependent variable), then that could mean your model won't be a very reliable one.

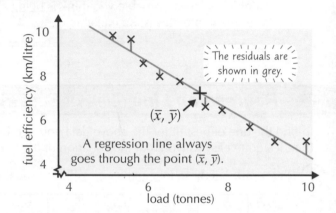

The residuals are shown in grey.

$(\bar{x}, \bar{y})$

A regression line always goes through the point $(\bar{x}, \bar{y})$.

EXAMPLE For the fuel efficiency example on the last page, calculate the residuals for: (i) $x = 5.6$, (ii) $x = 7.4$.

(i) When $x = 5.6$, the residual = $9.5 - (14.5 - 0.978 \times 5.6)$ = 0.477 (to 3 sig. fig.)

(ii) When $x = 7.4$, the residual = $6.8 - (14.5 - 0.978 \times 7.4)$ = –0.463 (to 3 sig. fig.)

A positive residual means the regression line is too low for that value of x.
A negative residual means the regression line is too high.

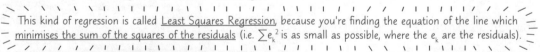

This kind of regression is called Least Squares Regression, because you're finding the equation of the line which minimises the sum of the squares of the residuals (i.e. $\sum e_k^2$ is as small as possible, where the e_k are the residuals).

Use Regression Lines With Care

You can use your regression line to predict values of y.
But it's best not to do this for x-values outside the range of your original table of values.

EXAMPLE Use your regression equation to estimate the value of y when: (i) $x = 7.6$, (ii) $x = 12.6$

(i) When $x = 7.6$, $y = 14.5 - 0.978 \times 7.6$ = 7.07 (to 3 sig. fig.). This should be a pretty reliable guess, since $x = 7.6$ falls in the range of x we already have readings for — this is called interpolation.

(ii) When $x = 12.6$, $y = 14.5 - 0.978 \times 12.6$ = 2.18 (to 3 sig. fig.). This may well be unreliable since $x = 12.6$ is bigger than the biggest x-value we already have — this is called extrapolation.

99% of all statisticians make sweeping statements...

Be careful with that extrapolation business — it's like me saying that because I grew at an average rate of 10 cm a year for the first few years of my life, by the time I'm 50 I should be 5 metres tall. Residuals are always errors in the values of y — these equations for working out the regression line all assume that you can measure x perfectly all the time.

S2 Section 1 — Practice Questions

That was a short section, but chock-full of <u>fiddly terms</u> and <u>hefty equations</u>. The only way to learn all those details is by using them — so stretch your maths muscles and take a jog around this obstacle course of <u>practice questions</u>.

Warm-up Questions

1) The table below shows the results of some measurements of randomly selected alcoholic cocktails. Here, x = total volume in ml, and y = percentage alcohol concentration by volume.

x	90	100	100	150	160	180	200	240	250	290	300
y	40	35	25	30	25	30	25	20	25	15	7

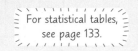
For statistical tables, see page 133.

a) Draw a scatter diagram representing this information.

b) Calculate the product-moment correlation coefficient (PMCC) of these values.

c) Carry out a hypothesis test at a significance level of 5% to determine whether this is evidence of a correlation between the volume of alcoholic drinks and their alcohol concentration.

2) These are the marks obtained by 9 pupils in their Physics and English exams.

Physics	54	34	23	57	56	58	13	65	69
English	16	73	89	83	23	81	56	62	61

Calculate Spearman's rank correlation coefficient, and determine if this is evidence at a 5% significance level of an association between the marks in Physics and English exams.

3) For each pair of variables below, state which would be the dependent variable and which would be the independent variable.

a) • the annual number of volleyball-related injuries
   • the annual number of sunny days

b) • the annual number of rainy days
   • the annual number of Monopoly-related injuries

c) • a person's disposable income
   • a person's spending on luxuries

d) • the number of trips to the loo per day
   • the number of cups of tea drunk per day

e) • the number of festival tickets sold
   • the number of pairs of Wellington boots bought

4) The radius in mm, r, and the weight in grams, w, of 10 randomly selected blueberry pancakes are given in the table below.

r	48.0	51.0	52.0	54.5	55.1	53.6	50.0	52.6	49.4	51.2
w	100	105	108	120	125	118	100	115	98	110

a) Find: (i) $S_{rr} = \sum r^2 - \dfrac{(\sum r)^2}{n}$, (ii) $S_{rw} = \sum rw - \dfrac{(\sum r)(\sum w)}{n}$

The regression line of w on r has equation $w = a + br$.

b) Find b, the gradient of the regression line.

c) Find a, the intercept of the regression line on the w-axis.

d) Write down the equation of the regression line of w on r.

e) Use your regression line to estimate the weight of a blueberry pancake of radius 60 mm.

f) Comment on the reliability of your estimate, giving a reason for your answer.

S2 Section 1 — Practice Questions

Exam Questions

1   Thirteen Year-7 pupils in a school were randomly selected. For each pupil, two variables were recorded:
    - the number of after-school catch-up sessions attended during a school year (x),
    - their score in a maths test (y%).

    The results are shown in the table below.

x	1	2	3	3	4	5	5	5	6	6	6	7	8
y	33	30	42	52	24	35	50	56	37	56	62	68	61

   a)   Represent this data on a scatter diagram.

(2 marks)

   b)   Calculate the product-moment correlation coefficient (PMCC) between the two variables.

(4 marks)

   c)   Carry out a hypothesis test at the 5% significance level to determine whether
        there is a correlation between the variables.

(6 marks)

2   The following times (in seconds) were taken by eight different runners to complete distances of
    20 metres and 60 metres.

Runner	A	B	C	D	E	F	G	H
20-metre time (x)	3.39	3.20	3.09	3.32	3.33	3.27	3.44	3.08
60-metre time (y)	8.78	7.73	8.28	8.25	8.91	8.59	8.90	8.05

   a)   Plot a scatter diagram to represent the data.

(2 marks)

   b)   Find the equation of the regression line of y on x, and plot it on your scatter diagram.

(8 marks)

   c)   Use the equation of the regression line to estimate the value of y when:
        (i) $x = 3.15$,   (ii) $x = 3.88$.
        Comment on the reliability of your estimates.

(4 marks)

   d)   Find the residuals for:
        (i) $x = 3.32$ (ii) $x = 3.27$.

        Illustrate them on your scatter diagram.

(4 marks)

3   A journalist believes there is a positive correlation between the distance in miles, x, cycled during a
    training ride by cyclists from a particular cycling club and the number of calories, y, eaten at lunch.
    He gathers data from 10 randomly selected members of the club, and calculates the following statistics:

$$S_{xx} = 155\,440 \qquad S_{yy} = 395.5 \qquad S_{xy} = 6333$$

   a)   Use these values to calculate the product-moment correlation coefficient.

(2 marks)

   b)   Carry out a hypothesis test at the 1% significance level to investigate the journalist's belief.
        State your hypotheses clearly.

(5 marks)

   c)   State the assumption necessary for this test to be valid.
        Explain how you might check whether this assumption is likely to be justified.

(2 marks)

4   The equation of the line of regression for a set of data is $y = 211.599 + 9.602x$.

   a)   Use the equation of the regression line to estimate the value of y when:
        (i) $x = 12.5$ (ii) $x = 14.7$.

(2 marks)

   b)   Calculate the residuals if the respective observed y-values were $y = 332.5$ and $y = 352.1$.

(2 marks)

The Poisson Distribution

It's time to introduce the Poisson distribution. If you speak French, you'll know that poisson means fish. I think.

A Poisson Distribution has **Only One Parameter**

The Greek letter lambda is often used for the Poisson parameter.

A Poisson Distribution has just <u>one parameter</u>: λ.
If the random variable X follows a Poisson distribution, then you can write <u>$X \sim$ Poisson(λ)</u>.

Poisson Probability Distribution: Poisson(λ)

If $X \sim$ Poisson(λ), then X can take values 0, 1, 2, 3... with probability:

$$P(X = x) = \frac{e^{-\lambda}\lambda^x}{x!}$$

Random variables following a Poisson distribution are <u>discrete</u> — there are 'gaps' between the possible values.

EXAMPLE   If $X \sim$ Poisson(2.8), find:
  a) $P(X = 0)$,   b) $P(X = 1)$,   c) $P(X = 2)$,   d) $P(X < 3)$,   e) $P(X \geq 3)$

Use the formula:

a) $P(X = 0) = \dfrac{e^{-2.8} \times 2.8^0}{0!} = e^{-2.8} = 0.061$ (to 3 d.p.).   *Remember... 0! = 1.*

b) $P(X = 1) = \dfrac{e^{-2.8} \times 2.8^1}{1!} = e^{-2.8} \times 2.8 = 0.170$ (to 3 d.p.).

c) $P(X = 2) = \dfrac{e^{-2.8} \times 2.8^2}{2!} = \dfrac{e^{-2.8} \times 2.8^2}{2 \times 1} = 0.238$ (to 3 d.p.).

If X ~ Poisson(λ), then it can only take whole number values, so P(X < 3) is the same as P(X ≤ 2).

d) $P(X < 3) = P(X \leq 2) = P(X = 0) + P(X = 1) + P(X = 2) = 0.061 + 0.170 + 0.238 = 0.469$.

e) $P(X \geq 3) = 1 - P(X < 3) = 1 - 0.469 = 0.531$.   *All the normal probability rules apply.*

For a Poisson Distribution: **Mean = Variance**

For a Poisson distribution, the <u>mean</u> and the <u>variance</u> are <u>the same</u> — and they <u>both</u> equal λ, the <u>Poisson parameter</u>. Remember that and you've probably learnt the most important Poisson fact. Ever.

Poisson Mean and Variance

If $X \sim$ Poisson(λ):   **Mean (μ) of X = E$(X) = \lambda$**

Variance (σ^2) of X = Var$(X) = \lambda$

So the standard deviation is:
$$\sigma = \sqrt{\lambda}$$

EXAMPLE   If $X \sim$ Poisson(7), find: a) E(X),   b) Var(X).
   It's Poisson, so $E(X) = Var(X) = \lambda = 7$.

This is the easiest question ever. So enjoy it while it lasts.

EXAMPLE   If $X \sim$ Poisson(1), find: a) $P(X \leq \mu)$,   b) $P(X \leq \mu - \sigma)$
   $E(X) = \mu = 1$, and $Var(X) = \sigma^2 = 1$, and so $\sigma = 1$.

a) $P(X \leq \mu) = P(X \leq 1) = P(0) + P(1) = \dfrac{e^{-1} \times 1^0}{0!} + \dfrac{e^{-1} \times 1^1}{1!} = 0.736$ (to 3 d.p.).

b) $P(X \leq \mu - \sigma) = P(X \leq 0) = P(0) = \dfrac{e^{-1} \times 1^0}{0!} = 0.368$ (to 3 d.p.).

The Poisson distribution is named after its inventor...

...the great French mathematician Monsieur Siméon-Denis Distribution. Boom boom. I always tell that joke at parties (which probably explains why I don't get to go to many parties these days). Most important thing here is that bit about the mean and variance being equal... so if you ever come across a distribution where $\mu = \sigma^2$, think 'Poisson' immediately.

The Poisson Parameter

I know what you're thinking... if only everything could be as accommodating as the Poisson distribution, with only one parameter and most things of interest being equal to it, then life would be so much easier. (Sigh.)

The Poisson Parameter is a **Rate**

The <u>number of events/things</u> that occur/are present <u>in a particular period</u> often follows a Poisson distribution. It could be a period of: <u>time</u> (e.g. minute/hour etc.), or <u>space</u> (e.g. litre/kilometre etc.).

Poisson Probability Distribution: Poisson(λ)

If X represents the number of events that occur in a particular space or time, then X will follow a Poisson distribution as long as:

1) The events occur <u>randomly</u>, and are all <u>independent</u> of each other.
2) The events happen <u>singly</u> (i.e. "<u>one at a time</u>").
3) The events happen (on average) at a <u>constant rate</u> (either in space or time).

The Poisson parameter λ is then the <u>average rate</u> at which these events occur (i.e. the average number of events in a given interval of space or time).

So the expected number of events that occur is <u>proportional</u> to the length of the period.

EXAMPLE   The random variable X represents the number of a certain type of cell in a particular volume of a blood sample. Assuming that the blood sample has been stirred, and that a given volume of blood always contains the same number of cells, show that X follows a Poisson distribution.

The sample has been stirred, so that should mean the cells of interest <u>aren't all clustered together</u>. This should ensure the 'events' (i.e. the cells you're interested in) occur <u>randomly</u> and <u>singly</u>. And since the total number of cells in a given volume is constant, the cells of interest should occur (on average) at a <u>constant rate</u>. Since X is the total number of 'events' in a given volume, <u>X must follow a Poisson distribution</u>.

The Poisson Parameter is **Additive**

Additive Property of the Poisson Distribution

- If X represents the number of events in <u>1 unit</u> of time/space (e.g. 1 minute / hour / m² / m³), and <u>$X \sim$ Poisson(λ)</u>, then the number of events in <u>x units</u> of time/space follows the distribution <u>Poisson($x\lambda$)</u>.

- If X and Y are <u>independent</u> variables with <u>$X \sim$ Poisson(λ)</u> and <u>$Y \sim$ Poisson(μ)</u>, then <u>$X + Y \sim$ Poisson($\lambda + \mu$)</u>.

EXAMPLE   Sunflowers grow singly and randomly in a field with an average of 10 sunflowers per square metre. What is the probability that a randomly chosen area of 0.25 m² contains no sunflowers?

The number of sunflowers in 1 m² follows the distribution Poisson(10).
So the number of sunflowers in 0.25 m² must follow the distribution Poisson(2.5) .
This means P(no sunflowers) $= \dfrac{e^{-2.5} \times 2.5^0}{0!} = e^{-2.5} = 0.082$ (to 3 d.p.) .

X ~ Poisson(10)

EXAMPLE   The number of radioactive atoms that decay per second follows the Poisson distribution Poisson(5). If the probability of no atoms decaying in t seconds is 0.5, verify that $t = 0.1386$.

If the random variable X represents the number of radioactive atoms that decay in t seconds, then $X \sim$ Poisson($5t$) .
This means P($X = 0$) $= \dfrac{e^{-5t}(5t)^0}{0!} = e^{-5t} = 0.5$.
This equation is satisfied by $t = 0.1386$, since $e^{-5 \times 0.1386} = e^{-0.693} = 0.500$ (to 3 d.p.) .

If events happen randomly, singly and at a constant rate, it's Poisson...

Lots of things follow a Poisson distribution — e.g. the number of radioactive atoms that decay in a given time, the number of sixes in 5 minutes of dice-throwing, the number of raindrops per minute that hit a bit of your tongue as you stare openmouthed at the sky on a rainy day. Think of a few others... make sure events happen <u>randomly</u>, <u>singly</u> and <u>at a constant rate</u>.

Using Poisson Tables

You've seen <u>statistical tables</u> before — for example, in S1 you saw how great they are for working out probabilities for the <u>binomial</u> distribution. So this should all seem <u>eerily familiar</u>.

Look up Probabilities in Poisson Tables

Going back to the <u>sunflowers</u> example near the bottom of the <u>previous page</u>...

EXAMPLE Sunflowers grow singly and randomly in a field with an average of 10 sunflowers per square metre. Find the probability that a randomly chosen square metre contains no more than 8 sunflowers.

If the random variable X represents the number of sunflowers in 1 m², then $X \sim$ Poisson(10). You need to find P($X \leq 8$).

① You could do this 'manually': $P(X = 0) + P(X = 1) + ... + P(X = 8) = \dfrac{e^{-10} \times 10^0}{0!} + \dfrac{e^{-10} \times 10^1}{1!} + ... + \dfrac{e^{-10} \times 10^8}{8!}$

② But it's much quicker and easier to use tables of the Poisson <u>cumulative distribution function</u> (c.d.f.). These show P($X \leq x$) if $X \sim$ Poisson(λ).

Here's a bit of a Poisson table:

- Find your <u>value of λ</u> (here, 10), and the <u>value of x</u> (here, 8).

- You can quickly see that P($X \leq 8$) = 0.3328.

x \ λ	10.00	10.10	10.20	10.30	10.40	10.50	10.60	10.70	10.80	10.90
0	0.0000	0.0000	0.0000	0.0000	0.0000	0.0000	0.0000	0.0000	0.0000	0.0000
1	0.0005	0.0005	0.0004	0.0004	0.0003	0.0003	0.0003	0.0003	0.0002	0.0002
2	0.0028	0.0026	0.0023	0.0022	0.0020	0.0018	0.0017	0.0016	0.0014	0.0013
3	0.0103	0.0096	0.0089	0.0083	0.0077	0.0071	0.0066	0.0062	0.0057	0.0053
4	0.0293	0.0274	0.0257	0.0241	0.0225	0.0211	0.0197	0.0185	0.0173	0.0162
5	0.0671	0.0634	0.0599	0.0566	0.0534	0.0504	0.0475	0.0448	0.0423	0.0398
6	0.1301	0.1240	0.1180	0.1123	0.1069	0.1016	0.0966	0.0918	0.0872	0.0828
7	0.2202	0.2113	0.2027	0.1944	0.1863	0.1785	0.1710	0.1636	0.1566	0.1498
8	0.3328	0.3217	0.3108	0.3001	0.2896	0.2794	0.2694	0.2597	0.2502	0.2410
9	0.4579	0.4455	0.4332	0.4210	0.4090	0.3971	0.3854	0.3739	0.3626	0.3515
10	0.5830	0.5705	0.5580	0.5456	0.5331	0.5207	0.5084	0.4961	0.4840	0.4719
11	0.6968	0.6853	0.6738	0.6622	0.6505	0.6387	0.6269	0.6150	0.6031	0.5912
⋮	⋮	⋮	⋮	⋮	⋮	⋮	⋮	⋮	⋮	⋮

You Need to Use Poisson Tables with a Bit of Cunning

Poisson tables will eventually tell you pretty much <u>anything</u> you want to know... as long as you know how to use them.

EXAMPLE When cloth is manufactured, faults occur randomly in the cloth at a rate of 10 faults per square metre. Use the above Poisson table to find:
- a) The probability of 7 or fewer faults in a square metre of cloth.
- b) The probability of more than 4 faults in a square metre of cloth.
- c) The probability of exactly 10 faults in a square metre of cloth.
- d) The probability of at least 9 faults in a square metre of cloth.
- e) The probability of exactly 4 faults in 1.05 m² of cloth.

See the full set of Poisson tables on p133.

The faults occur <u>randomly</u>, <u>singly</u> and <u>at a constant rate</u> (= 10 faults per square metre). So if X represents the number of faults in a square metre, then <u>$X \sim$ Poisson(10)</u>.

So use the column showing λ = 10.

a) P($X \leq 7$) = 0.2202

b) P($X > 4$) = 1 − P($X \leq 4$) = 1 − 0.0293 = 0.9707

c) P($X = 10$) = P($X \leq 10$) − P($X \leq 9$) = 0.5830 − 0.4579 = 0.1251

Now use the column showing λ = 10.5.

d) P($X \geq 9$) = 1 − P($X < 9$) = 1 − P($X \leq 8$) = 1 − 0.3328 = 0.6672

e) Let the random variable Y represent the number of faults in 1.05 m² of cloth. If the number of faults in 1 m² of cloth $\sim$ Poisson(10), then $Y \sim$ Poisson(1.05 × 10) = Poisson(10.5).

So P(exactly 4 faults in 1.05 m² of cloth) = P($Y \leq 4$) − P($Y \leq 3$) = 0.0211 − 0.0071 = 0.0140

Poisson tables — the best thing since binomial tables...

Learn the ways of the Poisson tables, and you shall prove your wisdom. In the exam, you'll be given a big booklet of fun containing all the statistical tables you could ever want. You need to think carefully about how to use them though — e.g. you might have to subtract one figure from another, or subtract one of the figures from 1. Or something else similar.

Poisson(λ) as an Approximation to B(n, p)

This page is largely about the binomial distribution B(n, p) — something you met in S1. If your memory of the binomial distribution is a little sketchy, it might be worth looking that up again before you tackle this page.

For **Big n** and **Small p** — **Poisson(np)** Approximates a Binomial Distribution

Sometimes, a Poisson distribution can be used as an approximation to a binomial distribution.

Poisson(np) as an Approximation to B(n, p)

If $X \sim$ B(n, p), and: 1) n is large, 2) p is small,

then X can be approximated by **Poisson(np)**.

> The mean of the binomial distribution is np, so use that as the mean of your Poisson distribution.

EXAMPLE In a school of 1825 students, what is the probability that at least 6 of them were born on June 21st? Use a suitable approximation to find your answer.
(You may assume that all birthdays are independent, and are distributed evenly throughout the year.)

If X represents the number of children in the school born on June 21st, then $X \sim$ B(1825, $\frac{1}{365}$).
You need to find P($X \geq 6$).

> So far so good. However, your binomial tables don't go past n = 20. And working this out 'by hand' isn't easy. But look at those values of n and p...

Since n is large and p is small, B(1825, $\frac{1}{365}$) can be approximated by Poisson($1825 \times \frac{1}{365}$) = Poisson(5).

So P($X \geq 6$) = 1 − P($X < 6$) = 1 − P($X \leq 5$) = 1 − 0.6160 = 0.3840. ← From Poisson tables — see p133.

If you work it out using B(1825, $\frac{1}{365}$), you also get 0.3840 — so this is a very good approximation.

The **Smaller** the Value of p, the **Better**

1) To use the Poisson approximation to B(n, p), you ideally want n "as large as possible" and p "as small as possible". The bigger n is and the smaller p is, the better the approximation will be.

2) It's important p is small because then the mean and the variance of B(n, p) are approximately equal — something you need if Poisson(np) is going to be a good approximation.

> If $X \sim$ B(n, p), then E(X) = np. And if p is small, $(1 - p) \approx 1$ — this means Var(X) = $np(1 - p) \approx np \times 1 = np$.

3) In your exam, you'll usually be told when to use an approximation.

> Though you might not be told which approximation to use, so you need to learn these conditions carefully. There's more about this on p122.

EXAMPLES:

① Factory A forgets to add icing to its chocolate cakes with a uniform probability of 0.02. Use a suitable approximation to find the probability that fewer than 6 of the next 100 cakes made will not be iced.

If X represents the number of "un-iced" cakes, then $X \sim$ B(100, 0.02).
Since n is quite large and p is quite small, $X \sim$ Poisson(100×0.02) = Poisson(2).
So P($X < 6$) = P($X \leq 5$) = 0.9834 ← If you work it out using B(100, 0.02), you get 0.9845.

Sometimes you can still use the approximation if p is very close to 1.

② Factory B adds icing to its chocolate cakes with a uniform probability of 0.99. Use a suitable approximation to find the probability that more than 95 of the next 100 cakes made will be iced.

- If Y represents the number of iced cakes produced by Factory B, then $Y \sim$ B(100, 0.99). Here, n is quite large, but p is not small.
- However, if you let W represent the number of "un-iced" cakes made, then $W \sim$ B(100, 0.01). Now you can use a Poisson approximation: $W \sim$ Poisson(100×0.01) = Poisson(1). So P($Y > 95$) = P($W < 5$) = P($W \leq 4$) = 0.9963 ← Using B(100, 0.01), you get 0.9966.

Remember — you need a small p...

This approximation only works if p is very small (although in the right circumstances, it'll also work if p is very close to 1). On a practical note... your tables go up to λ = 10.9 — so you can only use this approximation if np is less than this.

Worked Problems

Make sure you understand what's going on in these examples.

EXAMPLE 1: A breaking-down car

A car randomly breaks down twice a week on average.
The random variable X represents the number of times the car will break down next week.
a) What probability distribution could be used to model X? Explain your answer.
b) Find the probability that the car breaks down fewer than 3 times next week.
c) Find the probability that the car breaks down more than 4 times next week.
d) Find the probability that the car breaks down exactly 6 times in the next fortnight.

a) Since the breakdowns occur <u>randomly</u>, <u>singly</u> and (on average) <u>at a constant rate</u>, and X is the <u>total number</u> of breakdowns in one week, X follows a Poisson distribution: $X \sim$ Poisson(2)

b) Using tables for <u>$\lambda = 2$</u>: $P(X < 3) = P(X \le 2) = 0.6767$

c) Again, using tables for <u>$\lambda = 2$</u>: $P(X > 4) = 1 - P(X \le 4) = 1 - 0.9473 = 0.0527$

d) If the random variable Y represents the number of breakdowns in the next <u>fortnight</u>, then $Y \sim$ Poisson(2 × 2), i.e. $Y \sim$ Poisson(4). So using tables for <u>$\lambda = 4$</u>: $P(Y = 6) = P(Y \le 6) - P(Y \le 5) = 0.8893 - 0.7851 = 0.1042$

EXAMPLE 2: Bad apples

A restaurant owner needs to buy several crates of apples, so she visits a farm that sells apples by the crate.
Each crate contains 150 apples. On average 1.5% of the apples are bad, and these bad apples are randomly distributed between the crates. The restaurant owner opens a random crate and inspects each apple.
• If there are <u>no</u> bad apples in this crate, then the restaurant owner will <u>buy</u> the apples she needs from this farm.
• If <u>more than 2 apples</u> in this first crate are bad, then the restaurant owner will <u>not buy</u> from this farm.
• If <u>only 1 or 2 apples</u> in the first crate are bad, then a <u>second crate</u> is opened.
  The restaurant owner will then only buy from this farm if the second crate contains <u>at most 1 bad apple</u>.

a) Find the probability that none of the apples in the first crate are bad.
b) Find the probability that more than 2 apples in the first crate are bad.
c) Find the probability that a second crate is opened.
d) What is the probability of the restaurant owner buying the apples she needs from this farm?

a) The <u>average</u> number of bad apples in each crate is 150 × 0.015 = 2.25.
So if X represents the number of bad apples in each crate, then $X \sim$ Poisson(2.25).

$$P(X = 0) = \frac{e^{-2.25} \times 2.25^0}{0!} = e^{-2.25} = 0.1054 \text{ (to 4 d.p.)}.$$

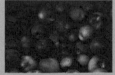

b) $$P(X = 1) = \frac{e^{-2.25} \times 2.25^1}{1!} = e^{-2.25} \times 2.25 = 0.2371 \text{ (to 4 d.p.)}.$$

$$P(X = 2) = \frac{e^{-2.25} \times 2.25^2}{2!} = \frac{e^{-2.25} \times 2.25^2}{2} = 0.2668 \text{ (to 4 d.p.)}.$$

Definitely Poisson.

So $P(X > 2) = 1 - P(X = 0) - P(X = 1) - P(X = 2) = 1 - 0.1054 - 0.2371 - 0.2668 = 0.3907$

c) A second crate is opened if $X = 1$ or $X = 2$. $P(X = 1 \text{ OR } X = 2) = 0.2371 + 0.2668 = 0.5039$

d) There are two ways the owner will buy apples from this farm:
  • <u>Either</u> the first crate will contain <u>no</u> bad apples (probability = 0.1054),
  • <u>Or</u> the first crate will contain <u>1 or 2</u> bad apples <u>AND</u> the second crate will contain <u>0 or 1</u> bad apples.
  P(1st crate has 1 or 2 bad AND 2nd crate has 0 or 1 bad) = 0.5039 × (0.1054 + 0.2371) = 0.1726
  So P(restaurant owner buys from this farm) = 0.1054 + 0.1726 = 0.278

All it takes is one bad apple question and everything starts to go wrong...

I admit that apple question looks a nightmare at first... but just hold your nerve and take things nice and slowly.
For example, in that last part, ask yourself: "What individual things need to happen before the restaurant owner will buy from this farm?" Work out the individual probabilities, add or multiply them as necessary, and Bob's your uncle.

S2 Section 2 — Practice Questions

Well, that's the section completed, which is as good a reason as most to celebrate. But wait... put that celebratory cup of tea on ice for a few minutes more, because you've still got some questions to answer to prove that you really do know everything. So try the questions... and if you get any wrong, do some more revision and try them again.

Warm-up Questions

1) If $X \sim$ Poisson(3.25), find (correct to 4 decimal places):
   a) P($X = 2$),　　b) P($X = 1$),　　c) P($X = 0$),　　d) P($X < 3$),　　e) P($X \geq 3$)

2) If $X \sim$ Poisson(8.7), find (correct to 4 decimal places):
   a) P($X = 2$),　　b) P($X = 1$),　　c) P($X = 0$),　　d) P($X < 3$),　　e) P($X \geq 3$)

3) For the following distributions, find: (i) E(X), (ii) Var(X), and (iii) the standard deviation of X.
   a) Poisson(8),　　　　b) Poisson(12.11)　　　　c) Poisson(84.2227)

4) For the following distributions, find: (i) P($X \leq \mu$),　(ii) P($X \leq \mu - \sigma$)
   a) Poisson(9),　　　　b) Poisson(4)

5) Which of the following would follow a Poisson distribution? Explain your answers.
   a) The number of defective products coming off a factory's production line in one day if defective products occur at random at an average of 25 per week.
   b) The number of heads thrown using a coin in 25 tosses if the probability of getting a head is always 0.5.
   c) The number of people joining a post-office queue each minute during lunchtime if people arrive at an average rate of 3 every five minutes.
   d) The total number of spelling mistakes in a document if mistakes are randomly made at an average rate of 3 per page.

6) In a radioactive sample, atoms decay at an average rate of 2000 per hour.
   State how the following quantities are distributed, giving as much detail as possible.
   a) The number of atoms decaying per minute.
   b) The number of atoms decaying per day.

7) Atoms in one radioactive sample decay at an average rate of 60 per minute, while in another they decay at an average rate of 90 per minute.
   a) How would the total number of atoms decaying each minute be distributed?
   b) How would the total number of atoms decaying each hour be distributed?

8) If $X \sim$ Poisson(8), use Poisson tables to find:
   a) P($X \leq 2$),　　b) P($X \leq 7$),　　c) P($X \leq 5$),　　d) P($X < 9$),　　e) P($X \geq 8$)
   f) P($X > 1$),　　g) P($X > 7$),　　h) P($X = 6$),　　i) P($X = 4$),　　j) P($X = 3$)

9) A gaggle of 100 geese is randomly scattered throughout a field measuring 10 m × 10m.
   What is the probability that in a randomly selected square metre of field, I find:
   a) no geese?　　　　b) 1 goose?　　　　c) 2 geese?　　　　d) more than 2 geese?

10) Which of the following random variables could be approximated by a Poisson distribution?
    Where it is possible, state the Poisson distribution that could be used.
    a) $X \sim$ B(4, 0.4),　　b) $Y \sim$ B(700, 0.01),　　c) $W \sim$ B(850, 0.34)
    d) $X \sim$ B(8, 0.1),　　e) $W \sim$ B(10 000, 0.00001),　f) $Y \sim$ B(80, 0.9) *(harder)*

11) Calculate the mean and variance of the following sample: 0, 0, 0, 1, 0, 1, 0, 1, 2, 2, 1, 1, 3, 0, 1
    Does the population the sample was taken from appear to follow a Poisson distribution?
    Explain your answer.

S2 Section 2 — Practice Questions

Nearly there — just... one... more... page...

Exam Questions

1 a) State two conditions needed for a Poisson distribution to be a suitable model for a quantity.

(2 marks)

   b) A birdwatcher knows that the number of chaffinches visiting a particular observation spot per hour follows a Poisson distribution with mean 7.
   Find the probability that in a randomly chosen hour during the day:

   (i) fewer than 4 chaffinches visit the observation spot,

(2 marks)

   (ii) at least 7 chaffinches visit the observation spot,

(2 marks)

   (iii) exactly 9 chaffinches visit the observation spot.

(2 marks)

   c) The number of birds <u>other than</u> chaffinches visiting the same observation spot per hour can be modelled by the Poisson distribution Poisson(22).
   Find the probability that exactly 3 birds (of any species) visit the observation spot in a random 15-minute period.

(4 marks)

2 The number of calls received at a call centre each hour can be modelled by a Poisson distribution with mean 20.
   a) Find the probability that in a random 30-minute period:

   (i) exactly 8 calls are received,

(3 marks)

   (ii) more than 8 calls are received.

(2 marks)

   b) For a Poisson distribution to be a suitable model, events have to occur independently.
   What is meant by "independently" in this context?

(1 mark)

3 When a particular engineer is called out to fix a fault, the probability of him being unable to fix the fault is always 0.02.
   a) The engineer's work is assessed after every 400 call-outs. The random variable X represents the number of faults the engineer is unable to fix over those 400 call-outs.
   Specify the statistical distribution that X will follow, stating the values of any parameters.

(2 marks)

   b) (i) Under what conditions can a binomial distribution be approximated by a Poisson distribution?

(2 marks)

   (ii) Write down a Poisson distribution that could be used to approximate X.

(1 mark)

   (iii) Write down the mean and variance of your Poisson distribution.

(1 mark)

   (iv) Using your Poisson approximation, calculate the probability that the engineer will be unable to fix fewer than 10 faults over a period of 400 call-outs.

(2 marks)

Chi-Squared (χ^2) Contingency-Table Tests

This section is dead short. Short but sweet, I say.

Contingency Tables show Frequencies for Two Variables

1) A contingency table is a way of showing information about two categorical variables for a number of items.
   (A 'categorical variable' is one where items are grouped into different categories or classes.)

2) For example, the data in this table shows how well n different plants grew in different types of soil.
   The variables are: (i) 'type of soil the plant was grown in',
                        (ii) 'amount of growth achieved'.

3) So here: • 14 plants achieved average growth in acidic soil,
             • a total of 40 plants achieved 'poor growth'
               (i.e. the total of the 'poor growth' column).
             • a total of 27 plants were planted in alkaline soil
               (i.e. the total of the 'alkaline soil' row).

Observed frequencies	Amount of growth achieved			Row totals
	Poor growth	Average growth	Good growth	
Acidic soil	28	14	8	50
Neutral soil	8	7	8	23
Alkaline soil	4	6	17	27
Column totals	40	27	33	100

(Type of soil — the row label for the three soil rows)

The columns show the categories for one of the variables, and the rows show the categories for the other.

These are the 'observed' frequencies — what actually happened.

If the variables are Independent, you can calculate Expected Frequencies

1) Assume for now that the two variables ('type of soil' and 'amount of growth') are completely independent.
   This would mean the type of soil doesn't affect the amount of growth at all.

2) Based on this assumption, you can work out what frequencies you would expect the different cells in the contingency table to contain using this formula:

$$\text{Expected frequency} = \frac{(\text{Row total}) \times (\text{Column total})}{\text{Overall total } (n)}$$

Expected frequencies	Poor growth	Average growth	Good growth	Total
Acidic soil	20	13.5	16.5	50
Neutral soil	9.2	6.21	7.59	23
Alkaline soil	10.8	7.29	8.91	27
Total	40	27	33	100

For example, the expected frequency for 'poor growth in acidic soil' is $\frac{50 \times 40}{100} = 20$.

3) You get this formula for the expected frequencies by saying that if 'type of soil' has no effect whatsoever on 'amount of growth', then the ratio of growth classes should be the same for each soil category.
   For example, $\frac{40}{100}$ of each row should show poor growth, $\frac{27}{100}$ of each row should show average growth, and so on.

You can see 'How far from expected' your observations are

1) You can use your expected frequencies to say whether, for example, more plants than you expected achieved good growth in each type of soil.

2) Remember... these expected values all assume that the variables 'soil type' and 'amount of growth' are completely independent (i.e. they're not associated).

EXAMPLE Comment briefly on how the observed growth of the above plants compares with what you would expect if there were no association between soil type and growth.

- The number of plants that achieved different levels of growth in neutral soil was close to what was expected.

  The numbers in the two tables are pretty similar for the 'neutral soil' row.

- However, for acidic soil the observed frequency for good growth was a lot lower than expected (while the observed frequency for poor growth was a lot higher than expected).

- In alkaline soil more plants than expected showed good growth (and fewer showed poor growth).

Your contingency plan should be to revise tables...

Well that could have been worse. You only had to do a little bit of multiplication and compare a few numbers and the page was done. Remember... all the way down this page, you've been assuming the two variables are not associated (i.e. neither has an effect on the other). On the next page you're going to test whether that assumption was a reasonable one to make.

Chi-Squared (χ^2) Contingency-Table Tests

Here we go with another ride on the hypothesis-testing train of fun...

Test your **Assumption** of '**No Association**' using a **Hypothesis Test**

1) You calculate expected frequencies by <u>assuming</u> the two variables in your contingency table are <u>not associated</u>. You can then use these expected frequencies in a <u>hypothesis test</u> to check whether this assumption is <u>supported</u> by <u>evidence</u> (the observed frequencies).

2) Use your assumption of 'no association' as the <u>null hypothesis</u>. For example...

> H_0: there is <u>no association</u> between the variables 'soil type' and 'amount of growth'.
>
> H_1: there is <u>some association</u> between the variables 'soil type' and 'amount of growth'.

Find the **Test Statistic** X^2 ('chi squared') and the **Degrees of Freedom**

1) Using your two tables (showing <u>observed frequencies</u> and <u>expected frequencies</u>), you can calculate your <u>test statistic</u> X^2 ('chi squared').

Capital 'chi' = X. Lower case 'chi' = χ.

The X^2 Statistic for Contingency-Table Tests

$$X^2 = \sum \frac{(O_i - E_i)^2}{E_i}$$, where O_i and E_i are the <u>observed</u> and <u>expected</u> frequencies for cell i.

Sometimes written $X^2 = \sum \frac{(f_o - f_e)^2}{f_e}$.

EXAMPLE Calculate the value of X^2 for the 'type of soil' and 'amount of growth' data on the previous page.

- First work out the '<u>contribution</u>' that each cell makes to X^2 — this is just $\frac{(O_i - E_i)^2}{E_i}$.
- Then <u>add up</u> these contributions to find X^2.

Contribution	Poor growth	Average growth	Good growth
Acidic soil	3.2000	0.0185	4.3788
Neutral soil	0.1565	0.1005	0.0221
Alkaline soil	4.2815	0.2283	7.3455

This is a <u>particular</u> value of X^2, so use a lower-case χ. $\Longrightarrow$ $\chi^2 = 3.2000 + 0.0185 + \cdots + 0.2283 + 7.3455 = 19.7317$

2) Before you can check whether this is significant, you need to know how many <u>degrees of freedom</u> (ν) your data has — this depends on how many <u>rows</u> and <u>columns</u> there are in your contingency table.

Greek letter 'nu'.

> $\nu = [(\text{no. of rows}) - 1] \times [(\text{no. of columns}) - 1]$

Not including the 'Total' row and column.

EXAMPLE Find the degrees of freedom for the 'soil' data above.

$\nu = [(\text{no. of rows}) - 1] \times [(\text{no. of columns}) - 1] = (3 - 1) \times (3 - 1) = 2 \times 2 = \underline{4}$

Find the **Critical Value** using the χ^2 **Table**

1) Under H_0, the statistic X^2 follows a χ^2 <u>distribution</u> with ν <u>degrees of freedom</u> (approximately) — i.e. $X^2 \sim \chi^2_{(\nu)}$.

2) A table showing percentage points of the χ^2 <u>distributions</u> is on p138. For these contingency-table tests, you need to use the <u>right-hand</u> part of the table.

For this <u>approximation</u> to be valid, all E_i must be <u>greater than 5</u>.

EXAMPLE Carry out a χ^2 test for the 'soil' data above at the 1% significance level. State your conclusion clearly.

For a <u>significance level</u> of <u>1%</u>, find the <u>critical value</u> by looking up 1% in the correct row of the χ^2 table. Here, the critical value is $x = 13.28$.

The 'soil' data gave $\chi^2 = 19.73$, which is <u>significant</u> at this level (i.e. it's <u>greater</u> than the critical value). So there is evidence to <u>reject H_0</u>, and to suggest there <u>is an association</u> between type of soil and growth for these plants.

This is the top-right corner of the χ^2 table. It shows <u>critical values</u> for different values of p and ν (i.e. values of x satisfying $P(X > x) = p\%$, where $X \sim \chi^2_{(\nu)}$).

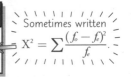

0	10	5.0	2.5	1.0	0.5	$p\%$
58	2.706	3.841	5.024	6.635	7.879	$\nu = 1$
11	4.605	5.991	7.378	9.210	10.60	2
84	6.251	7.815	9.348	11.34	12.84	3
64	7.779	9.488	11.14	13.28	14.86	4

While revising, allow yourself 3 degrees of freedom — food, sleep and toilet...

Quite a tricky page, that one — involving hypothesis tests, tables, a smattering of Greek, and all sorts. But the basic idea is familiar — set up your <u>hypotheses and significance level</u>, find a <u>test statistic</u>, and then compare this to a <u>critical value</u>.

Chi-Squared (χ^2) Contingency-Table Tests

You know what they say... practice makes perfect.

Make sure you can follow these Examples

EXAMPLE The contingency table on the right was produced after doing an investigation into newts. Carry out a χ^2 test at the 5% level of significance to test whether there is evidence of an association between the colour of a newt and its length.

	Red colour	Green colour	Brown colour	Total
Long	19	37	44	100
Short	22	30	33	85
Total	41	67	77	185

① Write down your hypotheses:

H_0: there is no association between colour and length.
H_1: there is some association between colour and length.

② Make a new table showing the expected frequencies (E), under H_0, where:

$$\text{Expected frequency} = \frac{\text{(Row total)} \times \text{(Column total)}}{\text{Overall total } (n)}$$

Expected frequencies	Red colour	Green colour	Brown colour	Total
Long	22.162	36.216	41.622	100
Short	18.838	30.784	35.378	85
Total	41	67	77	185

③ Make another table showing the contributions to the test statistic (X^2). Then sum them to find X^2 itself.

The individual contributions are $\dfrac{(O_i - E_i)^2}{E_i}$, so $X^2 = \sum \dfrac{(O_i - E_i)^2}{E_i}$.

Contribution	Red colour	Green colour	Brown colour
Long	0.451	0.017	0.136
Short	0.531	0.020	0.160

Adding up the individual contributions gives $\chi^2 = 1.315$.

④ Find the degrees of freedom: $\nu = [\text{(no. of rows)} - 1] \times [\text{(no. of columns)} - 1] = (2 - 1) \times (3 - 1) = 2$

⑤ Since $\nu = 2$, the test statistic's distribution is: $X^2 \sim \chi^2_{(2)}$ (approximately). ← Every value of E is greater than 5, so the approximation will be valid.

The significance level is 5%, so find the critical value in the χ^2 table by looking up $p = 5\%$ and $\nu = 2$.

The critical value is $x = 5.991$. Since $\chi^2 = 1.315 < 5.991$, the result is not significant at this level. So do not reject H_0 — there is no evidence at the 5% level of an association between the colour of a newt and its length.

EXAMPLE Use the data on the right to carry out a significance test at the 1% level to examine whether there is evidence of an association between level of revision and exam result.

	Pass	Fail	Total
Revised	56	8	64
Winged it	14	22	36
Total	70	30	100

H_0: there is no association between level of revision and exam result.
H_1: there is some association between level of revision and exam result.

The expected frequencies (E) under H_0 are:

Expected	Pass	Fail	Total
Revised	44.8	19.2	64
Winged it	25.2	10.8	36
Total	70	30	100

All are > 5.

And the contributions to the test statistic (X^2) are:

Contribution	Pass	Fail
Revised	2.800	6.533
Winged it	4.978	11.615

This gives $\chi^2 = 25.926$, where $X^2 \sim \chi^2_{(1)}$ (approximately).

$\nu = (2 - 1) \times (2 - 1) = 1 \times 1 = 1$

The significance level is 1%, so find the critical value in the χ^2 table by looking up $p = 1\%$ and $\nu = 1$. This gives a critical value of $x = 6.635$.

Since $\chi^2 = 25.926 > 6.635$, the result is significant at this level, and so you can reject H_0. There is evidence at the 1% level of an association between level of revision and exam result.

Now you can prove that 'reading this book' and 'exam grade' are linked...

These contingency-table tests are really just another hypothesis test with all the usual gubbins, plus a nice table.
Right... onwards and upwards... once you're happy you know all the stuff, give the practice questions a go.

S2 Section 3 — Practice Questions

That section was like a delicious main course of hypothesis-testing treats.
Finish off the meal with this dessert of lightly baked practice questions.

Warm-up Questions

1) The contingency table below shows data collected during a traffic survey.

   a) How many cars:

      (i)   were saloons with 2 occupants?

      (ii) were estates with 1 occupant?

      (iii) were neither saloons nor estates?

      (iv) contained 3 or more occupants?

      (v) were counted altogether?

		Type of car			
		Saloon	Estate	Other	**Total**
Number of occupants	1 person	42	21	17	**80**
	2 people	18	15	8	**41**
	3 or more people	8	5	2	**15**
	Total	**68**	**41**	**27**	**136**

   b) Draw a table showing the expected frequencies for the different cells in the table, assuming that the variables 'number of occupants' and 'type of car' are not associated.

   c) Comment on how the observed frequencies compare with your answers for b).

2) A χ^2 contingency-table test produces the test statistic $\chi^2 = 8.3$. By comparing this statistic to the $\chi^2_{(4)}$ distribution, test at the 1% level whether there is evidence of an association between the variables.

3) This contingency table shows survey data for the variables 'Age' and 'Marital status'.

   a) Write down null and alternative hypotheses for a test to examine whether there is any association between the variables.

		Marital status				
		Single	Married	Divorced	Other	**Total**
Age (years)	Less than 30	27	16	5	7	**55**
	30 or over	14	47	8	9	**78**
	Total	**41**	**63**	**13**	**16**	**133**

   b) Calculate the expected frequencies for each combination of categories, assuming that the two variables are not associated.

   c) Draw a new table showing the contributions to the test statistic for each combination of categories.

   d) Find the value of X^2 for this data, and state its degrees of freedom.

   e) Carry out the test at the 5% level of significance. State your conclusion clearly.

4) Test at the 5% level of significance whether there is an association between the variables in this table:

	Likes olives	Doesn't like olives	Total
Male	22	18	40
Female	30	30	60
Total	52	48	100

S2 Section 3 — Practice Questions

Aha, some exam-style practice questions to test whether you've got this section sussed. Wasn't expecting that.

Exam Questions

1   Each cell in the contingency table below shows how many people in a particular age group suffer from different severities of back pain.

		Severity of back pain			
		No pain	Mild	Severe	**Total**
Age (years)	30 and under	42	21	17	**80**
	31-50	18	15	8	**41**
	51 and over	8	9	14	**31**
	Total	**68**	**45**	**39**	**152**

a)   Write down null and alternative hypotheses for a test to examine whether the variables 'age' and 'severity of back pain' are associated.

(2 marks)

b)   Calculate the expected frequencies for each cell under your null hypothesis.

(3 marks)

c)   For each age group, comment briefly on how the observed pattern of back pain compares with what would be expected if the two variables were not associated.

(3 marks)

d)   (i)   Draw a table showing the contribution of each cell to your test statistic.

(3 marks)

(ii)   Calculate the overall value of your test statistic.

(1 mark)

e)   Carry out the test at the 5% level of significance, stating your conclusion clearly.

(5 marks)

2   A random sample of 100 shoppers is surveyed to determine whether age is associated with favourite flavour of ice cream. The results are shown in the table.

		Age in full years		
		0 – 40	41 +	Total
Flavour of ice cream	Vanilla	10	14	24
	Chocolate	24	26	50
	Strawberry	7	4	11
	Mint choc chip	7	8	15
	Total	48	52	100

a)   Use a χ^2 test at the 5% level of significance to examine whether there is any association between age and favourite flavour of ice cream.

(9 marks)

b)   If two of these shoppers are selected at random, one from each of the two age groups, find the probability that they both said that strawberry is their favourite flavour of ice cream.

(3 marks)

Normal Distributions

The normal distribution is everywhere in statistics. Everywhere, I tell you. So learn this well...

The Normal Distribution is 'Bell-Shaped'

1) Loads of things in real life are most likely to fall 'somewhere in the middle', and are much less likely to take extremely high or extremely low values. In this kind of situation, you often get a normal distribution.

2) If you were to draw a graph showing how likely different values are, you'd end up with a graph that looks a bit like a bell. There's a peak in the middle at the mean (or expected value). And the graph is symmetrical — so values the same distance above and below the mean are equally likely.

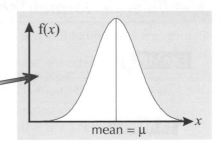

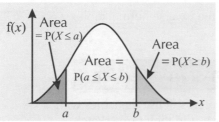

3) A normal distribution is continuous — there are no 'gaps' between possible values. To find the probability of a continuous random variable taking a value between two limits, you need to find the area under the graph between those limits.

And since the total probability is 1, the total area under the graph must be 1.

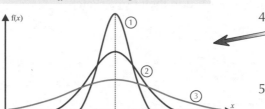

4) These three graphs all show normal distributions with the same mean (μ), but different variances (σ^2). Graph 1 has a small variance, and graph 3 has a larger variance — but the total area under all three curves is the same (= 1).

5) The most important normal distribution is the standard normal distribution, or Z — this has a mean of zero and a variance of 1.

Normal Distribution N(μ, σ^2)

- If X is normally distributed with **mean** μ and **variance** σ^2, it's written $X \sim N(\mu, \sigma^2)$.
- The standard normal distribution Z has **mean** 0 and **variance** 1, i.e. $Z \sim N(0, 1)$.

Use Tables to Work Out Probabilities of Z

Working out the area under a normal distribution curve is usually hard. But for Z, there are tables you can use (see p139). You look up a value of z and these tables (labelled $\Phi(z)$) tell you the probability that $Z \leq z$.

Area is
$\Phi(z) = P(Z \leq z)$

Or the probability that Z < z — it's the same thing for continuous distributions.

EXAMPLE Find the probability that:

a) $Z \leq 0.1$,   b) $Z < 0.64$,   c) $Z > 0.23$,   d) $Z \geq -0.42$,   e) $Z \leq -1.942$,   f) $0.123 < Z \leq 0.824$,   g) $Z = 1$

Tables only tell you the probability of Z being less than a particular value — use a sketch to work out anything else.

a) $P(Z \leq 0.1) = 0.5398$ ← Just look up z = 0.1 in the tables.

b) $P(Z < 0.64) = 0.7389$ ← For continuous distributions like Z: $P(Z < 0.64) = P(Z \leq 0.64)$.

c) $P(Z > 0.23) = 1 - P(Z \leq 0.23) = 1 - 0.5910 = 0.4090$

d) $P(Z \geq -0.42) = P(Z \leq 0.42) = 0.6628$ ← Use the symmetry of the graph:

e) $P(Z \leq -1.942) = P(Z \geq 1.942) = 1 - P(Z < 1.942) = 1 - 0.9739 = 0.0261$

f) $P(0.123 < Z \leq 0.824) = P(Z \leq 0.824) - P(Z \leq 0.123)$
   $= 0.7950 - 0.5490 = 0.2460$

Again, draw a graph and use the symmetry:

g) $P(Z = 1) = 0$ ← For a continuous distribution, $P(Z = k) = 0$ for any k (since the area under f(z) at a single point is zero).

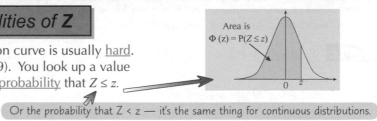

The Standard Normal Distribution, Z

You'll also be given a table showing the <u>inverse normal function</u> (labelled $\Phi^{-1}(p)$).
Use this if you're given a <u>probability</u> (value for p) and you need to <u>find z</u> for which $P(Z \le z) = p$.

The **Inverse Normal** Table Tells You z if You're Given a **Probability**

Remember... the probability you use in the inverse normal table is the probability that Z is <u>less</u> than a certain number.

EXAMPLE What is the value of z if: a) $P(Z \le z) = 0.9$?   b) $P(Z < z) = 0.758$?

Using the inverse normal table: a) $z = 1.282$,   b) $z = 0.6999$.

Get plenty of practice using the normal tables — they're not the easiest things in the world to understand.

EXAMPLE If $P(Z > z) = 0.355$, then what is the value of z?

If $P(Z > z) = 0.355$, then $P(Z \le z) = 1 - 0.355 = 0.645$. Again, using the inverse normal table, $z = 0.3719$.

A **Sketch** and some **Cunning** will help you get the most from tables

All the probabilities in the inverse normal table are <u>greater than 0.5</u>, but you can still use the tables with values <u>less</u> than this. You'll most likely need to <u>subtract the probability from 1</u>, and then <u>use a sketch</u>.

EXAMPLE If $P(Z < z) = 0.261$, then what is the value of z?

(1) Subtract from 1 to get a probability greater than 0.5: $1 - 0.261 = 0.739$

(2) If $P(Z < z) = 0.739$, then from the table, $z = 0.6403$.

(3) So if $P(Z < z) = 0.261$, then, $z = -0.6403$.

If $P(Z < z) = 0.261$, then z must be negative.

Area $= 1 - 0.261$
$= 0.739$

Area $= 0.261$

You need to **Practise** until you can **Use Tables** with your **Eyes Shut**

Not literally.

Here are a few more examples to get you started. There are loads more to have a go at yourself on p125.

EXAMPLE Find z if: a) $P(Z < z) = 0.999$,   b) $P(Z < z) = 0.05$,   c) $P(Z > z) = 0.444$,   d) $P(Z \ge z) = 0.618$

a) If $P(Z < z) = 0.999$, then $z = 3.090$.

b) $p = 0.05$ isn't in the inverse normal table, so look up $p = 1 - 0.05 = 0.95$.
   If $P(Z \le z) = 0.95$, then $z = 1.645$, which means $P(Z > 1.645) = 0.05$.
   This tells you $P(Z < -1.645) = 0.05$, so z must equal -1.645 .

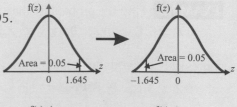

Area $= 0.05$

Area $= 0.05$

c) If $P(Z > z) = 0.444$, then $P(Z \le z) = 0.556$.
   Using the inverse normal table, $z = 0.1408$.

d) $P(Z \ge z) = 0.618$ — start by looking up $p = 0.618$ in the inverse normal table. This tells you that if $P(Z \le z) = 0.618$, then $z = 0.3002$. So if $P(Z \ge z) = 0.618$, then $z = -0.3002$.

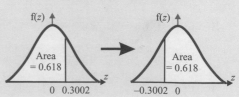

Area $= 0.618$

Area $= 0.618$

You should get used to drawing bell-shaped graphs...

It's definitely worth sketching the graph when you're using a normal distribution — you're much less likely to make a daft mistake. So even if the question looks a simple one, draw a quick sketch. And be warned... both normal tables in the formula booklet (i.e. the tables for <u>both</u> $\Phi(z)$ <u>and</u> $\Phi^{-1}(p)$) look pretty similar — so double-check you're using the right one before looking anything up. It all comes down to whether you're given a value of z or a probability, p.

Normal Distributions and Z-Tables

<u>All</u> normally-distributed variables can be transformed to Z — which is a marvellous thing.

$Z \sim N(0, 1)$
— see p115.

Transform to Z by **Subtracting** μ, then **dividing by** σ

1) You can convert <u>any</u> normally-distributed variable to Z by:

   i) <u>subtracting the mean</u>, and then

   ii) <u>dividing by the standard deviation</u>.

   This means that if you subtract μ from any numbers in the question and then divide by σ — you can use your tables for Z.

$$\text{If } X \sim N(\mu, \sigma^2), \text{ then } \frac{X - \mu}{\sigma} = Z, \text{ where } Z \sim N(0, 1)$$

2) Once you've transformed a variable like this, you can use the <u>Z-tables</u>.

EXAMPLE If $X \sim N(5, 16)$ find: a) $P(X < 7)$, b) $P(X > 9)$, c) $P(5 < X < 11)$

Subtract μ (= 5) from any numbers and divide by σ (= $\sqrt{16}$ = 4) — then you'll have a value for $Z \sim N(0, 1)$.

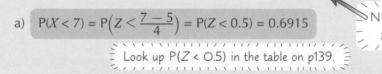

a) $P(X < 7) = P\left(Z < \frac{7-5}{4}\right) = P(Z < 0.5) = 0.6915$

N(5, 16) means the <u>variance</u> is 16 — take the <u>square root</u> to find the <u>standard deviation</u>.

Look up $P(Z < 0.5)$ in the table on p139.

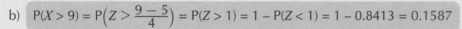

b) $P(X > 9) = P\left(Z > \frac{9-5}{4}\right) = P(Z > 1) = 1 - P(Z < 1) = 1 - 0.8413 = 0.1587$

c) $P(5 < X < 11) = P\left(\frac{5-5}{4} < Z < \frac{11-5}{4}\right) = P(0 < Z < 1.5)$

$= P(Z < 1.5) - P(Z < 0) = 0.9332 - 0.5 = 0.4332$

Find the area to the left of 1.5 and subtract the area to the left of 0.

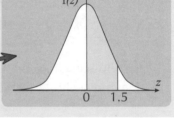

f(z)

0   1.5   z

The **Z-Distribution** Can be Used in **Real-Life** Situations

EXAMPLE The times taken by a group of people to complete an assault course are normally distributed with a mean of 600 seconds and a variance of 105 seconds. Find the probability that a randomly selected person took:
a) less than 575 seconds,   b) more than 620 seconds.

If X represents the time taken in seconds, then $X \sim N(600, 105)$.
It's a normal distribution — so your first thought should be to try and '<u>standardise</u>' it by converting it to Z.

a) <u>Subtract the mean</u> and <u>divide by the standard deviation</u>: $P(X < 575) = P\left(\frac{X - 600}{\sqrt{105}} < \frac{575 - 600}{\sqrt{105}}\right)$

$= P(Z < -2.440)$

Then $P(Z < -2.440) = 1 - P(Z \le 2.440) = 1 - 0.9927 = 0.0073$.

b) Again, <u>subtract the mean</u> and <u>divide by the standard deviation</u>: $P(X > 620) = P\left(\frac{X - 600}{\sqrt{105}} > \frac{620 - 600}{\sqrt{105}}\right)$

$= P(Z > 1.952)$

$= 1 - P(Z \le 1.952)$

$= 1 - 0.9745 = 0.0255$

Transform to Z and use Z-tables — I repeat: transform to Z and use Z-tables...

The basic idea is always the same — transform your normally-distributed variable to Z, and then use the Z-tables. Statisticians call this the "normal two-step". Well... some of them probably do, anyway. I admit, this stuff is all a bit weird and confusing at first. But as always, work through a few examples and it'll start to click. So get some practice.

Normal Distributions and Z-Tables

You might be given some <u>probabilities</u> and asked to find μ and σ. Just use the same old ideas...

Find μ and σ by First Transforming to Z

EXAMPLE $X \sim N(\mu, 2^2)$ and $P(X < 23) = 0.902$. Find μ.

This is a normal distribution — so your first thought should be to convert it to Z.

(1) $P(X < 23) = P\left(\dfrac{X - \mu}{2} < \dfrac{23 - \mu}{2}\right) = P\left(Z < \dfrac{23 - \mu}{2}\right) = 0.902$ Substitute Z for $\dfrac{X - \mu}{\sigma}$.

Now look up $p = 0.902$ in the inverse normal table.

(2) If $P(Z < z) = 0.902$, then $z = 1.293$.

(3) So $\dfrac{23 - \mu}{2} = 1.293$ — now solve this to find $\mu = 23 - (2 \times 1.293) = 20.41$ (to 2 d.p.).

EXAMPLE $X \sim N(53, \sigma^2)$ and $P(X < 50) = 0.1$. Find σ.

Again, this is a normal distribution — so you need to use that lovely <u>standardising equation</u> again.

(1) $P(X < 50) = P\left(Z < \dfrac{50 - 53}{\sigma}\right) = P\left(Z < -\dfrac{3}{\sigma}\right) = 0.1$.

Ideally, you'd look up 0.1 in the inverse normal table to find $-\dfrac{3}{\sigma}$.
Unfortunately, it isn't there, so you have to think a bit...

(2) $P\left(Z < -\dfrac{3}{\sigma}\right)$ is 0.1, so from the symmetry of the graph, $P\left(Z < \dfrac{3}{\sigma}\right)$ must be 0.9.

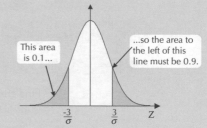

This area is 0.1... ...so the area to the left of this line must be 0.9.

So look up 0.9 in the inverse normal table to find that:

$$\frac{3}{\sigma} = 1.282, \text{ or } \sigma = 2.34 \text{ (to 3 sig. fig.)}$$

If You Have to Find μ and σ, You'll Need to Solve Simultaneous Equations

EXAMPLE The random variable $X \sim N(\mu, \sigma^2)$. If $P(X < 9) = 0.560$ and $P(X > 14) = 0.032$, then find μ and σ.

(1) $P(X < 9) = P\left(Z < \dfrac{9 - \mu}{\sigma}\right) = 0.560$.

Using the inverse normal table, this tells you that $\dfrac{9 - \mu}{\sigma} = 0.1510$, or $9 - \mu = 0.1510\sigma$.

(2) $P(X > 14) = P\left(Z > \dfrac{14 - \mu}{\sigma}\right) = 0.032$, which means that $P\left(Z < \dfrac{14 - \mu}{\sigma}\right) = 1 - 0.032 = 0.968$.

Using the inverse normal table, this tells you that $\dfrac{14 - \mu}{\sigma} = 1.852$, or $14 - \mu = 1.852\sigma$.

(3) Subtract the equations: $(14 - \mu) - (9 - \mu) = 1.852\sigma - 0.1510\sigma$, or $5 = 1.701\sigma$. This gives $\sigma = 5 \div 1.701 = 2.94$.
Now use one of the other equations to find μ: $\mu = 9 - (0.1510 \times 2.94) = 8.56$ (to 3 sig. fig.).   (to 3 sig. fig.)

The Norman distribution — came to England in 1066...

It's always the same — you always need to do the <u>normal two-step</u> of subtracting the mean and dividing by the standard deviation, and then using tables. Just make sure you don't use the <u>variance</u> by mistake — remember, in $N(\mu, \sigma^2)$, the second number always shows the variance. I'm sure you wouldn't make a mistake... it's just that I'm such a worrier.

Normal Approximation to B(n, p)

The binomial distribution (B(n, p)) is back. Again. Now then... if n is <u>big</u>, a <u>binomial</u> distribution can be <u>tricky</u> to use. You saw the Poisson approximation on p106, but sometimes a <u>normal</u> approximation is <u>better</u>. But there's a <u>snag</u>.

Use a **Continuity Correction** to Approximate a Binomial with a Normal

The binomial distribution is <u>discrete</u> (i.e. there are 'gaps' between the possible values), but the normal distribution is <u>continuous</u> (i.e. there are no 'gaps'). To allow for this you need to use a <u>continuity correction</u>.

- A <u>binomially-distributed</u> variable X is <u>discrete</u>, so you can work out P(X = 0), P(X = 1), etc.
- A <u>normally-distributed</u> variable is <u>continuous</u>, and so P(X = 0) = P(X = 1) = 0, etc.

So what you do is assume that the 'binomial 1' is <u>spread out</u> over the interval 0.5 - 1.5.

Then to approximate the <u>binomial P(X = 1)</u>, you find the <u>normal P(0.5 < X < 1.5)</u>.

Similarly, the 'binomial 2' is spread out over the interval 1.5 - 2.5, and so on.

Learn these **Continuity Corrections**

The interval you need to use with your normal distribution depends on the binomial probability you're trying to find out.

The general principle is the same, though — each <u>binomial value b</u> covers the <u>interval</u> from $b - \frac{1}{2}$ up to $b + \frac{1}{2}$.

Binomial	Normal	
P($X = b$)	P($b - \frac{1}{2} < X < b + \frac{1}{2}$)	
P($X \leq b$)	P($X < b + \frac{1}{2}$)	...to include b
P($X < b$)	P($X < b - \frac{1}{2}$)	...to exclude b
P($X \geq b$)	P($X > b - \frac{1}{2}$)	...to include b
P($X > b$)	P($X > b + \frac{1}{2}$)	...to exclude b

The **Normal Approximation** Only Works Well under **Certain Conditions**

Normal Approximation to the Binomial

Suppose the random variable X follows a binomial distribution, i.e. $X \sim$ **B(n, p)**.

If   (i) $p \approx \frac{1}{2}$,

and   (ii) n is large,

then $X \sim$ **N(np, npq)** (approximately), where $q = 1 - p$.

Since for a binomial distribution, $\mu = np$ and $\sigma^2 = npq$.

Even if p isn't all that close to 0.5, this approximation usually works fine as long as np and nq are both bigger than about 5.

EXAMPLE   If $X \sim$ B(80, 0.4), use a suitable approximation to find: (i) P(X < 35)   and   (ii) P($X \geq$ 40).

You need to make sure first that the normal approximation is <u>suitable</u>...

Also, np = 80 × 0.4 = 32 > 5, and nq = 80 × (1 − 0.4) = 48 > 5.

n is <u>fairly large</u>, and p is <u>not far</u> from $\frac{1}{2}$, so the normal approximation is valid.

Next, work out np and npq: $np = 80 \times 0.4 = 32$ and $npq = 80 \times 0.4 \times (1 - 0.4) = 19.2$ *$q = 1 - p$*

So the approximation you need is: $X \sim$ N(32, 19.2) *So the standard deviation is $\sqrt{19.2}$.*

Now apply a <u>continuity correction</u>, <u>transform</u> the variable to the standard normal distribution (Z), and use <u>tables</u>.

(i)   You need P(X < 35) — so with the <u>continuity correction</u> this is P(X < 34.5).

See page 139 for the normal distribution tables.

$$P(X < 34.5) = P\left(\frac{X - 32}{\sqrt{19.2}} < \frac{34.5 - 32}{\sqrt{19.2}}\right) = P(Z < 0.571) = 0.7160$$

(ii)   Now you need P($X \geq$ 40) — with the <u>continuity correction</u> this is P(X > 39.5).

$$P(X > 39.5) = P\left(\frac{X - 32}{\sqrt{19.2}} > \frac{39.5 - 32}{\sqrt{19.2}}\right) = P(Z > 1.712) = 1 - P(Z \leq 1.712) = 1 - 0.9566 = 0.0434$$

Normal Approximation to B(n, p)

I know what you're thinking — you want to know just how good a normal approximation actually is. Well, let's see...

EXAMPLE: Newborn babies

The average number of births per year in a hospital is 228. If each baby is equally likely to be a boy or a girl, then use a suitable approximation to find the probability that next year:
(i) there will be more boys born than girls,
(ii) exactly 100 boys will be born.

Mean = np = 228 × 0.5 = 114
Variance = npq = 228 × 0.5 × 0.5 = 57

If X represents the number of boys born next year, then you can assume that $X \sim B(228, 0.5)$. Since n is large, and p is 0.5, then you can use a normal approximation: $X \sim N(114, 57)$.

(i) You need to find P($X > 114$). With a continuity correction, this is P($X > 114.5$). It's a normal distribution, so transform this to Z, the standard normal distribution.

$$P(X > 114.5) = P\left(\frac{X - 114}{\sqrt{57}} > \frac{114.5 - 114}{\sqrt{57}}\right) = P(Z > 0.066)$$
$$= 1 - P(Z \leq 0.066) = 1 - 0.5263 = 0.4737$$

Using B(228, 0.5) instead of the normal approximation, you get 0.4736 — so this is a really good approximation.

(ii) With a continuity correction, you need to find P(99.5 < X < 100.5).

$$P(99.5 < X < 100.5) = P(X < 100.5) - P(X < 99.5)$$
$$= P\left(\frac{X - 114}{\sqrt{57}} < \frac{100.5 - 114}{\sqrt{57}}\right) - P\left(\frac{X - 114}{\sqrt{57}} < \frac{99.5 - 114}{\sqrt{57}}\right)$$
$$= P(Z < -1.788) - P(Z < -1.921)$$
$$= (1 - P(Z < 1.788)) - (1 - P(Z < 1.921))$$
$$= 1 - 0.9632 - 1 + 0.9727 = 0.0095$$

Using B(228, 0.5) instead of the normal approximation, you also get 0.0095.

EXAMPLE: Survival rates

a) On average, only 23% of the young of a particular species of bird survive to adulthood. If 80 chicks of this species are randomly selected, use a suitable approximation to find the probability that at least 30% of them survive.

b) If the survival rate were instead 18%, find the probability that more than three-quarters of the 80 chicks would die.

If X represents the number of survivors, then $X \sim B(80, 0.23)$.
Here, p isn't particularly close to 0.5, but n is quite large, so calculate np and nq:
$np = 80 \times 0.23 = 18.4$ and $nq = 80 \times (1 - 0.23) = 61.6$.

Both np and nq are much greater than 5, so a normal approximation should be okay to use — N(18.4, 14.168).
30% of 80 = 24, so with a continuity correction, you need to find P($X > 23.5$).

Mean = np = 80 × 0.23 = 18.4
Variance = npq = 80 × 0.23 × 0.77 = 14.168

$$P(X > 23.5) = P\left(Z > \frac{23.5 - 18.4}{\sqrt{14.168}}\right) = P(Z > 1.355) = 1 - P(Z \leq 1.355)$$
$$= 1 - 0.9123 = 0.0877$$

Using the original binomial distribution gives an answer of 0.0904, so this is a fairly good approximation.

b) This time, $X \sim B(80, 0.18)$, which means $np = 80 \times 0.18 = 14.4$ and $nq = 80 \times (1 - 0.18) = 65.6$.
So even though p is now quite far from 0.5, try the normal approximation — N(14.4, 11.808).
If more than three-quarters do not survive, that means $X < 20$, so you need to find P($X < 19.5$).

$$P(X < 19.5) = P\left(Z < \frac{19.5 - 14.4}{\sqrt{11.808}}\right) = P(Z < 1.484) = 0.9312$$

Using the original binomial distribution gives an answer of 0.9270, so this is another pretty good approximation.

Admit it — the normal distribution is the most amazing thing ever...

So the normal approximation works pretty well, even when p isn't really all that close to 0.5. But even so, you should always show that your approximation is 'suitable'. In fact, the question will usually tell you to use a 'suitable approximation', so part of your answer should be to show that you've made sure that it is actually okay. Remember that.

Normal Approximation to Poisson(λ)

More approximations, I'm afraid. But on the bright side, Mr Poisson is back. Good old Mr Poisson.

The Normal Approximation to **Poisson(λ)** Works Best if λ is **Big**

Normal Approximation to the Poisson Distribution

Suppose the random variable X follows a Poisson distribution, i.e. $X \sim$ **Poisson(λ)**.

If λ is large, then (approximately) $X \sim$ **N(λ, λ)**. ◄——

> Since for a Poisson distribution, mean = variance = λ (see page 103).

Ideally, you want λ 'as large as possible' — but in practice as long as $\underline{\lambda > 10}$, then you're fine.

Use a **Continuity Correction** to Approximate a Poisson with a Normal

Since a Poisson distribution is <u>discrete</u> (it can only take values 0, 1, 2...) but a normal distribution is <u>continuous</u>, you need to use a <u>continuity correction</u>. (See p119 for more about continuity corrections.)

EXAMPLE If $X \sim$ Poisson(49), find: a) P($X < 50$), b) P($X \geq 45$), c) P($X = 60$).

Since λ is <u>large</u> (it's greater than 10), you can use a <u>normal approximation</u> — $X \sim$ N(49, 49).

a) The <u>continuity correction</u> means you need to find P($X < 49.5$).

Transform to Z and use tables: $P(X < 49.5) = P\left(\frac{X - 49}{7} < \frac{49.5 - 49}{7}\right) = P(Z < 0.071) = 0.5283$

b) This time you need to find P($X > 44.5$): $P(X > 44.5) = P\left(Z > \frac{44.5 - 49}{7}\right) = P(Z > -0.643)$

$$= 1 - P(Z \leq -0.643) = P(Z \leq 0.643) = 0.7399$$

c) $P(X = 60) = P(59.5 < X < 60.5) = P(X < 60.5) - P(X < 59.5)$

$$= P\left(Z < \frac{60.5 - 49}{7}\right) - P\left(Z < \frac{59.5 - 49}{7}\right) = P(Z < 1.643) - P(Z < 1.5)$$

$$= 0.9498 - 0.9332 = 0.0166$$

EXAMPLE A sloppy publishing company produces books containing an average of 25 random errors per page.

Use a suitable approximation to find the probability of: a) fewer than 20 errors on a particular page,
b) exactly 25 errors on a particular page.

The errors happen <u>randomly</u>, <u>singly</u> and (on average) at a <u>constant rate</u>, and so the number of errors that occur on a <u>single page</u> (X) will follow a <u>Poisson</u> distribution. Since there's an average of 25 errors per page, $\underline{X \sim \text{Poisson(25)}}$.

a) Since λ is large (greater than 10), you can use a normal approximation — i.e. $X \sim$ N(25, 25).

You need to use a <u>continuity correction</u> here, so P(fewer than 20 errors) $\approx$ P($X < 19.5$).

Transform to Z and use tables: $P(X < 19.5) = P\left(\frac{X - 25}{5} < \frac{19.5 - 25}{5}\right) = P(Z < -1.1)$

$$= 1 - P(Z < 1.1)$$

$$= 1 - 0.8643 = 0.1357$$

b) P(exactly 25 errors on a page) $\approx$ P($24.5 < X < 25.5$) = P($X < 25.5$) − P($X < 24.5$).

Transform to Z and use tables: $P(X < 25.5) - P(X < 24.5) = P\left(Z < \frac{25.5 - 25}{5}\right) - P\left(Z < \frac{24.5 - 25}{5}\right)$

$$= P(Z < 0.1) - P(Z < -0.1)$$

$$= P(Z < 0.1) - (1 - P(Z < 0.1)) = 0.5398 - (1 - 0.5398) = 0.0796$$

The abnormal approximation — guess wildly then say 'Close enough'...

Lordy, lordy... the number of times you've had to read 'transform something to Z and use tables'. But that's the thing... if you can find probabilities from a normal distribution, then it's <u>bound</u> to be worth marks in the exam. On a different note, continuity corrections are fairly easy to use — it's remembering to use one in the first place that can be a bit tricky.

More About Approximations

You need to know a few different approximations for S2 — and to be honest, it can all get a bit <u>confusing</u>. But although the picture below looks like a complex wiring diagram, it's actually an easy-to-use flowchart to sum up your options.

Approximate if You're **Told to**, or if Your **Tables** 'Don't Go High Enough'

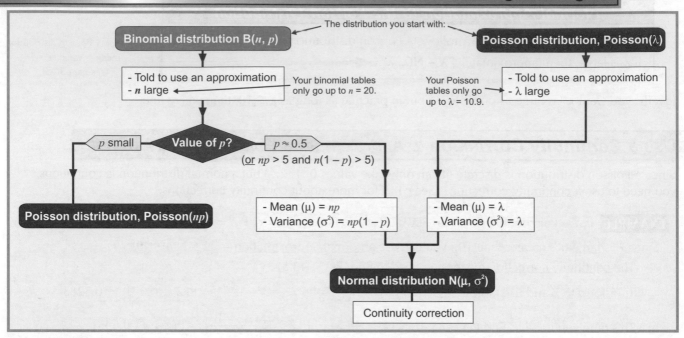

EXAMPLE:

A supermarket gives a customer a free bag when that customer can fit no more items into their existing bags. The number of bags given away was counted. It was found that 62% of customers needed at least one free bag, 2% of customers needed more than 5 free bags, and an average of 8 bags were given away each minute.

If the supermarket has 400 customers one particular morning, use suitable approximations to find:

a) the probability that more than 250 customers take at least one bag,
b) the probability that fewer than 10 customers take more than 5 bags,
c) the probability that more than 500 bags are given away in the first hour after the store opens.

a) Let X represent <u>how many</u> of the 400 customers take at least one bag.
Then $X \sim B(400, 0.62)$, and you need to find $P(X > 250)$.
Here, <u>n is large</u> and <u>p is not too far from 0.5</u> — so approximate X with $N(248, 94.24)$.

$$P(X > 250) \approx P(X > 250.5) = P\left(\frac{X - 248}{\sqrt{94.24}} > \frac{250.5 - 248}{\sqrt{94.24}}\right) = P(Z > 0.258) = 1 - P(Z \le 0.258) = 0.3982$$

b) Let M represent the <u>total number</u> of customers taking more than 5 bags.
Then $M \sim B(400, 0.02)$, and you need to find $P(M < 10)$.
Here, <u>n is large</u> and <u>p is very small</u> — use a <u>Poisson</u> approximation: Poisson(8)

$$P(M < 10) = P(M \le 9) = 0.7166$$

> Bags per minute ~ Poisson(8).
> So bags per hour ~ Poisson(8×60).

c) Let R represent the number of bags given away <u>in the first hour</u>. This is <u>not</u> a fixed number of <u>trials</u>, so it's <u>not</u> a binomial distribution. But the <u>period is fixed</u> (1 hour), so it's <u>Poisson</u> — in fact, $R \sim Poisson(480)$. You need to find $P(R > 500)$. Approximate R with $N(480, 480)$.

$$P(R > 500) \approx P(R > 500.5) = P\left(\frac{R - 480}{\sqrt{480}} > \frac{500.5 - 480}{\sqrt{480}}\right) = P(Z > 0.936) = 1 - 0.8253 = 0.1747$$

Check your p — then decide what to do...

The trickiest decision you face when approximating is whether to approximate $B(n, p)$ with a Poisson or a normal distribution — and it all depends on p really. So once you've made that decision, you should be off and running. But don't forget that continuity correction if you're using the normal approximation. You have been warned.

Hypothesis Tests and Normal Distributions

I tell you what would be a nice way to finish the section... more <u>hypothesis tests</u>. These next two pages describe how to use a <u>sample mean</u> ($\overline{X}$) to test a claim about the <u>population mean</u> (μ) of a normally distributed quantity.

You need a **Null Hypothesis** and an **Alternative Hypothesis**

1) Your <u>null hypothesis</u> will always be of the form: $H_0: \mu = k$ (for some number k)

2) You could be asked to use either a <u>one-tailed</u> or a <u>two-tailed</u> test.
   So your <u>alternative hypothesis</u> will look like one of these: ⟵
   one-tailed test: $H_1: \mu > k$ (or $H_1: \mu < k$)
   two-tailed test: $H_1: \mu \neq k$

Your **Test Statistic** is Z — where Z ~ N(0, 1)

The key to carrying out the hypothesis test is to know how the <u>sample mean</u> $\overline{X}$ is distributed.
Happily, if X is <u>normally</u> distributed, then $\overline{X}$ will be <u>normally</u> distributed too — so you can easily <u>transform</u> it to Z.

Distribution of the Sample Mean

Suppose X is a normally distributed random variable with <u>mean</u> μ and <u>variance</u> σ^2 — i.e. $X \sim N(\mu, \sigma^2)$.

If $\overline{X}$ is the sample mean of a <u>random sample</u> of size n taken from the distribution of X, then: $\overline{X} \sim N\left(\mu, \dfrac{\sigma^2}{n}\right)$ ⟵

Notice how this says:
(i) the <u>expected value</u> of $\overline{X}$ is: $E(\overline{X}) = \mu$,
(ii) the <u>variance</u> of $\overline{X}$ is: $Var(\overline{X}) = \dfrac{\sigma^2}{n}$.

In other words: $Z = \dfrac{\overline{X} - \mu}{\sigma / \sqrt{n}} \sim N(0, 1)$

You're going to use Z as your <u>test statistic</u>. That's why this is often called a <u>z-test</u>.

The test is **Easiest** when you **Know** the **Population Variance**

When you <u>know</u> the <u>population variance</u> σ^2, you can easily work out a value for Z using your sample mean $\overline{X}$.

EXAMPLE The times, in minutes, taken by the athletes in a running club to complete a certain run have been found to follow an N(12, 4) distribution. The coach increases the number of training sessions per week, and a random sample of 20 times run since the increase gives a mean time of 11.2 minutes.

Assuming that the variance has remained unchanged, test at the 5% significance level whether there is evidence that the average time has decreased.

① State your <u>hypotheses</u> and the <u>significance level</u>:
   Let μ = mean time since increase in training sessions.

   Then $H_0: \mu = 12$, and $H_1: \mu < 12$, and the significance level (α) is $\alpha = 0.05$.

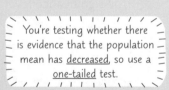
You're testing whether there is evidence that the population mean has <u>decreased</u>, so use a <u>one-tailed</u> test.

② State your <u>test statistic</u> and its <u>distribution under H_0</u> (i.e. assuming that H_0 is true):

   Under H_0, $\overline{X} \sim N(12, \frac{4}{20}) = N(12, 0.2)$, which means that $Z = \dfrac{\overline{X} - 12}{\sqrt{0.2}} \sim N(0, 1)$.

③ Calculate the value of the <u>test statistic</u> z: Since $\overline{x} = 11.2$, $z = \dfrac{11.2 - 12}{\sqrt{0.2}} = -1.789$

④ Find the <u>critical value</u>:
   This is a <u>one-tailed test</u>, and the <u>critical value</u> is z such that $P(Z < z) = 0.05$.
   Using the <u>inverse normal table</u>, $P(Z < 1.645) = 0.95$, and so by symmetry, $P(Z < -1.645) = 0.05$.
   This means the critical value is $z = -1.645$, and so the critical region is $Z < -1.645$.

⑤ Compare the value of your <u>test statistic</u> to the <u>critical value</u>, and decide whether to <u>reject</u> or <u>not reject</u> H_0:

   Since $z = -1.789 < -1.645$, the <u>result is significant</u> and there is <u>evidence</u> at the 5% level of significance to <u>reject</u> H_0 and to suggest that the <u>average time has decreased</u>.

Hypothesis Tests and Normal Distributions

On the previous page, you saw how to use a z-test if you already <u>know</u> the population variance σ^2.
Now you'll see that you can still use a z-test even if you <u>don't</u> know σ^2 — <u>as long as the sample size is large</u>.

If you **Don't Know** σ^2 but **n is large**, you can still use a **z-Test**

1) The <u>z-test</u> can also be used if the <u>population variance</u> σ^2 is <u>unknown</u>, but the <u>sample size is large</u> ($n > 30$).

2) You still use Z as the test statistic, but you need to replace σ^2 with the <u>sample variance s^2</u>.
   For large n, s^2 should be pretty close to σ^2.

Estimating σ^2 Using the Sample Variance s^2

If you have data from a sample of size n, then the formula for the sample variance (s^2) is:

$$s^2 = \frac{n}{n-1}\left[\frac{\sum x^2}{n} - \left(\frac{\sum x}{n}\right)^2\right] = \frac{\sum(x - \overline{x})^2}{n-1}$$

This is the formula for sample variance you met in S1.

where the x-values represent your sample data.

Apart from having to **Estimate** σ^2, the method is **Exactly the Same**

Don't be thrown off track by the extra step — the rest of the method is the same as before.

EXAMPLE The volumes of drinks dispensed by a drinks machine are normally distributed. The average volume is claimed to be 250 ml, but Greg thinks that the machine has developed a fault and wants to test whether the average volume has changed. He measures the volumes, x, of a random sample of 40 drinks from the machine and calculates the following:

$$\sum x = 9800 \quad \text{and} \quad \sum(x - \overline{x})^2 = 3900$$

Carry out Greg's test at the 5% level of significance.

Here, n is <u>fairly large</u>, so you can still use a z-test with σ^2 <u>estimated</u> by s^2.

$$\overline{x} = \frac{\sum x}{n} = \frac{9800}{40} = 245\,\text{ml} \quad \text{and} \quad s^2 = \frac{\sum(x - \overline{x})^2}{n-1} = \frac{3900}{39} = 100$$

Now you do exactly the same as before.

① The average volume is assumed to be 250 ml, so: $H_0: \mu = 250$, and $H_1: \mu \neq 250$.
   The significance level (α) is $\alpha = 0.05$.

You're testing whether the population mean has <u>changed</u> in either direction, so use a <u>two-tailed</u> test.

② Under H_0, $\overline{X} \sim N(250, {}^{100}\!/_{40}) = N(250, 2.5)$, which means that $Z = \frac{\overline{X} - 250}{\sqrt{2.5}} \sim N(0, 1)$.

③ Since $\overline{x} = 245$, $z = \frac{245 - 250}{\sqrt{2.5}} = -3.16$

i.e. $P(Z > z) = 0.025$.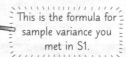

④ This is a <u>two-tailed test</u> at the 5% level.
   So to work out the <u>critical values</u>, use the 'normal' tables to find z such that $P(Z < z) = 0.975$.
   From <u>tables</u>, $P(Z < 1.960) = 0.975$, and this means the critical values are $z = \pm 1.960$.
   This gives a critical region of: $Z < -1.96$ or $Z > 1.96$.

⑤ Since $z = -3.16 < -1.96$, the <u>result is significant</u> and there is <u>evidence</u> at the 5% level of significance to <u>reject</u> H_0 and to suggest that the <u>average volume has changed</u>.

My hypothesis is — this is very likely to come up in the exam...

This really is the kind of stuff that examiners love. So if you learn the 5-step method above (with a possible extra step if you have to estimate σ^2 first), you should be in line for a fair few marks. But you need to get all the details right. For example, make sure your conclusion is either 'reject H_0' or 'not reject H_0' (and never 'accept H_1', for example). Best get plenty of practice.

S2 Section 4 — Practice Questions

You've come this far... don't give up now... only two more pages to go. And they're only questions — so it's not like there's loads more you're going to need to cram into your already crowded head. Loins girded? Good, here we go...

Warm-up Questions

1) Find the probability that:
   a) $Z < 0.84$,
   b) $Z < 2.95$,
   c) $Z > 0.68$,
   d) $Z \geq 1.55$,
   e) $Z < -2.10$,
   f) $Z \leq -0.01$,
   g) $Z > 0.10$,
   h) $Z \leq 0.64$,
   i) $Z > 0.23$,
   j) $0.10 < Z \leq 0.50$,
   k) $-0.62 \leq Z < 1.10$,
   l) $-0.99 < Z \leq -0.74$.

2) Find the value of z if:
   a) $P(Z < z) = 0.913$,
   b) $P(Z < z) = 0.587$,
   c) $P(Z > z) = 0.035$,
   d) $P(Z > z) = 0.01$,
   e) $P(Z \leq z) = 0.401$,
   f) $P(Z \geq z) = 0.995$.

3) If $X \sim N(50, 16)$ find: a) $P(X < 55)$, b) $P(X < 42)$, c) $P(X > 56)$, d) $P(47 < X < 57)$.

4) $X \sim N(\mu, 10)$ and $P(X < 8) = 0.892$. Find μ.

5) $X \sim N(11, \sigma^2)$ and $P(X < 13) = 0.6$. Find σ.

6) The random variable $X \sim N(\mu, \sigma^2)$. If $P(X < 15.2) = 0.978$ and $P(X > 14.8) = 0.106$, then find μ and σ.

7) The random variable X follows a binomial distribution: $X \sim B(100, 0.45)$.
   Using a normal approximation and continuity corrections, find:
   a) $P(X > 50)$,
   b) $P(X \leq 45)$,
   c) $P(40 < X \leq 47)$.

8) The random variable X follows a Poisson distribution: $X \sim Poisson(25)$.
   Using a normal approximation and continuity corrections, find:
   a) $P(X \leq 20)$,
   b) $P(X > 15)$,
   c) $P(20 \leq X < 30)$.

9) Seven people on average join the queue in the local post office every 15 minutes during the 7 hours it is open. The number of people working in the post office is constantly adjusted depending on how busy it is, with the result that there is a constant probability of 0.7 of any person being served within 1 minute.
   a) Find the probability of more than 200 people joining the queue in the post office on a particular day.
   b) If exactly 200 people come to the post office on a particular day, what is the probability that less than 70% of them are seen within a minute?

10) If $X \sim N(8, 2)$, find $P(\overline{X} < 7)$ where $\overline{X}$ is the mean of a random sample of 10 observations of X.

11) Carry out the following test of the mean, μ, of a normal distribution with variance $\sigma^2 = 9$.
   A random sample of 16 observations from the distribution was taken and the sample mean ($\overline{x}$) calculated.
   Test H_0: $\mu = 45$ against H_1: $\mu < 45$, at the 5% significance level, using $\overline{x} = 42$.

12) A random sample of 100 observations was taken from a normal distribution with unknown mean, μ.
   The following statistics were then calculated: $\sum x = 1360$ and $\sum x^2 = 19\,300$
   Test H_0: $\mu = 13.5$ against H_1: $\mu > 13.5$, at the 1% significance level.

S2 Section 4 — Practice Questions

One last hurdle before you can consider yourself fully up to speed with the normal distribution...

Exam Questions

1   The lifetimes of a particular type of battery are normally distributed with mean μ and standard deviation σ. A student using these batteries finds that 40% last less than 20 hours and 80% last less than 30 hours. Find μ and σ.

(7 marks)

2   The random variable X is binomially distributed with $X \sim B(100, 0.6)$.

a)   (i)   State the conditions needed for X to be well approximated by a normal distribution.

(2 marks)

   (ii)   Explain why a continuity correction is necessary in these circumstances.

(2 marks)

b)   Using a suitable approximation, find:

   (i) $P(X \geq 65)$

(4 marks)

   (ii) $P(50 < X < 62)$

(3 marks)

3   The heights of trees in an area of woodland are known to be normally distributed with a mean of 5.1 m. A random sample of 100 trees from a second area of woodland is selected and the heights, X, of the trees are measured giving the following results:

$$\sum x = 490 \text{ and } \sum x^2 = 2421$$

a)   Calculate unbiased estimates of the population mean, μ, and variance, σ^2, for this area.

(3 marks)

b)   Test at the 1% level of significance whether the trees in the second area of woodland have a different mean height from the trees in the first area.
You may assume the heights of trees in this area are normally distributed.

(6 marks)

4   The random variable X follows a binomial distribution: $X \sim B(n, p)$.
X is approximated by the normally distributed random variable Y.
Using this normal approximation, $P(X \leq 151) = 0.894$ and $P(X > 127) = 0.997$.

a)   Find the mean and standard deviation of the normal approximation.

(8 marks)

b)   Use your results from a) to find n and p. Give your answer for p to 2 decimal places, and your answer for n to the nearest whole number.

(4 marks)

5   The diameters of the pizza bases made at a restaurant are normally distributed.
The mean diameter is 12 inches, and 5% of the bases measure more than 13 inches.

a)   Find the standard deviation of the diameters of the pizza bases.

[4 marks]

Any pizza base with a diameter of less than 10.8 inches is considered too small and is discarded.

b)   If 100 pizza bases are made in an evening, approximately how many would you expect to be discarded due to being too small?

[3 marks]

Three pizza bases are selected at random.

c)   Find the probability that at least one of these bases is too small.

[3 marks]

General Certificate of Education
Advanced Subsidiary (AS) and Advanced Level

Statistics S2 — Practice Exam One

Time Allowed: 1 hour 30 min

Graphical calculators may be used for this exam.

Give any non-exact numerical answers to an appropriate degree of accuracy.

Statistical tables can be found on page 133.

There are 72 marks available for this paper.

1.   A teacher believes there is a positive correlation between students' marks (y) in an examination and the amount of revision undertaken in hours (x). To investigate this, she collects the following data from a random selection of 8 students.

x	12	10	9	5	14	11	12	6
y	88	72	65	59	92	75	80	69

($\Sigma x = 79$, $\Sigma y = 600$, $\Sigma x^2 = 847$, $\Sigma y^2 = 45\,884$ and $\Sigma xy = 6143$.)

A scatter diagram of the data is shown below.

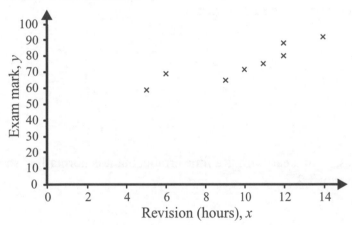

a)   Calculate S_{xx}, S_{yy} and S_{xy}.

(3 marks)

b)   Calculate the sample product-moment correlation coefficient for x and y.

(2 marks)

c)   Carry out a hypothesis test at the 5% significance level to investigate the teacher's belief concerning students' marks and the amount of revision they do. State your hypotheses clearly.

(5 marks)

d)   State an assumption you need to make for this test to be valid.
Explain how the validity of this assumption may be checked using the scatter diagram.

(2 marks)

e)   The teacher believes she can fit a linear regression line to the data.
Give one reason to support her conclusion.

(1 mark)

f)   Find the equation of the regression line of y on x.

(3 marks)

g)   The teacher must estimate the examination mark of a student who did not take the examination.
The teacher knows this student to have done 8 hours of revision.
Estimate the likely mark for this student.

(1 mark)

h)   Comment on the reliability of your estimate in g).

(1 mark)

2   The number of houses, X, sold each week by an estate agent in a small town can be modelled by a Poisson distribution. The estate agent sells houses at an average rate of 2 per week.

   a)   Find the probability that in a randomly selected week, the estate agent will sell:

       (i)   exactly 1 house,

(2 marks)

       (ii)   at least 2 houses but no more than 4 houses.

(3 marks)

   b)   To qualify for a "monthly bonus", the estate agent needs to sell at least 2 houses each week for 4 consecutive weeks. Find the probability that the estate agent qualifies for the "monthly bonus" over the next 4-week period.

(3 marks)

   c)   The number of houses, Y, sold each week by a second estate agent at the same firm can be modelled by a Poisson distribution with a mean of 3.

       (i)   Write down the distribution of H, the total number of houses sold by the two estate agents each week.

(1 mark)

       (ii)   Calculate the probability that in a randomly selected two-week period, the two estate agents will sell at least 9 houses altogether.

(3 marks)

   d)   Use a suitable approximation to find the probability that the two estate agents will sell fewer than 120 houses altogether over the next 26 weeks.

(6 marks)

3   The duration in minutes, X, of a car wash is a little erratic, but it is normally distributed with a mean of 8 minutes and a variance of 1.2.

   a)   Find:

       (i) $P(X < 7.5)$,

(3 marks)

       (ii)   the probability that the duration deviates from the mean by more than 1 minute,

(4 marks)

       (iii)   the duration in minutes, d, such that there is no more than a 1% probability that the car wash will take longer than this duration.

(4 marks)

   b)   After some maintenance work is carried out, the manager claims the mean duration of the car wash has fallen. A hypothesis test is to be carried out to investigate this claim.

      A random sample of 20 washes are timed, and the duration of each wash noted.

       (i)   Explain what is meant by a one-tailed hypothesis test.

(2 marks)

       (ii)   Write down suitable null and alternative hypotheses to test the manager's claim.

(1 mark)

       (iii)   The mean duration of the sample of 20 washes was 7.8 minutes.
            Carry out the test at the 5% significance level.
            You may assume that the variance of the washes' durations is unchanged.

(5 marks)

4   Jack wants to know whether there is a link between gender and the foreign language that students at his school choose to study for their GCSEs.

He carries out a survey of 50 students and gets the following results:

	French	Spanish	Total
Male	14	6	20
Female	8	22	30
Total	22	28	50

a)   Write down suitable null and alternative hypotheses for a test to investigate whether there is any association between the variables 'gender' and 'foreign language studied'.

(1 mark)

b)   Calculate the expected frequency for each combination of 'gender' and 'language studied' under your null hypothesis.

(3 marks)

c)   Carry out a χ^2 test at the 1% level of significance to determine whether there is an association between gender and the language chosen.

Your answer should include a table showing the contribution of each cell in the above table to your test statistic.

(8 marks)

d)   Comment briefly on how the observations compare with your predictions.

(2 marks)

e)   If 2 of the students are selected at random, calculate the probability that they are of different genders and study different languages.

(3 marks)

General Certificate of Education
Advanced Subsidiary (AS) and Advanced Level

Statistics S2 — Practice Exam Two

Time Allowed: 1 hour 30 min

Graphical calculators may be used for this exam.

Give any non-exact numerical answers to an appropriate degree of accuracy.

Statistical tables can be found on page 133.

There are 72 marks available for this paper.

1   The manager of a company believes that there is a positive correlation between the amount of money spent on marketing a new product (x, measured in thousands of pounds) and the awareness of that product among the general public (y, measured on a scale of 1-10).

She looks at a random selection of data showing the cost of previous marketing campaigns and the public awareness of the product shortly afterwards. The figures she finds are shown in the table below.

x (£'000)	5	6	7	9	24	25	26	27
y	2	3	3.5	3.2	3.6	5	7	9.5

a)   Draw a scatter diagram to show these results.

(2 marks)

b)   Calculate the sample product-moment correlation coefficient (PMCC) between x and y.
(You may use $\Sigma x^2 = 2797$, $\Sigma y^2 = 212.7$ and $\Sigma xy = 731.2$.)

(5 marks)

c)   The manager asks you to carry out a significance test to determine whether this value for the PMCC shows the two variables are correlated in a statistically significant way.

Explain why it is inappropriate to carry out a hypothesis test on the PMCC in this way.

(2 marks)

The manager instead asks you to investigate whether there is a positive association between the two variables using Spearman's rank correlation coefficient.

d)   Calculate Spearman's rank correlation coefficient (SRCC) for the values in the above table.

(4 marks)

e)   Carry out a hypothesis test using a significance level of 1% to investigate whether the two variables are positively associated. State your hypotheses clearly.

(5 marks)

2   A scientist is testing a household cleaning product. She cleans a tile on which bacteria have been grown, then examines how many bacteria survive. Surviving bacteria are spread randomly on the tile.

    a)   An average of 6 bacteria per square centimetre are initially assumed to survive.

         If the random variable X represents the number of surviving bacteria in a randomly chosen square centimetre of tile, find:

         (i) $P(X < 10)$

(2 marks)

         (ii) $P(5 \leq X \leq 7)$

(3 marks)

    b)   During one test, the scientist counts the total number of surviving bacteria (x) on 15 randomly chosen square centimetres of tile.

         The scientist's results can be summarised as: $\Sigma x = 83$ and $\Sigma x^2 = 538$.

         Calculate the sample mean and the sample variance of the data.
         Give your answers to 2 decimal places.

(3 marks)

    c)   Explain why the data in b) support the use of a Poisson distribution to model the number of surviving bacteria per square centimetre.

(1 mark)

    d)   Find $P(X = 5)$, using a Poisson distribution whose mean equals your sample mean from b).

(2 marks)

    e)   A different scientist is investigating an alternative cleaning product using a similar technique.

         He has found that after a tile has been cleaned using this product, there is a probability of 0.35 that the tile will contain no bacteria after 1 hour.

         The scientist cleans 100 tiles. The random variable Y describes the number of tiles that contain no bacteria after 1 hour.

         (i)   Specify the probability distribution of the random variable Y.
              Give the values of any parameters necessary to fully determine the distribution.

(2 marks)

         (ii)   Use a suitable approximation to find the probability that more than 40 of the tiles contain no bacteria after 1 hour.

(5 marks)

3   The average height of the sunflowers in a particular field is 150 cm.

a)   The heights of the sunflowers in a second field are known to follow a normal distribution, with a variance of 20. The heights (in cm) of a random sample of 6 of these sunflowers are:

$$140, \quad 142.5, \quad 137.5, \quad 141, \quad 140, \quad 139$$

Test at the 1% level of significance whether the average height of the sunflowers in this field is the same as for the sunflowers in the first field.

(8 marks)

b)   The heights (y cm) of 40 randomly selected sunflowers in a third field are measured. The summary statistics are given below.

$$\sum y = 5928 \qquad \sum y^2 = 884\,180$$

Test at the 5% level of significance whether the average height of the sunflowers in this third field is less than the average height of the sunflowers in the first field. You may assume the heights of the sunflowers in this field are normally distributed.

(10 marks)

4   The table below shows the results of a study of 150 trees.

	Leaf disease	No leaf disease	Total
Height < 3m	32	39	71
3m ≤ Height < 4m	19	27	46
Height ≥ 4m	19	14	33
Total	70	80	150

a)   Test at the 5% level of significance whether there is an association between the variables 'height of tree' and 'presence of leaf disease'.

Your working should include a table showing the contribution of each cell to the test statistic.

(12 marks)

b)   Comment briefly on how the observations compare with the expected frequencies under the null hypothesis.

(2 marks)

c)   If 3 trees are selected at random, one from each height category, find the probability that all 3 of them suffer from the leaf disease.

(4 marks)

OCR (MEI) S2 — STATISTICAL TABLES

Cumulative Poisson probabilities

λ	0.01	0.02	0.03	0.04	0.05	0.06	0.07	0.08	0.09
x = 0	0.9900	0.9802	0.9704	0.9608	0.9512	0.9418	0.9324	0.9231	0.9139
1	1.0000	0.9998	0.9996	0.9992	0.9988	0.9983	0.9977	0.9970	0.9962
2	- - - - -	1.0000	1.0000	1.0000	1.0000	1.0000	0.9999	0.9999	0.9999
3	- - - - -	- - - - -	- - - - -	- - - - -	- - - - -	- - - - -	1.0000	1.0000	1.0000

λ	0.10	0.20	0.30	0.40	0.50	0.60	0.70	0.80	0.90
x = 0	0.9048	0.8187	0.7408	0.6703	0.6065	0.5488	0.4966	0.4493	0.4066
1	0.9953	0.9825	0.9631	0.9384	0.9098	0.8781	0.8442	0.8088	0.7725
2	0.9998	0.9989	0.9964	0.9921	0.9856	0.9769	0.9659	0.9526	0.9371
3	1.0000	0.9999	0.9997	0.9992	0.9982	0.9966	0.9942	0.9909	0.9865
4	- - - - -	1.0000	1.0000	0.9999	0.9998	0.9996	0.9992	0.9986	0.9977
5	- - - - -	- - - - -	- - - - -	1.0000	1.0000	1.0000	0.9999	0.9998	0.9997
6	- - - - -	- - - - -	- - - - -	- - - - -	- - - - -	- - - - -	1.0000	1.0000	1.0000

λ	1.00	1.10	1.20	1.30	1.40	1.50	1.60	1.70	1.80	1.90
x = 0	0.3679	0.3329	0.3012	0.2725	0.2466	0.2231	0.2019	0.1827	0.1653	0.1496
1	0.7358	0.6990	0.6626	0.6268	0.5918	0.5578	0.5249	0.4932	0.4628	0.4337
2	0.9197	0.9004	0.8795	0.8571	0.8335	0.8088	0.7834	0.7572	0.7306	0.7037
3	0.9810	0.9743	0.9662	0.9569	0.9463	0.9344	0.9212	0.9068	0.8913	0.8747
4	0.9963	0.9946	0.9923	0.9893	0.9857	0.9814	0.9763	0.9704	0.9636	0.9559
5	0.9994	0.9990	0.9985	0.9978	0.9968	0.9955	0.9940	0.9920	0.9896	0.9868
6	0.9999	0.9999	0.9997	0.9996	0.9994	0.9991	0.9987	0.9981	0.9974	0.9966
7	1.0000	1.0000	1.0000	0.9999	0.9999	0.9998	0.9997	0.9996	0.9994	0.9992
8	- - - - -	- - - - -	- - - - -	1.0000	1.0000	1.0000	1.0000	0.9999	0.9999	0.9998
9	- - - - -	- - - - -	- - - - -	- - - - -	- - - - -	- - - - -	- - - - -	1.0000	1.0000	1.0000

λ	2.00	2.10	2.20	2.30	2.40	2.50	2.60	2.70	2.80	2.90
x = 0	0.1353	0.1225	0.1108	0.1003	0.0907	0.0821	0.0743	0.0672	0.0608	0.0550
1	0.4060	0.3796	0.3546	0.3309	0.3084	0.2873	0.2674	0.2487	0.2311	0.2146
2	0.6767	0.6496	0.6227	0.5960	0.5697	0.5438	0.5184	0.4936	0.4695	0.4460
3	0.8571	0.8386	0.8194	0.7993	0.7787	0.7576	0.7360	0.7141	0.6919	0.6696
4	0.9473	0.9379	0.9275	0.9162	0.9041	0.8912	0.8774	0.8629	0.8477	0.8318
5	0.9834	0.9796	0.9751	0.9700	0.9643	0.9580	0.9510	0.9433	0.9349	0.9258
6	0.9955	0.9941	0.9925	0.9906	0.9884	0.9858	0.9828	0.9794	0.9756	0.9713
7	0.9989	0.9985	0.9980	0.9974	0.9967	0.9958	0.9947	0.9934	0.9919	0.9901
8	0.9998	0.9997	0.9995	0.9994	0.9991	0.9989	0.9985	0.9981	0.9976	0.9969
9	1.0000	0.9999	0.9999	0.9999	0.9998	0.9997	0.9996	0.9995	0.9993	0.9991
10	- - - - -	1.0000	1.0000	1.0000	1.0000	0.9999	0.9999	0.9999	0.9998	0.9998
11	- - - - -	- - - - -	- - - - -	- - - - -	- - - - -	1.0000	1.0000	1.0000	1.0000	0.9999
12	- - - - -	- - - - -	- - - - -	- - - - -	- - - - -	- - - - -	- - - - -	- - - - -	- - - - -	1.0000

λ	3.00	3.10	3.20	3.30	3.40	3.50	3.60	3.70	3.80	3.90
x = 0	0.0498	0.0450	0.0408	0.0369	0.0334	0.0302	0.0273	0.0247	0.0224	0.0202
1	0.1991	0.1847	0.1712	0.1586	0.1468	0.1359	0.1257	0.1162	0.1074	0.0992
2	0.4232	0.4012	0.3799	0.3594	0.3397	0.3208	0.3027	0.2854	0.2689	0.2531
3	0.6472	0.6248	0.6025	0.5803	0.5584	0.5366	0.5152	0.4942	0.4735	0.4532
4	0.8153	0.7982	0.7806	0.7626	0.7442	0.7254	0.7064	0.6872	0.6678	0.6484
5	0.9161	0.9057	0.8946	0.8829	0.8705	0.8576	0.8441	0.8301	0.8156	0.8006
6	0.9665	0.9612	0.9554	0.9490	0.9421	0.9347	0.9267	0.9182	0.9091	0.8995
7	0.9881	0.9858	0.9832	0.9802	0.9769	0.9733	0.9692	0.9648	0.9599	0.9546
8	0.9962	0.9953	0.9943	0.9931	0.9917	0.9901	0.9883	0.9863	0.9840	0.9815
9	0.9989	0.9986	0.9982	0.9978	0.9973	0.9967	0.9960	0.9952	0.9942	0.9931
10	0.9997	0.9996	0.9995	0.9994	0.9992	0.9990	0.9987	0.9984	0.9981	0.9977
11	0.9999	0.9999	0.9999	0.9998	0.9998	0.9997	0.9996	0.9995	0.9994	0.9993
12	1.0000	1.0000	1.0000	1.0000	0.9999	0.9999	0.9999	0.9999	0.9998	0.9998
13	- - - - -	- - - - -	- - - - -	- - - - -	1.0000	1.0000	1.0000	1.0000	1.0000	0.9999
14	- - - - -	- - - - -	- - - - -	- - - - -	- - - - -	- - - - -	- - - - -	- - - - -	- - - - -	1.0000

OCR (MEI) S2 — STATISTICAL TABLES

Cumulative Poisson probabilities (continued)

λ	4.00	4.10	4.20	4.30	4.40	4.50	4.60	4.70	4.80	4.90
x = 0	0.0183	0.0166	0.0150	0.0136	0.0123	0.0111	0.0101	0.0091	0.0082	0.0074
1	0.0916	0.0845	0.0780	0.0719	0.0663	0.0611	0.0563	0.0518	0.0477	0.0439
2	0.2381	0.2238	0.2102	0.1974	0.1851	0.1736	0.1626	0.1523	0.1425	0.1333
3	0.4335	0.4142	0.3954	0.3772	0.3594	0.3423	0.3257	0.3097	0.2942	0.2793
4	0.6288	0.6093	0.5898	0.5704	0.5512	0.5321	0.5132	0.4946	0.4763	0.4582
5	0.7851	0.7693	0.7531	0.7367	0.7199	0.7029	0.6858	0.6684	0.6510	0.6335
6	0.8893	0.8786	0.8675	0.8558	0.8436	0.8311	0.8180	0.8046	0.7908	0.7767
7	0.9489	0.9427	0.9361	0.9290	0.9214	0.9134	0.9049	0.8960	0.8867	0.8769
8	0.9786	0.9755	0.9721	0.9683	0.9642	0.9597	0.9549	0.9497	0.9442	0.9382
9	0.9919	0.9905	0.9889	0.9871	0.9851	0.9829	0.9805	0.9778	0.9749	0.9717
10	0.9972	0.9966	0.9959	0.9952	0.9943	0.9933	0.9922	0.9910	0.9896	0.9880
11	0.9991	0.9989	0.9986	0.9983	0.9980	0.9976	0.9971	0.9966	0.9960	0.9953
12	0.9997	0.9997	0.9996	0.9995	0.9993	0.9992	0.9990	0.9988	0.9986	0.9983
13	0.9999	0.9999	0.9999	0.9998	0.9998	0.9997	0.9997	0.9996	0.9995	0.9994
14	1.0000	1.0000	1.0000	1.0000	0.9999	0.9999	0.9999	0.9999	0.9999	0.9998
15	- - - - -	- - - - -	- - - - -	- - - - -	1.0000	1.0000	1.0000	1.0000	1.0000	0.9999
16	- - - - -	- - - - -	- - - - -	- - - - -	- - - - -	- - - - -	- - - - -	- - - - -	- - - - -	1.0000

λ	5.00	5.10	5.20	5.30	5.40	5.50	5.60	5.70	5.80	5.90
x = 0	0.0067	0.0061	0.0055	0.0050	0.0045	0.0041	0.0037	0.0033	0.0030	0.0027
1	0.0404	0.0372	0.0342	0.0314	0.0289	0.0266	0.0244	0.0224	0.0206	0.0189
2	0.1247	0.1165	0.1088	0.1016	0.0948	0.0884	0.0824	0.0768	0.0715	0.0666
3	0.2650	0.2513	0.2381	0.2254	0.2133	0.2017	0.1906	0.1800	0.1700	0.1604
4	0.4405	0.4231	0.4061	0.3895	0.3733	0.3575	0.3422	0.3272	0.3127	0.2987
5	0.6160	0.5984	0.5809	0.5635	0.5461	0.5289	0.5119	0.4950	0.4783	0.4619
6	0.7622	0.7474	0.7324	0.7171	0.7017	0.6860	0.6703	0.6544	0.6384	0.6224
7	0.8666	0.8560	0.8449	0.8335	0.8217	0.8095	0.7970	0.7841	0.7710	0.7576
8	0.9319	0.9252	0.9181	0.9106	0.9027	0.8944	0.8857	0.8766	0.8672	0.8574
9	0.9682	0.9644	0.9603	0.9559	0.9512	0.9462	0.9409	0.9352	0.9292	0.9228
10	0.9863	0.9844	0.9823	0.9800	0.9775	0.9747	0.9718	0.9686	0.9651	0.9614
11	0.9945	0.9937	0.9927	0.9916	0.9904	0.9890	0.9875	0.9859	0.9841	0.9821
12	0.9980	0.9976	0.9972	0.9967	0.9962	0.9955	0.9949	0.9941	0.9932	0.9922
13	0.9993	0.9992	0.9990	0.9988	0.9986	0.9983	0.9980	0.9977	0.9973	0.9969
14	0.9998	0.9997	0.9997	0.9996	0.9995	0.9994	0.9993	0.9991	0.9990	0.9988
15	0.9999	0.9999	0.9999	0.9999	0.9998	0.9998	0.9998	0.9997	0.9996	0.9996
16	1.0000	1.0000	1.0000	1.0000	0.9999	0.9999	0.9999	0.9999	0.9999	0.9999
17	- - - - -	- - - - -	- - - - -	- - - - -	1.0000	1.0000	1.0000	1.0000	1.0000	1.0000

OCR (MEI) S2 — STATISTICAL TABLES

Cumulative Poisson probabilities (continued)

λ	6.00	6.10	6.20	6.30	6.40	6.50	6.60	6.70	6.80	6.90
x = 0	0.0025	0.0022	0.0020	0.0018	0.0017	0.0015	0.0014	0.0012	0.0011	0.0010
1	0.0174	0.0159	0.0146	0.0134	0.0123	0.0113	0.0103	0.0095	0.0087	0.0080
2	0.0620	0.0577	0.0536	0.0498	0.0463	0.0430	0.0400	0.0371	0.0344	0.0320
3	0.1512	0.1425	0.1342	0.1264	0.1189	0.1118	0.1052	0.0988	0.0928	0.0871
4	0.2851	0.2719	0.2592	0.2469	0.2351	0.2237	0.2127	0.2022	0.1920	0.1823
5	0.4457	0.4298	0.4141	0.3988	0.3837	0.3690	0.3547	0.3406	0.3270	0.3137
6	0.6063	0.5902	0.5742	0.5582	0.5423	0.5265	0.5108	0.4953	0.4799	0.4647
7	0.7440	0.7301	0.7160	0.7017	0.6873	0.6728	0.6581	0.6433	0.6285	0.6136
8	0.8472	0.8367	0.8259	0.8148	0.8033	0.7916	0.7796	0.7673	0.7548	0.7420
9	0.9161	0.9090	0.9016	0.8939	0.8858	0.8774	0.8686	0.8596	0.8502	0.8405
10	0.9574	0.9531	0.9486	0.9437	0.9386	0.9332	0.9274	0.9214	0.9151	0.9084
11	0.9799	0.9776	0.9750	0.9723	0.9693	0.9661	0.9627	0.9591	0.9552	0.9510
12	0.9912	0.9900	0.9887	0.9873	0.9857	0.9840	0.9821	0.9801	0.9779	0.9755
13	0.9964	0.9958	0.9952	0.9945	0.9937	0.9929	0.9920	0.9909	0.9898	0.9885
14	0.9986	0.9984	0.9981	0.9978	0.9974	0.9970	0.9966	0.9961	0.9956	0.9950
15	0.9995	0.9994	0.9993	0.9992	0.9990	0.9988	0.9986	0.9984	0.9982	0.9979
16	0.9998	0.9998	0.9997	0.9997	0.9996	0.9996	0.9995	0.9994	0.9993	0.9992
17	0.9999	0.9999	0.9999	0.9999	0.9999	0.9998	0.9998	0.9998	0.9997	0.9997
18	1.0000	1.0000	1.0000	1.0000	1.0000	0.9999	0.9999	0.9999	0.9999	0.9999
19	- - - - -	- - - - -	- - - - -	- - - - -	- - - - -	1.0000	1.0000	1.0000	1.0000	1.0000

λ	7.00	7.10	7.20	7.30	7.40	7.50	7.60	7.70	7.80	7.90
x = 0	0.0009	0.0008	0.0007	0.0007	0.0006	0.0006	0.0005	0.0005	0.0004	0.0004
1	0.0073	0.0067	0.0061	0.0056	0.0051	0.0047	0.0043	0.0039	0.0036	0.0033
2	0.0296	0.0275	0.0255	0.0236	0.0219	0.0203	0.0188	0.0174	0.0161	0.0149
3	0.0818	0.0767	0.0719	0.0674	0.0632	0.0591	0.0554	0.0518	0.0485	0.0453
4	0.1730	0.1641	0.1555	0.1473	0.1395	0.1321	0.1249	0.1181	0.1117	0.1055
5	0.3007	0.2881	0.2759	0.2640	0.2526	0.2414	0.2307	0.2203	0.2103	0.2006
6	0.4497	0.4349	0.4204	0.4060	0.3920	0.3782	0.3646	0.3514	0.3384	0.3257
7	0.5987	0.5838	0.5689	0.5541	0.5393	0.5246	0.5100	0.4956	0.4812	0.4670
8	0.7291	0.7160	0.7027	0.6892	0.6757	0.6620	0.6482	0.6343	0.6204	0.6065
9	0.8305	0.8202	0.8096	0.7988	0.7877	0.7764	0.7649	0.7531	0.7411	0.7290
10	0.9015	0.8942	0.8867	0.8788	0.8707	0.8622	0.8535	0.8445	0.8352	0.8257
11	0.9467	0.9420	0.9371	0.9319	0.9265	0.9208	0.9148	0.9085	0.9020	0.8952
12	0.9730	0.9703	0.9673	0.9642	0.9609	0.9573	0.9536	0.9496	0.9454	0.9409
13	0.9872	0.9857	0.9841	0.9824	0.9805	0.9784	0.9762	0.9739	0.9714	0.9687
14	0.9943	0.9935	0.9927	0.9918	0.9908	0.9897	0.9886	0.9873	0.9859	0.9844
15	0.9976	0.9972	0.9969	0.9964	0.9959	0.9954	0.9948	0.9941	0.9934	0.9926
16	0.9990	0.9989	0.9987	0.9985	0.9983	0.9980	0.9978	0.9974	0.9971	0.9967
17	0.9996	0.9996	0.9995	0.9994	0.9993	0.9992	0.9991	0.9989	0.9988	0.9986
18	0.9999	0.9998	0.9998	0.9998	0.9997	0.9997	0.9996	0.9996	0.9995	0.9994
19	1.0000	0.9999	0.9999	0.9999	0.9999	0.9999	0.9999	0.9998	0.9998	0.9998
20	1.0000	1.0000	1.0000	1.0000	1.0000	1.0000	1.0000	0.9999	0.9999	0.9999
21	- - - - -	- - - - -	- - - - -	- - - - -	- - - - -	- - - - -	- - - - -	1.0000	1.0000	1.0000

Cumulative Poisson probabilities (continued)

λ	8.00	8.10	8.20	8.30	8.40	8.50	8.60	8.70	8.80	8.90
x = 0	0.0003	0.0003	0.0003	0.0002	0.0002	0.0002	0.0002	0.0002	0.0002	0.0001
1	0.0030	0.0028	0.0025	0.0023	0.0021	0.0019	0.0018	0.0016	0.0015	0.0014
2	0.0138	0.0127	0.0118	0.0109	0.0100	0.0093	0.0086	0.0079	0.0073	0.0068
3	0.0424	0.0396	0.0370	0.0346	0.0323	0.0301	0.0281	0.0262	0.0244	0.0228
4	0.0996	0.0940	0.0887	0.0837	0.0789	0.0744	0.0701	0.0660	0.0621	0.0584
5	0.1912	0.1822	0.1736	0.1653	0.1573	0.1496	0.1422	0.1352	0.1284	0.1219
6	0.3134	0.3013	0.2896	0.2781	0.2670	0.2562	0.2457	0.2355	0.2256	0.2160
7	0.4530	0.4391	0.4254	0.4119	0.3987	0.3856	0.3728	0.3602	0.3478	0.3357
8	0.5925	0.5786	0.5647	0.5507	0.5369	0.5231	0.5094	0.4958	0.4823	0.4689
9	0.7166	0.7041	0.6915	0.6788	0.6659	0.6530	0.6400	0.6269	0.6137	0.6006
10	0.8159	0.8058	0.7955	0.7850	0.7743	0.7634	0.7522	0.7409	0.7294	0.7178
11	0.8881	0.8807	0.8731	0.8652	0.8571	0.8487	0.8400	0.8311	0.8220	0.8126
12	0.9362	0.9313	0.9261	0.9207	0.9150	0.9091	0.9029	0.8965	0.8898	0.8829
13	0.9658	0.9628	0.9595	0.9561	0.9524	0.9486	0.9445	0.9403	0.9358	0.9311
14	0.9827	0.9810	0.9791	0.9771	0.9749	0.9726	0.9701	0.9675	0.9647	0.9617
15	0.9918	0.9908	0.9898	0.9887	0.9875	0.9862	0.9848	0.9832	0.9816	0.9798
16	0.9963	0.9958	0.9953	0.9947	0.9941	0.9934	0.9926	0.9918	0.9909	0.9899
17	0.9984	0.9982	0.9979	0.9977	0.9973	0.9970	0.9966	0.9962	0.9957	0.9952
18	0.9993	0.9992	0.9991	0.9990	0.9989	0.9987	0.9985	0.9983	0.9981	0.9978
19	0.9997	0.9997	0.9997	0.9996	0.9995	0.9995	0.9994	0.9993	0.9992	0.9991
20	0.9999	0.9999	0.9999	0.9998	0.9998	0.9998	0.9998	0.9997	0.9997	0.9996
21	1.0000	1.0000	1.0000	0.9999	0.9999	0.9999	0.9999	0.9999	0.9999	0.9998
22	- - - - -	- - - - -	- - - - -	1.0000	1.0000	1.0000	1.0000	1.0000	1.0000	0.9999
23	- - - - -	- - - - -	- - - - -	- - - - -	- - - - -	- - - - -	- - - - -	- - - - -	- - - - -	1.0000

λ	9.00	9.10	9.20	9.30	9.40	9.50	9.60	9.70	9.80	9.90
x = 0	0.0001	0.0001	0.0001	0.0001	0.0001	0.0001	0.0001	0.0001	0.0001	0.0001
1	0.0012	0.0011	0.0010	0.0009	0.0009	0.0008	0.0007	0.0007	0.0006	0.0005
2	0.0062	0.0058	0.0053	0.0049	0.0045	0.0042	0.0038	0.0035	0.0033	0.0030
3	0.0212	0.0198	0.0184	0.0172	0.0160	0.0149	0.0138	0.0129	0.0120	0.0111
4	0.0550	0.0517	0.0486	0.0456	0.0429	0.0403	0.0378	0.0355	0.0333	0.0312
5	0.1157	0.1098	0.1041	0.0986	0.0935	0.0885	0.0838	0.0793	0.0750	0.0710
6	0.2068	0.1978	0.1892	0.1808	0.1727	0.1649	0.1574	0.1502	0.1433	0.1366
7	0.3239	0.3123	0.3010	0.2900	0.2792	0.2687	0.2584	0.2485	0.2388	0.2294
8	0.4557	0.4426	0.4296	0.4168	0.4042	0.3918	0.3796	0.3676	0.3558	0.3442
9	0.5874	0.5742	0.5611	0.5479	0.5349	0.5218	0.5089	0.4960	0.4832	0.4705
10	0.7060	0.6941	0.6820	0.6699	0.6576	0.6453	0.6329	0.6205	0.6080	0.5955
11	0.8030	0.7932	0.7832	0.7730	0.7626	0.7520	0.7412	0.7303	0.7193	0.7081
12	0.8758	0.8684	0.8607	0.8529	0.8448	0.8364	0.8279	0.8191	0.8101	0.8009
13	0.9261	0.9210	0.9156	0.9100	0.9042	0.8981	0.8919	0.8853	0.8786	0.8716
14	0.9585	0.9552	0.9517	0.9480	0.9441	0.9400	0.9357	0.9312	0.9265	0.9216
15	0.9780	0.9760	0.9738	0.9715	0.9691	0.9665	0.9638	0.9609	0.9579	0.9546
16	0.9889	0.9878	0.9865	0.9852	0.9838	0.9823	0.9806	0.9789	0.9770	0.9751
17	0.9947	0.9941	0.9934	0.9927	0.9919	0.9911	0.9902	0.9892	0.9881	0.9870
18	0.9976	0.9973	0.9969	0.9966	0.9962	0.9957	0.9952	0.9947	0.9941	0.9935
19	0.9989	0.9988	0.9986	0.9985	0.9983	0.9980	0.9978	0.9975	0.9972	0.9969
20	0.9996	0.9995	0.9994	0.9993	0.9992	0.9991	0.9990	0.9989	0.9987	0.9986
21	0.9998	0.9998	0.9998	0.9997	0.9997	0.9996	0.9996	0.9995	0.9995	0.9994
22	0.9999	0.9999	0.9999	0.9999	0.9999	0.9999	0.9998	0.9998	0.9998	0.9997
23	1.0000	1.0000	1.0000	1.0000	1.0000	0.9999	0.9999	0.9999	0.9999	0.9999
24	- - - - -	- - - - -	- - - - -	- - - - -	- - - - -	1.0000	1.0000	1.0000	1.0000	1.0000

OCR (MEI) S2 — STATISTICAL TABLES

Cumulative Poisson probabilities (continued)

λ	10.00	10.10	10.20	10.30	10.40	10.50	10.60	10.70	10.80	10.90
x = 0	0.0000	0.0000	0.0000	0.0000	0.0000	0.0000	0.0000	0.0000	0.0000	0.0000
1	0.0005	0.0005	0.0004	0.0004	0.0003	0.0003	0.0003	0.0003	0.0002	0.0002
2	0.0028	0.0026	0.0023	0.0022	0.0020	0.0018	0.0017	0.0016	0.0014	0.0013
3	0.0103	0.0096	0.0089	0.0083	0.0077	0.0071	0.0066	0.0062	0.0057	0.0053
4	0.0293	0.0274	0.0257	0.0241	0.0225	0.0211	0.0197	0.0185	0.0173	0.0162
5	0.0671	0.0634	0.0599	0.0566	0.0534	0.0504	0.0475	0.0448	0.0423	0.0398
6	0.1301	0.1240	0.1180	0.1123	0.1069	0.1016	0.0966	0.0918	0.0872	0.0828
7	0.2202	0.2113	0.2027	0.1944	0.1863	0.1785	0.1710	0.1636	0.1566	0.1498
8	0.3328	0.3217	0.3108	0.3001	0.2896	0.2794	0.2694	0.2597	0.2502	0.2410
9	0.4579	0.4455	0.4332	0.4210	0.4090	0.3971	0.3854	0.3739	0.3626	0.3515
10	0.5830	0.5705	0.5580	0.5456	0.5331	0.5207	0.5084	0.4961	0.4840	0.4719
11	0.6968	0.6853	0.6738	0.6622	0.6505	0.6387	0.6269	0.6150	0.6031	0.5912
12	0.7916	0.7820	0.7722	0.7623	0.7522	0.7420	0.7316	0.7210	0.7104	0.6996
13	0.8645	0.8571	0.8494	0.8416	0.8336	0.8253	0.8169	0.8083	0.7995	0.7905
14	0.9165	0.9112	0.9057	0.9000	0.8940	0.8879	0.8815	0.8750	0.8682	0.8612
15	0.9513	0.9477	0.9440	0.9400	0.9359	0.9317	0.9272	0.9225	0.9177	0.9126
16	0.9730	0.9707	0.9684	0.9658	0.9632	0.9604	0.9574	0.9543	0.9511	0.9477
17	0.9857	0.9844	0.9830	0.9815	0.9799	0.9781	0.9763	0.9744	0.9723	0.9701
18	0.9928	0.9921	0.9913	0.9904	0.9895	0.9885	0.9874	0.9863	0.9850	0.9837
19	0.9965	0.9962	0.9957	0.9953	0.9948	0.9942	0.9936	0.9930	0.9923	0.9915
20	0.9984	0.9982	0.9980	0.9978	0.9975	0.9972	0.9969	0.9966	0.9962	0.9958
21	0.9993	0.9992	0.9991	0.9990	0.9989	0.9987	0.9986	0.9984	0.9982	0.9980
22	0.9997	0.9997	0.9996	0.9996	0.9995	0.9994	0.9994	0.9993	0.9992	0.9991
23	0.9999	0.9999	0.9998	0.9998	0.9998	0.9998	0.9997	0.9997	0.9996	0.9996
24	1.0000	0.9999	0.9999	0.9999	0.9999	0.9999	0.9999	0.9999	0.9998	0.9998
25	- - - - -	1.0000	1.0000	1.0000	1.0000	1.0000	1.0000	0.9999	0.9999	0.9999
26	- - - - -	- - - - -	- - - - -	- - - - -	- - - - -	- - - - -	- - - - -	1.0000	1.0000	1.0000

OCR (MEI) S2 — STATISTICAL TABLES

Critical values for the product moment correlation coefficient, r

	5%	2.5%	1%	0.5%	1-tail test
	10%	5%	2%	1%	2-tail test
n					
1	-	-	-	-	
2	-	-	-	-	
3	0.9877	0.9969	0.9995	0.9999	
4	0.9000	0.9500	0.9800	0.9900	
5	0.8054	0.8783	0.9343	0.9587	
6	0.7293	0.8114	0.8822	0.9172	
7	0.6694	0.7545	0.8329	0.8745	
8	0.6215	0.7067	0.7887	0.8343	
9	0.5822	0.6664	0.7498	0.7977	
10	0.5494	0.6319	0.7155	0.7646	
11	0.5214	0.6021	0.6851	0.7348	
12	0.4973	0.5760	0.6581	0.7079	
13	0.4762	0.5529	0.6339	0.6835	
14	0.4575	0.5324	0.6120	0.6614	
15	0.4409	0.5140	0.5923	0.6411	

Critical values for Spearman's rank correlation coefficient, r_s

	5%	2.5%	1%	0.5%	1-tail test
	10%	5%	2%	1%	2-tail test
n					
1	–	–	–	–	
2	–	–	–	–	
3	–	–	–	–	
4	1.0000	–	–	–	
5	0.9000	1.0000	1.0000	–	
6	0.8286	0.8857	0.9429	1.0000	
7	0.7143	0.7857	0.8929	0.9286	
8	0.6429	0.7381	0.8333	0.8810	
9	0.6000	0.7000	0.7833	0.8333	
10	0.5636	0.6485	0.7455	0.7939	
11	0.5364	0.6182	0.7091	0.7545	
12	0.5035	0.5874	0.6783	0.7273	
13	0.4835	0.5604	0.6484	0.7033	
14	0.4637	0.5385	0.6264	0.6791	
15	0.4464	0.5214	0.6036	0.6536	

Percentage points of the χ^2 distribution

The table shows values of x satisfying $P(X > x) = p\%$, where X has the χ^2 distribution with v degrees of freedom.

$p\%$	99	97.5	95	90	10	5	2.5	1	0.5
$v = 1$	.0001	.0010	.0039	.0158	2.706	3.841	5.024	6.635	7.879
2	.0201	.0506	0.103	0.211	4.605	5.991	7.378	9.210	10.60
3	0.115	0.216	0.352	0.584	6.251	7.815	9.348	11.34	12.84
4	0.297	0.484	0.711	1.064	7.779	9.488	11.14	13.28	14.86
5	0.554	0.831	1.145	1.610	9.236	11.07	12.83	15.09	16.75
6	0.872	1.237	1.635	2.204	10.64	12.59	14.45	16.81	18.55
7	1.239	1.690	2.167	2.833	12.02	14.07	16.01	18.48	20.28
8	1.646	2.180	2.733	3.490	13.36	15.51	17.53	20.09	21.95
9	2.088	2.700	3.325	4.168	14.68	16.92	19.02	21.67	23.59

The table in your formula booklet will be in two halves like this — you only need the right-hand part for contingency-table tests.

OCR (MEI) S2 — STATISTICAL TABLES

The normal distribution function

The table below shows $\Phi(z) = P(Z \le z)$, where $Z \sim N(0, 1)$.

For negative z, use: $\Phi(-z) = 1 - \Phi(z)$.

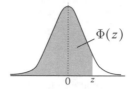

z	0	1	2	3	4	5	6	7	8	9	1	2	3	4	5	6	7	8	9
															ADD				
0.0	0.5000	0.5040	0.5080	0.5120	0.5160	0.5199	0.5239	0.5279	0.5319	0.5359	4	8	12	16	20	24	28	32	36
0.1	0.5398	0.5438	0.5478	0.5517	0.5557	0.5596	0.5636	0.5675	0.5714	0.5753	4	8	12	16	20	24	28	32	35
0.2	0.5793	0.5832	0.5871	0.5910	0.5948	0.5987	0.6026	0.6064	0.6103	0.6141	4	8	12	15	19	23	27	31	35
0.3	0.6179	0.6217	0.6255	0.6293	0.6331	0.6368	0.6406	0.6443	0.6480	0.6517	4	8	11	15	19	23	26	30	34
0.4	0.6554	0.6591	0.6628	0.6664	0.6700	0.6736	0.6772	0.6808	0.6844	0.6879	4	7	11	14	18	22	25	29	32
0.5	0.6915	0.6950	0.6985	0.7019	0.7054	0.7088	0.7123	0.7157	0.7190	0.7224	3	7	10	14	17	21	24	27	31
0.6	0.7257	0.7291	0.7324	0.7357	0.7389	0.7422	0.7454	0.7486	0.7517	0.7549	3	6	10	13	16	19	23	26	29
0.7	0.7580	0.7611	0.7642	0.7673	0.7704	0.7734	0.7764	0.7794	0.7823	0.7852	3	6	9	12	15	18	21	24	27
0.8	0.7881	0.7910	0.7939	0.7967	0.7995	0.8023	0.8051	0.8078	0.8106	0.8133	3	6	8	11	14	17	19	22	25
0.9	0.8159	0.8186	0.8212	0.8238	0.8264	0.8289	0.8315	0.8340	0.8365	0.8389	3	5	8	10	13	15	18	20	23
1.0	0.8413	0.8438	0.8461	0.8485	0.8508	0.8531	0.8554	0.8577	0.8599	0.8621	2	5	7	9	12	14	16	18	21
1.1	0.8643	0.8665	0.8686	0.8708	0.8729	0.8749	0.8770	0.8790	0.8810	0.8830	2	4	6	8	10	12	14	16	19
1.2	0.8849	0.8869	0.8888	0.8907	0.8925	0.8944	0.8962	0.8980	0.8997	0.9015	2	4	6	7	9	11	13	15	16
1.3	0.9032	0.9049	0.9066	0.9082	0.9099	0.9115	0.9131	0.9147	0.9162	0.9177	2	3	5	6	8	10	11	13	14
1.4	0.9192	0.9207	0.9222	0.9236	0.9251	0.9265	0.9279	0.9292	0.9306	0.9319	1	3	4	6	7	8	10	11	13
1.5	0.9332	0.9345	0.9357	0.9370	0.9382	0.9394	0.9406	0.9418	0.9429	0.9441	1	2	4	5	6	7	8	10	11
1.6	0.9452	0.9463	0.9474	0.9484	0.9495	0.9505	0.9515	0.9525	0.9535	0.9545	1	2	3	4	5	6	7	8	9
1.7	0.9554	0.9564	0.9573	0.9582	0.9591	0.9599	0.9608	0.9616	0.9625	0.9633	1	2	3	3	4	5	6	7	8
1.8	0.9641	0.9649	0.9656	0.9664	0.9671	0.9678	0.9686	0.9693	0.9699	0.9706	1	1	2	3	4	4	5	6	6
1.9	0.9713	0.9719	0.9726	0.9732	0.9738	0.9744	0.9750	0.9756	0.9761	0.9767	1	1	2	2	3	4	4	5	5
2.0	0.9772	0.9778	0.9783	0.9788	0.9793	0.9798	0.9803	0.9808	0.9812	0.9817	0	1	1	2	2	3	3	4	4
2.1	0.9821	0.9826	0.9830	0.9834	0.9838	0.9842	0.9846	0.9850	0.9854	0.9857	0	1	1	2	2	2	3	3	4
2.2	0.9861	0.9864	0.9868	0.9871	0.9875	0.9878	0.9881	0.9884	0.9887	0.9890	0	1	1	1	2	2	2	3	3
2.3	0.9893	0.9896	0.9898	0.9901	0.9904	0.9906	0.9909	0.9911	0.9913	0.9916	0	1	1	1	1	2	2	2	2
2.4	0.9918	0.9920	0.9922	0.9925	0.9927	0.9929	0.9931	0.9932	0.9934	0.9936	0	0	1	1	1	1	1	2	2
2.5	0.9938	0.9940	0.9941	0.9943	0.9945	0.9946	0.9948	0.9949	0.9951	0.9952									
2.6	0.9953	0.9955	0.9956	0.9957	0.9959	0.9960	0.9961	0.9962	0.9963	0.9964									
2.7	0.9965	0.9966	0.9967	0.9968	0.9969	0.9970	0.9971	0.9972	0.9973	0.9974									
2.8	0.9974	0.9975	0.9976	0.9977	0.9977	0.9978	0.9979	0.9979	0.9980	0.9981									
2.9	0.9981	0.9982	0.9982	0.9983	0.9984	0.9984	0.9985	0.9985	0.9986	0.9986			Not possible to calculate reliable differences in this format						
3.0	0.9987	0.9987	0.9987	0.9988	0.9988	0.9989	0.9989	0.9989	0.9990	0.9990									
3.1	0.9990	0.9991	0.9991	0.9991	0.9992	0.9992	0.9992	0.9992	0.9993	0.9993									
3.2	0.9993	0.9993	0.9994	0.9994	0.9994	0.9994	0.9994	0.9995	0.9995	0.9995									
3.3	0.9995	0.9995	0.9995	0.9996	0.9996	0.9996	0.9996	0.9996	0.9996	0.9997									
3.4	0.9997	0.9997	0.9997	0.9997	0.9997	0.9997	0.9997	0.9997	0.9997	0.9998									

OCR (MEI) S2 — STATISTICAL TABLES

The inverse normal function

The table below shows $\Phi^{-1}(p) = z$.

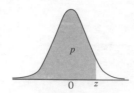

p	0.000	0.001	0.002	0.003	0.004	0.005	0.006	0.007	0.008	0.009
0.50	0.0000	0.0025	0.0050	0.0075	0.0100	0.0125	0.0150	0.0175	0.0201	0.0226
0.51	0.0251	0.0276	0.0301	0.0326	0.0351	0.0376	0.0401	0.0426	0.0451	0.0476
0.52	0.0502	0.0527	0.0552	0.0577	0.0602	0.0627	0.0652	0.0677	0.0702	0.0728
0.53	0.0753	0.0778	0.0803	0.0828	0.0853	0.0878	0.0904	0.0929	0.0954	0.0979
0.54	0.1004	0.1030	0.1055	0.1080	0.1105	0.1130	0.1156	0.1181	0.1206	0.1231
0.55	0.1257	0.1282	0.1307	0.1332	0.1358	0.1383	0.1408	0.1434	0.1459	0.1484
0.56	0.1510	0.1535	0.1560	0.1586	0.1611	0.1637	0.1662	0.1687	0.1713	0.1738
0.57	0.1764	0.1789	0.1815	0.1840	0.1866	0.1891	0.1917	0.1942	0.1968	0.1993
0.58	0.2019	0.2045	0.2070	0.2096	0.2121	0.2147	0.2173	0.2198	0.2224	0.2250
0.59	0.2275	0.2301	0.2327	0.2353	0.2378	0.2404	0.2430	0.2456	0.2482	0.2508
0.60	0.2533	0.2559	0.2585	0.2611	0.2637	0.2663	0.2689	0.2715	0.2741	0.2767
0.61	0.2793	0.2819	0.2845	0.2871	0.2898	0.2924	0.2950	0.2976	0.3002	0.3029
0.62	0.3055	0.3081	0.3107	0.3134	0.3160	0.3186	0.3213	0.3239	0.3266	0.3292
0.63	0.3319	0.3345	0.3372	0.3398	0.3425	0.3451	0.3478	0.3505	0.3531	0.3558
0.64	0.3585	0.3611	0.3638	0.3665	0.3692	0.3719	0.3745	0.3772	0.3799	0.3826
0.65	0.3853	0.3880	0.3907	0.3934	0.3961	0.3989	0.4016	0.4043	0.4070	0.4097
0.66	0.4125	0.4152	0.4179	0.4207	0.4234	0.4261	0.4289	0.4316	0.4344	0.4372
0.67	0.4399	0.4427	0.4454	0.4482	0.4510	0.4538	0.4565	0.4593	0.4621	0.4649
0.68	0.4677	0.4705	0.4733	0.4761	0.4789	0.4817	0.4845	0.4874	0.4902	0.4930
0.69	0.4959	0.4987	0.5015	0.5044	0.5072	0.5101	0.5129	0.5158	0.5187	0.5215
0.70	0.5244	0.5273	0.5302	0.5330	0.5359	0.5388	0.5417	0.5446	0.5476	0.5505
0.71	0.5534	0.5563	0.5592	0.5622	0.5651	0.5681	0.5710	0.5740	0.5769	0.5799
0.72	0.5828	0.5858	0.5888	0.5918	0.5948	0.5978	0.6008	0.6038	0.6068	0.6098
0.73	0.6128	0.6158	0.6189	0.6219	0.6250	0.6280	0.6311	0.6341	0.6372	0.6403
0.74	0.6433	0.6464	0.6495	0.6526	0.6557	0.6588	0.6620	0.6651	0.6682	0.6713
0.75	0.6745	0.6776	0.6808	0.6840	0.6871	0.6903	0.6935	0.6967	0.6999	0.7031
0.76	0.7063	0.7095	0.7128	0.7160	0.7192	0.7225	0.7257	0.7290	0.7323	0.7356
0.77	0.7388	0.7421	0.7454	0.7488	0.7521	0.7554	0.7588	0.7621	0.7655	0.7688
0.78	0.7722	0.7756	0.7790	0.7824	0.7858	0.7892	0.7926	0.7961	0.7995	0.8030
0.79	0.8064	0.8099	0.8134	0.8169	0.8204	0.8239	0.8274	0.8310	0.8345	0.8381
0.80	0.8416	0.8452	0.8488	0.8524	0.8560	0.8596	0.8633	0.8669	0.8705	0.8742
0.81	0.8779	0.8816	0.8853	0.8890	0.8927	0.8965	0.9002	0.9040	0.9078	0.9116
0.82	0.9154	0.9192	0.9230	0.9269	0.9307	0.9346	0.9385	0.9424	0.9463	0.9502
0.83	0.9542	0.9581	0.9621	0.9661	0.9701	0.9741	0.9782	0.9822	0.9863	0.9904
0.84	0.9945	0.9986	1.0027	1.0069	1.0110	1.0152	1.0194	1.0237	1.0279	1.0322
0.85	1.0364	1.0407	1.0450	1.0494	1.0537	1.0581	1.0625	1.0669	1.0714	1.0758
0.86	1.0803	1.0848	1.0893	1.0939	1.0985	1.1031	1.1077	1.1123	1.1170	1.1217
0.87	1.1264	1.1311	1.1359	1.1407	1.1455	1.1503	1.1552	1.1601	1.1650	1.1700
0.88	1.1750	1.1800	1.1850	1.1901	1.1952	1.2004	1.2055	1.2107	1.2160	1.2212
0.89	1.2265	1.2319	1.2372	1.2426	1.2481	1.2536	1.2591	1.2646	1.2702	1.2759
0.90	1.2816	1.2873	1.2930	1.2988	1.3047	1.3106	1.3165	1.3225	1.3285	1.3346
0.91	1.3408	1.3469	1.3532	1.3595	1.3658	1.3722	1.3787	1.3852	1.3917	1.3984
0.92	1.4051	1.4118	1.4187	1.4255	1.4325	1.4395	1.4466	1.4538	1.4611	1.4684
0.93	1.4758	1.4833	1.4909	1.4985	1.5063	1.5141	1.5220	1.5301	1.5382	1.5464
0.94	1.5548	1.5632	1.5718	1.5805	1.5893	1.5982	1.6072	1.6164	1.6258	1.6352
0.95	1.6449	1.6546	1.6646	1.6747	1.6849	1.6954	1.7060	1.7169	1.7279	1.7392
0.96	1.7507	1.7624	1.7744	1.7866	1.7991	1.8119	1.8250	1.8384	1.8522	1.8663
0.97	1.8808	1.8957	1.9110	1.9268	1.9431	1.9600	1.9774	1.9954	2.0141	2.0335
0.98	2.0537	2.0749	2.0969	2.1201	2.1444	2.1701	2.1973	2.2262	2.2571	2.2904
0.99	2.3263	2.3656	2.4089	2.4573	2.5121	2.5758	2.6521	2.7478	2.8782	3.0902

Discrete Groups of Particles in 1 Dimension

Welcome to the <u>Centre of Mass</u>. No, not your local Catholic church...

For **Particles in a Line** — Combine **Moments** about the **Origin**

1) The weight of an object is considered to act at its <u>centre of mass</u>.
   A <u>group</u> of objects <u>also</u> has a centre of mass, which isn't necessarily in the same position as any one of the objects.

2) It's often convenient to model these objects as <u>particles</u> (point masses) since the position of a particle is the position of its centre of mass. If a group of particles all lie in a <u>horizontal line</u>, then the centre of mass of the <u>group</u> will lie somewhere on the <u>same line</u>.

   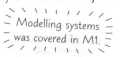
   — Modelling systems
   was covered in M1.

3) The <u>moment</u> (turning effect) of a particle from a fixed point is:

   | weight (mass × gravity) | × | perpendicular distance from point |

   This is <u>*mgx*</u> if the fixed point and the particle are <u>horizontally aligned</u> (see p154 for more on moments).

4) The moment of a <u>group</u> of particles in a <u>horizontal line</u> about a point in the horizontal line can be found by <u>adding together</u> all the <u>individual moments</u> about the point: Σmgx.

5) This has the same effect as the <u>combined weight</u> (Σmg) acting at the <u>centre of mass</u> of the <u>whole group</u> ($\overline{x}$).

   Writing this as a formula:

   $$\Sigma mgx = \overline{x}\Sigma mg$$
   e.g. for 3 particles in a horizontal line:
   $$m_1gx_1 + m_2gx_2 + m_3gx_3 = \overline{x}(m_1g + m_2g + m_3g)$$
   $$\Rightarrow m_1x_1 + m_2x_2 + m_3x_3 = \overline{x}(m_1 + m_2 + m_3)$$
   $$\Rightarrow \Sigma mx = \overline{x}\Sigma m$$

   The gs cancel out on each side.

   Use this simplified formula to find the centre of mass, $\overline{x}$, of a group of objects in a horizontal line.

EXAMPLE Three particles are placed at positions along the *x*-axis as shown.
Find the coordinates of the centre of mass of the group of particles.

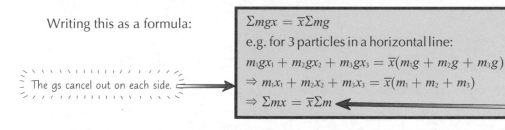

| $m_1 = 3$ kg | | $m_2 = 1.5$ kg | $m_3 = 0.5$ kg |
| (-2, 0) | 0 | (3, 0) | (5, 0) |

Negative coordinates go in the formula just as they are.

1) Use the formula $\Sigma mx = \overline{x}\Sigma m$ and put in what you know:
   $$m_1x_1 + m_2x_2 + m_3x_3 = \overline{x}(m_1 + m_2 + m_3)$$
   $$\Rightarrow (3 \times -2) + (1.5 \times 3) + (0.5 \times 5) = \overline{x}(3 + 1.5 + 0.5)$$
   $$\Rightarrow 1 = 5\overline{x} \quad \Rightarrow \quad \overline{x} = 0.2$$

2) So the centre of mass of the group has the coordinates (0.2, 0)

Use $\overline{y}$ for Particles in a Vertical Line

$$\Sigma my = \overline{y}\Sigma m$$

It's the same for particles arranged in a <u>vertical</u> line. The centre of mass has coordinates $(0, \overline{y})$.

EXAMPLE A light vertical rod AB has particles attached at various positions, as shown. At what height is the centre of mass of the rod?

A light rod has length but no width or depth, and no mass (as it's light).

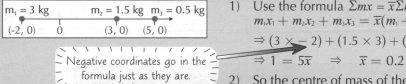

1) First, work out the positions of all the particles relative to a <u>single point</u> or 'origin'.
   Since you're asked for the <u>vertical height</u>, pick point A at the bottom of the rod:
   $$y_1 = 1, y_2 = 2, y_3 = 4, y_4 = 5.$$

2) Plug the numbers into the formula:
   $$\Sigma my = \overline{y}\Sigma m \quad \Rightarrow \quad m_1y_1 + m_2y_2 + m_3y_3 + m_4y_4 = \overline{y}(m_1 + m_2 + m_3 + m_4)$$
   $$\Rightarrow (3 \times 1) + (4 \times 2) + (1 \times 4) + (2 \times 5) = \overline{y} \times (3 + 4 + 1 + 2)$$
   $$\Rightarrow 25 = \overline{y} \times 10 \quad \Rightarrow \quad \overline{y} = 25 \div 10 = 2.5.$$

3) Make sure you've answered the question — $\overline{y}$ is the <u>vertical coordinate</u> from the 'origin' which we took as the bottom of the rod. So the vertical height of the centre of mass is <u>2.5 m</u>.

Take a moment to understand the basics...

Once you've got your head around what's going on with a system of particles, the number crunching is the easy part. You'll often have to tackle wordy problems where you first have to model a situation using rods and particles and things — you should be more than familiar with doing this from M1, and there's more practice to come later in the section.

Discrete Groups of Particles in 2 Dimensions

Let's face it, in the 'real world', you'll rarely come across a group in a perfectly orderly line (think of queuing up in the sales — madness). Luckily, the same principles apply in two dimensions — it's no harder than the stuff on the last page.

Use the **Position Vector r̄** for **Centre of Mass** of a **Group** on a **Plane**

There are two ways to find the centre of mass of a group of particles on a plane (i.e. in 2 dimensions, x and y, rather than just in a line). The quickest way uses position vectors, but I'll show you both methods and you can choose.

> **EXAMPLE** Find the coordinates of the centre of mass of the system of particles shown in the diagram.

The Long Way — find the x and y coordinates separately:

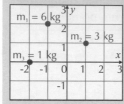

1) Find the x coordinate of the centre of mass first (pretend they're in a horizontal line...)
$x_1 = -1$, $x_2 = 1$, $x_3 = -2$, so:
$m_1x_1 + m_2x_2 + m_3x_3 = \bar{x}(m_1 + m_2 + m_3) \Rightarrow (6 \times -1) + (3 \times 1) + (1 \times -2) = \bar{x}(6 + 3 + 1)$
$\Rightarrow \bar{x} = -\frac{5}{10} = \underline{-0.5}$.

2) Now find the y coordinate in the same way: $y_1 = 2$, $y_2 = 1$, $y_3 = 0$, so:
$m_1y_1 + m_2y_2 + m_3y_3 = \bar{y}(m_1 + m_2 + m_3) \Rightarrow (6 \times 2) + (3 \times 1) + (1 \times 0) = \bar{y}(6 + 3 + 1)$
$\Rightarrow \bar{y} = \frac{15}{10} = \underline{1.5}$.

3) So the centre of mass has the coordinates $\underline{(-0.5, 1.5)}$.

Column position vectors like these are just like coordinates standing upright — $r = \binom{x}{y}$.

The Short Way — use position vectors:

1) Write out the position vector (**r**) for each particle: $\mathbf{r}_1 = \binom{-1}{2}$, $\mathbf{r}_2 = \binom{1}{1}$, $\mathbf{r}_3 = \binom{-2}{0}$.

2) Use the formula, but replace the xs and ys with **r**s: $\Sigma m\mathbf{r} = \bar{\mathbf{r}}\Sigma m \Rightarrow m_1\mathbf{r}_1 + m_2\mathbf{r}_2 + m_3\mathbf{r}_3 = \bar{\mathbf{r}}(m_1 + m_2 + m_3)$

$\Rightarrow 6\binom{-1}{2} + 3\binom{1}{1} + 1\binom{-2}{0} = \bar{\mathbf{r}}(6 + 3 + 1) \Rightarrow \binom{-6}{12} + \binom{3}{3} + \binom{-2}{0} = 10\bar{\mathbf{r}}$

$\Rightarrow \binom{-5}{15} = 10\bar{\mathbf{r}} \Rightarrow \bar{\mathbf{r}} = \binom{-0.5}{1.5}$. So the centre of mass has position vector $\binom{-0.5}{1.5}$, and coordinates $\underline{(-0.5, 1.5)}$.

> Using this method the formula becomes: $\Sigma m\mathbf{r} = \bar{\mathbf{r}}\Sigma m$

The **Formula** works for finding **Unknown Masses** and **Locations**

You won't always be asked to find the centre of mass of a system. You could be given the position of the centre of mass and asked to work out something else, like the mass or coordinates of a particle in the system. Use the same formula:

> **EXAMPLE** The diagram shows the position of the centre of mass (COM) of a system of three particles attached to the corners of a light rectangular lamina. Find m_2.

A lamina is just a flat (2D) shape.

1) First of all, pick your origin — bottom left looks as good as anywhere — and define all your positions from this point:
$\mathbf{r}_1 = \binom{0}{4}$, $\mathbf{r}_2 = \binom{6}{4}$, $\mathbf{r}_3 = \binom{6}{0}$. The COM, $\bar{\mathbf{r}}$, is at $\binom{3}{3.5}$.

2) Fill in what you know in the formula:
$\Sigma m\mathbf{r} = \bar{\mathbf{r}}\Sigma m \Rightarrow m_1\mathbf{r}_1 + m_2\mathbf{r}_2 + m_3\mathbf{r}_3 = \bar{\mathbf{r}}(m_1 + m_2 + m_3)$

$\Rightarrow 8\binom{0}{4} + m_2\binom{6}{4} + 2\binom{6}{0} = \binom{3}{3.5} \times (8 + m_2 + 2) \Rightarrow \binom{0}{32} + \binom{6m_2}{4m_2} + \binom{12}{0} = \binom{3}{3.5} \times (m_2 + 10)$

$\Rightarrow \binom{6m_2 + 12}{4m_2 + 32} = \binom{3m_2 + 30}{3.5m_2 + 35}$

3) Pick either the top row or bottom row to solve the equation for m_2 (it should be the same in both),
e.g. Top: $6m_2 + 12 = 3m_2 + 30 \Rightarrow m_2 = \underline{6\ kg}$. Bottom: $4m_2 + 32 = 3.5m_2 + 35 \Rightarrow m_2 = \underline{6\ kg}$.

2D or not 2D — that is the question...

Well actually the question's more likely to be 'Find the centre of mass of the following system of particles...', but then I doubt that would have made Hamlet quite such a gripping tale. Make sure you can do this stuff with your eyes shut because you'll need it again later on, and there's also a new compulsory blindfolded section to the M2 exam this year...

Standard Uniform Laminas

A page full of shapes for you to learn, just like in little school. However, you need to be able to find the centres of mass of these <u>uniform plane laminas</u>, not just colour them in. Even if you <u>can</u> do it neatly inside the lines.

Use **Lines of Symmetry** with **Regular** and **Standard Shapes**

<u>Uniform</u> laminas have <u>evenly spread</u> mass, so the centre of mass is in the centre of the shape, on all the <u>lines of symmetry</u>. So for shapes with more than one line of symmetry, the <u>centre of mass</u> is where the lines of symmetry <u>intersect</u>.

> **EXAMPLE** Find the coordinates of the centre of mass of a uniform rectangular lamina with vertices A(−4, 7), B (2, 7), C(−4, −3) and D(2, −3).
>
> 1) A little sketch never goes amiss...
>
> 2) $\bar{x}$ is the midpoint of AB (or CD), i.e. $(-4 + 2) \div 2 = -1$.
>
> 3) $\bar{y}$ is the midpoint of AC (or BD), i.e. $(7 + -3) \div 2 = 2$.
>
> 4) So the centre of mass is at (−1, 2). Easy peasy lemon squeezy*.

The **Centre of Mass** of a **Triangle** is the **Centroid**

1) In any triangle, the lines from each <u>vertex</u> to the <u>midpoint of the opposite side</u> are called <u>medians</u>.

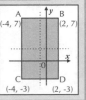
> In an equilateral triangle, the medians are lines of symmetry.

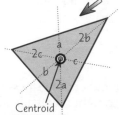
Centroid

2) If you draw in the medians on <u>any triangle</u>, the point where they meet will be <u>two thirds</u> of the way up each median from each vertex. This point is the <u>centroid</u>, and it's the <u>centre of mass</u> in a uniform triangle.

3) There's a formula for finding the coordinates of the centroid:

> For a triangle with vertices at (x_1, y_1), (x_2, y_2) and (x_3, y_3):
>
> **Centre of Mass** $(\bar{x}, \bar{y})$ **is at** $(\frac{x_1 + x_2 + x_3}{3}, \frac{y_1 + y_2 + y_3}{3})$
>
> (i.e. the mean x coordinate and mean y coordinate)

> For an <u>isosceles</u> triangle, the centroid is two thirds of the way down the <u>line of symmetry</u> from the vertex.

If you need this formula in your exam, you'll be given it — but it's handy to know how to use it.

Use the **Formula** to find the COM of a **Sector of a Circle**

Finding the centre of mass of a <u>sector of a circle</u> is a bit harder, so the <u>formula</u> is given to you in the exam:

> For a uniform circle sector, radius r and angle 2α radians:
>
> **Centre of Mass is at** $\frac{2r\sin\alpha}{3\alpha}$ **from the centre of the circle on the axis of symmetry.**

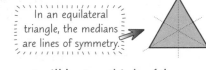
COM · Centre of Circle

> **EXAMPLE** A sector is cut from a uniform circle of radius 3 cm, centre P. The sector is an eighth of the whole circle. How far along the axis of symmetry is the centre of mass of the sector from P?
>
> 1) The angle of the sector is an eighth of the whole circle, so $2\alpha = \frac{2\pi}{8} \Rightarrow \alpha = \frac{\pi}{8}$.
>
> 2) Using the formula $\frac{2r\sin\alpha}{3\alpha}$, with $r = 3$ cm:
>
>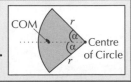
> Don't forget to set your calculator to work in radians rather than degrees.
>
> Centre of Mass $= \dfrac{2 \times 3 \times \sin\frac{\pi}{8}}{\frac{3\pi}{8}} = 1.9489... = \underline{1.95 \text{ cm}}$ from P (to 3 s.f.)

I love a lamina in uniform...

A nice easy page with lots of pretty shapes and colours. Before you start unleashing your inner toddler and demanding sweets and afternoon naps, make sure you fully understand what's been said on this page, because the tough stuff is coming right up. There's plenty of time for sweets and afternoon naps when the exams are over. Trust me...

*Squeezing lemons is actually quite tricky so I'm not sure where this saying comes from.

Composite Shapes

It's time to combine all the things covered so far in the section into one <u>lamina lump</u>. Yay.

For a **Composite Shape** — Find each COM **Individually** then **Combine**

A <u>composite</u> shape is one that can be broken up into standard <u>parts</u> such as rectangles and circles.
Once you've found the COM of a <u>part</u>, imagine replacing it with a <u>particle</u> of the <u>same mass</u> in the <u>position of the COM</u>.
Do this for each part, then find the COM of the <u>group</u> of 'particles' — this is the COM of the composite shape.

EXAMPLE A sign for the 'Rising Sun' restaurant is made from a uniform circular lamina attached to a uniform
rectangular lamina made from the same material. The dimensions of the two laminas are shown below.
Find the location of the centre of mass of the shape in relation to the point O.

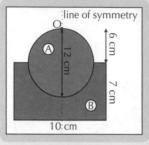

1) First, split up the shape into a circle (A) and rectangle (B). As both bits are made
    of the same material, the masses of A and B are in proportion to their areas,
    so we can say $m_A = \pi r^2 = \pi \times 6^2 = \underline{113.1}$, and $m_B = 10 \times 7 = \underline{70}$.

2) The shape has a line of symmetry, so the centre of mass <u>must be on that line</u>,
    directly below the point O.

3) Next find the vertical position of the centres of mass of both A and B individually:
    $y_A = \underline{6\ cm}$ from O $y_B = 6$ cm + (7 cm ÷ 2) = $\underline{9.5\ cm}$ from O
    since A and B each have a horizontal line of symmetry halfway down them (but B is 6 cm below O to start with).

> Use symmetry where you
> can — but make sure you
> explain what you've done.

4) Treat the shapes as two particles positioned at the centres of mass of each shape,
    and use the formula from page 141:
    $$\Sigma my = \overline{y}\Sigma m \quad \Rightarrow \quad m_A y_A + m_B y_B = \overline{y}(m_A + m_B)$$
    $$\Rightarrow (113.1 \times 6) + (70 \times 9.5) = \overline{y}(113.1 + 70) \quad \Rightarrow \quad 1343.6 = 183.1\overline{y} \quad \Rightarrow \quad \overline{y} = \underline{7.34\ cm}.$$

5) Make sure you've answered the question —
    The centre of mass of the whole shape is <u>7.34 cm</u> vertically below O on the line of symmetry. Job done.

You can use the **Removal Method** for **Some Shapes**

You may have a shape that looks like a 'standard' shape with other standard shapes '<u>removed</u>' rather than stuck together.
The <u>removal method</u> is like the one above, except the individual centres of mass are <u>subtracted</u> rather than added.

EXAMPLE Find the coordinates of the centre of mass of the lamina shown —
a circle of radius 3 with a quarter sector removed.

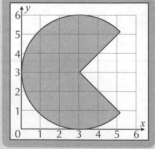

1) Let's call the 'whole' circle A and the sector that's been removed B.
    Since B is a quarter of A, we can say that the masses are $m_A = 4$ and $m_B = 1$.

2) We're working in 2D, so use position vectors $\mathbf{r}_A$ and $\mathbf{r}_B$ to
    describe the centres of mass. From the symmetry of the circle, $\mathbf{r}_A = \binom{3}{3}$.
    $\mathbf{r}_B$ can be worked out using the formula on page 142:
    $y_B = 3$ (from the symmetry of the sector) and $x_B = 3 + \dfrac{2r\sin\alpha}{3\alpha}$.
    The angle of the sector, $2\alpha = \dfrac{\pi}{2} \Rightarrow \alpha = \dfrac{\pi}{4}$, and r = 3,
    so: $x_B = 3 + \dfrac{2 \times 3 \times \sin\frac{\pi}{4}}{\frac{3\pi}{4}} = 4.8006...$ So $\mathbf{r}_B = \binom{4.8006}{3}$.

> Don't panic — you'll be
> given this formula in the
> exam if you need it.

3) Using the removal method, our formula becomes: $m_A\mathbf{r}_A - m_B\mathbf{r}_B = \overline{\mathbf{r}}(m_A - m_B)$
    $$4\binom{3}{3} - 1\binom{4.8006}{3} = \overline{\mathbf{r}}(4 - 1) \quad \Rightarrow \quad \binom{12 - 4.8006}{12 - 3} = 3\overline{\mathbf{r}} \quad \Rightarrow \quad \overline{\mathbf{r}} = \binom{7.1994}{9} \div 3 = \binom{2.3998}{3}.$$

4) So the coordinates of the centre of mass of the shape are <u>(2.40, 3)</u>.

Waxing is another effective removal method...

Now you've got all you need to find the centre of mass of any lamina shape, so long as you can spot how it breaks up into
circles, rectangles, etc. Quite arty-farty this. Set out your working neatly though, especially for the more complicated shapes.

Centres of Mass in 3 Dimensions

I know how much you must have enjoyed this centre of mass stuff so far. But if you're anything like me, you'll be hungry for more. MORE. So, I present to you today's special — Centres of Mass in 3 Dimensions. Delicious.

Use **Symmetry** to find the COM of a **Uniform 3D Shape**

Remember — uniform means that the mass is evenly distributed.

1) As you've seen on the previous few pages, using the symmetry of a shape makes finding the COM tonnes easier.

2) This is just as true for uniform 3D shapes as it is for laminas.

3) For example, spheres, cubes, cylinders and cuboids all have their centre of mass right slap bang in the centre.

4) In fact, for any uniform 3D shape, the COM will be at the point where all the planes of symmetry intersect.

5) So, for a shape with an axis of rotational symmetry, the centre of mass will be somewhere on that axis.

6) In your exam, you'll have to find the COM of any sphere or cuboid all on your own.
   For any other shapes, you'll be given a handy formula — you'll need to know how to use it though:

COM of Uniform Solids

Pyramid or **cone**, height h:
$\frac{1}{4}h$ above base on line from centre of base to vertex

Hemisphere, radius r and centre O:
$\frac{3}{8}r$ from O on axis of symmetry

COM of Uniform Shells

Conical Shell, height h:
$\frac{1}{3}h$ above 'base' on line from centre of 'base' to vertex

Hemispherical shell, radius r and centre O:
$\frac{1}{2}r$ from O on axis of symmetry

A shell is basically a solid with all the insides scooped out. And with no base.

Use the same method for **Composite Shapes** in **3D** as in **2D**

Just find the centre of mass for each shape individually, then combine.

EXAMPLE   A toy rocket, R, is made up of a solid uniform cone, A, of height 4 cm and mass 0.5 kg and a solid uniform cylinder, B, of height 12 cm and mass 1 kg. A and B are joined so that the base of A coincides with one of the plane faces of B, as shown below.
Find the position of the rocket's centre of mass in relation to O, the centre of its base.

1) The rocket has an axis of symmetry running through O and the vertex of A, so the centres of mass of A, B and R will all lie somewhere on this line.

This simplifies the question to particles in a vertical line. Just like p. 141

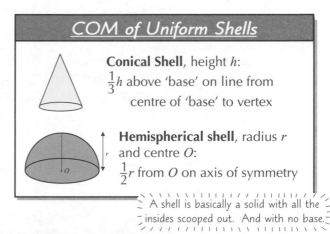

2) Find the vertical position of centres of mass of A and B individually:
$y_A = \frac{1}{4}(4) + 12 = 1 + 12 = \underline{13 \text{ cm}}$ above O

(using the formula for the centre of mass of a solid uniform cone and the fact that the base of A is 12 cm above O to start with)

$y_B = \frac{1}{2}h_B = \frac{1}{2}(12) = \underline{6 \text{ cm}}$ from O

(since the cylinder has a horizontal plane of symmetry halfway up)

3) Now, just like you did in 2D, treat the shapes as two particles positioned at the centre of mass of each shape and use the formula from p.141 to find the centre of mass of R:

$\Sigma my = \bar{y}\Sigma m \quad \Rightarrow \quad m_A y_A + m_B y_B = m_R y_R$

$\Rightarrow \quad 0.5(13) + 1(6) = 1.5 y_R \quad \Rightarrow \quad y_R = 12.5 \div 1.5 = 8\frac{1}{3} \text{ cm}.$

4) So the centre of mass of the rocket is $8\frac{1}{3}$ cm vertically above O on the axis of symmetry. Simple as that.

Centres of Mass in 3 Dimensions

As well as questions on 3D solids and shells, you might be asked about 3D shapes made from <u>laminas</u>.

Again, find each COM *Individually* then *Combine*

Isn't it great when you get to use the same method over and over again?

EXAMPLE   A tray is made from 4 uniform rectangular laminas of the same material, A, B, C and D, arranged as shown below. Find the coordinates of the centre of mass of the tray referred to the axes shown and the distance, d, of this point from the origin, O.

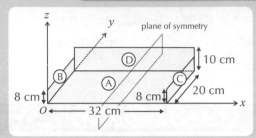

1) As A, B, C and D are made from the same material, their masses are in proportion to their areas. So:
$$m_A = 32 \times 20 = 640$$
$$m_B = m_C = 20 \times 8 = 160$$
$$m_D = 32 \times 10 = 320$$

2) The tray has a plane of symmetry at $x = 16$, so the x-coordinate of the tray's centre of mass must lie on this plane. So $\bar{x} = 16$.

> This has simplified the problem to just finding the COM in two dimensions — y and z.

3) Now find the <u>y-coordinate</u> of the centre of mass of the tray:
The centres of mass of the individual laminas can be found using symmetry.
They are at the centre of each lamina — so $y_A = 10$, $y_B = 10$, $y_C = 10$ and $y_D = 20$.
Use the formula to find the y-coordinate of the centre of mass of the tray:
$$\Sigma my = \bar{y}\Sigma m \Rightarrow m_A y_A + m_B y_B + m_C y_C + m_D y_D = \bar{y}(m_A + m_B + m_C + m_D)$$
$$\Rightarrow (640 \times 10) + (160 \times 10) + (160 \times 10) + (320 \times 20) = \bar{y}(640 + 160 + 160 + 320)$$
$$\Rightarrow \bar{y} = 16000 \div 1280 = 12.5$$

4) And do the same thing for the z-coordinate:
$$\Sigma mz = \bar{z}\Sigma m \Rightarrow m_A z_A + m_B z_B + m_C z_C + m_D z_D = \bar{z}(m_A + m_B + m_C + m_D)$$
$$\Rightarrow (640 \times 0) + (160 \times 4) + (160 \times 4) + (320 \times 5) = \bar{z}(640 + 160 + 160 + 320)$$
$$\Rightarrow \bar{z} = 2880 \div 1280 = 2.25$$

> Again, the z-coordinates of the COMs of A, B, C and D are found using symmetry.

So the coordinates of the centre of mass of the tray are $(\bar{x}, \bar{y}, \bar{z}) = (16, 12.5, 2.25)$.

5) Finally, use Pythagoras to find the distance, d, from O:
$$d = \sqrt{16^2 + 12.5^2 + 2.25^2} = 20.4 \text{ cm (3 s.f.)}$$

You can also use the *Formula* in *3 dimensions*

Sometimes you <u>won't be able</u> to use symmetry to simplify a 3D centre of mass question.
If you don't want to have to find each of the three coordinates <u>individually</u>, then you'll need to break out the <u>vector equation</u> from page 142 and use it with some <u>3D column vectors</u>. Go on, it'll be fun.

EXAMPLE   A system consists of 3 particles, A, B and C. A, B and C have coordinates (1, 2, 3), (1, –1, 0) and (–5, 4, 3) and masses 1 kg, 2 kg and 3 kg respectively. Find the centre of mass of the system.

Use the equation $\Sigma m\mathbf{r} = \bar{\mathbf{r}}\Sigma m$, where $\mathbf{r}_A = \begin{pmatrix} 1 \\ 2 \\ 3 \end{pmatrix}$, $\mathbf{r}_B = \begin{pmatrix} 1 \\ -1 \\ 0 \end{pmatrix}$, $\mathbf{r}_C = \begin{pmatrix} -5 \\ 4 \\ 3 \end{pmatrix}$ and $m_A = 1$ kg, $m_B = 2$ kg, $m_C = 3$ kg:

$$m_A\mathbf{r}_A + m_B\mathbf{r}_B + m_C\mathbf{r}_C = (m_A + m_B + m_C)\bar{\mathbf{r}} \Rightarrow 1\begin{pmatrix} 1 \\ 2 \\ 3 \end{pmatrix} + 2\begin{pmatrix} 1 \\ -1 \\ 0 \end{pmatrix} + 3\begin{pmatrix} -5 \\ 4 \\ 3 \end{pmatrix} = (1 + 2 + 3)\bar{\mathbf{r}} \Rightarrow \bar{\mathbf{r}} = \frac{1}{6}\begin{pmatrix} 1 + 2 - 15 \\ 2 - 2 + 12 \\ 3 + 0 + 9 \end{pmatrix} = \begin{pmatrix} -2 \\ 2 \\ 2 \end{pmatrix}$$

So the coordinates of the centre of mass of the system are (–2, 2, 2).

'Centres of Mass 3D' — the must-miss movie of the year...

...contact your local cinema for details. Or, if that's not your thing, then spend some time practising centre of mass questions.

Frameworks

More pretty shapes, this time made from <u>rods</u> rather than laminas — imagine bending a wire coathanger into something shapely (and infinitely more useful since wire hangers are rubbish). These shapes are called <u>frameworks</u>.

Treat **Each Side** as a **Rod** with its own **Centre of Mass**

In a framework, there's nothing in the middle, so all the mass is within the <u>rods</u> that make up the shape's <u>edges</u>. If the rods are <u>straight</u> and <u>uniform</u>, the centre of mass of each one is at the <u>midpoint</u> of the rod. Try to imagine each side of the shape as a <u>separate rod</u>, even if it's a single wire bent round into a shape.

EXAMPLE a) Find the coordinates of the centre of mass of the framework shown.

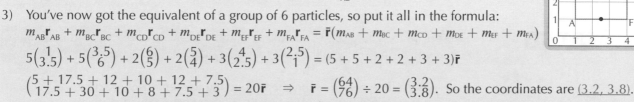

1) The black dots are the <u>centres of mass</u> of each of the rods that make up the frame
— so the position vectors can simply be written down for each one, e.g. $\mathbf{r}_{AB} = \binom{1}{3.5}$.

2) The mass of each rod is <u>proportional to its length</u>, so $m_{AB} = 5$ etc.

3) You've now got the equivalent of a group of 6 particles, so put it all in the formula:

$m_{AB}\mathbf{r}_{AB} + m_{BC}\mathbf{r}_{BC} + m_{CD}\mathbf{r}_{CD} + m_{DE}\mathbf{r}_{DE} + m_{EF}\mathbf{r}_{EF} + m_{FA}\mathbf{r}_{FA} = \bar{\mathbf{r}}(m_{AB} + m_{BC} + m_{CD} + m_{DE} + m_{EF} + m_{FA})$

$5\binom{1}{3.5} + 5\binom{3.5}{6} + 2\binom{6}{5} + 2\binom{5}{4} + 3\binom{4}{2.5} + 3\binom{2.5}{1} = (5 + 5 + 2 + 2 + 3 + 3)\bar{\mathbf{r}}$

$\binom{5 + 17.5 + 12 + 10 + 12 + 7.5}{17.5 + 30 + 10 + 8 + 7.5 + 3} = 20\bar{\mathbf{r}} \Rightarrow \bar{\mathbf{r}} = \binom{64}{76} \div 20 = \binom{3.2}{3.8}$. So the coordinates are <u>(3.2, 3.8)</u>.

b) A particle with the same mass as the whole framework is attached to the frame at A. Find the new centre of mass of the system.

Loaded frames are popular with examiners. Just set out your working clearly and step by step to make sure you've included everything.

1) The system consists of the framework mass which acts at (3.2, 3.8) (from a)), plus the mass of a particle at (1, 1). As they're the same mass, you can call each mass '1'.

2) $1\mathbf{r}_{Frame} + 1\mathbf{r}_{Particle} = 2\bar{\mathbf{r}} \Rightarrow \binom{3.2}{3.8} + \binom{1}{1} = 2\bar{\mathbf{r}} \Rightarrow \bar{\mathbf{r}} = \binom{4.2}{4.8} \div 2 = \binom{2.1}{2.4}$.

So the coordinates of the new COM are <u>(2.1, 2.4)</u>.

Arcs have their own Formula

<u>Arcs</u> sometimes crop up in framework questions. They're parts of the edge of a circle, and just like <u>sectors</u> have their own <u>formula</u> to work out their centre of mass. You'll be given the formula in the exam if you need it.

For a uniform arc of a circle of radius r and angle 2α radians:

Centre of Mass is at $\frac{r\sin\alpha}{\alpha}$ from the centre of the circle on the axis of symmetry.

EXAMPLE A wire is bent to form a sector of a circle with a radius of 4 cm and angle $\phi = \frac{\pi}{3}$, as shown. Find, to 3 s.f., the horizontal distance of the centre of mass of the framework from the point C.

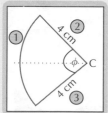

1) The mass of each rod that forms the 3 edges of the shape is in proportion to its length. The length of the arc is $\frac{4\pi}{3}$ (from arc length = $r\theta$ — see C2), and the other two sides are each 4.

2) To find the COM of the arc, use the formula $\frac{r\sin\alpha}{\alpha}$ (where $2\alpha = \frac{\pi}{3}$, so $\alpha = \frac{\pi}{6}$):

$x_1 = \dfrac{4 \times \sin\frac{\pi}{6}}{\frac{\pi}{6}} = \dfrac{12}{\pi}$ cm from C.

3) Then for the straight rods: each has its centre of mass 2 cm along its length, and the horizontal distance from C can be found using basic trig:

$x_2 = x_3 = 2$ cm $\times \cos\frac{\pi}{6} = \sqrt{3}$ cm. (They're the same because of the symmetry.)

4) Treat the 3 rods like particles on a horizontal line: $m_1x_1 + m_2x_2 + m_3x_3 = \bar{x}(m_1 + m_2 + m_3)$

$\left(\frac{4\pi}{3} \times \frac{12}{\pi}\right) + (4 \times \sqrt{3}) + (4 \times \sqrt{3}) = \bar{x}\left(\frac{4\pi}{3} + 4 + 4\right) \Rightarrow 16 + 8\sqrt{3} = \left(8 + \frac{4\pi}{3}\right)\bar{x} \Rightarrow \bar{x} = \underline{2.45 \text{ cm to 3 s.f.}}$

Arc-asm is the lowest form of wit — yet still funnier than this gag...

There's been a lot to take in on the last few pages. You'll notice every 'new' bit needs you to do all the 'old' bits too, and more besides. Maths is kinda like that. Make sure you're astoundingly marvellous at the section so far before you move on.

Laminas in Equilibrium

This is what the whole section's been working up to. The raison d'être for centres of mass, if you'll pardon my French. The position of the centre of mass will tell you what happens when you hang it up or tilt it. Très intéressant, non?

Laminas **Hang** with the Centre of Mass **Directly Below** the **Pivot**

When you <u>suspend</u> a shape, either from a point on its edge or from a <u>pivot</u> point within the shape, it will hang in <u>equilibrium</u> so that the centre of mass is <u>vertically below</u> the suspension point.

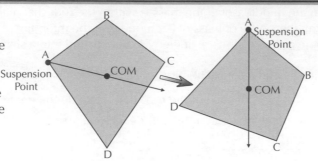

Knowing where the centre of mass lies will let you work out the <u>angle</u> that the shape hangs at.

This also applies to composite shapes — the centre of mass of the composite shape hangs directly below the pivot.

EXAMPLE   In the shape above, A is at (0, 6), C is at (8, 6), and the COM is at (4, 5). Find, in radians to 3 s.f., the angle AC makes with the vertical when the shape is suspended from A.

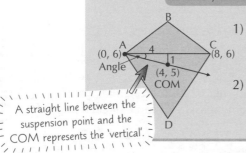

1) Do a little <u>sketch</u> of the shape showing the lengths you know. Draw in the line representing the <u>vertical</u> from the suspension point to the COM and <u>label</u> the angle you need to find.

A straight line between the suspension point and the COM represents the 'vertical'.

2) The angle should now be an easy piece of <u>trig</u> away:
Angle = $\tan^{-1} \frac{1}{4}$ = <u>0.245 radians</u> to 3 s.f.

In an exam question, you'll usually have to find the position of the centre of mass first and THEN do this bit to finish.

Shapes **Topple** if the COM is not **Directly Above** the **Bottom Edge**

<u>SAFE</u>

<u>Tilting</u> a shape on an inclined plane will make it <u>topple over</u> eventually (assuming there's enough <u>friction</u> to stop it sliding).

To make it fall over, you need to <u>incline</u> the plane above an angle, α, where the centre of mass is <u>vertically above</u> the bottom corner or edge of the shape, as shown in the pictures on the left.

EXAMPLE   The house-shaped lamina shown is in equilibrium on a plane inclined at an angle α. Find the value of α at the point where the shape is about to topple (in rads to 3 s.f.).

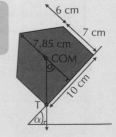

1) Draw in a line between the COM and the corner point (T) of the shape — this line will be vertical at the tipping point.

Use what you know about the position of the COM to draw a right-angled triangle containing α.
Height of COM from bottom edge = 7 + 6 − 7.85 = 5.15 cm.
COM is also halfway along the bottom edge, i.e. 10 ÷ 2 = 5 cm from T.

<u>MORTAL PERIL</u>

2) Use basic trig to work out the size of the angle:
$\alpha = \tan^{-1}\left(\frac{5}{5.15}\right)$ = <u>0.771 rads to 3 s.f.</u>

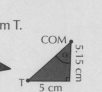

You might get a question about a solid 3D object, or a 3D shape made of laminas, standing on an inclined plane. You go about solving it in exactly the same way.

Don't hang around — get practising or you're heading for a fall...

This page may seem deceptively easy because in both examples it's assumed you've already found the centre of mass (that's what all the other pages were about in case you'd forgotten). In the exam you'll more than likely have to <u>find</u> the COM first and <u>then</u> work out the hanging or toppling angles. Luckily, there's plenty of practice at doing this on the next few pages...

M2 Section 1 — Practice Questions

Hurrah and huzzah — it's time to put your <u>slick Section 1 skills</u> (try saying that in a hurry) to the test.
As with all <u>strenuous exercise</u>, you need to <u>warm up</u> properly — and, as if by chance, look what we have here...

Warm-up Questions

1) Three particles have mass $m_1 = 1$ kg, $m_2 = 2$ kg, and $m_3 = 3$ kg.
Find the centre of mass of the system of particles if their coordinates are, respectively:
a) (1, 0), (2, 0), (3, 0)   b) (0, 3), (0, 2), (0, 1)   c) (3, 4), (3, 1), (1, 0)

2) A system of particles located at coordinates A(0, 0), B(0, 4), C(5, 4) and D(5, 0) have masses
m kg, $2m$ kg, $3m$ kg and 12 kg respectively. Find m, if the centre of mass of the system is at (3.5, 2).

3) Find the coordinates of the centres of mass of each of the uniform laminas shown below.

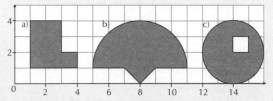

For b) you can check back to
p143 for the formulas for the
COM of a sector and a triangle.

4) A square uniform lamina of width 10 cm has a smaller square of width 2 cm cut from its top left
corner. Find the vertical distance of the centre of mass of the remaining shape from its top edge.

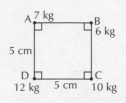

5) a) A light square framework has side lengths of 5 cm.
Masses are attached to the corners, as shown on the left.
Find the distance of the centre of mass from: i) side AB   ii) side AD.

b) The frame is suspended from corner A and hangs in equilibrium.
Find the angle AB makes with the vertical. Give your answer in
degrees to the nearest degree.

6) A solid uniform cylinder, P, of height 6 cm and radius 2.5 cm is placed on a
rough plane inclined at an angle α to the horizontal, as shown.
If P is on the point of toppling, find the value of α to the nearest degree.

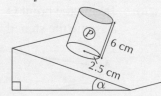

The universe is full of seemingly <u>unanswerable questions</u> to ponder.
Fortunately for those not particularly inclined towards philosophy, there are some perfectly good <u>answerable</u> ones here.

Exam Questions

1   The diagram shows three particles attached to a light rectangular
lamina at coordinates A(1, 3), B(5, 1) and C(4, y). The centre of
mass of the system is at ($\overline{x}$, 2).

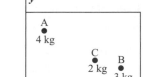

a)   Show that $y = 1.5$.

(3 marks)

b)   Show that $\overline{x} = 3$.

(3 marks)

The light lamina is replaced with a uniform rectangle PQRS, having a mass of 6 kg and vertices at
P(0, 0), Q(0, 5), R(7, 5) and S(7, 0). Particles A, B and C remain at their existing coordinates.

c)   Find the coordinates of the new centre of mass of the whole system.

(6 marks)

M2 Section 1 — Practice Questions

2   A cardboard 'For Sale' sign is modelled as a uniform lamina consisting of two squares and an isosceles triangle. The line of symmetry through the triangle coincides with that of the larger square, as shown.

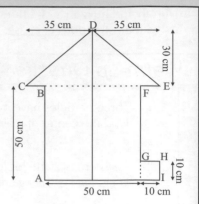

     a)   Show that the centre of mass of the sign, to 3 s.f., is 25.8 cm from AB and 34.5 cm from AI.

                                                           (6 marks)

The sign, with a mass of 1 kg, is suspended from the point D, and hangs in equilibrium, at an angle. A small weight, modelled as a particle, is attached at A, so that the sign hangs with AI horizontal.

     b)   Find the mass of the particle needed to make the sign hang in this way. Give your answer in kg to 3 s.f.

                                                            (3 marks)

3   A stencil is made from a uniform sheet of metal by removing a quarter of a circle with centre at the point O.

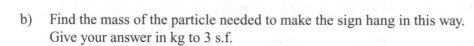

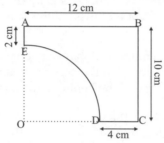

     a)   Taking the point O as the origin, find the coordinates of the centre of mass of the stencil, to 3 s.f. Assume the stencil can be modelled as a lamina.

                                                            (7 marks)

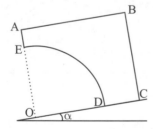

Particles are added to the stencil to adjust the centre of mass so that it now acts at coordinates (9, 6) from O. The stencil rests in equilibrium on a rough inclined plane, as shown. The angle of incline is increased until the shape is just about to fall over, balanced on the point D.

     b)   Find the angle of incline above which the shape will topple. Give your answer in radians to 3 s.f.

                                                            (3 marks)

4   A wire sculpture is modelled as a frame made from two uniform rods, one straight with mass $2m$, and one a semicircular arc with mass πm, with 2 particles of mass $3m$ and $4m$ attached to each corner, as shown.

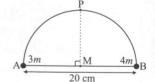

     a)   Find, in cm to 4 decimal places, the distance of the centre of mass of the loaded framework from:

         (i)   MP, where M is the mid-point of AB,

                                                            (3 marks)

         (ii)   AB.

                                                            (3 marks)

The sculpture is suspended from the point P, and hangs in equilibrium.

     b)   Find the angle MP makes with the vertical. Give your answer in radians to 3 s.f.

                                                            (3 marks)

5   A piece of jewellery is made by cutting a triangle from a thin circle of metal, as shown below.

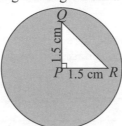

P is the centre of the circle, which has a radius of 2 cm. Triangle *PQR* is right-angled and isosceles.
The shape can be modelled as a uniform lamina.

a)   Show that the centre of mass of the shape is 0.070 cm from *P*, to 3 decimal places.

           (5 marks)

The shape hangs in equilibrium from a pin at point *Q*, about which it is able to rotate freely.
The pin can be modelled as a smooth peg.

b)   Find the angle that *PQ* makes with the vertical.
      Give your answer in degrees, to 1 decimal place.

           (3 marks)

6   The shape shown in Fig. 1 is formed by folding a uniform lamina through
      90° about the *z*-axis so the edge *AO* coincides with the *y*-axis and the edge
      OB with the *x*-axis.

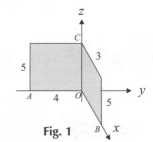

a)   Find the coordinates of the centre of mass of the shape,
      referred to the axes shown.

           (6 marks)   **Fig. 1**

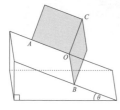

Fig. 2

b)   The folded lamina is placed on a rough plane, inclined at an angle of
      θ degrees to the horizontal, such that *AO* runs along the line of maximum
      slope and *OC* is perpendicular to the slope, as shown in Fig. 2. Assuming
      that the lamina is prevented from sliding, calculate the maximum value
      that θ can take before the lamina topples about *OB*.

           (4 marks)

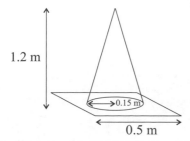

7   A traffic cone, C, is modelled as an open conical shell, A, of height 1.2 m
      and base radius 0.15 m attached to a square lamina, B, of side 0.5 m.
      A and B are combined so that the vertex of A is vertically above the centre
      of B, the point *O*.
      It is assumed that A and B are made from the same uniform material.
      Find the position of the centre of mass of the cone in relation to *O*.
      Use the fact that the curved surface of a cone has area $\pi r l$, where *l* is the
      length of the sloped edge.

           (6 marks)

Friction

Friction tries to prevent motion, but don't let it prevent you getting marks in the exam — revise this page and it won't.

Friction Tries to Prevent Motion

Push hard enough and a particle will move, even though there's friction opposing the motion. A <u>friction force</u>, <u>F</u>, has a <u>maximum value</u>. This depends on the <u>roughness</u> of the surface and the value of the <u>normal reaction</u> from the surface.

$$F \leq \mu R \quad \text{OR} \quad F \leq \mu N$$

(where R and N both stand for normal reaction)

μ has no units.
μ is pronounced as 'mu'.

μ is called the "<u>coefficient of friction</u>". The <u>rougher</u> the surface, the <u>bigger</u> μ gets.

EXAMPLE

What range of values can a friction force take in resisting a horizontal force P acting on a particle Q, of mass 12 kg, resting on a rough horizontal plane which has a coefficient of friction of 0.4? (Take $g = 9.8 \text{ ms}^{-2}$.)

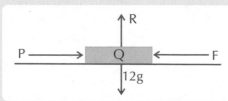

Resolving vertically: $R = 12g$

Use formula from above:

$F \leq \mu R$

$F \leq 0.4(12g)$

$F \leq 47.0 \text{ N}$ (3 s.f.)

So friction can take any value between 0 and 47.0 N, depending on how large P is.

If $P \leq 47.0$ N then Q remains in equilibrium. If P = 47.0 N then Q is <u>on the point of sliding</u> — i.e. friction is at its <u>limit</u>. If P > 47.0 then Q will start to move.

Limiting Friction is When Friction is at Maximum (F = μR)

EXAMPLE

A particle of mass 6 kg is placed on a rough horizontal plane which has a coefficient of friction of 0.3. A horizontal force Q is applied to the particle. Describe what happens if Q is: a)   16 N
Take $g = 9.8 \text{ ms}^{-2}$ b)   20 N

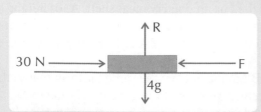

Resolving vertically: $R = 6g$

Using formula above:

$F \leq \mu R$
$F \leq 0.3(6g)$
$F \leq 17.6 \text{ N}$ (3 s.f.)

a)   Since Q < 17.6 it <u>won't move</u>.

b)   Since Q > 17.6 it'll <u>start moving</u>. No probs.

EXAMPLE

A particle of mass 4 kg at rest on a rough horizontal plane is being pushed by a horizontal force of 30 N. Given that the particle is on the point of moving, find the coefficient of friction.

30 N → [ ] ← F
              ↑ R
              ↓ 4g

Resolving horizontally: F = 30
Resolving vertically: R = 4g
The particle's about to move, so friction is at its limit:

$F = \mu R$

$30 = \mu(4g)$

$\mu = \dfrac{30}{4g} = 0.765$ (3 s.f.)

Sometimes friction really rubs me up the wrong way...

Friction can be a right nuisance, but without it we'd just slide all over the place, which would be worse (I imagine).

Friction and Inclined Planes

Solving these problems involves careful use of $F_{net} = ma$, $F = \mu R$ and the equations of motion.

> That's right — you're expected to remember everything you learnt in M1, including $F = ma$ and all that *uvast* malarkey.

Use F = ma in *Two Directions* for *Inclined Plane* questions

For <u>inclined slope</u> questions, it's much easier to resolve forces <u>parallel</u> and <u>perpendicular</u> to the plane's surface. Remember that friction always acts in the <u>opposite</u> direction to the motion.

EXAMPLE

A small body of weight 20 N accelerates from rest and moves a distance of 5 m down a rough plane angled at 15° to the horizontal. Draw a force diagram and find the coefficient of friction between the body and the plane given that the motion takes 6 seconds. Take g = 9.8 ms⁻².

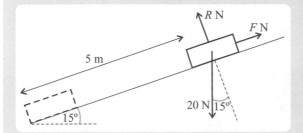

Taking down the slope as positive:

$u = 0$, $\quad s = 5$, $\quad t = 6$, $\quad a = ?$

Use one of the equations of motion: $\quad s = ut + \frac{1}{2}at^2$

$5 = (0 \times 6) + (\frac{1}{2}a \times 6^2)$ so **$a = 0.2778$ ms⁻²**

Resolving in ↖ direction:

$F_{net} = ma$

$R - 20\cos15° = \dfrac{20}{g} \times 0$

So: $\quad R = 20\cos15° = \mathbf{19.32\ N}$

> There is no acceleration <u>perpendicular</u> to the slope.

Resolving in ↙ direction:

$F_{net} = ma$

$20\sin15° - F = \dfrac{20}{g} \times 0.2778$

$F = 4.609$ N

It's sliding, so $\quad F = \mu R$

$4.609 = \mu \times 19.32$

$\mu = 0.24$ (to 2 d.p.)

EXAMPLE

An object rests on a rough plane inclined at an angle of θ° to the horizontal. The coefficient of friction between the object and the plane is 0.7. Determine the smallest value of θ for which the object will begin to slide down the plane.

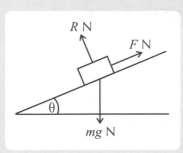

Resolving in ↙ direction: $\quad F_{net} = ma$

$mg\sin\theta - F = 0$

$\Rightarrow F = mg\sin\theta$, call this equation ①.

Resolving in ↖ direction: $\quad F_{net} = ma$

$R - mg\cos\theta = 0$

$\Rightarrow R = mg\cos\theta$, call this equation ②.

When the object is about to slide, friction is limiting, so $F = \mu R$.

So, using equations ① and ② :

$F = \mu R \Rightarrow mg\sin\theta = \mu mg\cos\theta$

Cancel mg: $\sin\theta = \mu\cos\theta \Rightarrow \mu = \tan\theta$

So, $\theta = \tan^{-1}\mu = \tan^{-1}(0.7) = 35.0°$ (3 s.f.)

> In general, a particle on an inclined plane will slide if $\tan\theta \geq \mu$.

Inclined planes — nothing to do with suggestible Boeing 737s...

The main thing to remember about inclined planes is that you can choose to resolve in any two directions as long as they're <u>perpendicular</u>. It makes sense to choose the directions that involve doing as little work as possible. Obviously.

Moments

In this lifetime there are moments — moments of joy and of sorrow, and those moments where you have to answer questions on moments in exams.

Moments are *Clockwise* or *Anticlockwise*

A 'moment' is the turning effect a force has around a point.
The larger the force, and the greater the distance from the point, then the larger the moment.

Moment = Force × Perpendicular Distance

EXAMPLE A plank 2 m long is attached horizontally to a ship at one end, O, as shown.
A bird lands on the other end of the plank, applying a force of 15 N.
Model the plank as a light rod and find the moment applied by the bird.

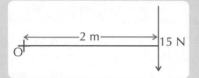

Moment   = F × d
           = 15 × 2
           = 30 Nm

The units are just newtons × metres = Nm. Couldn't they have thought of a cleverer name?

Actually, Moment = Force × Perpendicular Distance from Force's Line of Action

Often, you'll be given a distance between the point and the force, but this distance won't be perpendicular to the force's 'line of action'. You'll need to resolve to find the perpendicular distance.

EXAMPLE Find the sum of the moments of the forces shown about the point A.

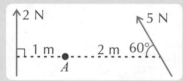

Calculating the clockwise moment is simple as the line of action is perpendicular to A:

$2 \times 1 = 2$ Nm

The anticlockwise moment is trickier as the line of action of the force isn't perpendicular to A.
There are two ways to go about finding the moment — by finding the perpendicular distance or finding the perpendicular component of the force.

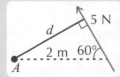

Finding the perpendicular distance:

$d = 2\sin60°$

So, moment = $5 \times 2\sin60° = 10\sin60° = 5\sqrt{3}$ Nm

Both methods give the same moment. Just choose whichever you find simplest — and be sure to show your workings.

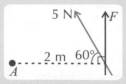

Finding the perpendicular component of the force:

$F = 5\sin60°$

So, moment = $5\sin60° \times 2 = 10\sin60° = 5\sqrt{3}$ Nm

We can now find the sum of the moments (in this case, taking anticlockwise as negative):

Clockwise + anticlockwise moments = $2 + (-5\sqrt{3}) = -6.66$ Nm (3 s.f.) = 6.66 Nm anticlockwise

Resolve the force, Luke — use the perpendicular distance...
Why do I want to write a musical every time I read a page about moments? Clearly a sci-fi epic would be more appropriate.

Moments

You'll remember from M1 that if a body is in <u>equilibrium</u>, then the <u>resultant force</u> in any direction is <u>zero</u>. Well, as if that wasn't enough, at equilibrium, <u>moments</u> about <u>any point</u> equal <u>zero</u> too. How about that?

In **Equilibrium** Moments Total **Zero**

In equilibrium, the moments about <u>any</u> point total zero — so <u>anticlockwise moments = clockwise moments</u>.

EXAMPLE Two weights of 30 N and 45 N are placed on a light 8 m beam. The 30 N weight is at one end of the beam, as shown, whilst the other weight is a distance d from the midpoint M. The beam is horizontal and held in equilibrium by a single wire with tension T attached at M. Find T and the distance d.

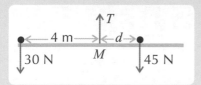

Resolving vertically: $30 + 45 = T = 75$ N

Take moments about M:
Clockwise Moment = Anticlockwise Moment
$$45 \times d = 30 \times 4$$
$$d = \frac{120}{45} = 2\frac{2}{3} = 2.67 \text{ m (3 s.f.)}$$

EXAMPLE A rod, AB, of length 6 m is held in equilibrium in a horizontal position by two strings, as shown. By taking moments, find the mass, m, of the rod. Take $g = 9.8$ ms⁻².

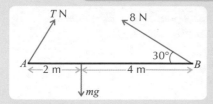

By taking moments about A:
clockwise moments = anticlockwise moments
$2mg = 6\sin30° \times 8$
$mg = 12 \Rightarrow m = 12 \div 9.8 = \boxed{1.22 \text{ kg (3 s.f.)}}$

Although you can take moments about any point (even one not on the rod), it's always easier to take moments about a point that has an unknown force going through it.

The **Weight** acts at the **Centre** of a **Uniform** rod

Mostly, you'll be dealing with <u>rods</u>. A model rod has <u>negligible thickness</u>, so you only need to consider where along its <u>length</u> the centre of mass lies. If the rod is <u>uniform</u> then the weight acts at the <u>centre</u> of the rod.

The entire weight of the rod can be considered to act at the <u>centre of mass</u>.

EXAMPLE A 6 m long uniform beam AB of weight 40 N is supported at A by a vertical reaction R. AB is held horizontal by a vertical wire attached 1 m from the other end. A particle of weight 30 N is placed 2 m from the support R. Find the tension T in the wire and the force R.

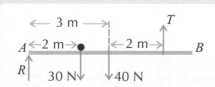

Take <u>moments</u> about A.
Clockwise Moment = Anticlockwise Moment
$$(30 \times 2) + (40 \times 3) = T \times 5$$
$$T = 36 \text{ N}$$
Resolve vertically: $T + R = 30 + 40$
So: $R = 34 \text{ N}$

EXAMPLE A uniform rod, AB, of length l m and mass m kg is suspended in horizontal equilibrium by two inextensible wires, with tensions as shown. Find m. Take $g = 9.8$ ms⁻².

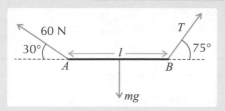

Take <u>moments</u> about B:
$60\sin30° \times l = mg \times \frac{1}{2}l$
so $m = \frac{60l}{gl} = \frac{60}{g} = 6.12$ kg (3 s.f.)

Again, it makes sense to take moments about B so you don't have to worry about the unknown force T.

Moments

You can **Calculate** the Centre of Mass for **Non-Uniform** rods

If the weight acts at an <u>unknown</u> point along a rod, the point can be found in the usual way — by taking <u>moments</u>.
You might also have to <u>resolve</u> the forces <u>horizontally</u> or <u>vertically</u> to find some missing information.

EXAMPLE A plank of length 7 m and mass 5 kg is supported horizontally by a vertical string attached at a point B, as shown. One end of the plank, A, rests upon a pole. The tension in the string is T and the normal reaction at the pole is 70 N. A particle, P, of mass 9 kg rests on the plank 2 m from A, as shown. The system is in equilibrium. Find T and the distance, x, from A to the centre of mass of the plank.

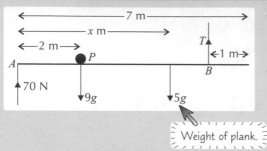

<u>Resolve vertically</u>: upward forces = downward forces:

$T + 70 = 9g + 5g$
so, $T = 14g - 70 = 67.2$ N

<u>Moments about A</u>: clockwise moments = anticlockwise moments:

$(9g \times 2) + (5g \times x) = 67.2 \times 6$
$49x = 403.2 - 176.4$
so $x = \dfrac{226.8}{49} = 4.63$ m (3 s.f.)

> Weight of plank.

EXAMPLE A Christmas banner, AB, is attached to a ceiling by two pieces of tinsel at A and C, where $BC = 0.6$ m. The banner has mass 8 kg and is held in a horizontal position. The tensions in the pieces of tinsel are equal. The banner can be modelled as a non-uniform rod held in equilibrium and the tinsel as light strings. Find the tension in the tinsel and the distance, x, between A and the centre of mass of the rod. Take $g = 9.8$ ms^{-2}.

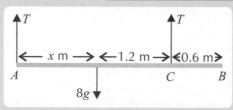

<u>Resolve vertically</u>:

$2T = 8g \Rightarrow T = 4g = 39.2$ N

Take <u>moments about A</u>:

$8g \times x = T \times (x + 1.2)$
$\Rightarrow 8gx = 4g(x + 1.2)$
$\Rightarrow 2x = x + 1.2 \Rightarrow x = 1.2$ m

The tinsel at A snaps and a downward force is applied at B to keep the banner horizontal.
Find the magnitude of the force applied at B and the tension in the tinsel attached at C.

Take <u>moments about C</u>:

$8g \times 1.2 = F_B \times 0.6$
So, $F_B = \dfrac{8 \times 9.8}{0.6} = 157$ N (3 s.f.)

<u>Resolve vertically</u>: $T_C = 8g + 157$
So, $T_C = 235$ N (3 s.f.)

EXAMPLE A non-uniform rod, AB, of mass 2 kg and length 1 m, is suspended in equilibrium at an angle of θ to the vertical by two vertical strings, as shown. The tensions in the strings are T N and 12 N respectively. Find the distance, x, from A to the rod's centre of mass. Take $g = 9.8$ ms^{-2}.

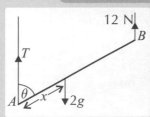

Taking <u>moments about A</u>: $2g\sin\theta \times x = 12\sin\theta \times 1$
$2\sin\theta$ cancels, so:
$gx = 6$
$x = 0.612$ m (3 s.f.)

Significant moments in life — birthdays, exams, exam results...

Don't worry that the models used in Mechanics aren't that realistic — it's the ability to do the maths (and pass those exams)
that counts. Anyway, you can worry about real life when you're done with school (when there'll be fewer exams).

Rigid Bodies

If reactions are at a weird angle, rather than horizontal, vertical or perpendicular to something else, then it's easier to think of them as <u>two components</u> — in two nice, convenient perpendicular directions.

Reactions can have *Horizontal and Vertical Components*

If a rod is connected to a plane (such as a wall) by a <u>hinge</u> or <u>pivot</u> and the forces holding it in equilibrium <u>aren't parallel</u>, then the reaction at the wall <u>won't be perpendicular</u> to the wall. Don't panic though, components are super-helpful here.

EXAMPLE A uniform rod, AB, is freely hinged on a vertical wall at A. The rod is held in horizontal equilibrium by a light inextensible string attached at a point C, 0.4 m from the end B at an angle of 45° to the rod, as shown. Given that the rod is 1.2 m long and has mass 2 kg, find the tension in the string and the magnitude of the reaction at the wall.

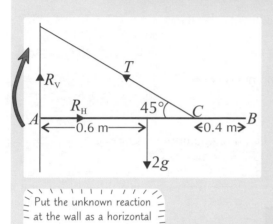

Put the unknown reaction at the wall as a horizontal and a vertical component.

Moments about A: ◄———— *Choose A so that you can ignore the unknown reaction components while finding T.*
$T\sin45° \times (1.2 - 0.4) = 2g \times 0.6$
so, $T\sin45° = 14.7$
and $\boxed{T = 20.788... = 20.8 \text{ N (3 s.f.)}}$

Resolving horizontally: ◄———— *The rod is in equilibrium, so the resultant force in any direction is zero.*
$R_H = T\cos45° = 20.788... \times \cos45°$
so, $R_H = 14.7$ N

Resolving vertically:
$R_V + T\sin45° = 2g$
so $R_V = 4.9$ N

Magnitude of reaction:
$|R| = \sqrt{R_H^2 + R_V^2} = \sqrt{14.7^2 + 4.9^2}$
so $\boxed{|R| = 15.5 \text{ N (3 s.f.)}}$

EXAMPLE A non-uniform rod, AB, of length $6a$ and mass 4 kg is supported by a light strut at an angle of 70° to a vertical wall, as shown. The distance from A to the centre of mass, X, of the rod is xa m. The strut exerts a thrust of 16 N at the centre of the rod. A particle of weight 2 N is placed at B. Find x, and the magnitude and direction of the reaction at A.

Moments about A:
$16\cos70° \times 3a = (4g \times xa) + (2 \times 6a)$
so $4gxa = 4.4169... \times a$
and $\boxed{x = 0.113 \text{ (3 s.f.)}}$

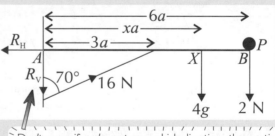

Resolving horizontally:
$R_H = 16\sin70°$
$\Rightarrow R_H = 15.04$ N (4 s.f.)

Resolving vertically:
$R_V + 4g + 2 = 16\cos70°$
so $R_V = 16\cos70° - 39.2 - 2 \Rightarrow R_V = -35.73$ N (4 s.f.)

Don't worry if you're not sure which directions the reaction components act in. You'll just get negative numbers if you're wrong (the magnitude will be the same).

Magnitude of reaction:
$|R| = \sqrt{R_H^2 + R_V^2} = \sqrt{15.04^2 + 35.73^2}$
so $\boxed{|R| = 38.8 \text{ N (3 s.f.)}}$

R_V is negative — so it must go upwards instead of downwards.

Direction of reaction:
$\tan\theta = \dfrac{15.04}{35.73}$

so $\boxed{\theta = 22.8° \text{ (3 s.f.) to the wall}}$

I'm trying to resist making a pun about rigor mortis...

...so I'll just tell you that it's due to irreversible muscular contraction caused by a shortage of adenosine triphosphate. Nice.

Rigid Bodies and Friction

Where would we be without friction? Well, using a ladder would certainly be trickier. Before getting too distracted by that thought you should really revise this page instead — ladders are featured, I promise.

Friction lets you assume the Reaction is Perpendicular

From the previous page, you know that a rod attached to a wall has a reaction at the wall with a horizontal and vertical component. If the rod is held by friction instead, then the frictional force 'replaces' the vertical component.

EXAMPLE A rod, AB, rests against a rough vertical wall and is held in limiting equilibrium perpendicular to the wall by a light inextensible string attached at B at an angle of θ, as shown, where $\tan\theta = \frac{7}{17}$.
The tension in the string is 42 N. The length AB is 5.5 m and the centre of mass is located 3.8 m from B. Find the mass of the rod, m, and the coefficient of friction, μ, between the wall and the rod.

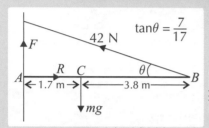

$\tan\theta = \frac{7}{17}$

First take moments about A so you can find mg while ignoring the unknowns F and R.

Moments about A: $mg \times 1.7 = 42\sin\theta \times 5.5$
so $mg = 51.737...$ N
and $m = 5.28$ kg (3 s.f.)

Now take moments about a different point to find F. I've taken them about C, but you could have used B.

Moments about C: $1.7 \times F = 3.8 \times 42\sin\theta$
so $F = 35.7$ N (3 s.f.)

Now you know F, you only need to find R before you can find μ.

Resolving horizontally:
$R = 42\cos\theta$
$R = 38.8$ N (3 s.f.)

Limiting equilibrium, so $F = \mu R$:
$35.7 = 38.8\mu$
so $\mu = 0.92$ (2 s.f.)

Limiting equilibrium first appeared on p. 152 — it means that the body is on the point of moving.

Multiple Surfaces can exert a Frictional Force

'Ladder' questions, where a rod rests at an angle against the ground and a wall, are common in M2 exams. Often, the ground is modelled as rough and the wall as smooth. Can't take these things for granted though...

The 4 possible combinations of surfaces for 'ladder' questions:

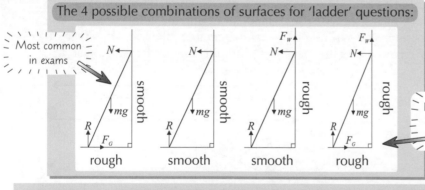

Most common in exams

Friction acts to prevent motion — so think about which way the ladder would slip and draw the frictional force in the opposite direction.

EXAMPLE A ladder rests against a smooth wall at an angle of 65° to the rough ground, as shown. The ladder has mass 1.3 kg and length $5x$ m. A cat of mass 4.5 kg sits on the ladder at C, $4x$ m from the base. The ladder is in limiting equilibrium. Model the ladder as a uniform rod and the cat as a particle. Find the coefficient of friction between the ground and the ladder.

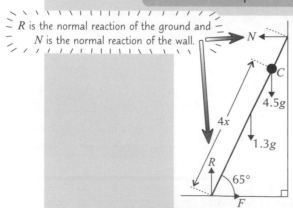

R is the normal reaction of the ground and N is the normal reaction of the wall.

Resolving horizontally: $F = N$

Take moments about the base of the ladder to find N:
$N\sin65° \times 5x = (1.3g\cos65° \times 2.5x) + (4.5g\cos65° \times 4x)$
$4.532xN = 13.46x + 74.55x$
so, $N = \dfrac{88.01x}{4.532x} = 19.4$ N (3 s.f.)

Resolve vertically to find R:
$R = 1.3g + 4.5g$
$\Rightarrow R = 56.84$ N

The ladder is in limiting equilibrium, so $F = \mu R$:
Resolving horizontally shows $F = N$, so, $19.4 = 56.84\mu$
and $\mu = 0.34$ (2 s.f.)

Rigid Bodies and Friction

A *Reaction* is always *Perpendicular to the Surface*

Sometimes a body may be leaning against a surface that isn't vertical. This blows my mind.

EXAMPLE
A uniform ladder of length 3 m rests against a smooth wall slanted at 10° to the vertical, as shown. The ladder is at an angle of 60° to the ground. The magnitude of the normal reaction of the wall is 18 N. Find the mass of the ladder.

If the wall was vertical then the angles shown in red would be <u>identical</u> as both the weight and the wall would be perpendicular to the ground. Simple. However, the 18 N reaction at the wall is perpendicular to the <u>wall</u>, so be careful when resolving forces <u>relative to the ladder</u>.

Moments about the base of the ladder:
$mg\sin 30° \times 1.5 = 18\sin 70° \times 3$
so $m = 6.90$ kg (3 s.f.)

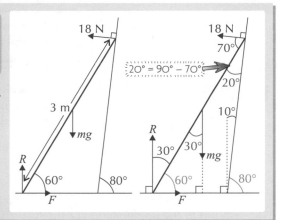

Bodies can be Supported *Along Their Lengths*

If a rod is <u>resting</u> on something along its length then the reaction is <u>perpendicular</u> to the <u>rod</u>.

EXAMPLE
A uniform rod, AB, rests with end A on rough ground and upon a smooth peg at C, 0.9 m from B. The rod has length 3.3 m and weight 10 N. A particle, P, with weight 25 N is placed at B. Given that the rod is held in limiting equilibrium at an angle of 28° above the horizontal, find the magnitude of the normal reaction, R_2, at the peg and the friction, F, between the rod and the ground.

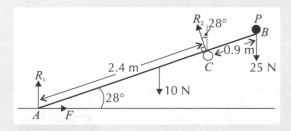

It's a uniform rod, so its weight acts in the middle.

Moments about A:
$2.4R_2 = (10\cos 28° \times 1.65) + (25\cos 28° \times 3.3)$
so $R_2 = 36.421... = 36.4$ N (3 s.f.)

Resolving horizontally:
$F = R_2\sin 28° = 36.421... \times \sin 28°$
$\Rightarrow F = 17.1$ N (3 s.f.)

If you *Don't Know* that equilibrium is *Limiting*, F ≤ μR

In <u>limiting equilibrium</u>, friction is at its <u>maximum</u> (i.e. $F = \mu R$). You might be asked to find μ when you don't know if equilibrium is limiting. Just find it in the same way as if equilibrium was limiting, but replace $F = \mu R$ with $F \leq \mu R$.

EXAMPLE
A rough peg supports a rod of mass 3 kg at a point B, 0.2 m from one end of the rod, as shown. The other end of the rod, A, rests on a smooth horizontal plane. The rod is 1.5 m long, with its centre of mass located 1.2 m from A at point C. Given that the rod is in equilibrium at an angle of 15° to the horizontal plane and that the friction at the peg exerts a force of 8 N, show that $\mu \geq 0.30$.

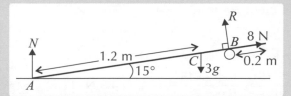

You know F, but to find μ you also need to know R.
Take moments about A to find R:
$R \times (1.5 - 0.2) = 3g\cos 15° \times 1.2$
so $R = 26.2$ N (3 s.f.)

$F \leq \mu R$
so $\mu \geq \dfrac{8}{26.2}$
$\mu \geq 0.30$ (2 s.f.)

A body can also be supported along its length by a bed...

... but rough ground and a smooth peg sound much more comfortable. The thing to remember about these questions is to keep an eye on whether the points of contact are rough or smooth — that tells you whether or not you need to worry about friction. It's a bit of a pain, but you've just got to take the rough with the smooth I guess...

Laminas and Moments

I'm getting a bit fed up with thin rods and beams — I'm ready to take it to another dimension. Pay close attention. Just like with rods, the entire weight of an object can be considered to act at the <u>centre of mass</u>.

Remember to measure to the **Line of Action** of a Force

You probably don't need me to tell you again that to find the moment of a force about a point, you need to use the <u>perpendicular distance</u> from the point to the <u>line of action</u> of the force. Well, it's that 'line of action' bit that starts to become more important when you're dealing with 2D shapes:

> **EXAMPLE** A uniform lamina, *ABCD*, of weight 8 N is freely hinged to the corner of a wall at *A*. The lamina is held in equilibrium by a vertical force *F* acting at point *C* as shown. Find the value of *F* by taking moments about *A*.

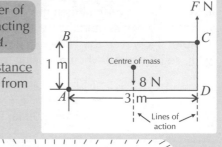

1) The lamina is uniform, so the mass acts at the centre. The <u>perpendicular distance</u> from *A* to the line of action of the lamina's weight is the <u>horizontal distance</u> from *AB* to the centre of mass (1.5 m).

2) The force *F* also acts <u>vertically</u> and the <u>perpendicular distance</u> from *A* to the line of action of the force is 3 m.

3) So, taking moments about *A*: $8 \times 1.5 = F \times 3 \Rightarrow F = 4$ N

Flick back to p. 143 for a reminder about laminas and their centres of mass.

The <u>vertical</u> distances between A and the forces don't matter. Because both forces are only <u>acting vertically</u>, you only need to use the <u>horizontal distance</u> to work out the moments.

Split **Angled Forces** into **Perpendicular Components**, then take Moments

1) When you've got a lamina held in equilibrium at a funny angle, the easiest thing to do is just <u>split each force</u> acting on the lamina into <u>two perpendicular components</u>.

2) Then, when you take moments, just use the <u>perpendicular distance</u> to the line of action of <u>each component</u>.

3) And remember — when you take moments about a point on a 2D shape, you need to look for forces acting in <u>all</u> directions. (With 1D shapes like rods, you can ignore any forces acting parallel to the rod when taking moments.)

> **EXAMPLE** The house-shaped lamina shown has a mass of 8 kg and its centre of mass lies on the axis of symmetry, 5.15 cm above the centre of the base. The lamina is smoothly pivoted at point *P* and is supported in equilibrium by a light, inextensible vertical wire at point *Q*, as shown.
>
> The base of the lamina makes an angle of 15° with the horizontal. Find the tension, *T*, in the wire.

<u>Split</u> the forces acting on the shape into components acting <u>parallel</u> and <u>perpendicular</u> to the base of the lamina:

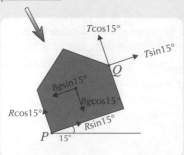

Now take <u>moments</u> about *P* (so *R* can be ignored):

- Total <u>clockwise</u> moment = $(8g\cos15° \times 5) + (T\sin15° \times 7)$

- Total <u>anticlockwise</u> moment = $(8g\sin15° \times 5.15) + (T\cos15° \times 10)$

The lamina is in <u>equilibrium</u>, so:

$(8g\cos15° \times 5) + (T\sin15° \times 7) = (8g\sin15° \times 5.15) + (T\cos15° \times 10)$

$\Rightarrow 7T\sin15° - 10T\cos15° = (8g\sin15° \times 5.15) - (8g\cos15° \times 5)$

$\Rightarrow T = \dfrac{(8g\sin15° \times 5.15) - (8g\cos15° \times 5)}{7\sin15° - 10\cos15°} = 34.9$ N (3 s.f.)

Let's just take a moment to resolve the issue...

You don't have to split the forces into perpendicular components first — you could just take moments straight away. But more often than not, that leads to tricky Pythagoras and trig to get the distances right. I reckon this way makes it a bit easier.

Forces in Frameworks

Remember <u>frameworks</u> from page 147? Well they're about to <u>thrust</u> themselves back into your life. Awesome.

Internal Forces in rods can be Thrusts or Tensions

In a framework of light, pin-jointed rods, <u>each rod</u> experiences a <u>single internal force</u>, which is <u>constant</u> throughout the rod. There are <u>two types</u> of internal force:

1) Forces acting '<u>inwards</u>', towards the <u>centres of the rods</u>, are known as <u>tensions</u>.

2) Forces acting '<u>outwards</u>', towards the <u>ends of the rods</u>, are called <u>thrusts</u> (or <u>compressions</u>).

3) In the diagram on the right, rods AB and BC are in <u>tension</u>, and rod AC is in <u>compression</u>.

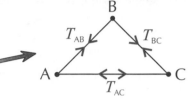

> ### Internal Forces in a Framework
> **ABC is a framework of light, rigid rods freely pin-jointed together at A, B and C.**
>
> T_{AB}, T_{BC} and T_{AC} are the <u>internal</u> <u>forces</u> acting in the rods.

Resolve at Each Joint to find Unknown Forces

1) The rods in a framework are in <u>equilibrium</u>, so the resultant force at <u>each joint</u> will be zero.

2) This means you can <u>resolve</u> forces at <u>each joint</u> to find any <u>unknown forces</u>. ◄ — *This is likely to require some deft use of trig. Again.*

3) To resolve at a joint, you <u>consider only the forces acting at that joint</u>. Don't forget that there may also be <u>external forces</u> acting at the joint, such as a weight or reaction forces.

4) Working out whether each internal force is a <u>tension</u> or <u>thrust</u> is easy. Just <u>assume</u> that all the internal forces are <u>one type</u> (e.g. tensions), and then if any forces turn out <u>negative</u>, then they must be the <u>other</u> (i.e. thrusts). Cool, eh?

EXAMPLE

The diagram shows a framework of light rigid rods AB and AC in a vertical plane. The rods are freely pin-jointed to each other at A and to fixed points on a vertical wall at B and C. A load of weight 4 N is attached at point A.

a) Draw and label a diagram of the forces acting on the framework and the internal forces in the rods.

b) Calculate the internal forces in the two rods, and state whether they are tensions or thrusts.

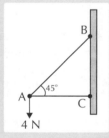

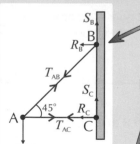

a) The diagram of the forces acting on the framework can be seen here. The forces S_B, R_B, S_C and R_C are the reaction forces of the wall on the framework, and T_{AB} and T_{AC} are the <u>internal forces</u> acting on the rods. Both internal forces have been drawn as <u>tensions</u>.

b) <u>Resolve</u> at A to find the internal forces:

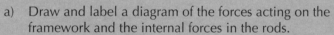

Vertically:
$$4 = T_{AB}\sin45°$$
$$\Rightarrow T_{AB} = 4 \div \sin45° = 4\sqrt{2} \text{ N}$$

Horizontally:
$$T_{AB}\cos45° + T_{AC} = 0$$
$$\Rightarrow T_{AC} = -T_{AB}\cos45° = \frac{-4\sqrt{2}}{\sqrt{2}} = -4 \text{ N}$$

As the internal forces were all assumed to be tensions, T_{AB} is a <u>tension</u> of $4\sqrt{2}$ N and T_{AC} is a <u>thrust</u> of 4 N.

Resolve at A rather than B or C so you don't have to deal with the unknown reactions on the wall.

Remember that internal forces are the same throughout a rod — so the magnitude of T_{AC} is 4 N at <u>both</u> A and C. That would be handy to know if you were trying to find R_C.

I'm sensing a lot of tension in the room — maybe it's all this talk of rigid rods...

There's nothing too tricky on this page. Once you get your head around resolving at a point, it's all stuff you've done before. Make sure you understand that 'assuming all to be tensions' business, and then crack on with some questions...

M2 Section 2 — Practice Questions

Time to make like a tree and ~~half leave sway gently in the breeze.~~ Darn it, that analogy wasn't really working...
Anyway, time to be a <u>dedicated student</u> and practise your forces know-how. Ace.

Warm-up Questions

Whenever a numerical value of g is required in the following questions, take $g = 9.8$ ms^{-2}.

1) A brick of mass 1.2 kg is sliding down a rough plane which is inclined at 25° to the horizontal. Given that its acceleration is 0.3 ms^{-2} down the plane, find the coefficient of friction between the brick and the plane.

2) A 60 kg uniform beam AE of length 14 m is in equilibrium, supported by two vertical ropes attached to B and D as shown.

   Find the tensions in the ropes to 1 d.p.

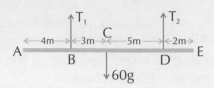

3) What is meant by a 'non-uniform rod'?

4) A uniform ladder, of length l m, is placed on rough horizontal ground and rests against a smooth vertical wall at an angle of 20° to the wall. Draw a diagram illustrating this system with forces labelled. State what assumptions you would make.

5) Calculate the perpendicular distance from the particle, P, to the forces shown in the diagrams below:
   a)   b)   c)

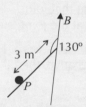

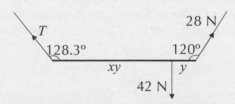

6) a) Given that the beam shown is in equilibrium, calculate the magnitude of T.

   b) Find the value of x.

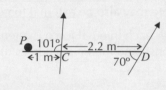

Those <u>practice questions</u> should've been a <u>doddle</u>. Time to step it up a notch with some questions more like those you'll get in the exam. In the words of a fictional <u>dance-squad commander</u>, "don't let me down".

Exam Questions

Whenever a numerical value of g is required in the following questions, take $g = 9.8$ ms^{-2}.

1 A non-uniform rod, AB, is freely hinged at a vertical wall. It is held in horizontal equilibrium by a beam attached to the wall at C at an angle of 55°. The tension in the beam is 30 N, as shown. The rod has mass 2 kg, centred 0.4 m from A. The total length of the rod is x m.

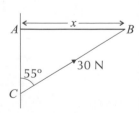

   a) Find the length of the rod, x.

   (3 marks)

   b) Find the magnitude and direction of the reaction at A.

   (5 marks)

M2 Section 2 — Practice Questions

If the previous question was a struggle, then you know what to do — go back a few pages and have another look. These questions will still be here while you're gone. Lurking.

2   A horizontal uniform beam with length x and weight 18 N is held in equilibrium by two vertical strings. One string is attached to one end of the beam and the other at point A, 3 m from the first string. The tension in the string at point A is 12 N.
Show that $x = 4$ m.

(3 marks)

3   A 6 m long uniform beam of mass 20 kg is in equilibrium. One end is resting on a vertical pole, and the other end is held up by a vertical wire attached to that end so that the beam rests horizontally. There are two 10 kg weights attached to the beam, situated 2 m from either end.

a)   Draw a diagram of the beam including all the forces acting on it.

(2 marks)

Find, in terms of g:

b) T, the tension in the wire.

(3 marks)

c) R, the normal reaction at the pole.

(2 marks)

4   A uniform rod, AB, is held in limiting horizontal equilibrium against a rough wall by an inextensible string connected to the rod at point C and the wall at point D, as shown. A particle of mass m kg rests at point B. The magnitude of the normal reaction of the wall at A is 72.5 N. The mass of the rod is 3 kg.

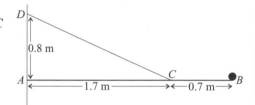

a)   Find the tension, T, in the string.

(4 marks)

b)   Find m.

(3 marks)

c)   Find the magnitude of the frictional force, F, between the wall and the rod.

(3 marks)

5   A uniform rod of mass m kg rests in equilibrium against rough horizontal ground at point A and a smooth peg at point B, making an angle of θ with the ground, as shown.
The rod is l m long and B is $\frac{3}{4}l$ from A.

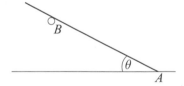

a)   Show that the perpendicular reaction at the peg, $P = \frac{2}{3}mg\cos\theta$.

(3 marks)

b)   Given that $\sin\theta = \frac{3}{5}$, find the range of values which the coefficient of friction between the rod and the ground could take.

(6 marks)

6   A horizontal force of 8 N just stops a mass of 7 kg from sliding down a plane inclined at 15° to the horizontal, as shown.

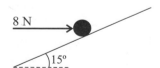

a)   Calculate the coefficient of friction between the mass and the plane to 2 d.p.

(5 marks)

b)   The 8 N force is now removed. Find how long the mass takes to slide a distance of 3 m down the line of greatest slope.

(7 marks)

7   A uniform ladder, *AB*, is positioned against a smooth vertical wall and rests upon rough horizontal ground at an angle of θ, as shown. Clive stands on the ladder at point *C*, two-thirds of the way along the ladder's length from *A*. The ladder is 4.2 m long and weighs 180 N. The normal reaction at A is 490 N.

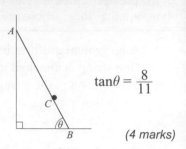

$\tan\theta = \dfrac{8}{11}$

The ladder rests in limiting equilibrium. Model Clive as a particle and find:

a)   the mass of Clive, *m*, to the nearest kg.

(4 marks)

b)   the coefficient of friction, μ, between the ground and the ladder.

(5 marks)

8   The diagram shows a framework of light, rigid rods freely pin-jointed to each other at A, B and C and to a fixed horizontal surface at D. The framework rests on the horizontal surface at C and experiences a reaction force of *R* N. There is also a force of *F* N acting at A at an angle of 30° to the vertical, as shown.

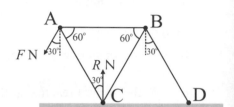

a)   Draw a diagram showing the internal forces acting on the rods. Also include *R* and *F* in your diagram.

(1 mark)

b)   Find the magnitude of each of the internal forces in terms of *F* and state whether each rod is under tension or compression. Also find *R* in terms of *F*.

(7 marks)

9   A shape is made up of a uniform square lamina and a uniform rectangular lamina as shown. The centre of mass of the shape is located 2 m from AB and 2.28 m from AC.

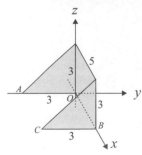

The shape is smoothly pivoted at A and rests in equilibrium against a smooth vertical wall. The angle between AC and the horizontal ground is 30°. Given that the weight of the shape is 4 N, find the magnitude of the reaction force, *R*, of the wall on the shape.

(4 marks)

10   Two uniform laminas in the shape of right-angled triangles are fixed to either end of a uniform rectangular lamina to make a sign, as shown. The edge *OA* coincides with the *y*-axis, *BC* runs parallel to *OA*, and *OB* coincides with the *x*-axis. The three laminas are made from the same material. The coordinates of the centre of mass of the shape are (2.5, –0.375, 1.3125), referred to the axes shown.

The *x*- and *y*-axes are on rough horizontal ground. A horizontal force of magnitude *H* is applied to the sign at the point (2.5, 0, 1.5). The force acts perpendicular to *OB* in the positive *y* direction. The mass of the sign is 3 kg.

a)   Given that the lamina is prevented from sliding and is on the point of tipping about the *x*-axis, calculate *H*.

(4 marks)

The coefficient of friction between the sign and the ground is 0.35.

b)   Given that the sign is no longer prevented from sliding, determine whether the force *H* will cause the sign to slide before it tips.

(3 marks)

Work Done

Hello, good evening, welcome to Section 3 — where <u>work</u> and <u>energy</u> are tonight's chef's specials...

You Can Find the **Work Done** by a Force Over a Certain **Distance**

When a force is acting on a particle, you can work out the <u>work done</u> by the force using the formula:

> **Work done = force (F) × distance moved in the direction of the force (s)**

For F in newtons, and s in metres, the unit of work done is joules (J).

E.g. if an object is pushed <u>4 m</u> across a horizontal floor by a force of magnitude <u>12 N</u> acting horizontally, the <u>work done</u> by the force will be 12 × 4 = <u>48 J</u>

EXAMPLE   A rock is dragged across horizontal ground by a rope attached to the rock at an angle of 25° to the horizontal. Given that the work done by the force is 470 J and the tension in the rope is 120 N, find the distance the rock is moved.

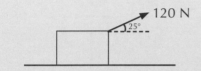

120 N

Work = horizontal component of force × s

$470 = 120\cos25 \times s$

$s = 4.32$ m (3 s.f.)

Because the force and the distance moved have to be in the same direction.

EXAMPLE   A sack of flour of mass m kg is attached to a vertical rope and raised h m at a constant speed. Show that the work done against gravity by the tension in the rope, T, can be expressed as mgh.

T N

mg N

Resolve vertically:

$F = ma$

$T - mg = m \times 0$

$\Rightarrow T = mg$

Work done = Fs

$= T \times h$

$= mgh$

Work and gravity

You can always use the formula mgh to find the work done by a force against gravity.

Gravity is a <u>conservative</u> force. The work done by (or against) a conservative force depends only on the <u>start</u> and <u>end</u> points of motion, not the path between the two points. So if the sack of flour above was <u>raised</u> and <u>then lowered</u> by h m, the total work done would be <u>zero</u>. Forces that aren't conservative are called <u>dissipative</u> (e.g. friction).

A Particle Moving **Up a Rough Slope** does Work against **Friction and Gravity**

EXAMPLE   A block of mass 3 kg is pulled 9 m up a rough plane inclined at an angle of 20° to the horizontal by a force, T. The block moves at a constant speed. The work done by T against friction is 154 J.

Find: a)   the work done by T against gravity
          b)   the coefficient of friction between the block and the plane.

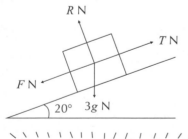

R N

T N

F N

20° $3g$ N

a)   Work done against gravity = mgh

    $= 3g \times 9\sin20$

    $= \textbf{90.5 J}$ (3 s.f.)

You need to use the <u>vertical</u> height, because it's only vertically that T does work against gravity.

b)   Resolve perpendicular to the slope to find R:

    $R - 3g\cos20 = m \times 0$

    $\Rightarrow R = 3g\cos20$

Particle is moving, so:

$F = \mu R$

$= \mu \times 3g\cos20$

Work done by T against friction

    $= F \times s = 154$

So, $\mu \times 3g\cos20 \times 9 = 154$

    $\mu = \textbf{0.619}$ (3 s.f.)

Remember — for a moving particle, $F = \mu R$, where μ is the coefficient of friction and R is the normal reaction.

The bit of T that is working against friction must be equal to F as the block is moving with constant speed (i.e. a = O), so you can just use F here.

My work done = coffee × flapjack...

The really important thing to remember from this page is that the distance moved must be in the <u>same direction as the force</u>. Also, don't forget that a particle moving at constant velocity has no resultant force acting on it — this makes resolving forces easy.

Kinetic and Potential Energy

Here are couple of jokers you might remember from GCSE Science. I know, I know — Science. This means we're skirting dangerously close to the <u>real world</u> here. :| Don't be too afraid though — it's not as scary as you might think...

A *Moving Particle* Possesses *Kinetic Energy*

Any particle that is <u>moving</u> has <u>kinetic energy</u> (K.E.). You can find the kinetic energy of a particle using the formula:

$$\text{K.E.} = \tfrac{1}{2}mv^2$$

You need to learn this formula — you won't be given it in the exam.

If mass, m, is measured in kg and velocity, v, in ms^{-1}, then kinetic energy is measured in joules.

EXAMPLE

An ice skater of mass 60 kg is moving at a constant velocity of 8 ms^{-1}. Find the ice skater's kinetic energy.

Kinetic energy $= \tfrac{1}{2}mv^2$

$\qquad\qquad = \tfrac{1}{2} \times 60 \times 8^2 = 1920\,\text{J}$

Work Done is the same as the *Change* in a Particle's *Kinetic Energy*

The <u>work done</u> by a force to <u>change the velocity</u> of a particle moving <u>horizontally</u> is equal to the change in that particle's kinetic energy:

Work done = change in kinetic energy

$$\textbf{Work done} = \tfrac{1}{2}mv^2 - \tfrac{1}{2}mu^2 = \tfrac{1}{2}m(v^2 - u^2)$$

EXAMPLE

A particle P of mass 6 kg is pulled along a rough horizontal plane by a force of 40 N, acting parallel to the plane. The particle travels 4 m in a straight line between two points on the plane, A and B. The coefficient of friction between P and the plane is 0.35.

a) Find the work done against friction in moving P from A to B.

At B, P has a speed of 8 ms^{-1}.

b) Calculate the speed of P at A.

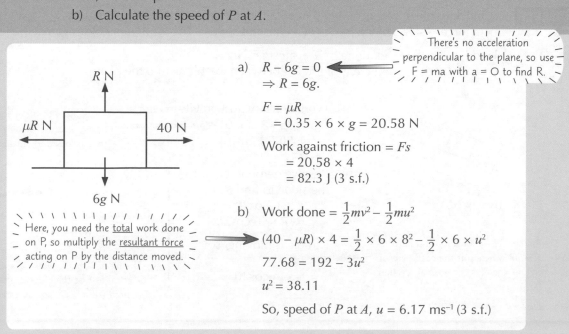

a) $R - 6g = 0$
$\Rightarrow R = 6g.$

There's no acceleration perpendicular to the plane, so use $F = ma$ with $a = 0$ to find R.

$F = \mu R$
$\quad = 0.35 \times 6 \times g = 20.58\,\text{N}$

Work against friction $= Fs$
$\quad = 20.58 \times 4$
$\quad = 82.3\,\text{J}$ (3 s.f.)

b) Work done $= \tfrac{1}{2}mv^2 - \tfrac{1}{2}mu^2$

$(40 - \mu R) \times 4 = \tfrac{1}{2} \times 6 \times 8^2 - \tfrac{1}{2} \times 6 \times u^2$

$77.68 = 192 - 3u^2$

$u^2 = 38.11$

So, speed of P at A, $u = 6.17$ ms^{-1} (3 s.f.)

Here, you need the <u>total</u> work done on P, so multiply the <u>resultant force</u> acting on P by the distance moved.

Kinetic and Potential Energy

Gravitational Potential Energy is all about a Particle's Height

The gravitational potential energy (G.P.E.) of a particle can be found using the formula:

$$\text{G.P.E.} = mgh$$ ← You need to learn this formula as well.

If mass (m) is measured in kg, acceleration due to gravity (g) in ms^{-2} and the vertical height above some base level (h) in m, then G.P.E. is measured in <u>joules</u>.

The <u>greater the height</u> of a particle above the 'base level', the <u>greater</u> that particle's gravitational <u>potential energy</u>.

EXAMPLE

A lift and its occupants have a combined mass of 750 kg. The lift moves vertically from the ground to the first floor of a building, 6.1 m above the ground. After pausing, it moves vertically to the 17th floor, 64.9 m above the ground. Find the gravitational potential energy gained by the lift and its occupants in moving:

a) from the ground floor to the first floor,

b) from the first floor to the 17th floor.

a) G.P.E. gained = $mg \times$ increase in height
$= 750 \times 9.8 \times 6.1$
$= 44\,800$ J (3 s.f)

b) G.P.E. gained = $mg \times$ increase in height
$= 750 \times 9.8 \times (64.9 - 6.1)$
$= 432\,000$ J (3 s.f.)

Gravitational Potential Energy Always uses the Vertical Height

When you're working out the gravitational potential energy of a particle, the value of h you use should <u>always, always, always</u> be the <u>vertical height</u> above the 'base level'. This means that for a particle moving on a <u>slope</u>, it's only the <u>vertical component</u> of the distance you're interested in:

EXAMPLE

A skateboarder and her board have a combined mass of 65 kg. The skateboarder starts from rest at a point X and freewheels down a slope inclined at 15° to the horizontal. She travels 40 m down the line of greatest slope. Find the gravitational potential energy lost by the skateboarder.

The skateboarder has moved a distance of 40 m down the slope, so this is a vertical distance of: 40sin15° m.
G.P.E. = mgh
$= 65 \times 9.8 \times 40\sin 15°$
$= 6590$ J $= 6.59$ kJ (both to 3 s.f.)

Mechanical Energy is the Sum of a Particle's Kinetic and Potential Energies

Over the next couple of pages, you're going to see a fair bit about '<u>mechanical energy</u>'. This is nothing to freak out about — it's just the sum of the kinetic and potential energies of a particle:

Total Mechanical Energy = Kinetic Energy + Gravitational Potential Energy

Strictly speaking, it also includes Elastic Potential Energy, but you don't need to know about that in M2 — hooray!

Particle P has so much potential — if only he could apply himself...

There shouldn't be anything earth-shattering on these two pages — I'd bet my completed 1994-95 Premier League sticker album that you've seen both of these types of energy before*. Still, it's worth refreshing yourself for what comes next.

*I won't though, it's too dear to me. Ahh, shinies...

The Work-Energy Principle

Those pages refreshing your memory on potential and kinetic energy weren't just for fun and giggles. Behold...

Learn the **Principle of Conservation of Mechanical Energy...**

The principle of conservation of mechanical energy says that:

> **If there are no external forces doing work on an object, the total mechanical energy of the object will remain constant.**

An external force is any force other than the weight of the object, e.g. friction, air resistance, tension in a rope, etc. This means that the sum of potential and kinetic energies remains the same throughout an object's motion. This is a pretty useful bit of knowledge:

EXAMPLE

A BASE jumper with mass 88 kg jumps from a ledge on a building, 150 m above the ground. He falls with an initial velocity of 6 ms^{-1} towards the ground. He releases his parachute at a point 60 m above the ground.

a) Find the initial kinetic energy of the jumper in kJ.

b) Use the principle of conservation of mechanical energy to find the jumper's kinetic energy and speed at the point where he releases his parachute.

c) State one assumption you have made in modelling this situation.

a) Initial K.E. $= \frac{1}{2}mu^2 = \frac{1}{2} \times 88 \times (6)^2$

$= 1584 = 1.58$ kJ (3 s.f.)

b) Decrease in G.P.E. as he falls:

You can just use the change in height here, as it's the change in G.P.E. that you're interested in.

$mgh = 88 \times 9.8 \times (150 - 60)$

$= 77\,616$ J

Using conservation of mechanical energy: Increase in K.E. = Decrease in G.P.E.

So, K.E. when parachute released − Initial K.E. = Decrease in G.P.E.

$$\frac{1}{2}mv^2 = \text{Decrease in G.P.E.} + \text{Initial K.E.}$$

$$= 77616 + 1584 = 79.2 \text{ kJ}$$

Rearrange $\frac{1}{2}mv^2 = 79\,200$ to find the speed of the jumper when parachute is released:

If you don't assume this, then you can't use the principle of conservation of energy.

$$v = \sqrt{\frac{79\,200}{\frac{1}{2} \times 88}} = 42.4 \text{ ms}^{-1} \text{ (3 s.f.)}$$

c) That the only force acting on the jumper is his weight.

...and the **Work-Energy Principle**

1) As you saw above, if there are no external forces doing work on an object, then the total mechanical energy of the object remains constant.

2) So, if there *is* an external force doing work on an object, then the total mechanical energy of the object must change.

3) This leads to the work-energy principle:

> **The work done on an object by external forces is equal to the change in the total mechanical energy of that object.**

4) The work-energy principle is pretty similar to the result on page 166. It's generally more useful though, because you can use it for objects moving in any direction — not just horizontally.

Turn the page for a **HOT** and **SEXY** example...

The Work-Energy Principle

As promised, a <u>lovely example</u> of the work-energy principle...

Example

A particle of mass 3 kg is projected up a rough plane inclined at an angle θ to the horizontal, where $\tan\theta = \frac{5}{12}$. The particle moves through a point A at a speed of 11 ms^{-1}.

The particle continues to move up the line of greatest slope and comes to rest at a point B before sliding back down the plane. The coefficient of friction between the particle and the slope is $\frac{1}{3}$.

a) Use the work-energy principle to find the distance AB.

b) Find the speed of the particle when it returns to A.

a) Call the distance AB x.

You're told to use the work-energy principle, so first find the change in total mechanical energy:

Change in K.E. of the particle = Final K.E. – Initial K.E.

$$= \tfrac{1}{2}mv^2 - \tfrac{1}{2}mu^2 = 0 - \left(\tfrac{1}{2} \times 3 \times 11^2\right) = \textbf{–181.5 J}$$

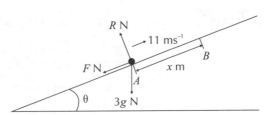

Change in G.P.E. of the particle = $mg \times$ (change in height)

$$= 3gx\sin\theta = 3gx \times \frac{5}{13} = \frac{\textbf{15gx}}{\textbf{13}} \textbf{ J}$$

⟵ $\tan\theta = \frac{5}{12} \Rightarrow \sin\theta = \frac{5}{13}$

So, change in total mechanical energy

$$= \textbf{–181.5} + \frac{\textbf{15gx}}{\textbf{13}}$$

Displacement is <u>negative</u> because the particle is moving in the <u>opposite direction to F</u>.

The only external force doing work on the particle is the frictional force, F. So you need to find the work done by F.

First, resolve perpendicular to slope:

$$R - 3g\cos\theta = 0 \Rightarrow R = 3g \times \frac{12}{13} = \frac{36g}{13}$$

$$F = \mu R = \frac{1}{3} \times \frac{36g}{13} = \frac{12g}{13}$$

$\tan\theta = \frac{5}{12} \Rightarrow \cos\theta = \frac{12}{13}$

Work done by $F = Fs = \frac{12g}{13} \times -x = -\frac{12gx}{13}$

Using the work-energy principle:
Change in total mechanical energy = Work done by F

So: $-181.5 + \dfrac{15gx}{13} = -\dfrac{12gx}{13}$

$$\frac{27gx}{13} = 181.5$$

$$x = \frac{181.5 \times 13}{27g} = 8.92 \text{ m (3 s.f.)}$$

b) The particle moves from A, up to B and back down to A, so overall change in G.P.E. = 0

So, the change in total mechanical energy between the first and second time the particle is at A is just the change in Kinetic Energy, i.e. Final K.E. – Initial K.E. = $\tfrac{1}{2}mv^2 - \tfrac{1}{2}mu^2$

Work done on the particle = $Fs = F \times -2x$

The particle has travelled the distance AB twice and is always moving in the opposite direction to the frictional force.

$$= \frac{12g}{13} \times -2(8.917) = \textbf{–161.3}$$

Using the work-energy principle:

$u = 11$ ms^{-1}, as this is the speed of the particle when it's first at A.

$$\tfrac{1}{2} \times 3 \times v^2 - \tfrac{1}{2} \times 3 \times 11^2 = -161.3$$

$$\tfrac{3}{2}v^2 = 181.5 - 161.3 \quad \Rightarrow \quad v = 3.67 \text{ ms}^{-1} \text{ (3 s.f.)}$$

Does this mean we can save energy by doing less work...

There are a few different ways you could tackle part b). You could just look at the motion back down the slope and look at the K.E. gained and the G.P.E. lost. Or you could resolve parallel to the slope, work out the acceleration and use $v^2 = u^2 + 2as$. If the question doesn't tell you what method to use, you'll get marks for using any correct method. <u>Correct</u> being the key word.

Power

Right, last page of learnin' in this section. It's a good 'un as well. And just think: after this — practice questions. Get in.

Power is the Rate at which Work is done on an Object

Power is a measure of the <u>rate a force does work on an object</u>. ◄

So Power = $\dfrac{\text{Work Done}}{\text{Time}}$

The unit for power is the <u>watt</u>, where 1 watt (1 W) = 1 joule per second.

For an <u>engine</u> producing a <u>driving force</u> of F newtons, and moving a vehicle at a speed of v ms⁻¹, the power in watts can be found using the formula:

Power = $F \times v$ ◄

Power = $\dfrac{\text{Work Done}}{\text{Time}} = \dfrac{\text{Force} \times \text{Distance}}{\text{Time}} = \text{Force} \times \text{Velocity}$

This is the formula you'll end up using most of the time — those examiners can't resist a question about engines. But don't forget what power means, just in case they throw you a curveball — it's the <u>rate of doing work</u>.

EXAMPLE

A train of mass 500 000 kg is travelling along a straight horizontal track with a constant speed of 20 ms⁻¹. The train experiences a constant resistance to motion of magnitude 275 000 N.

a) Find the rate at which the train's engine is working. Give your answer in kW.

b) The train now moves up a hill inclined at 2° to the horizontal. If the engine continues to work at the same rate and the magnitude of the non-gravitational resistance to motion remains the same, find the new constant speed of the train.

a) Call the driving force of the train T N and the speed of the train u ms⁻¹.

Resolve horizontally to find T:

$T - 275\,000 = m \times 0$

So $T = 275\,000$ N

Power = $T \times u = 275\,000 \times 20 = 5500$ kW.

b) Call the new driving force T' and resolve parallel to the slope:

$T' - 275\,000 - 500\,000g\sin2° = m \times 0$

$\Rightarrow T' = 275\,000 + 500\,000g\sin2°$ N $= 446\,008$ N

Power = $T' \times v$

$5\,500\,000 = 446\,008 \times v \quad \Rightarrow \quad v = \dfrac{5\,500\,000}{446\,008} = 12.3$ ms⁻¹ (3 s.f.)

EXAMPLE

A tractor of mass 3000 kg is moving down a hill inclined at an angle of θ to the horizontal, where $\sin\theta = \dfrac{1}{24}$. The acceleration of the tractor is 1.5 ms⁻² and its engine is working at a constant rate of 30 kW. Find the magnitude of the non-gravitational resistance to motion at the instant when the tractor is travelling at a speed of 8 ms⁻¹.

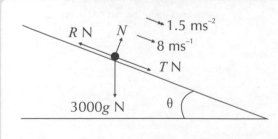

Use Power = $F \times v$ to find T:

$30\,000 = T \times 8 \Rightarrow T = 3750$ N

Add the component of weight, as the tractor is moving down the slope.

Resolve parallel to the slope: $T + mg\sin\theta - R = ma$

$3750 + (3000 \times 9.8 \times \dfrac{1}{24}) - R = 3000 \times 1.5$

$R = 3750 + 1225 - 4500$

There is acceleration here, so this term doesn't disappear for once.

$R = 475$ N

All together now — Watt's the unit for power...

Well that pretty much wraps up this section on Work and Energy. Plenty of formulas to learn and plenty of fun force diagrams to draw. If you're itching for some practice at all this then turn over and crack on. Even if you're not, do it anyway.

M2 Section 3 — Practice Questions

I don't know about you, but I enjoyed that section. Lots of <u>engines</u> and <u>energy</u> and <u>blocks</u> moving on <u>slopes</u> and GRRRRR look how manly I am as I do work against <u>friction</u>. *Ahem* sorry about that. Right-oh — practice questions...

Warm-up Questions

1) A crate is pushed across a smooth horizontal floor by a force of 250 N, acting in the direction of motion. Find the work done in pushing the crate 3 m.

2) A crane lifts a concrete block 12 m vertically at constant speed. If the crane does 34 kJ of work against gravity, find the mass of the concrete block. Take $g = 9.8$ ms^{-1}.

3) A horse of mass 450 kg is cantering at a speed of 13 ms^{-1}. Find the horse's kinetic energy.

4) An ice skater of mass 65 kg sets off from rest. After travelling 40 m in a straight line across horizontal ice, she has done 800 J of work. Find the speed of the ice skater at this point.

5) A particle of mass 0.5 kg is projected upwards from ground level and reaches a maximum height of 150 m above the ground. Find the increase in the particle's gravitational potential energy. Take $g = 9.8$ ms^{-2}.

6) State the principle of conservation of mechanical energy.
   Explain why you usually need to model an object as a particle if you are using this principle.

7) A jubilant cowboy throws his hat vertically upwards with a velocity of 5 ms^{-1}. Use conservation of energy to find the maximum height the hat reaches above the point of release. Take $g = 9.8$ ms^{-2}.

8) State the work-energy principle. Explain what is meant by an 'external force'.

9) A car's engine is working at a rate of 350 kW. If the car is moving with speed 22 ms^{-1}, find the driving force of the engine.

Well those warm-up questions should have got your maths juices flowing, and you should now be eager to move on to something a bit more <u>exam-like</u>. It's probably best not to ask what maths juice is.

Exam Questions

Whenever a numerical value of g is required in the questions below, take $g = 9.8$ ms^{-2}.

1

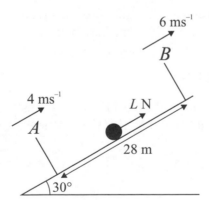

A skier is pulled up a sloping plane by a force, L, acting parallel to the plane which is inclined at an angle of 30° to the horizontal. The skier and his skis have a combined mass of 90 kg and he experiences a constant frictional force of 66 N as he moves up the slope. The skier passes through two gates, A and B, which are 28 m apart. His speed at gate A is 4 ms^{-1}. At gate B, his speed has increased to 6 ms^{-1}. Find:

a) the increase in the skier's total mechanical energy as he moves from gate A to gate B,

(5 marks)

b) the magnitude of the force, L, pulling the skier up the slope.

(3 marks)

M2 Section 3 — Practice Questions

I hope you've still got the energy left to power through this last bit of work. I don't want to have to force you...

2   A stone of mass 0.3 kg is dropped down a well. The stone hits the surface of the water in the well with a speed of 20 ms⁻¹.

   a)   Calculate the kinetic energy of the stone as it hits the water.

(2 marks)

   b)   By modelling the stone as a particle and using conservation of energy, find the height above the surface of the water from which the stone was dropped.

(3 marks)

   c)   When the stone hits the water, it begins to sink vertically and experiences a constant resistive force of 23 N. Use the work-energy principle to find the depth the stone has sunk to when the speed of the stone is reduced to 1 ms⁻¹.

(5 marks)

3   A van of mass 2700 kg is travelling at a constant speed of 16 ms⁻¹ up a road inclined at an angle of 12° to the horizontal. The non-gravitational resistance to motion is modelled as a single force of magnitude 800 N.

   a)   Find the rate of work of the engine.

(4 marks)

When the van passes a point A, still travelling at 16 ms⁻¹, the engine is switched off and the van comes to rest without braking, a distance x m from A. If all resistance to motion remains constant, find:

   b)   the distance x,

(4 marks)

   c)   the time taken for the van to come to rest.

(4 marks)

4

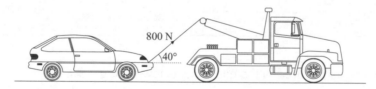

A car of mass 1500 kg is towed 320 m along a straight horizontal road by a rope attached to a pick-up truck. The rope is attached to the car at an angle of 40° to the horizontal and the tension in the rope is 800 N. The car experiences a constant resistance to motion from friction.

   a)   Find the work done by the towing force.

(3 marks)

   b)   Over the 320 m, the car increases in speed from 11 ms⁻¹ to 16 ms⁻¹. Assuming that the magnitude of the towing force remains constant at 800 N, find the coefficient of friction between the car and the road.

(4 marks)

5   A cyclist is riding up a road at a constant speed of 4 ms⁻¹. The road is inclined at an angle α to the horizontal. The cyclist is working at a rate of 250 W and experiences a constant non-gravitational resistance to motion of magnitude 35 N. The cyclist and his bike have a combined mass of 88 kg.

   a)   Find the angle of the slope, α.

(4 marks)

   b)   The cyclist now increases his work rate to 370 W. If all resistances to motion remain unchanged, find the cyclist's acceleration when his speed is 4 ms⁻¹.

(4 marks)

Linear Momentum

Momentum has Magnitude and Direction

Momentum is a measure of how much "umph" a _moving object_ has, due to its _mass_ and _velocity_.
Total momentum _before_ a collision equals total momentum _after_ a collision.
This idea is called "Conservation of Momentum".

$$\boxed{\text{Momentum} = \text{Mass} \times \text{Velocity}}$$

The unit of momentum is kgms^{-1} or Ns

EXAMPLE Particles A and B, each of mass 5 kg, move in a straight line with velocities
6 ms⁻¹ and 2 ms⁻¹ respectively. After collision mass A continues in the same
direction with velocity 4.2 ms⁻¹. Find the velocity of B after impact.

Before

A (5kg) 6 ms⁻¹   B (5kg) 2 ms⁻¹

Before: Momentum A + Momentum B = $(5 \times 6) + (5 \times 2) = 40$

After: Momentum A + Momentum B = $(5 \times 4.2) + (5 \times v) = 21 + 5v$

Using conservation of momentum: $40 = 21 + 5v$

After

A (5kg) 4.2 ms⁻¹   B (5kg) v

So: $v = 3.8$ ms⁻¹ in the same direction as before

Stick to saying 'same' or 'opposite' direction, rather than left or right — there's less chance of confusion.

Draw 'before' and 'after' diagrams to help you see what's going on.

Masses Joined Together have the Same Velocity

Particles that <u>stick together</u> after impact are said to "<u>coalesce</u>". After that you can treat them as just <u>one object</u>.

EXAMPLE Two particles of mass 40 g and M kg move towards each other with speeds of 6 ms⁻¹ and
3 ms⁻¹ respectively. Given that the particles coalesce after impact and move with a speed
of 2 ms⁻¹ in the same direction as that of the 40 g particle's initial velocity, find M.

Before   **After**

A (0.04kg) 6 ms⁻¹   3 ms⁻¹ B (M)   (M + 0.04) kg 2 ms⁻¹

$(0.04 \times 6) + (M \times -3) = (M + 0.04) \times 2$

$0.24 - 3M = 2M + 0.08$

$5M = 0.16$

$\boxed{M = 0.032 \text{ kg}}$

Don't forget to convert all masses to the same units.

Momentum is a vector, so the sign of the velocity is important.

Momentum works the same in 2 Dimensions

In your exam you could be asked about the momentum of particles
moving on a <u>plane</u>. Don't worry though — everything is the <u>same</u> as
in the previous examples, just with <u>two components of velocity</u>.

$$\boxed{m_1\mathbf{u}_1 + m_2\mathbf{u}_2 = m_1\mathbf{v}_1 + m_2\mathbf{v}_2}$$

EXAMPLE Two particles, A and B, collide as shown. Following the collision they
move separately at different velocities. Find B's velocity after the collision.

1) Again, it's just a matter of plugging the numbers in:
$$m_A\mathbf{u}_A + m_B\mathbf{u}_B = m_A\mathbf{v}_A + m_B\mathbf{v}_B,$$
where $m_A = 5$, $m_B = 3$, $\mathbf{u}_A = 4\mathbf{i} + 3\mathbf{j}$, $\mathbf{u}_B = -2\mathbf{i} + 7\mathbf{j}$ and $\mathbf{v}_A = -2\mathbf{i}$.

2) $5(4\mathbf{i} + 3\mathbf{j}) + 3(-2\mathbf{i} + 7\mathbf{j}) = 5(-2\mathbf{i}) + 3\mathbf{v}_B$
$\Rightarrow 20\mathbf{i} + 15\mathbf{j} - 6\mathbf{i} + 21\mathbf{j} = -10\mathbf{i} + 3\mathbf{v}_B$
$\Rightarrow 3\mathbf{v}_B = 24\mathbf{i} + 36\mathbf{j}$
$\Rightarrow \mathbf{v}_B = 8\mathbf{i} + 12\mathbf{j}$

So B's new velocity is $\boxed{(8\mathbf{i} + 12\mathbf{j}) \text{ ms}^{-1}}$.

You might be expected to use column vectors too. They're not complicated, e.g. $(8\mathbf{i} + 12\mathbf{j})$ is $\begin{pmatrix} 8 \\ 12 \end{pmatrix}$.

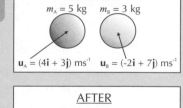
BEFORE
$m_A = 5$ kg $m_B = 3$ kg
$\mathbf{u}_A = (4\mathbf{i} + 3\mathbf{j})$ ms⁻¹ $\mathbf{u}_B = (-2\mathbf{i} + 7\mathbf{j})$ ms⁻¹

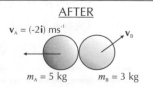
AFTER
$\mathbf{v}_A = (-2\mathbf{i})$ ms⁻¹ $\mathbf{v}_B$
$m_A = 5$ kg $m_B = 3$ kg

Ever heard of Hercules?

Well, he carried out 12 tasks. Nothing to do with momentum, but if you're feeling sorry for yourself for doing M2, think on.

Momentum and Impulse

An impulse <u>changes the momentum</u> of a particle. That's important so let me say it again for you, but in a green box...

An *Impulse* causes a *Change* in *Momentum*

If an object receives an <u>impulse</u> (*I* — measured in newton seconds, or Ns) its momentum will <u>change</u>.
The <u>size</u> of the change is the <u>size of the impulse</u>.

Impulse = final momentum − initial momentum

$$I = mv - mu \quad \text{or} \quad \mathbf{I} = m\mathbf{v} - m\mathbf{u}$$

This is the vector form.

Remember, since <u>velocity</u> is a <u>vector</u>, momentum and impulse are <u>vectors</u> too.

EXAMPLE A body of mass 500 g is travelling in a straight line. Find the magnitude of the impulse needed to increase its speed from 2 ms⁻¹ to 5 ms⁻¹.

This is called the impulse-momentum principle. Ooooh, aaaaaah.

Impulse = Change in momentum $= mv - mu$
$= (0.5 \times 5) - (0.5 \times 2)$
$= 1.5$ Ns

EXAMPLE A ball ($m = 0.1$ kg) travels with a velocity of $(5\mathbf{i} + 12\mathbf{j})$ ms⁻¹ before receiving an impulse of **I** Ns. If the ball's new velocity is $(15\mathbf{i} + 22\mathbf{j})$ ms⁻¹, find **I**.

1) Don't be put off by the vector notation.
   Just plug the info in the formula:
   $\mathbf{I} = m\mathbf{v} - m\mathbf{u}$, where $m = 0.1$, $\mathbf{v} = 15\mathbf{i} + 22\mathbf{j}$ and $\mathbf{u} = 5\mathbf{i} + 12\mathbf{j}$.

2) $\mathbf{I} = 0.1(15\mathbf{i} + 22\mathbf{j}) - 0.1(5\mathbf{i} + 12\mathbf{j})$
   $= 1.5\mathbf{i} + 2.2\mathbf{j} - 0.5\mathbf{i} - 1.2\mathbf{j}$
   $= 1\mathbf{i} + 1\mathbf{j} = \mathbf{i} + \mathbf{j}$.

3) So the ball received an impulse of $(\mathbf{i} + \mathbf{j})$ Ns.

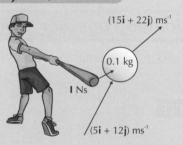
$(15\mathbf{i} + 22\mathbf{j})$ ms⁻¹
0.1 kg
I Ns
$(5\mathbf{i} + 12\mathbf{j})$ ms⁻¹

Use *Pythagoras* and *Trig* for the *Magnitude* and *Angle* of *Impulse*

With vectors, you can use the <u>horizontal</u> **i** component and the <u>vertical</u> **j** component to form a <u>right-angled triangle</u>. Then simply use <u>basic trig</u> and <u>Pythagoras</u> to find any <u>angles</u>, or the <u>magnitude</u> (scalar size) of impulses or velocities.

EXAMPLE A badminton player smashes a shuttlecock ($m = 0.005$ kg) with an impulse of $(0.035\mathbf{i} - 0.065\mathbf{j})$ Ns. If the shuttle was initially travelling at $(-3\mathbf{i} + \mathbf{j})$ ms⁻¹, find its <u>speed</u> after the smash, and the <u>angle</u> it makes with the horizontal.

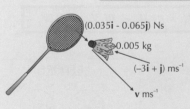
(0.035i - 0.065j) Ns
0.005 kg
(−3i + j) ms⁻¹
v ms⁻¹

1) Find the final velocity as a vector first, so: $\mathbf{I} = m\mathbf{v} - m\mathbf{u}$,
   where $\mathbf{I} = 0.035\mathbf{i} - 0.065\mathbf{j}$, $m = 0.005$ and $\mathbf{u} = -3\mathbf{i} + \mathbf{j}$.
   $0.035\mathbf{i} - 0.065\mathbf{j} = 0.005\mathbf{v} - 0.005(-3\mathbf{i} + \mathbf{j})$
   $\Rightarrow 0.035\mathbf{i} - 0.065\mathbf{j} = 0.005\mathbf{v} + 0.015\mathbf{i} - 0.005\mathbf{j}$
   $\Rightarrow 0.005\mathbf{v} = 0.02\mathbf{i} - 0.06\mathbf{j}$
   $\Rightarrow \mathbf{v} = (0.02\mathbf{i} - 0.06\mathbf{j}) \div 0.005 = 4\mathbf{i} - 12\mathbf{j}$.

2) Draw a right-angled triangle of the velocity vector:

3) Use Pythagoras to find the speed (the <u>magnitude</u> of the velocity):
   $|\mathbf{v}| = \sqrt{4^2 + 12^2} = 12.6$ ms⁻¹ to 3 s.f.

4) Use trig to find the angle of motion with the horizontal:
   $\theta = \tan^{-1}\left(\frac{12}{4}\right) = 71.6°$ to 3 s.f.

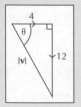
4
θ
|v|
12

Finding the magnitude of a vector this way should be familiar to you from M1.

Mo' mentum mo' problems...

Nothing too tricky here — you've just got to mind your **i**'s and **j**'s. As always, I find drawing a picture of the situation helps when you're trying to visualise the particles bouncing in all directions. Or, you could just draw inspirational doodles and think about that emo type you fancy who sits at the back of class. Not quite as productive though...

Momentum and Impulse

Impulses always *Balance* in *Collisions*

During <u>impact</u> between particles A and B, the impulse that A gives to B is the <u>same</u> as the impulse that B gives to A, but in the opposite direction.

EXAMPLE A mass of 2 kg moving at 2 ms⁻¹ collides with a mass of 3 kg which is moving in the same direction at 1 ms⁻¹. The 2 kg mass continues to move in the same direction at 1 ms⁻¹ after impact. Find the impulse given by the 2 kg mass to the other mass.

Using "conservation of momentum":

$(2 \times 2) + (3 \times 1) = (2 \times 1) + 3v$

So $v = 1\frac{2}{3}$ ms⁻¹

Before

After

Impulse (on B) $= mv - mu$ (for B)

$= (3 \times 1\frac{2}{3}) - (3 \times 1)$

$= $ **2 Ns**

*The impulse B gives to A is $(2 \times 1) - (2 \times 2) = $ **−2 Ns**. Aside from the different direction, you can see it's the same — so you didn't actually need to find v for this question.*

EXAMPLE Two snooker balls A and B have a mass of 0.6 kg and 0.9 kg respectively. The balls are initially at rest on a snooker table. Ball A is given an impulse of magnitude 4.5 Ns towards ball B. Modelling the snooker table as a smooth horizontal plane, find the speed of ball A before it collides with B.

Impulse $= mv - mu$

$\Rightarrow 4.5 = (0.6 \times v) - (0.6 \times 0) = 0.6v$

$\Rightarrow v = \dfrac{4.5}{0.6} = 7.5$ ms⁻¹. So speed of A before collision is 7.5 ms⁻¹.

The balls collide and move away in the direction A was travelling before the collision. Find the speed of ball A after the collision, given that the speed of ball B is 4 ms⁻¹.

Using conservation of momentum:

$(0.6 \times 7.5) + (0.9 \times 0) = 0.6v + (0.9 \times 4)$

So, $v = 1.5$ ms⁻¹. So speed of A after collision is 1.5 ms⁻¹.

Impulse is linked to *Force* too

Impulse is also related to the force needed to <u>change the momentum</u> and the <u>time</u> it takes.

| **Impulse = Force × Time** |

If there are no external forces acting on a system of particles, then there will be no change in total momentum.

EXAMPLE A 0.9 tonne car increases its speed from 30 kmh⁻¹ to 40 kmh⁻¹. Given that the maximum additional constant forward force the car's engine can produce is 1 kN, find the shortest time it will take to achieve this change in speed.

To change kmh⁻¹ to ms⁻¹, multiply by 1000 (to change km to m), then divide by 3600 (to change h⁻¹ to s⁻¹).

Impulse $= mv - mu$

$= (900 \times \dfrac{40\,000}{3600}) - (900 \times \dfrac{30\,000}{3600})$

$= 2500$ Ns

Now use Impulse = Force × Time:

$2500 = 1000 \times t$

$t = 2.5$ s

Doctor, this man is sick — 'im pulse is very weak...

...a little bit like that pun actually. Anyway, naff humour aside, make sure you've got your head round all of this momentum and impulse stuff, 'cos we're about to move on to something completely similar. And you thought M2 would be dull...

Collisions

Oh yes, you've not seen the last of those colliding particles. If you like things loud and dramatic, think demolition balls and high speed crashes. If you're anything like me though you'll be picturing a nice sedate game of snooker.

The **Coefficient of Restitution** is always between **0 and 1**

When two particles collide in a <u>direct impact</u> (i.e. they're moving on the <u>same straight line</u>), the speeds they bounce away at depend on the <u>coefficient of restitution</u>, <u>e</u>. This is known as <u>Newton's Law of Restitution</u> (or Newton's experimental law), and looks like this:

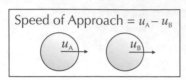

Speed of Approach $= u_A - u_B$

$$e = \frac{\text{speed of separation of particles}}{\text{speed of approach of particles}}$$

$$e = \frac{v_B - v_A}{u_A - u_B}$$

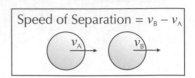

Speed of Separation $= v_B - v_A$

1) The value of e depends on the <u>material</u> that the particles are made of.

2) e always lies between <u>0 and 1</u>.

3) When <u>$e = 0$</u> the particles are called 'inelastic', and they'll <u>coalesce</u>.

4) When <u>$e = 1$</u> the particles are '<u>perfectly elastic</u>' and they'll bounce apart with <u>no loss of speed</u>.

> Balls of modelling clay would be near the $e = 0$ end of the scale, while ping pong balls are nearer to $e = 1$.

> **EXAMPLE** Two particles collide as shown. Find the coefficient of restitution.

1) Firstly, work out the speeds of approach and separation, taking care with positives and negatives:
Speed of approach $= u_A - u_B = 5 - (-7) = 12$ ms⁻¹.
Speed of separation $= v_B - v_A = 2 - (-4) = 6$ ms⁻¹.

> Think of 'left to right' as positive, and so particles travelling 'right to left' will have a negative speed.

2) Use $e = \dfrac{\text{speed of separation of particles}}{\text{speed of approach of particles}}$:

$e = \dfrac{6}{12} = 0.5$. So the coefficient of restitution is <u>0.5</u>.

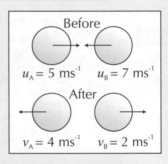

Before

$u_A = 5$ ms⁻¹ $u_B = 7$ ms⁻¹

After

$v_A = 4$ ms⁻¹ $v_B = 2$ ms⁻¹

For **Two Unknown Speeds** — use **Momentum Conservation** too

Often you'll be <u>given</u> the value of e and asked to find the <u>velocities</u> of <u>both particles</u> either before or after impact. As there are <u>two unknowns</u>, you'll need to use the formula for <u>conservation of momentum</u> (on p.173) along with the Law of Restitution to form <u>simultaneous equations</u>.

> **EXAMPLE** Two particles, A and B, are moving in opposite directions in the same straight line, as shown. If $e = \frac{1}{3}$, find the velocities of both particles after impact.

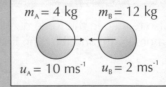

$m_A = 4$ kg $m_B = 12$ kg

$u_A = 10$ ms⁻¹ $u_B = 2$ ms⁻¹

1) Use $e = \frac{v_B - v_A}{u_A - u_B}$ to get the first equation:

$\frac{1}{3} = \frac{v_B - v_A}{10 - (-2)} \Rightarrow v_B - v_A = 4$. Call this **equation 1**.

2) Use $m_A u_A + m_B u_B = m_A v_A + m_B v_B$ to get the second equation:
$(4 \times 10) + (12 \times -2) = 4v_A + 12v_B$
$\Rightarrow 16 = 4v_A + 12v_B \Rightarrow v_A + 3v_B = 4$. Call this **equation 2**.

3) **Equation 1 + equation 2** gives:
$4v_B = 8$, so $v_B = 2$ ms⁻¹ (i.e. 2 ms⁻¹ in the opposite direction to its motion before the collision).

4) Substituting in **equation 1** gives:
$2 - v_A = 4$, so $v_A = -2$ ms⁻¹ (i.e. 2 ms⁻¹ also in the opposite direction to before the collision).

Collisions

There's a saying in Stoke-on-Trent that goes: 'cost kick a bo againt a wo till it bosses?'*
Well, that's kinda what this next bit's about, a.k.a. 'the collision of a particle with a plane surface'.

The **Law of Restitution** *also works with a* **Smooth Plane Surface**

Particles don't just collide with each other. They can collide with a <u>fixed flat surface</u> —
such as when a ball is kicked against a <u>vertical wall</u>, or dropped onto a <u>horizontal floor</u>.

As long as the surface can be modelled as <u>smooth</u> (i.e. no friction) and <u>perpendicular</u> to
the <u>motion of the particle</u>, the law can be simplified to:

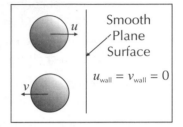

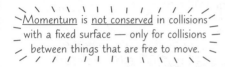
<u>Momentum</u> is <u>not conserved</u> in collisions
with a fixed surface — only for collisions
between things that are free to move.

$$e = \frac{\text{speed of rebound of particle}}{\text{speed of approach of particle}} = \frac{v}{u}$$

EXAMPLE A ball rolling along a smooth horizontal floor at 6 ms⁻¹ hits a smooth vertical wall,
with a coefficient of restitution $e = 0.65$. Find the speed of the ball as it rebounds.

BEFORE $u = 6$ ms⁻¹ $e = 0.65$

Using $e = \frac{v}{u}$:

$0.65 = \frac{v}{6} \Rightarrow v = 0.65 \times 6 = 3.9$ ms⁻¹.

AFTER v

So the ball rebounds at a speed of 3.9 ms⁻¹. Piece of cake.

Use the **Laws of Motion** *for things being* **Dropped**

Things get a tiny bit trickier when a particle is dropped onto a <u>horizontal surface</u> because acceleration under gravity
comes into play. You should be pretty nifty with <u>equations of motion</u> now though — just remember to use them here.

EXAMPLE A basketball is dropped vertically from rest at a height of 1.4 m onto a horizontal floor.
It rebounds to a height of 0.9 m. Find e for the impact with the floor.

1) Assuming the ball is a particle, and the floor is smooth, we can use $e = \frac{v}{u}$.
For the diagram shown, this would be $e = \frac{u_2}{v_1}$, as we need the
velocity <u>just before</u> the impact (v_1) and the velocity <u>just after</u> (u_2).

2) Using $v^2 = u^2 + 2as$ <u>before</u> the impact with the floor
(where $a = g \approx 9.8$ ms⁻²):
$v_1^2 = 0 + 2 \times 9.8 \times 1.4 = 27.44$
$\Rightarrow v_1 = 5.238$ ms⁻¹ to 4 s.f.

3) Using $v^2 = u^2 + 2as$ <u>after</u> the impact with the floor
(where $a = -g$ since the motion is against gravity):
$0 = u_2^2 + 2 \times -9.8 \times 0.9$
$\Rightarrow u_2 = 4.2$ ms⁻¹.

4) Finally, we can find e: $e = \frac{u_2}{v_1} = \frac{4.2}{5.238} = 0.802$ to 3 s.f.

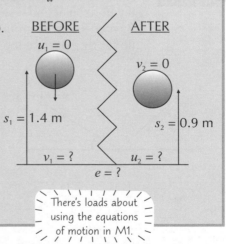

BEFORE $u_1 = 0$ $s_1 = 1.4$ m $v_1 = ?$

AFTER $v_2 = 0$ $s_2 = 0.9$ m $u_2 = ?$ $e = ?$

There's loads about using the equations of motion in M1.

Dating Tip #107 — Avoid them if they're on the rebound...

Just when you were thinking this section was a load of balls, along come walls and floors to shake things up a bit. The Law
of Restitution is a pretty straightforward formula, but chances are there'll be added complications in the exam questions.
Learn how to tackle the four types of question on these last two pages and you'll be laughing.

*For those unfamiliar with Potteries dialect, this means

Oblique Collisions

Don't let the title worry you — there's nothing too difficult on this page. It's pretty similar to what was on the last page, but now the collisions are at funny angles. It's time to get your trig on. Again.

In an *Oblique Impact* with a Plane, Impulse acts *Perpendicular* to the Plane

1) When an object collides with a smooth plane at an <u>oblique</u> angle (i.e. not perpendicular to the surface), the <u>impulse</u> on the object acts <u>perpendicular</u> to the plane.

2) This means that only the component of the object's velocity in the direction <u>perpendicular to the plane</u> is changed by the collision. The component of velocity <u>parallel</u> to the surface remains <u>unchanged</u>.

3) The <u>direction</u> of the perpendicular component of velocity will be <u>reversed</u> by the collision (because the object is moving away from the surface after the collision instead of towards it).

4) The <u>Law of Restitution</u> still applies in oblique collisions. The <u>magnitude</u> of the perpendicular component of velocity after the collision is the original magnitude multiplied by *e*, the <u>coefficient of restitution</u> between the object and the surface.

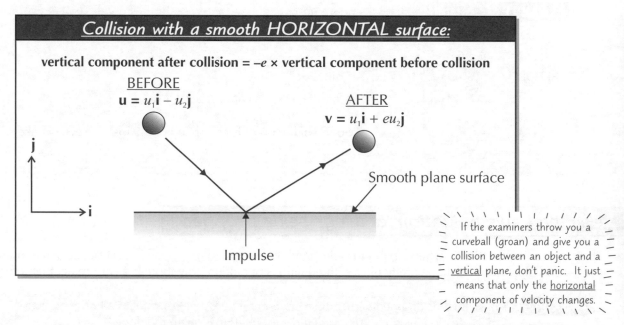

Collision with a smooth HORIZONTAL surface:

vertical component after collision = −*e* × vertical component before collision

BEFORE
$\mathbf{u} = u_1\mathbf{i} - u_2\mathbf{j}$

AFTER
$\mathbf{v} = u_1\mathbf{i} + eu_2\mathbf{j}$

Smooth plane surface

Impulse

If the examiners throw you a curveball (groan) and give you a collision between an object and a <u>vertical</u> plane, don't panic. It just means that only the <u>horizontal</u> component of velocity changes.

EXAMPLE

A tennis ball hits the horizontal ground with velocity $12\mathbf{i} - 8\mathbf{j}$ ms^{-1} (where $\mathbf{i}$ and $\mathbf{j}$ are the horizontal and vertical unit vectors respectively), and rebounds at an angle of $\alpha°$ to $\mathbf{i}$. By modelling the ground as a smooth plane surface with coefficient of restitution $e = 0.5$, find v, the speed of the ball after the collision, and α.

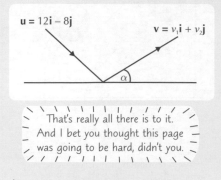

$\mathbf{u} = 12\mathbf{i} - 8\mathbf{j}$

$\mathbf{v} = v_1\mathbf{i} + v_2\mathbf{j}$

α

That's really all there is to it. And I bet you thought this page was going to be hard, didn't you.

1) The ground is parallel to $\mathbf{i}$, so the component of velocity in this direction is <u>unchanged</u>, i.e. $v_1 = 12$.

2) Perpendicular to the wall, the component of the velocity is <u>reversed</u> and <u>multiplied by *e*</u>, so $v_2 = -0.5(-8) = 4$.

3) So the velocity of the ball after the collision is $\mathbf{v} = 12\mathbf{i} + 4\mathbf{j}$ ms^{-1}. Use Pythagoras to find the speed after the collision:
$v = \sqrt{12^2 + 4^2} = 12.6$ ms^{-1} (3 s.f.)

4) You can now calculate α: $\tan\alpha = \frac{4}{12} \Rightarrow \alpha = 18.4°$ (3 s.f.)

Feel like you're on a collision course with your exams?

You might not always be given an object's velocity in terms of $\mathbf{i}$ and $\mathbf{j}$ vectors. In that case, you just have to do a bit of trig to find the components parallel and perpendicular to the surface — then it's just the same as the method on this page. Lovely.

Complex Collisions

You've had an easy ride so far this section, but now it's time to fasten your seatbelt, don your crash helmet, and prepare for some pretty scary collisions. Don't say I didn't warn you...

Solve *Successive* Collisions Step by Step...

Think of this as a <u>multi-particle pile-up</u>. One particle collides with another, which then shoots off to collide with a third. No extra maths required, but quite a bit of <u>extra thinking</u>.

EXAMPLE Particles P, Q and R are travelling at different speeds along the same smooth straight line, as shown. Particles P and Q collide first ($e = 0.6$), then Q goes on to collide with R ($e = 0.2$). What are the velocities of P, Q and R after the second collision?

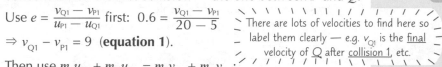

1) Take things step by step. Forget about R for the moment and concentrate on the first collision — the one between P and Q:

Use $e = \frac{v_{Q1} - v_{P1}}{u_{P1} - u_{Q1}}$ first: $0.6 = \frac{v_{Q1} - v_{P1}}{20 - 5}$

$\Rightarrow v_{Q1} - v_{P1} = 9$ (**equation 1**).

There are lots of velocities to find here so label them clearly — e.g. v_{Q1} is the <u>final</u> velocity of Q after <u>collision 1</u>, etc.

Then use $m_P u_{P1} + m_Q u_{Q1} = m_P v_{P1} + m_Q v_{Q1}$:

$(0.1 \times 20) + (0.4 \times 5) = 0.1 v_{P1} + 0.4 v_{Q1}$

$\Rightarrow 4 = 0.1 v_{P1} + 0.4 v_{Q1}$ $\Rightarrow$ $v_{P1} + 4 v_{Q1} = 40$ (**equation 2**).

Equation 1 + equation 2 gives:
$5 v_{Q1} = 49$ $\Rightarrow$ $v_{Q1} = 9.8$ ms⁻¹.

Substituting in **equation 1** gives:
$9.8 - v_{P1} = 9$ $\Rightarrow$ $v_{P1} = 9.8 - 9 = 0.8$ ms⁻¹.

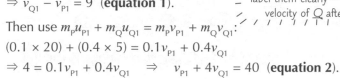

2) For the second collision, which is between Q and R: $e = \frac{v_{R2} - v_{Q2}}{u_{Q2} - u_{R2}}$. u_{Q2} is the same as the velocity of Q after the first collision — you found this above (9.8 ms⁻¹), so:

$0.2 = \frac{v_{R2} - v_{Q2}}{9.8 - (-1)}$ $\Rightarrow$ $v_{R2} - v_{Q2} = 2.16$ (**equation 3**).

Then $m_Q u_{Q2} + m_R u_{R2} = m_Q v_{Q2} + m_R v_{R2}$:

$(0.4 \times 9.8) + (2 \times -1) = 0.4 v_{Q2} + 2 v_{R2}$

$\Rightarrow 1.92 = 0.4 v_{Q2} + 2 v_{R2}$ $\Rightarrow$ $0.2 v_{Q2} + v_{R2} = 0.96$ (**equation 4**).

Equation 4 – equation 3 gives:
$1.2 v_{Q2} = -1.2$ $\Rightarrow$ $v_{Q2} = -1$ ms⁻¹.

Substituting in **equation 3** gives:
$v_{R2} - (-1) = 2.16$ $\Rightarrow$ $v_{R2} = 2.16 - 1 = 1.16$ ms⁻¹.

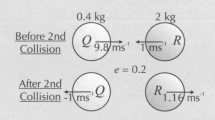

3) Velocities after both collisions are: $P = 0.8$ ms⁻¹, $Q = -1$ ms⁻¹ and $R = 1.16$ ms⁻¹:

... as well as *Subsequent Collisions* with a *Plane Surface*

EXAMPLE Following the second collision, P is removed and R hits a smooth vertical wall at a right angle. How big would e have to be for this impact to allow R to collide again with Q, assuming Q is moving with velocity -1 ms⁻¹?

1) Think things through carefully. Q is currently going at 1 ms⁻¹ in the <u>opposite direction</u>. To hit it again, R needs to bounce off the wall with a rebound speed <u>higher</u> than 1 ms⁻¹, so it can 'catch up'. So $v_{R3} > 1$.

2) For the impact with the wall, $e = \frac{v_{R3}}{u_{R3}}$ $\Rightarrow$ $v_{R3} = e u_{R3}$, and so $e u_{R3} > 1$.

3) From the example above, $u_{R3} = v_{R2} = 1.16$ ms⁻¹, so $1.16e > 1$ $\Rightarrow$ $e > \frac{1}{1.16}$ $\Rightarrow$ $e > 0.8620...$

4) So, to 3 s.f., e must be <u>higher than 0.862</u> for R to collide again with Q.

Collisions and Energy

Almost the end of the section, and I guess your energy might be waning. Most things lose kinetic energy when they collide — you need to know how to work out how much. It's enough to make you want a quiet lie down...

Kinetic Energy is only Conserved in Perfectly Elastic Collisions

For any collision where $e < 1$, some kinetic energy will be lost (it changes into things like heat and sound). The formula for working out how much has been lost is fairly straightforward:

The units of K.E. are joules, if mass is given in kg and speed in ms^{-1}

$$\begin{aligned} \text{Loss of K.E.} &= \text{Total K.E. before} - \text{Total K.E. after} \\ \text{on Impact} &= (\tfrac{1}{2}m_1u_1^2 + \tfrac{1}{2}m_2u_2^2) - (\tfrac{1}{2}m_1v_1^2 + \tfrac{1}{2}m_2v_2^2) \end{aligned}$$

For velocities given in vector (i and j) form, find their magnitude (speed) to put into the K.E. formula.

The tricky bit is finding the u's and v's to put in the formula...

EXAMPLE A tiny cannon fires a ball in a straight line across a smooth horizontal table, as shown. The ball collides directly with another, stationary, ball with $e = 0.7$, and moves away from this collision at 7.5 ms^{-1}.

a) Find the loss of K.E. when the balls collide.

$m_c = 0.05$ kg $m_1 = m_2 = 0.001$ kg
C   1   2

1) We first need to find u_1 (the speed of the fired ball before it hits the other) and v_2 (the final speed of the other ball). Use the law of restitution and conservation of momentum (as on p. 176) where $e = 0.7$, $v_1 = 7.5$, and $u_2 = 0$.

2) $e = \dfrac{v_2 - v_1}{u_1 - u_2} \Rightarrow 0.7 = \dfrac{v_2 - 7.5}{u_1 - 0} \Rightarrow v_2 - 0.7u_1 = 7.5$ (**eqn 1**).

   $m_1u_1 + m_2u_2 = m_1v_1 + m_2v_2$ and since $m_1 = m_2$:

   $u_1 + 0 = 7.5 + v_2 \Rightarrow u_1 - v_2 = 7.5$ (**eqn 2**).

   Eqn 1 + eqn 2: $0.3u_1 = 15 \Rightarrow u_1 = \boxed{50 \text{ ms}^{-1}}$.

   Sub in **eqn 2**: $50 - v_2 = 7.5 \Rightarrow v_2 = 50 - 7.5 = \boxed{42.5 \text{ ms}^{-1}}$.

3) Finally, putting all the values in the K.E. formula:

   $\text{Loss of K.E.} = (\tfrac{1}{2}m_1u_1^2 + \tfrac{1}{2}m_2u_2^2) - (\tfrac{1}{2}m_1v_1^2 + \tfrac{1}{2}m_2v_2^2)$

   $= \tfrac{1}{2}m[(u_1^2 + u_2^2) - (v_1^2 + v_2^2)]$

   $= \tfrac{1}{2} \times 0.001 \times [(50^2 + 0^2) - (7.5^2 + 42.5^2)]$

   $= 0.31875 = \boxed{0.319 \text{ J to 3 s.f.}}$

b) Find the K.E. gained by firing the cannon.

1) Since both the cannon and the ball are stationary before firing, there is no initial K.E. The gain in K.E. is simply $\tfrac{1}{2}m_cv_c^2 + \tfrac{1}{2}m_1v_1^2$, where v_1 is the speed of the ball after firing, i.e. 50 ms^{-1}, as calculated in part a). You need to work out the velocity of the cannon (v_c) though.

2) Momentum is conserved so:

   $m_cu_c + m_1u_1 = m_cv_c + m_1v_1$

   $\Rightarrow 0 + 0 = 0.05v_c + (0.001 \times 50)$

   $\Rightarrow v_c = -(0.001 \times 50) \div 0.05 = \boxed{-1 \text{ ms}^{-1}}.$

   (i.e. the cannon moves backwards at 1 ms^{-1}).

3) Gain in K.E. $= \tfrac{1}{2}m_cv_c^2 + \tfrac{1}{2}m_1v_1^2$

   $= (\tfrac{1}{2} \times 0.05 \times (-1)^2) + (\tfrac{1}{2} \times 0.001 \times 50^2)$

   $= 1.275 = \boxed{1.28 \text{ J to 3 s.f.}}$

An Impulse will cause a Change in K.E.

EXAMPLE A fly of mass 0.002 kg is moving at a velocity of $(2\mathbf{i} - \mathbf{j})$ ms^{-1} when it is swatted with an impulse of $(0.01\mathbf{i} - 0.06\mathbf{j})$ Ns. How much kinetic energy is gained by the fly following the impulse?

1) Using the impulse formula from p. 174: $I = m\mathbf{v} - m\mathbf{u}$, so

   $0.01\mathbf{i} - 0.06\mathbf{j} = 0.002\mathbf{v} - 0.002(2\mathbf{i} - \mathbf{j}) \Rightarrow 0.002\mathbf{v} = 0.01\mathbf{i} - 0.06\mathbf{j} + 0.004\mathbf{i} - 0.002\mathbf{j} = 0.014\mathbf{i} - 0.062\mathbf{j}$

   $\Rightarrow \mathbf{v} = (0.014\mathbf{i} - 0.062\mathbf{j}) \div 0.002 = (7\mathbf{i} - 31\mathbf{j})$ ms^{-1}.

2) The initial speed of the fly $|\mathbf{u}| = \sqrt{2^2 + 1^2} = \sqrt{5}$, so $u^2 = 5$.

   After the impulse this becomes $|\mathbf{v}| = \sqrt{7^2 + 31^2} = \sqrt{1010}$, so $v^2 = 1010$.

The formula's been tweaked to suit the situation — there's only one 'particle', and there will be an increase rather than a loss in K.E.

3) Increase in K.E. $= \tfrac{1}{2}mv^2 - \tfrac{1}{2}mu^2 = (\tfrac{1}{2} \times 0.002 \times 1010) - (\tfrac{1}{2} \times 0.002 \times 5) = \boxed{1.005 \text{ J}}.$

I'm not lazy — I'm just conserving my kinetic energy...

There are plenty of different situations where you could be asked to find a change in kinetic energy — but they all use pretty much the same formula, and no doubt require you to calculate some speeds. Just think it through logically to decide whether K.E. will go up or down or whatever. Now make yourself a quick bevvy and a light snack — it's practice time...

M2 Section 4 — Practice Questions

Well that's been a <u>crash course</u> in collisions (ho ho). Don't just <u>sit and hope</u> that you've understood it all — come and have a go. Have a <u>practice lap</u> first...

Warm-up Questions

1) Each diagram represents the motion of two particles moving in a straight line.
   Find the missing mass or velocity (all masses are in kg and all velocities are in ms⁻¹).

| Before | After |

2) Two particles A and B collide, where $m_A = 0.5$ kg and $m_B = 0.4$ kg.
   Their <u>initial</u> velocities are $\mathbf{u}_A = (2\mathbf{i} + \mathbf{j})$ ms⁻¹ and $\mathbf{u}_B = (-\mathbf{i} - 4\mathbf{j})$ ms⁻¹. Find, to 3 s.f.:
   a) the speed of B <u>after impact</u> if A moves away from the collision at a velocity of $(-\mathbf{i} - 2\mathbf{j})$ ms⁻¹,
   b) their <u>combined speed</u> after the impact if they <u>coalesce</u> instead.

3) An impulse of 2 Ns acts against a ball of mass 300 g moving with a velocity of 5 ms⁻¹.
   Find the ball's new velocity.

4) Find the velocity of a particle of mass 0.1 kg, travelling at $(\mathbf{i} + \mathbf{j})$ ms⁻¹, after receiving an impulse of:
   a) $2\mathbf{i} + 5\mathbf{j}$ Ns   b) $-3\mathbf{i} + \mathbf{j}$ Ns   c) $-\mathbf{i} - 6\mathbf{j}$ Ns   d) $4\mathbf{i}$ Ns.

5) A 2 kg particle, travelling at $(4\mathbf{i} - \mathbf{j})$ ms⁻¹, receives an impulse, $\mathbf{Q}$, changing its velocity to $(-2\mathbf{i} + \mathbf{j})$ ms⁻¹.
   Find:
   a) $\mathbf{Q}$ b) $|\mathbf{Q}|$, in Ns to 3 s.f.   c) the angle $\mathbf{Q}$ makes with $\mathbf{i}$, in degrees to 3 s.f.

6) Two particles travelling directly towards each other at the <u>same speed</u> collide. The impact causes one particle to <u>stop</u>, and the other to go in the <u>opposite direction</u> at <u>half</u> its original speed. Find the value of e.

7) A particle of mass 1 kg travelling at 10 ms⁻¹ on a horizontal plane has a collision, where $e = 0.4$.
   Find the particle's <u>rebound speed</u> if it collides head-on with:
   a) a smooth vertical wall,   b) a particle of mass 2 kg travelling at 12 ms⁻¹ towards it.

8) A particle of mass 2 kg collides with a smooth horizontal surface at a velocity of $\mathbf{u} = 4\mathbf{i} - \mathbf{j}$ ms⁻¹, where $\mathbf{i}$ and $\mathbf{j}$ are the horizontal and vertical unit vectors respectively. The coefficient of restitution for the impact is $e = 0.5$. Find the velocity, $\mathbf{v}$, of the particle after the impact and the kinetic energy lost in the collision.

9) Particles A (mass 1 kg), B (4 kg) and C (5 kg) travel in the same line at speeds of $3u$, $2u$ and u, respectively.
   If A collides with B first ($e = \frac{1}{4}$), then B with C ($e = \frac{1}{3}$), determine whether A and B will collide <u>again</u>.

10) Find the <u>loss in kinetic energy</u> when a particle of mass 2 kg travelling at 3 ms⁻¹ collides with a stationary particle of mass 3 kg on a smooth horizontal plane surface, where $e = 0.3$.

Ready to notch it up a gear? Think you're the <u>Stig</u> of M2?
Well rev her up and let rip — just watch out for those <u>hairpin bends</u>.

Exam Questions

1   A marble of mass 0.02 kg, travelling at 2 ms⁻¹, collides with another, stationary, marble of mass 0.06 kg.
    Both can be modelled as smooth spheres on a smooth horizontal plane.
    If the collision is perfectly elastic, find the speed of each marble immediately after the collision.

(4 marks)

M2 Section 4 — Practice Questions

Encore encore, more more more...

2   A particle of mass 0.4 kg receives an impulse of $(3\mathbf{i} - 8\mathbf{j})$ Ns.
The velocity of the particle just before the impulse is $(-6\mathbf{i} + \mathbf{j})$ ms^{-1}.

    a)   Find the speed of the particle immediately after the impulse.
        Give your answer in ms^{-1} to 3 s.f.

                          (5 marks)

    b)   Find the angle between the motion of the particle and the horizontal following the impulse.
        Give your answer in degrees to 3 s.f.

                          (2 marks)

3   Particles P (of mass $2m$) and Q (of mass m), travelling in a straight line towards each other at the same speed (u) on a smooth horizontal plane surface, collide with a coefficient of restitution of $\frac{3}{4}$.

    a)   Show that the collision reverses the direction of both particles,
        with Q having eight times the rebound speed of P.

                          (6 marks)

    Following the collision, Q goes on to collide with a smooth vertical wall, perpendicular to its path.
The coefficient of restitution for the impact with the wall is e_{wall}.
Q goes on to collide with P again on the rebound from the wall.

    b)   Show that $e_{\text{wall}} > \frac{1}{8}$.

                          (3 marks)

    c)   Suppose that $e_{\text{wall}} = \frac{3}{5}$. If after the second collision with P, Q continues to move away from the wall, but with a speed of 0.22 ms^{-1}, find the value of u, the initial speed of both particles, in ms^{-1}.

                          (7 marks)

4   Particle P, of mass m kg and velocity $\binom{8}{4}$ ms^{-1}, collides with the stationary particle Q, of mass $3m$ kg. The velocities of P and Q immediately following the collision are $\binom{v_P}{1}$ ms^{-1} and $\binom{1}{v_Q}$ ms^{-1} respectively. Find:

    a) v_P and v_Q,

                          (3 marks)

    b)   the speeds of both P and Q immediately following the collision.

                          (3 marks)

5   A particle, A, of mass 7 kg is moving on a smooth horizontal plane with velocity $6\mathbf{i} - 4\mathbf{j}$ ms^{-1}.

    Another particle, B, of mass 2 kg is at rest. B experiences a force of magnitude F N for 5 seconds, which causes it to begin moving with velocity $\mathbf{v}_B$ ms^{-1}.
B collides with A and the two particles coalesce to form a new particle, C, with velocity $3\mathbf{i} + 4\mathbf{j}$ ms^{-1}.
Find $\mathbf{v}_B$ and F.

                          (7 marks)

6   Two particles of mass 0.8 kg and 1.2 kg are travelling in the same direction along a straight line with speeds of 4 ms^{-1} and 2 ms^{-1} respectively until they collide. After the collision the 0.8 kg mass has a velocity of 2.5 ms^{-1} in the same direction. The 1.2 kg mass then continues with its new velocity until it collides with a mass of m kg travelling with a speed of 4 ms^{-1} in the opposite direction to it.

    Given that both particles are brought to rest by this collision, find the mass m.

                          (4 marks)

M2 Section 4 — Practice Questions

7 Particles A (mass m), B (mass $2m$) and C (mass $4m$) lie on a straight line, as shown:

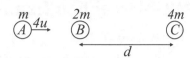

B and C are initially stationary when A collides with B at a speed of $4u$ ($u > 0$), causing B to collide with C. The coefficient of restitution between B and C is $2e$, where e is the coefficient of restitution between A and B.

a) Show that the collision between A and B does not reverse the direction of A.

(7 marks)

By the time B and C collide, A has travelled a distance of $\frac{d}{4}$ since the first collision.

b) Show that $e = \frac{1}{3}$.

(3 marks)

c) Hence find, in terms of u, the speed of C following its collision with B.

(5 marks)

8 A particle of mass $2m$, travelling at a speed of $3u$ on a smooth horizontal plane, collides directly with a particle of mass $3m$ travelling at $2u$ in the same direction. The coefficient of restitution is $\frac{1}{4}$.

a) Find expressions for the speeds of both particles after the collision.
    Give your answers in terms of u.

(4 marks)

b) Show that the amount of kinetic energy lost in the collision is $\frac{9mu^2}{16}$.

(4 marks)

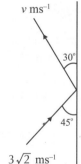

9 A particle of mass 1 kg bounces off a smooth vertical metal plate. It hits the plate at an angle of 45° to the vertical and with speed $u = 3\sqrt{2}$ ms⁻¹. It rebounds at an angle of 30°. By modelling the plate as a smooth vertical plane, find:

a) v, the speed of the particle after the collision,

(3 marks)

b) the coefficient of restitution, e, for the collision,

(3 marks)

c) the kinetic energy lost in the collision.

(2 marks)

10 Two particles, A and B, move on a smooth horizontal plane. A has mass m kg and velocity $\binom{u}{1}$ ms⁻¹. B has mass 5 kg and velocity $\binom{0}{-5}$ ms⁻¹.

a) Find an expression for the total momentum of the system.

(1 mark)

b) The particles collide and coalesce to form a new single particle. This particle has velocity $\binom{2}{-1}$ ms⁻¹. Find:

(i) the value of m,

(3 marks)

(ii) the speed of A before the collision

(3 marks)

General Certificate of Education
Advanced Subsidiary (AS) and Advanced Level

Mechanics M2 — Practice Exam One

Time Allowed: 1 hour 30 min

Calculators may be used for this exam (except those with
facilities for symbolic algebra, differentiation or integration).

Whenever a numerical value of g is required, take g = 9.8 ms⁻².

Give any non-exact numerical answers to an appropriate degree of accuracy.

There are 72 marks available for this paper.

1 a) A particle A, of mass 1 kg, moves in a straight line on a smooth, horizontal surface with speed
        $5u$ ms⁻¹. It collides with a stationary particle, B, of mass M kg. Immediately following the
        collision, A has speed u ms⁻¹ in the opposite direction to its original motion.

        Given that the coefficient of restitution for the collision is $\frac{4}{5}$, find:

   (i)   the speed of B after the collision, in terms of u,

        (3 marks)

   (ii) the value of M.

        (3 marks)

   Particle B goes on to collide with a smooth vertical wall, perpendicular to its direction of travel.
   The coefficient of restitution between B and the wall is e.

   (iii) Find the range of values of e that would allow B to collide again with particle A.

        (3 marks)

   b) A tennis ball of mass 60 g is projected horizontally with speed 15 ms⁻¹ from a point 2 m
       vertically above horizontal ground. The ball moves under the influence of gravity before
       colliding with the ground. The coefficient of restitution in the impact is $\frac{5}{8}$.
       Ignoring the effect of air resistance, find:

   (i)   the speed and direction of motion of the ball immediately following its impact with the
         ground,

        (6 marks)

   (ii) the ball's loss of kinetic energy as a result of its impact with the ground.

        (3 marks)

2 A uniform wire is bent into a frame shaped as a right-angled triangle, as shown in Fig. 1.

   a) Find the distance of the centre of mass of the frame from side OA.

        (4 marks)

   b) Show that the centre of mass of the frame is 1 cm away from side OB.

        (3 marks)

   The frame is suspended freely from point O, where it hangs in equilibrium.

   c) Find the angle that side AB makes with the horizontal.

        (5 marks)

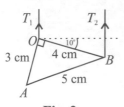

Fig. 2

   The frame is now suspended by two vertical light strings attached to the
   frame at O and B, so that OB is at an angle of 10° below the horizontal,
   as shown in Fig. 2.

   d) Given that the weight of the frame is 3 N, find the tension in each
       string.

        (6 marks)

3   a)   A freely-hinged beam, *AB*, attached to a vertical wall is held in equilibrium perpendicular to the wall by a strut attached to the beam at *C*. The strut is fastened to the wall at point *D*, making an angle of 60° with the wall, as shown. A particle, *P*, with a mass of 1.8 kg rests upon the beam at a point 0.2 m from *A*. The weight of the beam acts at point *C*. The length of the beam is 1.5 m and the distance from *A* to the centre of mass of the beam is 1.1 m.

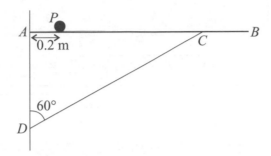

Given that the magnitude of the horizontal component of the reaction at *A* is 35 N, find:

(i)   the magnitude and direction of the reaction at *A*,

(5 marks)

(ii)   the tension in the strut,

(3 marks)

(iii)   the mass of the beam.

(3 marks)

b)   The strut is now removed and the beam rests with *B* on smooth horizontal ground and *A* against a vertical wall. A horizontal force of 10 N is applied at *B*, acting towards the wall, as shown. The beam is held in limiting equilibrium at an angle of 55° to the horizontal.

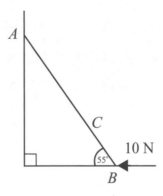

Show that the vertical wall is rough, and hence find the coefficient of friction between the wall and the beam.

(7 marks)

4

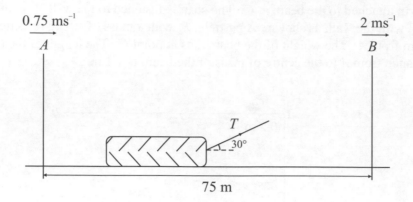

A man is dragging a tractor tyre of mass 160 kg along a straight, horizontal road by means of a light, inextensible rope attached to the tyre at an angle of 30° to the horizontal, as shown in the diagram above.

The man drags the tyre in a straight line between two checkpoints on the road, 75 m apart. The tyre passes through checkpoint A with a speed of 0.75 ms^{-1}, and checkpoint B with a speed of 2 ms^{-1}. Between the two checkpoints, the tyre experiences a constant resistive force of 270 N. Find:

a)   the work done by the tension in the rope in moving the tyre from A to B,

(4 marks)

b) T, the constant magnitude of the tension in the rope.

(3 marks)

The tyre is now used to make a swing. It is attached to one end of a light, inextensible rope of length 3 m. The other end of the rope is attached to a fixed horizontal tree branch. The tyre is allowed to swing freely and the rope remains taut throughout the tyre's motion. The tyre can be modelled as a particle, as shown:

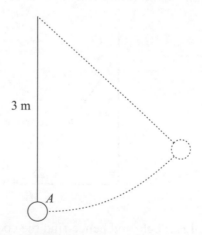

The tyre passes through the lowest point of its swing, A, with speed 6 ms^{-1}.

c)   Explain why the tension in the rope does no work on the tyre.

(1 mark)

d)   Assuming the tyre experiences no resistance to motion, show that the tyre reaches a maximum vertical height above A of 1.84 m (3 s.f.).

(3 marks)

Now assume that the tyre experiences a constant resistive force of 380 N parallel to its direction of motion.

e)   From the tyre's maximum height, as found in part d), it begins to swing back towards A.
     Find the speed of the tyre as it passes back through A.

(7 marks)

General Certificate of Education
Advanced Subsidiary (AS) and Advanced Level

Mechanics M2 — Practice Exam Two

Time Allowed: 1 hour 30 min

Calculators may be used for this exam (except those with facilities for symbolic algebra, differentiation or integration).

Whenever a numerical value of g is required, take g = 9.8 ms^{-2}.

Give any non-exact numerical answers to an appropriate degree of accuracy.

There are 72 marks available for this paper.

1   a)   A uniform rod, AB, rests in equilibrium against rough horizontal ground, as shown. It is held at an angle of θ to the horizontal by a smooth peg, C, where $\cos\theta = 0.91$. AB is 3 m in length and has a mass of 8 kg. The distance $CB = l$ m. The magnitude of the normal reaction at the peg is 54 N.

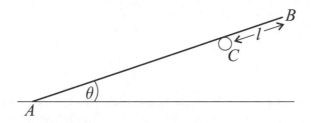

   (i)   Find l.

(3 marks)

   (ii)   Find μ, the coefficient of friction between the ground and the rod.

(5 marks)

   b)   Four light rods are freely pin-jointed together at P, Q and S and to a vertical wall at R and S to make a bracket for a shop sign, as shown. Weights of 100 N and 80 N are attached at P and Q respectively.

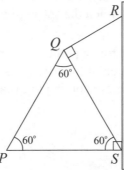

   (i)   Draw a diagram showing the loads and the internal forces acting on the framework.

(1 mark)

   (ii)   Find the internal forces in rods PQ and PS, and state whether each is a tension or a thrust.

(4 marks)

   (iii)   By considering forces acting at P and Q, form a pair of simultaneous equations describing the internal forces in rods QR and QS, and hence find the internal forces in QR and QS, stating whether they are tensions or thrusts.

(6 marks)

2   Three stationary particles, P, Q and R, lie in a line on a smooth horizontal surface. The particles have masses 0.2 kg, 0.6 kg and 0.7 kg respectively. Particle P is projected towards Q at a speed of 5 ms⁻¹, and collides directly with Q, with a coefficient of restitution of 0.65. Find:

   a)   the velocities of P and Q immediately after their collision,

(4 marks)

   b)   the size of the impulse P exerts on Q during the collision,

(2 marks)

   c)   the total kinetic energy lost in the collision.

(3 marks)

Particle Q then collides directly with R. Q is brought to rest by the collision.

   d)   Find the size of the coefficient of restitution between Q and R.

(4 marks)

A fourth particle, S, is projected from a point vertically above the surface and moves under the influence of gravity. S collides with the surface with velocity $4\mathbf{i} - 3\mathbf{j}$ ms⁻¹, where $\mathbf{i}$ and $\mathbf{j}$ are horizontal and vertical unit vectors respectively. It rebounds at an angle of θ above the horizontal, where $\tan\theta = \dfrac{5}{12}$.

   e)   Find the coefficient of restitution, e, in the impact, and the velocity of S immediately following the collision.

(4 marks)

3   a)   A bus of mass 13 000 kg is travelling along a straight, horizontal road at a constant speed of 14 ms⁻¹. The bus experiences a constant resistance to motion from non-gravitational forces which is modelled as a single force of magnitude 4500 N.

      (i)   Find the rate at which the engine of the bus is working. Give your answer in kW.

(3 marks)

      The bus now moves up a hill inclined at an angle, α, to the horizontal, where $\sin\alpha = \dfrac{1}{35}$. The engine in the bus now works at a rate of 72 kW.

      (ii)   Assuming that the non-gravitational resistance to motion remains constant at 4500 N, find the acceleration of the bus when the speed of the bus is 12 ms⁻¹.

(4 marks)

   b)   A particle of mass 9 kg is projected from a point A up a rough plane inclined at an angle of 30° to the horizontal. The speed of projection of the particle is 11 ms⁻¹. The particle travels 8 m up the line of greatest slope of the plane, before coming to instantaneous rest at point B.

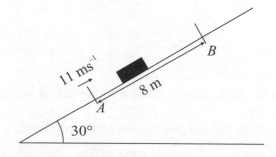

      (i)   Find the work done by friction in bringing the particle to rest.

(6 marks)

      (ii)   Find the coefficient of friction between the particle and the plane.

(5 marks)

4   A 3D shape is made by folding a uniform lamina, as shown below.

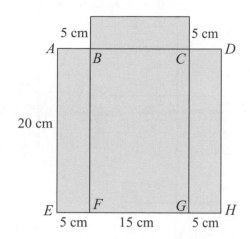

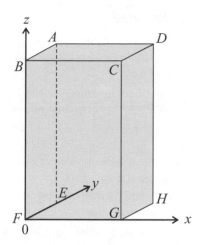

a)   Find the coordinates of the centre of mass of the shape relative to the axes shown on the diagram.

(7 marks)

The x- and y-axes are on horizontal ground. A horizontal force of magnitude P N is applied to the mid-point of BC, acting in the positive y-direction, perpendicular to the x-axis.

b)   Given that the mass of the shape is 0.5 kg, calculate the value of P if the shape is on the point of tipping about the line that runs through E and H.

(4 marks)

The horizontal force is now removed and the shape is placed on a rough plane inclined at an angle of α to the horizontal, such that GH is parallel to the plane and CG is perpendicular to the plane, as shown. The coefficient of friction between the shape and the plane is μ.

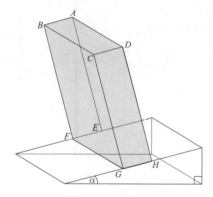

c)   Find the values of α and μ if the shape begins to slide when it is on the point of tipping about FG.

(7 marks)

Answers

C3 Section 1 — Functions

Warm-up Questions

1) a) Range f(x) ≥ –16. This is a function, and it's one-to-one (the domain is restricted so every x-value is mapped to only one value of f(x)).

b) To find the range of this function, you need to find the minimum point of $x^2 - 7x + 10$ — do this by completing the square: $x^2 - 7x + 10 = (x - 3.5)^2 - 12.25 + 10$
$$= (x - 3.5)^2 - 2.25.$$
As $(x - 3.5)^2 \geq 0$ the minimum value of $x^2 - 7x + 10$ is –2.25, so the range is f(x) ≥ –2.25.
This is a function, and it's many-to-one (as more than one x-value is mapped to the same value of f(x)).

You could also have found the minimum point by differentiating, setting the derivative equal to O and solving for x.

c) Range f(x) ≥ 0. This is not a function as f(x) doesn't exist for x < 0.

d) Sketch the graph for this one:

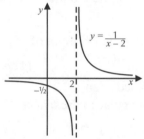

From the graph, the range is f(x) ∈ ℝ, f(x) ≠ 0.
This is not a function as it's not defined for x = 2.

If you're not sure about any of the domains or ranges for the other parts, draw the graphs and see if that helps you figure it out.

2) a) fg(2) = f(2(2) + 3) = f(7) = ³⁄₇.
gf(1) = g(3/1) = g(3) = 2(3) + 3 = 9.
$fg(x) = f(2x + 3) = \dfrac{3}{2x + 3}$.

b) fg(2) = f(2 + 4) = f(6) = 3(6²) = 3 × 36 = 108.
gf(1) = g(3(1²)) = g(3) = 3 + 4 = 7.
fg(x) = f(x + 4) = 3(x + 4)².

3) f is a one-to-one function so it has an inverse. The domain of the inverse is the range of the function and vice versa, so the domain of f⁻¹(x) is x ≥ 3 and the range is f⁻¹(x) ∈ ℝ.

4) Let y = f(x). Then $y = \sqrt{2x - 4}$
$$y^2 = 2x - 4$$
$$y^2 + 4 = 2x$$
$$x = \frac{y^2 + 4}{2} = \frac{y^2}{2} + 2$$
Writing in terms of x and f⁻¹(x) gives the inverse function as $f^{-1}(x) = \dfrac{x^2}{2} + 2$, which has domain x ≥ 0 (as the range of f is f(x) ≥ 0) and range f⁻¹(x) ≥ 2.

5) a) $\sin^{-1}\dfrac{1}{\sqrt{2}} = \dfrac{\pi}{4}$

b) $\cos^{-1}0 = \dfrac{\pi}{2}$

c) $\tan^{-1}\sqrt{3} = \dfrac{\pi}{3}$

6) See p4.

7) a)   b)

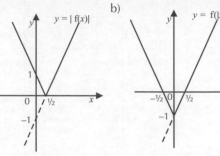

8)

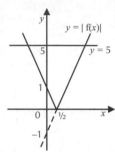

From the graph, |2x – 1| = 5 has 2 solutions, one where 2x – 1 = 5 (so x = 3) and one where –(2x – 1) = 5 (so x = –2).

9)

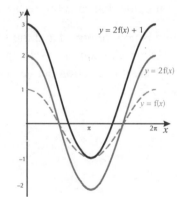

10) a) y = x² is even (but not periodic).

b) y = tan x is odd and periodic (with period π).

c) y = x³ is odd (but not periodic).

Exam Questions

1 For an even function, f(–x) = f(x).
f(–x) = (–x)sin(–x) = (–x)(–sin x) *[1 mark]* (as sin(–x) = –sin x)
= xsin x = f(x) *[1 mark]*, so f is an even function.
The graph of f(x) will be symmetrical about the y-axis *[1 mark]*.

2 To transform the curve y = x³ into y = (x – 1)³, translate it 1 unit *[1 mark]* in the positive x-direction *[1 mark]*.
To transform this into the curve y = 2(x – 1)³, stretch it vertically *[1 mark]* by a scale factor of 2 *[1 mark]*.
Finally, to transform into the curve y = 2(x – 1)³ + 4, the whole curve is translated 4 units *[1 mark]* in the positive y-direction *[1 mark]*.

Answers

3 a) $fg(6) = f(\sqrt{(3 \times 6) - 2}) = f(\sqrt{16})$ *[1 mark]*
      $= f(4) = 2^4 = 16$ *[1 mark]*

   b) $gf(2) = g(2^2) = g(4)$ *[1 mark]*
      $= \sqrt{(3 \times 4) - 2} = \sqrt{10}$ *[1 mark]*

   c) (i) First, write $y = g(x)$ and rearrange to make x the subject:
      $$y = \sqrt{3x - 2}$$
      $$\Rightarrow y^2 = 3x - 2$$
      $$\Rightarrow y^2 + 2 = 3x$$
      $$\Rightarrow \frac{y^2 + 2}{3} = x \qquad \text{[1 mark]}$$
      Then replace x with $g^{-1}(x)$ and y with x: $g^{-1}(x) = \frac{x^2 + 2}{3}$
      [1 mark].

      (ii) $fg^{-1}(x) = f\left(\frac{x^2 + 2}{3}\right)$ *[1 mark]*
      $= 2^{\frac{x^2 + 2}{3}}$ *[1 mark]*

4 a) The start and end points of the cos curve (with restricted domain) are $(0, 1)$ and $(\pi, -1)$, so the coordinates of the start point of arccos (point A) are $(-1, \pi)$ *[1 mark]* and the coordinates of the end point (point B) are $(1, 0)$ *[1 mark]*.

   b) $y = \arccos x$, that is, $y = \cos^{-1}x$, so $x = \cos y$ *[1 mark]*.

   c) $\arccos x = 2$, so $x = \cos 2$ *[1 mark]* $\Rightarrow x = -0.416$ *[1 mark]*.

5 a) The range of f is $f(x) > 0$ *[1 mark]*.

   b) Let $y = f(x)$. Then $y = \frac{1}{x + 5}$.
      Rearrange this to make x the subject:
      $$y(x + 5) = 1$$
      $$\Rightarrow x + 5 = \frac{1}{y} \quad \text{[1 mark]}$$
      $$\Rightarrow x = \frac{1}{y} - 5 \quad \text{[1 mark]}$$
      Finally, write out in terms of x and $f^{-1}(x)$: $f^{-1}(x) = \frac{1}{x} - 5$
      [1 mark]. The domain of the inverse is the same as the range of the function, so $x > 0$ *[1 mark]*. The range of the inverse is the same as the domain of the function, so $f^{-1}(x) > -5$ *[1 mark]*.

   c)

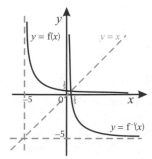

   [3 marks available — 1 mark for each correct curve, 1 mark for correct intersection and asymptotes as shown]

6 a)

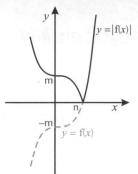

   [2 marks available — 1 mark for reflecting in x-axis at x = n, 1 mark for crossing y-axis at y = m]

   b)

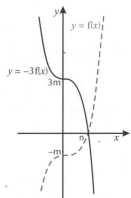

   [2 marks available — 1 mark for reflecting in y-axis and 1 mark for crossing y-axis at y = 3m (due to stretch by scale factor 3)]

   c)

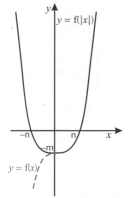

   [2 marks available — 1 mark for reflecting in y-axis and 1 mark for crossing the x-axis at −n]

Answers

C3 Section 2
— Exponentials, Logarithms and Proof
Warm-up Questions

1) a)-d)

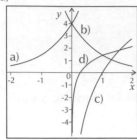

2) a) $e^{2x} = 6 \Rightarrow 2x = \ln 6 \Rightarrow x = \ln 6 \div 2 = 0.8959$ to 4 d.p.

b) $\ln (x + 3) = 0.75 \Rightarrow x + 3 = e^{0.75} \Rightarrow x = e^{0.75} - 3$
$= -0.8830$ to 4 d.p.

c) $3e^{-4x+1} = 5 \Rightarrow e^{-4x+1} = \frac{5}{3} \Rightarrow e^{4x-1} = \frac{3}{5} \Rightarrow 4x - 1 = \ln \frac{3}{5}$
$\Rightarrow x = (\ln \frac{3}{5} + 1) \div 4 = 0.1223$ to 4 d.p.

d) $\ln x + \ln 5 = \ln 4 \Rightarrow \ln (5x) = \ln 4 \Rightarrow 5x = 4$
$\Rightarrow x = 0.8$

3) a) $\ln (2x - 7) + \ln 4 = -3 \Rightarrow \ln (4(2x - 7)) = -3$
$\Rightarrow 8x - 28 = e^{-3} \Rightarrow x = \frac{e^{-3} + 28}{8}$ or $\frac{1}{8e^3} + \frac{7}{2}$.

b) $2e^{2x} + e^x = 3$, so if $y = e^x$, $2y^2 + y - 3 = 0$,
which will factorise to: $(2y + 3)(y - 1) = 0$,
so $e^x = -1.5$ (not possible), and $e^x = 1$,
so $x = 0$ is the only solution.

4) a) $y = 2 - e^{x+1}$

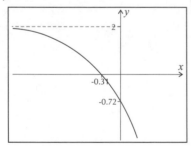

Goes through (0, –0.72) and (–0.31, 0),
with asymptote at $y = 2$.

b) $y = 5e^{0.5x} + 5$

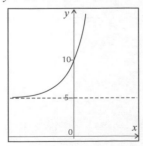

Goes through (0, 10), with asymptote at $y = 5$.

c) $y = \ln (2x) + 1$

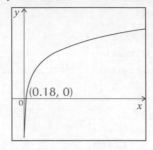

Goes through (0.18, 0), with asymptote at $x = 0$.

d) $y = \ln (x + 5)$

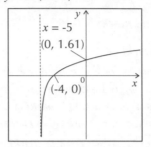

Goes through (0, 1.61) and (–4, 0), with asymptote at $x = -5$.

*You can use your 'graph transformation' skills to work out what
they'll look like, e.g. d) is just $y = \ln x$ shifted 5 to the left.*

5) a) $V = 7500e^{-0.2t}$, so when $t = 0$, $V = 7500 \times e^0 = £7500$.

b) $V = 7500 \times e^{(-0.2 \times 10)} = £1015$ to the nearest £.

c) When $V = 500$, $500 = 7500e^{-0.2t}$
$\Rightarrow e^{-0.2t} = \frac{500}{7500} \Rightarrow e^{0.2t} = \frac{7500}{500} \Rightarrow 0.2t = \ln \frac{7500}{500} = 2.7080...$
$\Rightarrow t = 2.7080... \div 0.2 = 13.5$ years.

d)

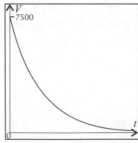

Goes through (0, 7500) with an asymptote at $V = 0$.

6) The simplest way to disprove the statement is to find a
counter-example. Try some values of n and see if the
statement is true for them:
$n = 3 \Rightarrow n^2 - n - 1 = 3^2 - 3 - 1 = 5$ — prime
$n = 4 \Rightarrow n^2 - n - 1 = 4^2 - 4 - 1 = 11$ — prime
$n = 5 \Rightarrow n^2 - n - 1 = 5^2 - 5 - 1 = 19$ — prime
$n = 6 \Rightarrow n^2 - n - 1 = 6^2 - 6 - 1 = 29$ — prime
$n = 7 \Rightarrow n^2 - n - 1 = 7^2 - 7 - 1 = 41$ — prime
$n = 8 \Rightarrow n^2 - n - 1 = 8^2 - 8 - 1 = 55$ — not prime
$n^2 - n - 1$ is not prime when $n = 8$.
So the statement is false.

*Sometimes good old trial and error is the easiest way to find a
counter-example. Don't forget, if you've been told to disprove a
statement like this, then a counter-example must exist.*

Answers

Exam Questions

1 a) $6e^x = 3 \Rightarrow e^x = 0.5$ **[1 mark]** $\Rightarrow x = \ln 0.5$ **[1 mark]**.

b) $e^{2x} - 8e^x + 7 = 0$.

(This looks like a quadratic, so use $y = e^x$...)

If $y = e^x$, then $y^2 - 8y + 7 = 0$. This will factorise to give:
$(y - 7)(y - 1) = 0 \Rightarrow y = 7$ and $y = 1$.
So $e^x = 7 \Rightarrow x = \ln 7$, and $e^x = 1 \Rightarrow x = \ln 1 = 0$.

[4 marks available — 1 mark for factorisation of a quadratic, 1 mark for both solutions for e^x, and 1 mark for each correct solution for x.]

c) $4 \ln x = 3 \Rightarrow \ln x = 0.75$ **[1 mark]** $\Rightarrow x = e^{0.75}$ **[1 mark]**.

d) $\ln x + \dfrac{24}{\ln x} = 10$

(You need to get rid of that fraction, so multiply through by $\ln x$...)

$(\ln x)^2 + 24 = 10 \ln x$
$\Rightarrow (\ln x)^2 - 10 \ln x + 24 = 0$

(...which looks like a quadratic, so use $y = \ln x$...)

$y^2 - 10y + 24 = 0 \Rightarrow (y - 6)(y - 4) = 0$
$\Rightarrow y = 6$ or $y = 4$.
So $\ln x = 6 \Rightarrow x = e^6$, or $\ln x = 4 \Rightarrow x = e^4$.

[4 marks available — 1 mark for factorisation of a quadratic, 1 mark for both solutions for $\ln x$, and 1 mark for each correct solution for x.]

2   $y = e^{ax} + b$

The sketch shows that when $x = 0$, $y = -6$, so:
$-6 = e^0 + b$ **[1 mark]**
$-6 = 1 + b \Rightarrow b = -7$ **[1 mark]**.

The sketch also shows that when $y = 0$, $x = \frac{1}{4} \ln 7$, so:
$0 = e^{(\frac{a}{4} \ln 7)} - 7$ **[1 mark]**
$\Rightarrow e^{(\frac{a}{4} \ln 7)} = 7$
$\Rightarrow \frac{a}{4} \ln 7 = \ln 7 \Rightarrow \frac{a}{4} = 1 \Rightarrow a = 4$ **[1 mark]**.

The asymptote occurs as $x \to -\infty$, so $e^{4x} \to 0$,
and since $y = e^{4x} - 7$, $y \to -7$.
So the equation of the asymptote is $y = -7$ **[1 mark]**.

3 a) When $t = 0$ (i.e. when the mink were introduced to the habitat) $M = 74 \times e^0 = 74$, so there were 74 mink originally **[1 mark]**.

b) After 3 years, $M = 74 \times e^{0.6 \times 3}$ **[1 mark]** $= 447$ mink **[1 mark]**.

You can't round up here as there are only 447 whole mink.

c) For $M = 10\ 000$:
$10\ 000 = 74e^{0.6t}$
$\Rightarrow e^{0.6t} = 10\ 000 \div 74 = 135.1351$
$\Rightarrow 0.6t = \ln 135.1351 = 4.9063$ **[1 mark]**
$\Rightarrow t = 4.9063 \div 0.6 = 8.2$ years to reach 10 000, so it would take 9 complete years for the population to exceed 10 000 **[1 mark]**.

d)

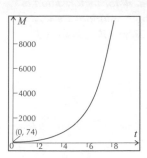

[2 marks available — 1 mark for correct shape of graph, 1 mark for (0, 74) as a point on the graph.]

4 a) $y = \ln (4x - 3)$, and $x = a$ when $y = 1$.
$1 = \ln (4a - 3) \Rightarrow e^1 = 4a - 3$ **[1 mark]**
$\Rightarrow a = (e^1 + 3) \div 4 = 1.43$ to 2 d.p. **[1 mark]**.

b) The curve can only exist when $4x - 3 > 0$ **[1 mark]** so $x > 3 \div 4$, $x > 0.75$. If $x > b$, then $b = 0.75$ **[1 mark]**.

c)

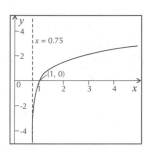

When $y = 0$, $4x - 3 = e^0 = 1$, so $x = 1$.
As $x \to \infty$, $y \to \infty$ gradually.
From (b), there will be an asymptote at $x = 0.75$.

[2 marks available — 1 mark for correct shape including asymptote at x = 0.75, 1 mark for (1, 0) as a point on the graph.]

5 a) Proof by exhaustion: let n be even. $n^2 - n = n(n - 1)$.
If n is even, $n - 1$ is odd so $n(n - 1)$ is even (as even × odd = even). This means that $n(n - 1) - 1$ is odd **[1 mark]**.
Let n be odd. If n is odd, $n - 1$ is even, so $n(n - 1)$ is even (as odd × even = even). This means that $n(n - 1) - 1$ is odd **[1 mark]**. As any integer n has to be either odd or even, $n^2 - n - 1$ is odd for any value of n **[1 mark]**.

b) As $n^2 - n - 1$ is odd, $n^2 - n - 2$ is even **[1 mark]**. The product of even numbers is also even **[1 mark]**, so as $(n^2 - n - 2)^3$ is the product of 3 even numbers, it will always be even **[1 mark]**.

6 a) $2e^x + 18e^{-x} = 20$

(Multiply through by e^x to remove the e^{-x}, since $e^x \times e^{-x} = 1$)

$2e^{2x} + 18 = 20e^x$
$\Rightarrow 2e^{2x} - 20e^x + 18 = 0 \Rightarrow e^{2x} - 10e^x + 9 = 0$

(This now looks like a quadratic equation, so use $y = e^x$ to simplify...)

$y^2 - 10y + 9 = 0$
$\Rightarrow (y - 1)(y - 9) = 0 \Rightarrow y = 1$ or $y = 9$.

So $e^x = 1 \Rightarrow x = 0$
or $e^x = 9 \Rightarrow x = \ln 9$.

Answers

[4 marks available — 1 mark for factorisation of a quadratic, 1 mark for both solutions for e^x, and 1 mark for each correct exact solution for x.]

b) $2 \ln x - \ln 3 = \ln 12$

$\Rightarrow 2 \ln x = \ln 12 + \ln 3$

(Use the log laws to simplify at this point...)

$\Rightarrow \ln x^2 = \ln 36$ *[1 mark]*

$\Rightarrow x^2 = 36$ *[1 mark]*

$\Rightarrow x = 6$ *[1 mark]*

(x must be positive as ln (−6) does not exist.)

7 a) B is the value of A when $t = 0$.
From the table, $B = 50$ *[1 mark]*.

b) Substitute $t = 5$ and $A = 42$ into $A = 50e^{-kt}$:

$42 = 50e^{-5k} \Rightarrow e^{-5k} = \frac{42}{50} \Rightarrow e^{5k} = \frac{50}{42}$ *[1 mark]*

$\Rightarrow 5k = \ln\left(\frac{50}{42}\right) = 0.17435$

$\Rightarrow k = 0.17435 \div 5 = 0.0349$ to 3 s.f. *[1 mark]*.

c) $A = 50e^{-0.0349t}$ (using values from (a) and (b)),
so when $t = 10$, $A = 50 \times e^{-0.0349 \times 10}$ *[1 mark]*
= 35 to the nearest whole *[1 mark]*.

d) The half-life will be the value of t when A reaches half of the original value of 50, i.e. when $A = 25$.

$25 = 50e^{-0.0349t}$

$\Rightarrow \frac{25}{50} = e^{-0.0349t} \Rightarrow \frac{50}{25} = e^{0.0349t} \Rightarrow e^{0.0349t} = 2$ *[1 mark]*.

$0.0349t = \ln 2$ *[1 mark]*

$\Rightarrow t = \ln 2 \div 0.0349 = 20$ days to the nearest day *[1 mark]*.

C3 Section 3 — Differentiation 1
Warm-up Questions

1) a) $y = u^{\frac{1}{2}} \Rightarrow \frac{dy}{du} = \frac{1}{2}u^{-\frac{1}{2}} = \frac{1}{2\sqrt{u}} = \frac{1}{2\sqrt{x^3 + 2x^2}}$

$u = x^3 + 2x^2 \Rightarrow \frac{du}{dx} = 3x^2 + 4x$

$\Rightarrow \frac{dy}{dx} = \frac{3x^2 + 4x}{2\sqrt{x^3 + 2x^2}}$.

b) $y = u^{-\frac{1}{2}} \Rightarrow \frac{dy}{du} = -\frac{1}{2}u^{-\frac{3}{2}} = -\frac{1}{2(\sqrt{u})^3} = -\frac{1}{2(\sqrt{x^3 + 2x^2})^3}$

$u = x^3 + 2x^2 \Rightarrow \frac{du}{dx} = 3x^2 + 4x$

$\Rightarrow \frac{dy}{dx} = -\frac{3x^2 + 4x}{2(\sqrt{x^3 + 2x^2})^3}$.

c) $y = e^u \Rightarrow \frac{dy}{du} = e^u = e^{5x^2}$.

$u = 5x^2 \Rightarrow \frac{du}{dx} = 10x$

$\Rightarrow \frac{dy}{dx} = 10xe^{5x^2}$.

d) $y = \ln u \Rightarrow \frac{dy}{du} = \frac{1}{u} = \frac{1}{(6 - x^2)}$

$u = 6 - x^2 \Rightarrow \frac{du}{dx} = -2x$

$\Rightarrow \frac{dy}{dx} = -\frac{2x}{(6 - x^2)}$.

2) a) $x = 2e^y \Rightarrow \frac{dx}{dy} = 2e^y \Rightarrow \frac{dy}{dx} = \frac{1}{2e^y}$.

b) $x = \ln u$ where $u = 2y + 3$

$\frac{dx}{du} = \frac{1}{u} = \frac{1}{2y + 3}$ and $\frac{du}{dy} = 2 \Rightarrow \frac{dx}{dy} = \frac{2}{2y + 3}$

$\Rightarrow \frac{dy}{dx} = \frac{2y + 3}{2} = y + 1.5$.

3) a) For $f(x) = y = \sin^2 (x + 2)$, use the chain rule twice:

$y = u^2$, where $u = \sin (x + 2)$

$\frac{dy}{du} = 2u = 2 \sin (x + 2)$ and $\frac{du}{dx} = \cos (x + 2) \cdot 1$ (by chain rule)

$\Rightarrow \frac{dy}{dx} = f'(x) = 2 \sin (x + 2) \cos (x + 2)$.

This could also be written as sin (2x + 4) — see C4 Section 2.

b) $f(x) = y = 2 \cos 3x$:

$y = 2 \cos u$, where $u = 3x$

$\frac{dy}{du} = -2 \sin u = -2 \sin 3x$ and $\frac{du}{dx} = 3$

$\Rightarrow \frac{dy}{dx} = f'(x) = -6 \sin 3x$.

4) a) For $y = e^{2x}(x^2 - 3)$, use the product rule:

$u = e^{2x} \Rightarrow \frac{du}{dx} = 2e^{2x}$ (from the chain rule),

$v = x^2 - 3 \Rightarrow \frac{dv}{dx} = 2x$.

$\frac{dy}{dx} = u\frac{dv}{dx} + v\frac{du}{dx} = 2xe^{2x} + 2e^{2x}(x^2 - 3) = 2e^{2x}(x^2 + x - 3)$.

When $x = 0$, $\frac{dy}{dx} = 2e^0(0 + 0 - 3) = 2 \times 1 \times -3 = -6$.

b) For $y = \ln x \sin x$, use the product rule:

$u = \ln x \Rightarrow \frac{du}{dx} = \frac{1}{x}$,

$v = \sin x \Rightarrow \frac{dv}{dx} = \cos x$.

$\frac{dy}{dx} = u\frac{dv}{dx} + v\frac{du}{dx} = \ln x \cos x + \frac{\sin x}{x}$.

When $x = 1$, $\frac{dy}{dx} = \ln 1 \cos 1 + \frac{\sin 1}{1} = 0 + \sin 1$
= 0.841 (to 3 s.f.).

5) For $y = \frac{6x^2 + 3}{4x^2 - 1}$, use the quotient rule:

$u = 6x^2 + 3 \Rightarrow \frac{du}{dx} = 12x$,

$v = 4x^2 - 1 \Rightarrow \frac{dv}{dx} = 8x$.

$\frac{dy}{dx} = \frac{v\frac{du}{dx} - u\frac{dv}{dx}}{v^2} = \frac{12x(4x^2 - 1) - 8x(6x^2 + 3)}{(4x^2 - 1)^2}$.

At (1, 3), $x = 1$ and so gradient =

$\frac{dy}{dx} = \frac{12(4 - 1) - 8(6 + 3)}{(4 - 1)^2} = \frac{36 - 72}{9} = -4$.

Equation of a straight line is:

$y - y_1 = m(x - x_1)$, where m is the gradient.

So the equation of the tangent at (1, 3) is:

$y - 3 = -4(x - 1) \Rightarrow y = -4x + 7$ (or equivalent).

6) For $y = \frac{e^x}{\sqrt{x}}$, use the quotient rule:

$u = e^x \Rightarrow \frac{du}{dx} = e^x$,

$v = x^{\frac{1}{2}} \Rightarrow \frac{dv}{dx} = \frac{1}{2}x^{-\frac{1}{2}} = \frac{1}{2\sqrt{x}}$.

$\frac{dy}{dx} = \frac{v\frac{du}{dx} - u\frac{dv}{dx}}{v^2} = \frac{e^x \sqrt{x} - \frac{e^x}{2\sqrt{x}}}{(\sqrt{x})^2}$.

Multiplying top and bottom by $2\sqrt{x}$ gives:

$\frac{dy}{dx} = \frac{2xe^x - e^x}{2x\sqrt{x}} = \frac{e^x(2x - 1)}{2x\sqrt{x}}$.

At the stationary point, $\frac{dy}{dx} = 0$,

$\Rightarrow \frac{e^x(2x - 1)}{2x\sqrt{x}} = 0 \Rightarrow e^x(2x - 1) = 0$,

so either $e^x = 0$ or $2x - 1 = 0$. e^x never equals 0, so the stationary point must be at $2x - 1 = 0$, $x = \frac{1}{2}$.

Answers

To find out the nature of the stationary point,

differentiate again: $\frac{dy}{dx} = \frac{e^x(2x-1)}{2x\sqrt{x}}$, so use quotient rule and product rule:

$u = e^x(2x - 1) \Rightarrow$ using product rule $\frac{du}{dx} = 2e^x + e^x(2x - 1)$
$= e^x(2x - 1 + 2) = e^x(2x + 1)$.

$v = 2x^{\frac{3}{2}} \Rightarrow \frac{dv}{dx} = 3x^{\frac{1}{2}} = 3\sqrt{x}$.

$\frac{d^2y}{dx^2} = \frac{v\frac{du}{dx} - u\frac{dv}{dx}}{v^2} = \frac{2x\sqrt{x}\,e^x(2x+1) - 3\sqrt{x}\,e^x(2x-1)}{(2x\sqrt{x})^2}$
$= \frac{\sqrt{x}\,e^x(4x^2 - 4x + 3)}{4x^3}$.

When $x = \frac{1}{2}$, $\frac{d^2y}{dx^2} > 0$, so it is a minimum point.

Give yourself a big pat on the back if you survived question 6. I told you it was hard...

Exam Questions

1 a) For $y = \ln(3x + 1)\sin(3x + 1)$,
   use the product rule and the chain rule:
   Product rule: $u = \ln(3x + 1)$ and $v = \sin(3x + 1)$.
   Using the chain rule for $\frac{du}{dx} = \frac{3}{3x+1}$ *[1 mark]*.
   Using the chain rule for $\frac{dv}{dx} = 3\cos(3x + 1)$ *[1 mark]*.

   So $\frac{dy}{dx} = u\frac{dv}{dx} + v\frac{du}{dx}$
   $= [\ln(3x + 1) \cdot 3\cos(3x + 1)] + [\sin(3x + 1) \cdot \frac{3}{3x+1}]$ *[1 mark]*
   $= 3\ln(3x + 1)\cos(3x + 1) + \frac{3\sin(3x+1)}{3x+1}$ *[1 mark]*.

   b) For $y = \frac{\sqrt{x^2+3}}{\cos 3x}$, use the quotient rule and the chain rule:
   Quotient rule: $u = \sqrt{x^2 + 3}$ and $v = \cos 3x$.
   Using the chain rule for $\frac{du}{dx} = \frac{2x}{2\sqrt{x^2+3}} = \frac{x}{\sqrt{x^2+3}}$ *[1 mark]*.
   Using the chain rule for $\frac{dv}{dx} = -3\sin 3x$ *[1 mark]*.

   So $\frac{dy}{dx} = \frac{v\frac{du}{dx} - u\frac{dv}{dx}}{v^2} = \frac{[\cos 3x \cdot \frac{x}{\sqrt{x^2+3}}] - [\sqrt{x^2+3} \cdot -3\sin 3x]}{\cos^2 3x}$
   [1 mark]. Then multiply top and bottom by $\sqrt{x^2+3}$ to get:
   $\frac{dy}{dx} = \frac{x\cos 3x + 3(x^2+3)\sin 3x}{(\sqrt{x^2+3})\cos^2 3x} = \frac{x + 3(x^2+3)\tan 3x}{(\sqrt{x^2+3})\cos 3x}$
   [1 mark].

   c) For $y = \sin^3(2x^2)$, use the chain rule twice:
   $y = u^3$ where $u = \sin(2x^2)$.
   $\frac{dy}{du} = 3u^2 = 3\sin^2(2x^2)$ *[1 mark]*.
   $\frac{du}{dx} = 4x\cos(2x^2)$ (using chain rule again) *[1 mark]*.
   So $\frac{dy}{dx} = 12x\sin^2(2x^2)\cos(2x^2)$ *[1 mark]*.

2 $f(x) = \frac{1}{\cos x}$, so using the quotient rule:
   $u = 1 \Rightarrow \frac{du}{dx} = 0$ and $v = \cos x \Rightarrow \frac{dv}{dx} = -\sin x$.

   $\frac{dy}{dx} = \frac{v\frac{du}{dx} - u\frac{dv}{dx}}{v^2} = \frac{(\cos x \cdot 0) - (-1)(-\sin x)}{\cos^2 x} = \frac{\sin x}{\cos^2 x}$.

   Since $\tan x = \frac{\sin x}{\cos x}$, $f'(x) = \frac{dy}{dx} = \frac{\sin x}{\cos x} \times \frac{1}{\cos x} = \frac{\tan x}{\cos x}$.
   [4 marks available — 1 mark for u and du/dx, 1 mark for v and dv/dx, 1 mark for correct answer from quotient rule, and 1 mark for correct rearrangement.]

3 a) For $x = \sqrt{y^2 + 3y}$, find $\frac{dx}{dy}$ first (using the chain rule):
   $x = u^{\frac{1}{2}}$ where $u = y^2 + 3y$.
   $\frac{dx}{du} = \frac{1}{2}u^{-\frac{1}{2}} = \frac{1}{2\sqrt{u}} = \frac{1}{2\sqrt{y^2+3y}}$ *[1 mark]*.
   $\frac{du}{dy} = 2y + 3$ *[1 mark]*.

   So $\frac{dx}{dy} = \frac{2y+3}{2\sqrt{y^2+3y}}$ *[1 mark]*.
   (Now, flip the fraction upside down for dy/dx...)
   $\frac{dy}{dx} = \frac{2\sqrt{y^2+3y}}{2y+3}$ *[1 mark]*.
   At the point (2, 1), $y = 1$, so:
   $\frac{dy}{dx} = \frac{2\sqrt{1^2+3}}{2+3} = \frac{4}{5} = 0.8$ *[1 mark]*.

   b) Equation of a straight line is:
   $y - y_1 = m(x - x_1)$, where m is the gradient.
   For the tangent at (2, 1), $y_1 = 1$, $x_1 = 2$, and $m = \frac{dy}{dx} = 0.8$.
   So the equation is:
   $y - 1 = 0.8(x - 2) \Rightarrow y = 0.8x - 0.6$ (or equivalent fractions)
   [2 marks available — 1 mark for correct substitution of (2, 1) and gradient from (a), and 1 mark for final answer.]

4 a) For $y = \sqrt{e^x + e^{2x}}$, use the chain rule:
   $y = u^{\frac{1}{2}}$ where $u = e^x + e^{2x}$.
   $\frac{dy}{du} = \frac{1}{2}u^{-\frac{1}{2}} = \frac{1}{2\sqrt{u}} = \frac{1}{2\sqrt{e^x+e^{2x}}}$ *[1 mark]*.
   $\frac{du}{dx} = e^x + 2e^{2x}$ *[1 mark]*.
   So $\frac{dy}{dx} = \frac{e^x + 2e^{2x}}{2\sqrt{e^x+e^{2x}}}$ *[1 mark]*.

   b) For $y = 3e^{2x+1} - \ln(1 - x^2) + 2x^3$, use the chain rule for the first 2 parts separately:

   For $y = 3e^{2x+1}$, $y = 3e^u$ where $u = 2x + 1$, so $\frac{dy}{du} = 3e^u = 3e^{2x+1}$
   and $\frac{du}{dx} = 2$, so $\frac{dy}{dx} = 6e^{2x+1}$ *[1 mark]*.
   For $y = \ln(1 - x^2)$, $y = \ln u$ where $u = 1 - x^2$,
   so $\frac{dy}{du} = \frac{1}{u} = \frac{1}{(1-x^2)}$ and $\frac{du}{dx} = -2x$, so $\frac{dy}{dx} = -\frac{2x}{(1-x^2)}$
   [1 mark].
   So overall: $\frac{dy}{dx} = 6e^{2x+1} + \frac{2x}{(1-x^2)} + 6x^2$ *[1 mark]*.

5 a) For $y = e^x\sin x$, use the product rule:
   $u = e^x \Rightarrow \frac{du}{dx} = e^x$
   $v = \sin x \Rightarrow \frac{dv}{dx} = \cos x$
   So $\frac{dy}{dx} = u\frac{dv}{dx} + v\frac{du}{dx} = (e^x \cdot \cos x) + (\sin x \cdot e^x)$
   $= e^x(\cos x + \sin x)$ *[1 mark]*.

   At the turning points, $\frac{dy}{dx} = 0$, so:
   $e^x(\cos x + \sin x) = 0$ *[1 mark]*

   $\Rightarrow$ turning points are when $e^x = 0$ or $\cos x + \sin x = 0$.
   e^x cannot be 0, so the turning points are when
   $\cos x + \sin x = 0$ *[1 mark]*

   $\Rightarrow \sin x = -\cos x \Rightarrow \frac{\sin x}{\cos x} = -1 \Rightarrow \tan x = -1$ *[1 mark]*.

   Look back at C2 for the graph of tan x to help you find all the solutions — it repeats itself every π radians...

Answers

There are two solutions for $\tan x = -1$ in the interval $-\pi \le x \le \pi$: $x = -\frac{\pi}{4}$ and $x = \pi - \frac{\pi}{4} = \frac{3\pi}{4}$, so the values of x at each turning point are $-\frac{\pi}{4}$ *[1 mark]* and $\frac{3\pi}{4}$ *[1 mark]*.

b) To determine the nature of the turning points, find $\frac{d^2y}{dx^2}$ at the points:

For $\frac{dy}{dx} = e^x(\cos x + \sin x)$, use the product rule:

$u = e^x \Rightarrow \frac{du}{dx} = e^x$

$v = \cos x + \sin x \Rightarrow \frac{dv}{dx} = \cos x - \sin x$, so:

$\frac{d^2y}{dx^2} = u\frac{dv}{dx} + v\frac{du}{dx} = [e^x \cdot (\cos x - \sin x)] + [(\cos x + \sin x) \cdot e^x]$
$= 2e^x \cos x$ *[1 mark]*.

When $x = -\frac{\pi}{4}$, $\frac{d^2y}{dx^2} > 0$ *[1 mark]*, so this is a minimum point *[1 mark]*.

When $x = \frac{3\pi}{4}$, $\frac{d^2y}{dx^2} < 0$ *[1 mark]*, so this is a maximum point *[1 mark]*.

6   For $y = \sin^2 x - 2\cos 2x$, use the chain rule on each part:

For $y = \sin^2 x$, $y = u^2$ where $u = \sin x$, so $\frac{dy}{du} = 2u = 2\sin x$ and $\frac{du}{dx} = \cos x$, so $\frac{dy}{dx} = 2\sin x \cos x$ *[1 mark]*.

For $y = 2\cos 2x$, $y = 2\cos u$ where $u = 2x$, so $\frac{dy}{du} = -2\sin u = -2\sin 2x$ and $\frac{du}{dx} = 2$, so $\frac{dy}{dx} = -4\sin 2x$ *[1 mark]*.

Overall $\frac{dy}{dx} = 2\sin x \cos x + 4\sin 2x$ *[1 mark]*.

(For gradient of the tangent, put the x value into dy/dx...)

Gradient of the tangent when $x = \frac{\pi}{12}$ is:

$2\sin\frac{\pi}{12}\cos\frac{\pi}{12} + 4\sin 2(\frac{\pi}{12}) = 2.5$ *[1 mark]*.

7   For $y = \frac{e^x + x}{e^x - x}$, use the quotient rule:

$u = e^x + x \Rightarrow \frac{du}{dx} = e^x + 1$.

$v = e^x - x \Rightarrow \frac{dv}{dx} = e^x - 1$.

$\frac{dy}{dx} = \frac{v\frac{du}{dx} - u\frac{dv}{dx}}{v^2} = \frac{(e^x - x)(e^x + 1) - (e^x + x)(e^x - 1)}{(e^x - x)^2}$.

When $x = 0$, $e^x = 1$, and $\frac{dy}{dx} = \frac{(1-0)(1+1) - (1+0)(1-1)}{(1-0)^2}$
$= \frac{2 - 0}{1^2} = 2$.

[3 marks available — 1 mark for finding u, v and their derivatives, 1 mark for dy/dx (however rearranged), and 1 mark for dy/dx = 2 when x = 0.]

8   For $x = \sin 4y$, $\frac{dx}{dy} = 4\cos 4y$ *[1 mark]* (using chain rule), and so $\frac{dy}{dx} = \frac{1}{4\cos 4y}$ *[1 mark]*.

At $(0, \frac{\pi}{4})$, $y = \frac{\pi}{4}$ and so $\frac{dy}{dx} = \frac{1}{4\cos \pi} = -\frac{1}{4}$ *[1 mark]*.

(This is the gradient of the tangent at that point, so to find the gradient of the normal do −1 ÷ gradient of tangent...)

Gradient of normal at $(0, \frac{\pi}{4}) = -1 \div -\frac{1}{4} = 4$ *[1 mark]*.

Equation of a straight line is:

$y - y_1 = m(x - x_1)$, where m is the gradient.

For the normal at $(0, \frac{\pi}{4})$, $x_1 = 0$, $y_1 = \frac{\pi}{4}$, and m = 4.

So the equation is:

$y - \frac{\pi}{4} = 4(x - 0)$ *[1 mark]* $\Rightarrow y = 4x + \frac{\pi}{4}$ (or equivalent) *[1 mark]*.

9   a) For f(x) = 4 ln 3x, use the chain rule:

$y = 4\ln u$ where $u = 3x$, so $\frac{dy}{du} = \frac{4}{u} = \frac{4}{3x}$, and $\frac{du}{dx} = 3$ *[1 mark for both]*, so $f'(x) = \frac{dy}{dx} = \frac{12}{3x} = \frac{4}{x}$ *[1 mark]*.
So for $x = 1$, $f'(1) = 4$ *[1 mark]*.

b) Equation of a straight line is:

$y - y_1 = m(x - x_1)$, where m is the gradient.

For the tangent at $x_1 = 1$, $y_1 = 4\ln 3$, and $m = \frac{dy}{dx} = 4$.

So the equation is:

$y - 4\ln 3 = 4(x - 1) \Rightarrow y = 4(x - 1 + \ln 3)$ (or equivalent).

[3 marks available — 1 mark for finding y = 4ln 3, 1 mark for correct substitution of (1, 4ln3) and gradient from (a), and 1 mark for correct final answer.]

C3 Section 4 — Differentiation 2
Warm-up Questions

1) a) Differentiate each term separately with respect to x:

$\frac{d}{dx}4x^2 - \frac{d}{dx}2y^2 = \frac{d}{dx}7x^2y$

Differentiate $4x^2$ first:

$\Rightarrow 8x - \frac{d}{dx}2y^2 = \frac{d}{dx}7x^2y$

Differentiate $2y^2$ using chain rule:

$\Rightarrow 8x - \frac{d}{dy}2y^2\frac{dy}{dx} = \frac{d}{dx}7x^2y$

$\Rightarrow 8x - 4y\frac{dy}{dx} = \frac{d}{dx}7x^2y$

Differentiate $7x^2y$ using product rule:

$\Rightarrow 8x - 4y\frac{dy}{dx} = 7x^2\frac{d}{dx}y + y\frac{d}{dx}7x^2$

$\Rightarrow 8x - 4y\frac{dy}{dx} = 7x^2\frac{dy}{dx} + 14xy$

Rearrange to make $\frac{dy}{dx}$ the subject:

$\Rightarrow (4y + 7x^2)\frac{dy}{dx} = 8x - 14xy$

$\Rightarrow \frac{dy}{dx} = \frac{8x - 14xy}{4y + 7x^2}$

b) Differentiate each term separately with respect to x:

$\frac{d}{dx}3x^4 - \frac{d}{dx}2xy^2 = \frac{d}{dx}y$

Differentiate $3x^4$ first:

$\Rightarrow 12x^3 - \frac{d}{dx}2xy^2 = \frac{dy}{dx}$

Differentiate $2xy^2$ using product rule:

$\Rightarrow 12x^3 - \left(y^2\frac{d}{dx}2x + 2x\frac{d}{dy}y^2\frac{dy}{dx}\right) = \frac{dy}{dx}$

$\Rightarrow 12x^3 - 2y^2 - 4xy\frac{dy}{dx} = \frac{dy}{dx}$

Answers

Rearrange to make $\dfrac{dy}{dx}$ the subject:

$\Rightarrow (1 + 4xy)\dfrac{dy}{dx} = 12x^3 - 2y^2$

$\Rightarrow \dfrac{dy}{dx} = \dfrac{12x^3 - 2y^2}{1 + 4xy}$

c) Use the product rule to differentiate each term separately with respect to x:

$\dfrac{d}{dx}\cos x \sin y = \dfrac{d}{dx}xy$

$\Rightarrow \cos x\dfrac{d}{dx}(\sin y) + \sin y\dfrac{d}{dx}(\cos x) = x\dfrac{d}{dx}y + y\dfrac{d}{dx}x$

Use the chain rule on $\dfrac{d}{dx}(\sin y)$:

$\Rightarrow \cos x\dfrac{d}{dy}(\sin y)\dfrac{dy}{dx} + \sin y\dfrac{d}{dx}(\cos x) = x\dfrac{d}{dx}y + y\dfrac{d}{dx}x$

$\Rightarrow (\cos x \cos y)\dfrac{dy}{dx} - \sin y \sin x = x\dfrac{dy}{dx} + y$

Rearrange to make $\dfrac{dy}{dx}$ the subject:

$\Rightarrow (\cos x \cos y - x)\dfrac{dy}{dx} = y + \sin x \sin y$

$\Rightarrow \dfrac{dy}{dx} = \dfrac{\sin x \sin y + y}{\cos x \cos y - x}$

Make sure you learn how to differentiate trig functions. Chances are they'll come up in your C3 exam. And even if they don't, that sort of skill will make you a hit at parties. Trust me.

2) a) At $(1, -4)$, $\dfrac{dy}{dx} = \dfrac{8x - 14xy}{4y + 7x^2}$

$= \dfrac{8(1) - 14(1)(-4)}{4(-4) + 7(1)^2} = \dfrac{8 + 56}{-16 + 7} = -\dfrac{64}{9}$

b) At $(1, 1)$, $\dfrac{dy}{dx} = \dfrac{12x^3 - 2y^2}{1 + 4xy}$

$= \dfrac{12(1)^3 - 2(1)^2}{1 + 4(1)(1)} = \dfrac{12 - 2}{1 + 4} = \dfrac{10}{5} = 2$

So the gradient of the normal is $-\dfrac{1}{2}$.

3) $A = 2(x)(2x) + 2(x)(3x) + 2(2x)(3x)$
$= 4x^2 + 6x^2 + 12x^2$
$= 22x^2$

So $\dfrac{dA}{dx} = 44x$

$V = (x)(2x)(3x) = 6x^3$
So $\dfrac{dV}{dx} = 18x^2$

By the chain rule:
$\dfrac{dA}{dt} = \dfrac{dA}{dx} \times \dfrac{dx}{dt} = 44x \times \dfrac{dx}{dt}$

To find $\dfrac{dx}{dt}$, use the chain rule again:

$\dfrac{dx}{dt} = \dfrac{dx}{dV} \times \dfrac{dV}{dt} = \dfrac{1}{\left(\dfrac{dV}{dx}\right)} \times \dfrac{dV}{dt} = \dfrac{1}{18x^2} \times 3 = \dfrac{1}{6x^2}$

So $\dfrac{dA}{dt} = 44x \times \dfrac{1}{6x^2} = \dfrac{22}{3x}$

1 a) (i) Using implicit differentiation:

$3e^x + 6y = 2x^2y \Rightarrow \dfrac{d}{dx}3e^x + \dfrac{d}{dx}6y = \dfrac{d}{dx}2x^2y$ *[1 mark]*

$\Rightarrow 3e^x + 6\dfrac{dy}{dx} = 2x^2\dfrac{dy}{dx} + y\dfrac{d}{dx}2x^2$

$\Rightarrow 3e^x + 6\dfrac{dy}{dx} = 2x^2\dfrac{dy}{dx} + 4xy$ *[1 mark]*

$\Rightarrow 2x^2\dfrac{dy}{dx} - 6\dfrac{dy}{dx} = 3e^x - 4xy$

$\Rightarrow \dfrac{dy}{dx} = \dfrac{3e^x - 4xy}{2x^2 - 6}$ *[1 mark]*

(ii) At the stationary points of C, $\dfrac{dy}{dx} = 0$

$\Rightarrow \dfrac{3e^x - 4xy}{2x^2 - 6} = 0$ *[1 mark]*

$\Rightarrow 3e^x - 4xy = 0$

$\Rightarrow y = \dfrac{3e^x}{4x}$ *[1 mark]*

b) Substitute $y = \dfrac{3e^x}{4x}$ into the original equation of curve C:

$3e^x + 6y = 2x^2y \Rightarrow 3e^x + 6\dfrac{3e^x}{4x} = 2x^2\dfrac{3e^x}{4x}$ *[1 mark]*

$\Rightarrow 3e^x(1 + \dfrac{3}{2x} - \dfrac{x}{2}) = 0$

$3e^x = 0$ has no solutions, so $(1 + \dfrac{3}{2x} - \dfrac{x}{2}) = 0$ *[1 mark]*

$\Rightarrow x^2 - 2x - 3 = 0$

$\Rightarrow (x + 1)(x - 3) = 0$

$\Rightarrow x = -1$ or $x = 3$ *[1 mark]*

$x = -1 \Rightarrow y = \dfrac{3e^{-1}}{4(-1)} = -\dfrac{3}{4e}$

$x = 3 \Rightarrow y = \dfrac{3e^3}{4(3)} = \dfrac{1}{4}e^3$

So the stationary points of C are $(-1, -\dfrac{3}{4e})$ and $(3, \dfrac{1}{4}e^3)$

[1 mark for correct y-coordinates]

If the question asks you for an exact answer, that usually means leaving it in terms of something like π or ln or, in this case, e.

2 a) c is the value of y when $x = 2$. If $x = 2$, then
$6x^2y - 7 = 5x - 4y^2 - x^2$

$\Rightarrow 6(2)^2y - 7 = 5(2) - 4y^2 - (2)^2$ *[1 mark]*

$\Rightarrow 24y - 7 = 6 - 4y^2$

$\Rightarrow 4y^2 + 24y - 13 = 0$

$\Rightarrow (2y + 13)(2y - 1) = 0$

$\Rightarrow y = -6.5$ or $y = 0.5$ *[1 mark]*

$c > 0$, so $c = 0.5$ *[1 mark]*

b) (i) Q is another point on C where $y = 0.5$.
If $y = 0.5$, then $6x^2y - 7 = 5x - 4y^2 - x^2$

$\Rightarrow 6x^2(0.5) - 7 = 5x - 4(0.5)^2 - x^2$ *[1 mark]*

$\Rightarrow 3x^2 - 7 = 5x - 1 - x^2$

$\Rightarrow 4x^2 - 5x - 6 = 0$

$\Rightarrow (x - 2)(4x + 3) = 0$ *[1 mark]*

$\Rightarrow x = 2$ or $x = -0.75$

$x \neq 2$, as $x = 2$ at the other point where T crosses C.
So the coordinates of Q are $(-0.75, 0.5)$. *[1 mark]*

(ii) To find the gradient of C, use implicit differentiation.
Differentiate each term separately with respect to x:

$\dfrac{d}{dx}6x^2y - \dfrac{d}{dx}7 = \dfrac{d}{dx}5x - \dfrac{d}{dx}4y^2 - \dfrac{d}{dx}x^2$ *[1 mark]*

Differentiate x-terms and constant terms:

$\Rightarrow \dfrac{d}{dx}6x^2y - 0 = 5 - \dfrac{d}{dx}4y^2 - 2x$ *[1 mark]*

Answers

Differentiate y-terms using chain rule:

$\Rightarrow \frac{d}{dx}6x^2y = 5 - \frac{d}{dy}4y^2\frac{dy}{dx} - 2x$

$\Rightarrow \frac{d}{dx}6x^2y = 5 - 8y\frac{dy}{dx} - 2x$ *[1 mark]*

Differentiate xy-terms using product rule:

$\Rightarrow 6x^2\frac{dy}{dx} + y\frac{d}{dx}6x^2 = 5 - 8y\frac{dy}{dx} - 2x$

$\Rightarrow 6x^2\frac{dy}{dx} + 12xy = 5 - 8y\frac{dy}{dx} - 2x$ *[1 mark]*

Rearrange to make $\frac{dy}{dx}$ the subject:

$\Rightarrow 6x^2\frac{dy}{dx} + 8y\frac{dy}{dx} = 5 - 2x - 12xy$

$\Rightarrow \frac{dy}{dx} = \frac{5 - 2x - 12xy}{6x^2 + 8y}$ *[1 mark]*

So at $Q = (-0.75, 0.5)$,

$\frac{dy}{dx} = \frac{5 - 2\left(-\frac{3}{4}\right) - 12\left(-\frac{3}{4}\right)\left(\frac{1}{2}\right)}{6\left(-\frac{3}{4}\right)^2 + 8\left(\frac{1}{2}\right)} = \frac{5 + \frac{3}{2} + \frac{9}{2}}{\frac{27}{8} + 4}$

$= \frac{11}{\left(\frac{59}{8}\right)} = 11 \times \frac{8}{59} = \frac{88}{59}$ *[1 mark]*

3 a) Start by finding the missing side length of the triangular faces. Call the missing length s:

$\frac{3}{4}x$ m

$s = \sqrt{x^2 + \left(\frac{3}{4}x\right)^2}$

$= \sqrt{x^2 + \frac{9}{16}x^2}$

$= \sqrt{\frac{25}{16}x^2}$

$= \frac{5}{4}x$ *[1 mark]*

Now find A by adding up the area of each of the faces:

$A = 2(\frac{1}{2} \times \frac{3}{2}x \times x) + (\frac{3}{2}x \times 4x) + 2(\frac{5}{4}x \times 4x)$ *[1 mark]*

$= \frac{3}{2}x^2 + 6x^2 + 10x^2$

$= \frac{35}{2}x^2$ *[1 mark]*

b) $\frac{dA}{dt} = 0.07$

$A = \frac{35}{2}x^2 \Rightarrow \frac{dA}{dx} = 35x$ *[1 mark]*

Using chain rule, $\frac{dx}{dt} = \frac{dx}{dA} \times \frac{dA}{dt}$ *[1 mark]*

$= \frac{1}{\left(\frac{dA}{dx}\right)} \times \frac{dA}{dt} = \frac{1}{35x} \times 0.07$

$= \frac{0.07}{35 \times 0.5} = 0.004$ m s^{-1} *[1 mark]*

c) First you need to figure out what the question is asking for. 'Find the rate of change of V' means we're looking for $\frac{dV}{dt}$. Start by finding an expression for V:

$V = (\frac{1}{2} \times \frac{3}{2}x \times x) \times 4x = 3x^3$ *[1 mark]*

So $\frac{dV}{dx} = 9x^2$ *[1 mark]*

Using chain rule, $\frac{dV}{dt} = \frac{dV}{dx} \times \frac{dx}{dt}$ *[1 mark]*

$= 9x^2 \times \frac{0.07}{35x} = \frac{9(1.2)^2 \times 0.07}{35 \times 1.2} = 0.0216$ m^3 s^{-1} *[1 mark]*

C3 Section 5 — Integration
Warm-up Questions

1) $2e^{2x} + C$

2) $\frac{1}{3}e^{3x-5} + C$

3) $\frac{2}{3}\ln|x| + C$

4) $\ln|2x + 1| + C$

5) $\frac{1}{4}\sin 4x + C$

6) $\ln|\sin x| + C$

7) $e^{x^3} + C$

8) $4\ln|x^5 + x^3 - 3x| + C$

9) If $u = e^x - 1$, then $\frac{du}{dx} = e^x$ (so $\frac{du}{e^x} = dx$) and $e^x + 1 = u + 2$. Substituting this into the integral gives:

$\int e^x(u + 2)u^2\frac{du}{e^x} = \int (u + 2)u^2 du$

$= \int u^3 + 2u^2 du = \frac{1}{4}u^4 + \frac{2}{3}u^3 + C$

$= \frac{1}{4}(e^x - 1)^4 + \frac{2}{3}(e^x - 1)^3 + C$

Make sure you put $u = e^x - 1$ back into your final answer.

10) Let $u = \ln x$ and let $\frac{dv}{dx} = 3x^2$. So $\frac{du}{dx} = \frac{1}{x}$ and $v = x^3$. Putting these into the formula gives:

$\int 3x^2\ln x \, dx = x^3\ln x - \int \frac{x^3}{x}dx = [x^3\ln x] - \int x^2 dx$

$= x^3\ln x - \frac{1}{3}x^3 + C = x^3(\ln x - \frac{1}{3}) + C$

11) Let $u = 4x$, and let $\frac{dv}{dx} = \cos 4x$. So $\frac{du}{dx} = 4$ and $v = \frac{1}{4}\sin 4x$. Putting these into the formula gives:

$\int 4x\cos 4x \, dx = 4x(\frac{1}{4}\sin 4x) - \int 4(\frac{1}{4}\sin 4x)dx$

$= x\sin 4x + \frac{1}{4}\cos 4x + C$

Exam Questions

1 $-\frac{1}{2}e^{(5-6x)} + C$

*[1 mark for answer in the form $ke^{(5-6x)} + C$,
1 mark for the correct value of k]*

2 Let $u = x$, so $\frac{du}{dx} = 1$. Let $\frac{dv}{dx} = \sin x$, so $v = -\cos x$ *[1 mark for both parts correct]*. Using integration by parts,

$\int_0^\pi x\sin x \, dx = [-x\cos x]_0^\pi - \int_0^\pi -\cos x \, dx$ *[1 mark]*

$= [-x\cos x]_0^\pi + [\sin x]_0^\pi$ *[1 mark]*

$= (\pi - 0) + (0) = \pi$ *[1 mark]*

If you'd tried to use $u = \sin x$, you'd have ended up with a more complicated function to integrate ($x^2\cos x$).

3 If $u = \ln x + 2$, then $\frac{du}{dx} = \frac{1}{x}$, so $x\,du = dx$. Changing the limits: when $x = 1$, $u = \ln 1 + 2 = 2$. When $x = 2$, $u = \ln 2 + 2$.

Answers

Substituting all this into the integral gives:

$$\int_1^2 \frac{8}{x}(\ln x + 2)^3 \, dx = \int_0^{\ln 2 + 2} \frac{8}{x}u^3 x du = \int_0^{\ln 2 + 2} 8u^3 \, du$$
$$= [2u^4]_0^{\ln 2 + 2}$$
$$= [2(\ln 2 + 2)^4] - [2(2)^4]$$
$$= 105.21 - 32 = 73.21 \text{ (4 s.f.)}.$$

[6 marks available — 1 mark for finding substitution for dx, 1 mark for finding correct limits, 1 mark for correct integral in terms of u, 2 marks for correct integration (1 for an answer in the form $k(u)^n$, 1 mark for correct values of k and n), 1 mark for final answer (to 4 s.f.)]

C3 Section 6 — Numerical Methods
Practice Questions

1) There are 2 roots (graph crosses the x-axis twice in this interval).

2) a) Sin $(2 \times 3) = -0.2794...$ and sin $(2 \times 4) = 0.9893...$
Since sin(2x) is a continuous function, the change of sign means there is a root between 3 and 4.

b) ln $(2.1 - 2) + 2 = -0.3025...$
and ln $(2.2 - 2) + 2 = 0.3905...$
Since the function is continuous for $x > 2$, the change of sign means there is a root between 2.1 and 2.2.

c) Rearrange first to give $x^3 - 4x^2 - 7 = 0$, then:
$4.3^3 - 4 \times (4.3^2) - 7 = -1.453$ and
$4.5^3 - 4 \times (4.5^2) - 7 = 3.125$.
The function is continuous, so the change of sign means there is a root between 4.3 and 4.5.

3) a) f(1) = 3, f(2) = −13.
f(1.1) = 2.85359
f(1.2) = 2.58528
f(1.3) = 2.14317
f(1.4) = 1.46336
f(1.5) = 0.46875
f(1.6) = −0.93216
There's a sign change, so the root lies in the interval (1.5, 1.6)
f(1.51) = 0.3485...
f(1.52) = 0.2242...
f(1.53) = 0.0956...
f(1.54) = −0.0372....
The root lies in the interval (1.53, 1.54). Both these values round to 1.5, so $x = 1.5$ to 1 d.p.

b) 1.5 bisects the interval (1, 2). f(1.5) = 0.46875 — so the root lies in the interval (1.5, 2). 1.75 bisects this interval and f(1.75) = −4.0341... so the root lies in (1.5, 1.75). 1.625 bisects this interval and f(1.625) = −1.3580... so the root lies in the interval (1.5, 1.625). 1.5625 bisects the interval, and f(1.5625) = −0.3527... so the root is in (1.5, 1.5625). 1.53125 bisects this interval, and f(1.53125) = 0.0793... so the root is in the interval (1.53125, 1.5625). 1.546875 bisects this interval, and f(1.546875) = −0.1311... so the root lies in the interval (1.53125, 1.546875). Both these values round to 1.5, so $x = 1.5$ to 1 d.p.

c) Put the values of f(1) and f(2) into the formula:
$$x = \frac{1(|-13|) + 2(|3|)}{|(3)| + |(-13)|} = \frac{19}{16} = 1.1875$$
f(1.1875) = 2.6271... so the root lies in the interval (1.1875, 2). Using the values of f(1.1875) and f(2):
$$x = \frac{1.1875(|-13|) + 2(|2.6271...|)}{|(2.6271...)| + |(-13)|} = 1.3240...$$
f(1.3240...) = 2.0038... so the root lies in the interval (1.3240..., 2). Using these new values on the formula:
$$x = \frac{1.3240...(|-13|) + 2(|2.0038...|)}{|(2.0038...)| + |(-13)|} = 1.4143...$$
f(1.4143...) = 1.3418... so the root is in the interval (1.4143..., 2). Using these new values on the formula:
$$x = \frac{1.4143...(|-13|) + 2(|1.3418...|)}{|(1.3418...)| + |(-13)|} = 1.4691...$$
f(1.4691...) = 0.8143... so the root is in the interval (1.4691..., 2).

Phew, there was a lot of working and fiddly numbers in that last part. The good news is that you only need to use one of the three methods (decimal search, bisection and linear interpolation) in your coursework — I found the decimal search method the easiest, but you can use whichever one you prefer.

4) If 1.2 is a root to 1 d.p. then there should be a sign change for f(x) between the error bounds:
f(1.15) = 1.15^3 + 1.15 − 3 = −0.3291...
f(1.25) = 1.25^3 + 1.25 − 3 = 0.2031...
There is a change of sign, and the function is continuous, so the root must lie between 1.15 and 1.25, so to 1 d.p. the root is at $x = 1.2$.

5) $x_1 = -\frac{1}{2} \cos(-1) = -0.2701...$
$x_2 = -\frac{1}{2} \cos(-0.2701...) = -0.4818...$
$x_3 = -\frac{1}{2} \cos(-0.4818...) = -0.4430...$
$x_4 = -\frac{1}{2} \cos(-0.4430...) = -0.4517...$
$x_5 = -\frac{1}{2} \cos(-0.4517...) = -0.4498...$
$x_6 = -\frac{1}{2} \cos(-0.4498...) = -0.4502...$
x_4, x_5 and x_6 all round to −0.45, so to 2 d.p. $x = -0.45$.

6) $x_1 = \sqrt{\ln 2 + 4} = 2.1663...$
$x_2 = \sqrt{\ln 2.1663... + 4} = 2.1847...$
$x_3 = \sqrt{\ln 2.1847... + 4} = 2.1866...$
$x_4 = \sqrt{\ln 2.1866... + 4} = 2.1868...$
$x_5 = \sqrt{\ln 2.1868... + 4} = 2.1868...$
x_3, x_4 and x_5 all round to 2.187, so to 3 d.p. $x = 2.187$.

7) a) (i) $2x^2 - x^3 + 1 = 0 \Rightarrow 2x^2 - x^3 = -1$
$\Rightarrow x^2(2 - x) = -1 \Rightarrow x^2 = \frac{-1}{2 - x} \Rightarrow x = \sqrt{\frac{-1}{2 - x}}$.

(ii) $2x^2 - x^3 + 1 = 0 \Rightarrow x^3 = 2x^2 + 1$
$\Rightarrow x = \sqrt[3]{2x^2 + 1}$.

(iii) $2x^2 - x^3 + 1 = 0 \Rightarrow 2x^2 = x^3 - 1$
$\Rightarrow x^2 = \frac{x^3 - 1}{2} \Rightarrow x = \sqrt{\frac{x^3 - 1}{2}}$.

b) Using $x_{n+1} = \sqrt{\frac{-1}{2 - x_n}}$ with $x_0 = 2.3$ gives:
$$x_1 = \sqrt{\frac{-1}{2 - 2.3}} = 1.8257...$$

Answers

$x_2 = \sqrt{\dfrac{-1}{2 - 1.8257\ldots}}$ has no real solution

so this formula does not converge to a root.

Using $x_{n+1} = \sqrt[3]{2x_n^2 + 1}$ with $x_0 = 2.3$ gives:

$x_1 = \sqrt[3]{2 \times (2.3)^2 + 1} = 2.2624\ldots$

$x_2 = \sqrt[3]{2 \times (2.2624\ldots)^2 + 1} = 2.2398\ldots$

$x_3 = \sqrt[3]{2 \times (2.2398\ldots)^2 + 1} = 2.2262\ldots$

$x_4 = \sqrt[3]{2 \times (2.2262\ldots)^2 + 1} = 2.2180\ldots$

$x_5 = \sqrt[3]{2 \times (2.2180\ldots)^2 + 1} = 2.2131\ldots$

$x_6 = \sqrt[3]{2 \times (2.2131\ldots)^2 + 1} = 2.2101\ldots$

$x_7 = \sqrt[3]{2 \times (2.2101\ldots)^2 + 1} = 2.2083\ldots$

x_5, x_6 and x_7 all round to 2.21,
so to 2 d.p. $x = 2.21$ is a root.

Using $x_{n+1} = \sqrt{\dfrac{x_n^3 - 1}{2}}$ with $x_0 = 2.3$ gives:

$x_1 = \sqrt{\dfrac{2.3^3 - 1}{2}} = 2.3629\ldots$

$x_2 = \sqrt{\dfrac{2.3629\ldots^3 - 1}{2}} = 2.4691\ldots$

$x_3 = \sqrt{\dfrac{2.4691\ldots^3 - 1}{2}} = 2.6508\ldots$

$x_4 = \sqrt{\dfrac{2.6508\ldots^3 - 1}{2}} = 2.9687\ldots$

This sequence is diverging so does not converge to a root.
The only formula that converges to a root is
$x_{n+1} = \sqrt[3]{2x_n^2 + 1}$.

8)

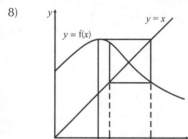

9) Rearranging the equation to get it in the form $f(x) = 0$ gives
$x^4 - 2x^3 - 5 = 0$. Differentiating this gives $f'(x) = 4x^3 - 6x^2$. Putting this into the Newton-Raphson formula gives:

$x_{n+1} = x_n - \dfrac{x_n^4 - 2x_n^3 - 5}{4x_n^3 - 6x_n^2}$. Starting with $x_0 = 2.5$,

$x_1 = 2.5 - \dfrac{2.5^4 - 2(2.5)^3 - 5}{4(2.5)^3 - 6(2.5)^2} = 2.3875$

$x_2 = 2.373982\ldots$

$x_3 = 2.373799\ldots$

$x_4 = 2.373799\ldots$

so $x = 2.3738$ to 5 s.f.

10) a) There will be a change of sign between $f(0.7)$ and $f(0.8)$ if
p lies between 0.7 and 0.8.
$f(0.7) = (2 \times 0.7 \times e^{0.7}) - 3 = -0.1807\ldots$
$f(0.8) = (2 \times 0.8 \times e^{0.8}) - 3 = 0.5608\ldots$
$f(x)$ is continuous, and there is a change of sign,
so $0.7 < p < 0.8$.

b) If $2xe^x - 3 = 0$, then $2xe^x = 3 \Rightarrow xe^x = \dfrac{3}{2}$
$\Rightarrow x = \dfrac{3}{2e^x} \Rightarrow x = \dfrac{3}{2}e^{-x}$.

c) $x_{n+1} = \dfrac{3}{2}e^{-x_n}$ and $x_0 = 0.7$, so:

$x_1 = \dfrac{3}{2}e^{-0.7} = 0.74487\ldots = 0.7449$ to 4 d.p.

$x_2 = \dfrac{3}{2}e^{-0.74487\ldots} = 0.71218\ldots = 0.7122$ to 4 d.p.

$x_3 = \dfrac{3}{2}e^{-0.71218\ldots} = 0.73585\ldots = 0.7359$ to 4 d.p.

$x_4 = \dfrac{3}{2}e^{-0.73585\ldots} = 0.71864\ldots = 0.7186$ to 4 d.p.

d) If the root of $f(x) = 0$, p, is 0.726 to 3 d.p. then there must
be a change of sign in $f(x)$ between the error bounds of p.
Error bounds = 0.7255, 0.7265.
$f(0.7255) = (2 \times 0.7255 \times e^{0.7255}) - 3 = -0.0025\ldots$
$f(0.7265) = (2 \times 0.7265 \times e^{0.7265}) - 3 = 0.0045\ldots$
$f(x)$ is continuous, and there's a change of sign,
so $p = 0.726$ to 3 d.p.

11) a) Where $y = \sin 3x + 3x$ and $y = 1$ meet,
$\sin 3x + 3x = 1 \Rightarrow \sin 3x + 3x - 1 = 0$.
$x = a$ is a root of this equation, so if $x = 0.1$ and $x = 0.2$
produce different signs, then a lies between them. So for
the continuous function $f(x) = \sin 3x + 3x - 1$:
$f(0.1) = \sin(3 \times 0.1) + (3 \times 0.1) - 1 = -0.4044\ldots$
$f(0.2) = \sin(3 \times 0.2) + (3 \times 0.2) - 1 = 0.1646\ldots$
There is a change of sign, so $0.1 < a < 0.2$.

b) $\sin 3x + 3x = 1 \Rightarrow 3x = 1 - \sin 3x \Rightarrow x = \dfrac{1}{3}(1 - \sin 3x)$.

c) $x_{n+1} = \dfrac{1}{3}(1 - \sin 3x_n)$ and $x_0 = 0.2$:
$x_1 = \dfrac{1}{3}(1 - \sin(3 \times 0.2)) = 0.1451\ldots$
$x_2 = \dfrac{1}{3}(1 - \sin(3 \times 0.1451\ldots)) = 0.1927\ldots$
$x_3 = \dfrac{1}{3}(1 - \sin(3 \times 0.1927\ldots)) = 0.1511\ldots$
$x_4 = \dfrac{1}{3}(1 - \sin(3 \times 0.1511\ldots)) = 0.1873\ldots$
So $x_4 = 0.187$ to 3 d.p.

d) Putting the equation in the form $f(x) = 0$: $\sin 3x + 3x - 1 = 0$.
Differentiating this gives: $f'(x) = 3\cos 3x + 3$. So the
Newton-Raphson formula is $x_{n+1} = x_n - \dfrac{\sin 3x_n + 3x_n - 1}{3\cos 3x_n + 3}$.
Starting with $x_0 = 0.2$,
$x_1 = 0.2 - \dfrac{\sin 3(0.2) + 3(0.2) - 1}{3\cos 3(0.2) + 3} = 0.169933\ldots$
$x_2 = 0.170324\ldots$
$x_3 = 0.170324\ldots$
So the root is 0.170 to 3 d.p. This method was much better
that the method used in part c), as it converged much
quicker. The iterations in part c) hadn't homed in on a root
by x_3, whereas they had for the Newton-Raphson method.

12) a) $x_{n+1} = \sqrt[3]{x_n^2 - 4}$, $x_0 = -1$:
$x_1 = \sqrt[3]{(-1)^2 - 4} = -1.44224\ldots = -1.4422$ to 4 d.p.
$x_2 = \sqrt[3]{(-1.4422\ldots)^2 - 4} = -1.24287\ldots = -1.2429$ to 4 d.p.
$x_3 = \sqrt[3]{(-1.2428\ldots)^2 - 4} = -1.34906\ldots = -1.3491$ to 4 d.p.
$x_4 = \sqrt[3]{(-1.3490\ldots)^2 - 4} = -1.29664\ldots = -1.2966$ to 4 d.p.

b) If b is a root of $x^3 - x^2 + 4 = 0$, then $x^3 - x^2 + 4 = 0$ will
rearrange to form $x = \sqrt[3]{x^2 - 4}$, the iteration formula used
in (a).

(This is like finding the iteration formula in reverse...)

$x^3 - x^2 + 4 = 0 \Rightarrow x^3 = x^2 - 4 \Rightarrow x = \sqrt[3]{x^2 - 4}$, and so b must
be a root of $x^3 - x^2 + 4 = 0$.

c) If the root of $f(x) = x^3 - x^2 + 4 = 0$, b, is -1.315 to 3 d.p.
then there must be a change of sign in $f(x)$ between the
error bounds of b, which are -1.3155 and -1.3145.

f(−1.3155) = (−1.3155)³ − (−1.3155)² + 4 = −0.00706...
f(−1.3145) = (−1.3145)³ − (−1.3145)² + 4 = 0.00075...
f(x) is continuous, and there's a change of sign,
so b = −1.315 to 3 d.p.

13) a) For f(x) = ln(x + 3) − x + 2, there will be a change in sign
between f(3) and f(4) if the root lies between those values.

f(3) = ln (3 + 3) − 3 + 2 = 0.7917...
f(4) = ln (4 + 3) − 4 + 2 = −0.0540...

There is a change of sign, and the function is continuous for
x > −3, so the root, m, must lie between 3 and 4.

b) x_{n+1} = ln (x_n + 3) + 2, and x_0 = 3, so:
x_1 = ln (3 + 3) + 2 = 3.7917...
x_2 = ln (3.7917... + 3) + 2 = 3.9157...
x_3 = ln (3.9157... + 3) + 2 = 3.9337...
x_4 = ln (3.9337... + 3) + 2 = 3.9364...
x_5 = ln (3.9364... + 3) + 2 = 3.9367...

So m = 3.94 to 2 d.p.

c) From b), m = 3.94 to 2 d.p. If this is correct then there will
be a change of sign in f(x) between the error bounds of m,
which are 3.935 and 3.945.
f(3.935) = ln (3.935 + 3) − 3.935 + 2 = 0.00158...
f(3.945) = ln (3.945 + 3) − 3.945 + 2 = −0.00697...

f(x) is continuous for x > −3, and there's a change of sign,
so m = 3.94 is correct to 2 d.p.

Practice Exam One

1 a) For 3ln x − ln 3x = 0, use the log laws to simplify to:
ln x^3 − ln 3x = 0 ⇒ ln $\frac{x^3}{3x}$ = 0 ⇒ ln $\frac{x^2}{3}$ = 0 *[1 mark]*.
Taking e to the power of both sides gives:
$\frac{x^2}{3}$ = e⁰ = 1 ⇒ x^2 = 3 ⇒ x = $\sqrt{3}$ (ignore the negative
solution as x > 0) *[1 mark]*.

b) Let y = f(x). Now, to find the inverse of y = 3ln x − ln 3x,
make x the subject then swap x and y:
y = ln $\frac{x^2}{3}$ (from (a)) ⇒ e^y = $\frac{x^2}{3}$ ⇒ x^2 = 3e^y
⇒ x = $\sqrt{3e^y}$ *[1 mark]*.

So f⁻¹(x) = $\sqrt{3e^x}$ *[1 mark]*.

2 a) gh(4) = g(h(4)) = g$\left(\frac{6}{4^2 - 4}\right)$ = g(0.5) *[1 mark]*
= $\sqrt{(2 \cdot 0.5) + 3}$ = $\sqrt{1 + 3}$ = $\sqrt{4}$ = 2. *[1 mark]*

b hg(3) = h(g(3)) = h($\sqrt{(2 \cdot 3) + 3}$) = h(3) *[1 mark]*
= $\frac{6}{3^2 - 4}$ = $\frac{6}{9 - 4}$ = $\frac{6}{5}$ = 1.2 *[1 mark]*.

c) hg(x) = h(g(x)) = h($\sqrt{2x + 3}$)
$\frac{6}{(\sqrt{2x + 3})^2 - 4}$ = $\frac{6}{2x + 3 - 4}$ = $\frac{6}{2x - 1}$.

*[3 marks available — 1 mark for functions in the correct
order, 1 mark for substituting g(x) into formula for h, 1
mark for simplifying]*.

3 a)

*[2 marks available — 1 mark for reflection in the x-axis
at 4/5 and 1 mark for y-intercept at 4]*

b) From the graph, it is clear that there are two points where
the graph would cross the line y = 2. One is the solution of
the equation −(5x − 4) = 2 and the other is the solution of
5x − 4 = 2. *[1 mark]*.
Solving the first equation gives: 2 = −5x + 4 ⇒ 5x = 2,
so x = 0.4 *[1 mark]*. Solving the second equation gives:
5x − 4 = 2 ⇒ 5x = 6 so x = 1.2 *[1 mark]*.

4 a)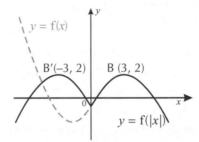

*[3 marks available — 1 mark for reflection
in the y-axis, 1 mark for each coordinate
of B' after transformation]*

b)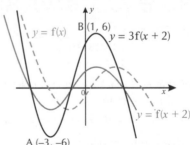

*[3 marks available — 1 mark for shape (stretch
and translation), 1 mark each for coordinates of
A and B after transformation]*

*The solid grey line shows the graph of y = f(x + 2) —
it's easier to do the transformation in two stages,
instead of doing it all at once.*

Answers

5 a) For $x = \dfrac{e^y + 2y}{e^y - 2y}$, use the quotient rule to find $\dfrac{dx}{dy}$:

$u = e^y + 2y \Rightarrow \dfrac{du}{dy} = e^y + 2$

$v = e^y - 2y \Rightarrow \dfrac{dv}{dy} = e^y - 2$

$\dfrac{dx}{dy} = \dfrac{v\dfrac{du}{dy} - u\dfrac{dv}{dy}}{v^2} = \dfrac{(e^y - 2y)(e^y + 2) - (e^y + 2y)(e^y - 2)}{(e^y - 2y)^2}$

$= \dfrac{(e^{2y} + 2e^y - 2ye^y - 4y) - (e^{2y} - 2e^y + 2ye^y - 4y)}{(e^y - 2y)^2}$

$= \dfrac{4e^y - 4ye^y}{(e^y - 2y)^2} = \dfrac{4e^y(1 - y)}{(e^y - 2y)^2}$.

$\dfrac{dy}{dx} = \dfrac{1}{\dfrac{dx}{dy}} = \dfrac{(e^y - 2y)^2}{4e^y(1 - y)}$.

[3 marks available — 1 mark for correct expressions for du/dy and dv/dy, 1 mark for finding expression for dx/dy using the quotient rule, and 1 mark for correct (or equivalent) expression for dy/dx]

b) At the point $(1, 0)$, $y = 0$ and so $e^y = e^0 = 1$.
So the gradient at that point is:

$\dfrac{dy}{dx} = \dfrac{(1 - 0)^2}{4(1 - 0)} = \dfrac{1}{4}$.

The gradient of the normal at that point is $-1 \div \dfrac{1}{4} = -4$.
Equation of a straight line is $y - y_1 = m(x - x_1)$, so at $(1, 0)$ with m = -4, the equation of the normal is:

$y - 0 = -4(x - 1) \Rightarrow y = -4x + 4$.

[3 marks available — 1 mark for finding gradient of the normal, 1 mark for correct substitution of −4 and (1, 0) into equation, and 1 mark for rearrangement into the correct form.]

6 a) $P = 5700e^{-0.15t}$, so when $t = 0$, $P = 5700e^0 = 5700$ ***[1 mark]***.

b) At the start of 2020, $t = 10$,
so $P = 5700e^{-0.15 \times 10} = 1271.8419... = 1271$

[2 marks available — 1 mark for correct substitution of t = 10, 1 mark for correct final answer]

Remember — round down as there are only 1271 whole birds.

c) When $P = 1000$: $1000 = 5700e^{-0.15t} \Rightarrow 1000 = \dfrac{5700}{e^{0.15t}}$
$\Rightarrow e^{0.15t} = \dfrac{5700}{1000} = 5.7$ ***[1 mark]***. Take ln of both sides:
$0.15t = \ln 5.7 \Rightarrow t = \dfrac{\ln 5.7}{0.15} = 11.6031...$ years.
So the population will drop below 1000 in the year 2021 ***[1 mark]***.

d)

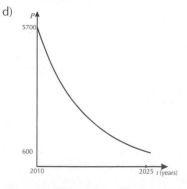

[3 marks available — 1 mark for correct shape of graph, 1 mark for (0, 5700) labelled, 1 mark for calculating P when t = 15 (the population ≈ 600 in 2025)]

7 a) Let $u = \ln x$, so $\dfrac{du}{dx} = \dfrac{1}{x}$. Let $\dfrac{dv}{dx} = \dfrac{3}{x^2}$, so $v = -\dfrac{3}{x}$.
Putting this into the formula for integration by parts gives:

$3\displaystyle\int_1^3 \dfrac{\ln x}{x^2}\,dx = 3\left[-\dfrac{\ln x}{x}\right]_1^3 - 3\int_1^3 -\dfrac{1}{x}\dfrac{1}{x}\,dx$

$= 3\left[-\dfrac{\ln x}{x}\right]_1^3 + 3\int_1^3 \dfrac{1}{x^2}\,dx = 3\left[-\dfrac{\ln x}{x}\right]_1^3 + 3\left[-\dfrac{1}{x}\right]_1^3$

$= \dfrac{-3\ln 3}{3} + \dfrac{3\ln 1}{1} - \dfrac{3}{3} + \dfrac{3}{1}$

$= -\ln 3 - 1 + 3 = 2 - \ln 3 = 0.90139$

[5 marks available — 1 mark for correct expression for du/dx, 1 mark for correct expression for v, 1 mark for correct formula for integration by parts, 1 mark for correct working and 1 mark for correct answer]

If the question asked for the exact value, you'd leave your answer as 2 − ln 3.

b) (i) To find $\dfrac{dy}{dx}$, use the quotient rule. Let $u = 3\ln x$, so $\dfrac{du}{dx} = \dfrac{3}{x}$ ***[1 mark]*** and let $v = x^2$, so $\dfrac{dv}{dx} = 2x$ ***[1 mark]***.
Putting this into the quotient rule formula gives:

$\dfrac{dy}{dx} = \dfrac{x^2\left(\dfrac{3}{x}\right) - 6x\ln x}{(x^2)^2}$ ***[1 mark]***

$= \dfrac{3x - 6x\ln x}{x^4} = \dfrac{3 - 6\ln x}{x^3}$ ***[1 mark]***.

(ii) Putting $x = 1$ into the expression for $\dfrac{dy}{dx}$ gives:

$\dfrac{dy}{dx} = \dfrac{3 - 6\ln 1}{1^3}$ ***[1 mark]*** $= \dfrac{3}{1} = 3$ ***[1 mark]***
Remember that ln 1 = 0.

c) If $u = 1 - x^2$, then $\dfrac{du}{dx} = -2x$, so $dx = -\dfrac{1}{2x}du$ ***[1 mark]***.
Change the limits: $u = 1 - x^2$, so when $x = 0$, $u = 1$ ***[1 mark]*** and when $x = \frac{1}{2}$, $u = \frac{3}{4}$ ***[1 mark]***.
Putting all this into the integral gives:

$\displaystyle\int_0^{\frac{1}{2}} \dfrac{x}{1 - x^2}\,dx = \int_1^{\frac{3}{4}} \dfrac{x}{u}\left(\dfrac{-1}{2x}\right)du$ ***[1 mark]***

$= \displaystyle\int_1^{\frac{3}{4}} \dfrac{-1}{2u}\,du$ ***[1 mark]*** $= \left[-\dfrac{1}{2}\ln|u|\right]_1^{\frac{3}{4}}$ ***[1 mark]***

$= -\dfrac{1}{2}\ln\dfrac{3}{4} - \left(-\dfrac{1}{2}\ln 1\right) = -\dfrac{1}{2}\ln\dfrac{3}{4}$

$= -\ln\sqrt{3} + \ln 2$

$= \ln 2 - \ln\sqrt{3}\ \left(= \ln\dfrac{2}{\sqrt{3}}\right)$ ***[1 mark]***

Use the laws of logs to rearrange −½ln ¾.

8 a) Differentiate each term with respect to x:
$x^3 + x^2y = y^2 - 1$

$\Rightarrow \dfrac{d}{dx}x^3 + \dfrac{d}{dx}x^2y = \dfrac{d}{dx}y^2 - \dfrac{d}{dx}1$

Differentiate x^3 and 1 first:

$\Rightarrow 3x^2 + \dfrac{d}{dx}x^2y = \dfrac{d}{dx}y^2 - 0$ ***[1 mark]***

Differentiate y^2 using the chain rule:

$\Rightarrow 3x^2 + \dfrac{d}{dx}x^2y = \dfrac{d}{dy}y^2 \dfrac{dy}{dx}$ ***[1 mark]***

$\Rightarrow 3x^2 + \dfrac{d}{dx}x^2y = 2y\dfrac{dy}{dx}$

Differentiate x^2y using the product rule:

$\Rightarrow 3x^2 + x^2\dfrac{d}{dx}y + y\dfrac{d}{dx}x^2 = 2y\dfrac{dy}{dx}$

Answers

$\Rightarrow 3x^2 + x^2\dfrac{dy}{dx} + 2xy = 2y\dfrac{dy}{dx}$ *[1 mark]*

Rearrange to make $\dfrac{dy}{dx}$ the subject:

$\Rightarrow (2y - x^2)\dfrac{dy}{dx} = 3x^2 + 2xy$

$\Rightarrow \dfrac{dy}{dx} = \dfrac{3x^2 + 2xy}{2y - x^2}$ *[1 mark]*

b) (i) Substitute $x = 1$ into the original equation:

$x = 1 \Rightarrow (1)^3 + (1)^2 y = y^2 - 1$ *[1 mark]*

$\Rightarrow y^2 - y - 2 = 0$

$\Rightarrow (y - 2)(y + 1) = 0$

$\Rightarrow y = 2$ or $y = -1$

$a > b$, so $a = 2$, $b = -1$ *[1 mark]*

(ii) At $Q = (1, -1)$,

$\dfrac{dy}{dx} = \dfrac{3(1)^2 + 2(1)(-1)}{2(-1) - (1)^2} = \dfrac{3 - 2}{-2 - 1} = -\dfrac{1}{3}$ *[1 mark]*

So the gradient of the normal at $Q = 3$. *[1 mark]*

$(y - y_1) = m(x - x_1)$

$\Rightarrow (y + 1) = 3(x - 1)$

$\Rightarrow y = 3x - 4$ *[1 mark]*

c) (i) $f(-x) = \dfrac{4}{3 - (-x)^2} = \dfrac{4}{3 - x^2} = f(x)$ *[1 mark]*. $f(-x) = f(x)$

so f is an even function *[1 mark]*. This means that the graph of y is symmetrical about the y-axis *[1 mark]*.

(ii) Using the chain rule, $y = \dfrac{4}{u}$, so $\dfrac{dy}{du} = \dfrac{-4}{u^2} = \dfrac{-4}{(3 - x^2)^2}$

[1 mark]. $u = 3 - x^2$, so $\dfrac{du}{dx} = -2x$ *[1 mark]*.

Putting it all together:

$\dfrac{dy}{dx} = \dfrac{(-2x)(-4)}{(3 - x^2)^2} = \dfrac{8x}{(3 - x^2)^2}$ *[1 mark]*.

(iii) At P, the x-coordinate is 1. Putting this value into $\dfrac{dy}{dx}$:

$\dfrac{dy}{dx} = \dfrac{8 \times 1}{(3 - 1^2)^2}$ *[1 mark]* $= \dfrac{8}{2^2} = \dfrac{8}{4} = 2$ *[1 mark]*.

(iv) At a turning point, $\dfrac{dy}{dx} = 0$. To verify that R is a turning

point, put $x = 0$ into the expression for $\dfrac{dy}{dx}$:

$\dfrac{dy}{dx} = \dfrac{8 \times 0}{(3 - 0^2)^2} = 0$, so R is a turning point *[1 mark]*.

Practice Exam Two

1 a) g has range $g(x) \geq -9$ *[1 mark]*, as the minimum value of g is -9.

b) Neither f nor g are one-to-one functions, so they don't have inverses *[1 mark]*.

f and g are many-to-one not one-to-one, as more than one value of x is mapped to the same f(x) or g(x) value, e.g. x = 1 and x = -1 are both mapped to f(x) = 1 and g(x)= -8.

c) (i) $fg(4) = f(4^2 - 9) = f(7)$ *[1 mark]* $= \dfrac{1}{7^2} = \dfrac{1}{49}$ *[1 mark]*.

(ii) $gf(1) = g(1/1^2) = g(1)$ *[1 mark]* $= 1^2 - 9 = -8$ *[1 mark]*.

2 Let $u = 4x$, so $\dfrac{du}{dx} = 4$. Let $\dfrac{dv}{dx} = e^{-2x}$, so $v = -\frac{1}{2}e^{-2x}$.

Putting this into the integral gives:

$\int 4xe^{-2x}dx = [4x(-\frac{1}{2}e^{-2x})] - \int 4(-\frac{1}{2}e^{-2x})\,dx$

$= -2xe^{-2x} + \int 2e^{-2x}dx$

$= -2xe^{-2x} - e^{-2x} + C \,(= -e^{-2x}(2x + 1) + C)$

[4 marks available — 1 mark for correct choice of u and dv/dx, 1 mark for correct differentiation and integration to obtain du/dx and v, 1 mark for correct integration by parts method, 1 mark for answer]

3 a) Proof by exhaustion: if n is even, n^3 is also even (as the product of even numbers is even), so $n^3 - n$ is even too (the difference between two even numbers is always even) *[1 mark]*. If n is odd, n^3 is also odd (as the product of odd numbers is odd), so $n^3 - n$ is even *[1 mark]*. n is an integer so must be odd or even, so $n^3 - n$ is always even.

You could have factorised $n^3 - n$ instead — you'd get $n(n + 1)(n - 1)$. Then if n is odd, (n + 1) and (n - 1) are even, so the product is even. If n is even, the product will be even too.

b) Disproof by contradiction: take integers $p = 2$ and $q = -4$. Then $2 > -4$, so $p > q$ *[1 mark]*, but $2^2 < (-4)^2$ (as $4 < 16$), so $p^2 < q^2$ *[1 mark]*, hence the statement is false.

4 a) $f(x) = (\sqrt{x + 2})\ln(x + 2)$,

so $f(7) = (\sqrt{7 + 2})\ln(7 + 2) = (\sqrt{9})\ln 9 = 3\ln 9$ *[1 mark]*

Using the log laws:

$f(7) = 3\ln(3^2) = 2 \times 3\ln 3 = 6\ln 3$ *[1 mark]*.

b) For $y = (\sqrt{x + 2})\ln(x + 2)$, use the product rule:

$u = \sqrt{x + 2} = (x + 2)^{\frac{1}{2}} \Rightarrow \dfrac{du}{dx} = \dfrac{1}{2}(x + 2)^{-\frac{1}{2}} = \dfrac{1}{2\sqrt{x + 2}}$

$v = \ln(x + 2) \Rightarrow \dfrac{dv}{dx} = \dfrac{1}{x + 2}$.

$f'(x) = \dfrac{dy}{dx} = u\dfrac{dv}{dx} + v\dfrac{du}{dx} = \dfrac{\sqrt{x + 2}}{x + 2} + \dfrac{\ln(x + 2)}{2\sqrt{x + 2}}$.

So $f'(7) = \dfrac{\sqrt{7 + 2}}{7 + 2} + \dfrac{\ln(7 + 2)}{2\sqrt{7 + 2}} = \dfrac{3}{9} + \dfrac{\ln 9}{2 \times 3}$.

Since, using log laws, $\ln 9 = \ln 3^2 = 2\ln 3$,

$f'(7) = \dfrac{1}{3} + \dfrac{2\ln 3}{2 \times 3} = \dfrac{1}{3} + \dfrac{\ln 3}{3} = \dfrac{1}{3}(1 + \ln 3)$.

[4 marks available — 1 mark for correct expressions for du/dx and dv/dx, 1 mark for correct use of product rule formula, 1 mark for correct substitution of x = 7, and 1 mark for correct rearrangement using the log laws]

c) Equation of a straight line is $y - y_1 = m(x - x_1)$. For the tangent at $x = 7$, $y = 6\ln 3$ (from (a)) and $m = \dfrac{1}{3}(1 + \ln 3)$ (from (b)), so the equation of the tangent is:

$y - 6\ln 3 = \dfrac{1}{3}(1 + \ln 3)(x - 7)$

$\Rightarrow y = \dfrac{1}{3}(1 + \ln 3)(x - 7) + 6\ln 3$

$\Rightarrow 3y = (1 + \ln 3)(x - 7) + 18\ln 3$

$\Rightarrow 3y = x + x\ln 3 - 7 - 7\ln 3 + 18\ln 3$

$\Rightarrow 3y = x + x\ln 3 + 11\ln 3 - 7$.

[2 marks available — 1 mark for correct substitution of m, y_1 and x_1 into equation, 1 mark for correct rearrangement to give final answer]

Answers

5 As $u = \ln x$, $\frac{du}{dx} = \frac{1}{x}$, so $x\,du = dx$ *[1 mark]*. The limits $x = 1$ and $x = 2$ become $u = \ln 1 = 0$ and $u = \ln 2$ *[1 mark]*.

$\left(\frac{\ln x}{\sqrt{x}}\right)^2 = \frac{(\ln x)^2}{x}$ *[1 mark]*. So the integral is:

$\int_0^{\ln 2} \frac{u^2}{x} x \, du = \int_0^{\ln 2} u^2 \, du$ *[1 mark]*

$= \left[\frac{u^3}{3}\right]_0^{\ln 2} = \frac{(\ln 2)^3}{3} = 0.111$ (3 s.f.) *[1 mark]*.

6 **a)** Differentiate each term with respect to x:

$\sin \pi x - \cos \frac{\pi y}{2} = 0.5$

$\Rightarrow \frac{d}{dx}(\sin \pi x) - \frac{d}{dx}\left(\cos \frac{\pi y}{2}\right) = \frac{d}{dx}(0.5)$

Differentiate $\sin \pi x$ and 0.5 first:

$\Rightarrow \pi \cos \pi x - \frac{d}{dx}\left(\cos \frac{\pi y}{2}\right) = 0$

Differentiate $\cos \frac{\pi y}{2}$ using the chain rule:

$\Rightarrow \pi \cos \pi x - \frac{d}{dy}\left(\cos \frac{\pi y}{2}\right)\frac{dy}{dx} = 0$ *[1 mark]*

$\Rightarrow \pi \cos \pi x + \left(\frac{\pi}{2}\sin \frac{\pi y}{2}\right)\frac{dy}{dx} = 0$

Rearrange to make $\frac{dy}{dx}$ the subject:

$\Rightarrow \frac{dy}{dx} = -\frac{\pi \cos \pi x}{\frac{\pi}{2}\sin \frac{\pi y}{2}} = -\frac{2\cos \pi x}{\sin \frac{\pi y}{2}}$ *[1 mark]*

b) **(i)** The stationary point is where the gradient is zero.

$\frac{dy}{dx} = 0 \Rightarrow -\frac{2\cos \pi x}{\sin \frac{\pi y}{2}} = 0 \Rightarrow \cos \pi x = 0$ *[1 mark]*

$\Rightarrow x = \frac{1}{2}$ or $x = \frac{3}{2}$ *[1 mark]*

$x = \frac{3}{2} \Rightarrow \sin \frac{3\pi}{2} - \cos \frac{\pi y}{2} = 0.5$

$\Rightarrow -1 - \cos \frac{\pi y}{2} = 0.5$

$\Rightarrow \cos \frac{\pi y}{2} = -1.5$

So y has no solutions when $x = \frac{3}{2}$ *[1 mark]*

$x = \frac{1}{2} \Rightarrow \sin \frac{\pi}{2} - \cos \frac{\pi y}{2} = 0.5$

$\Rightarrow 1 - \cos \frac{\pi y}{2} = 0.5$

$\Rightarrow \cos \frac{\pi y}{2} = 0.5$

$\Rightarrow \frac{\pi y}{2} = \frac{\pi}{3}$

$\Rightarrow y = \frac{2}{3}$

So the only stationary point of the graph of $\sin \pi x - \cos \frac{\pi y}{2} = 0.5$ for the given ranges of x and y is at $\left(\frac{1}{2}, \frac{2}{3}\right)$. *[1 mark]*

(ii) $x = \frac{1}{6} \Rightarrow \sin \frac{\pi}{6} - \cos \frac{\pi y}{2} = 0.5$

$\Rightarrow 0.5 - \cos \frac{\pi y}{2} = 0.5$

$\Rightarrow \cos \frac{\pi y}{2} = 0$

$\Rightarrow \frac{\pi y}{2} = \frac{\pi}{2}$

$\Rightarrow y = 1$ *[1 mark]*

At $\left(\frac{1}{6}, 1\right)$, $\frac{dy}{dx} = -\frac{2\cos \frac{\pi}{6}}{\sin \frac{\pi}{2}} = \frac{-2\left(\frac{\sqrt{3}}{2}\right)}{1} = -\sqrt{3}$ *[1 mark]*

so the equation of the tangent to the curve is:

$y - 1 = -\sqrt{3}\left(x - \frac{1}{6}\right)$ *[1 mark]* (or $y = -\sqrt{3}x + \frac{6 + \sqrt{3}}{6}$).

7 **a)** **(i)** $y = e^{2x} - 5e^x + 3x$, so, using chain rule:

$\frac{dy}{dx} = 2e^{2x} - 5e^x + 3$.

[2 marks available — 1 mark for $2e^{2x}$, 1 mark for rest of answer.]

(ii) Differentiating again gives: $\frac{d^2y}{dx^2} = 4e^{2x} - 5e^x$.

[2 marks available — 1 mark for $4e^{2x}$, 1 mark for $-5e^x$]

(iii) Stationary points occur when $\frac{dy}{dx} = 0$, so:

$2e^{2x} - 5e^x + 3 = 0$ *[1 mark]*.

(This looks like a quadratic, so substitute $y = e^x$ and factorise...)

$2y^2 - 5y + 3 = 0 \Rightarrow (2y - 3)(y - 1) = 0$ *[1 mark]*.

So the solutions are:

$2y - 3 = 0 \Rightarrow y = \frac{3}{2} \Rightarrow e^x = \frac{3}{2} \Rightarrow x = \ln \frac{3}{2}$ *[1 mark]*, and $y - 1 = 0 \Rightarrow y = 1 \Rightarrow e^x = 1 \Rightarrow x = \ln 1 = 0$ *[1 mark]*.

(iv) To determine the nature of the stationary points, find $\frac{d^2y}{dx^2}$ at $x = 0$ and $x = \ln \frac{3}{2}$:

$\frac{d^2y}{dx^2} = 4e^{2x} - 5e^x$ (from (b)), so when $x = 0$:

$\frac{d^2y}{dx^2} = 4e^0 - 5e^0 = 4 - 5 = -1$ *[1 mark]*,

so $\frac{d^2y}{dx^2} < 0$, which means the point is a maximum *[1 mark]*.

When $x = \ln \frac{3}{2}$:

$\frac{d^2y}{dx^2} = 4e^{2\ln \frac{3}{2}} - 5e^{\ln \frac{3}{2}} = 4\left(\frac{3}{2}\right)^2 - 5\left(\frac{3}{2}\right) = \frac{3}{2}$ *[1 mark]*,

so $\frac{d^2y}{dx^2} > 0$, which means the point is a minimum *[1 mark]*.

b) **(i)** Write the equation in terms of x and y: $y = e^{x^2 - 4}$, then rearrange to make x the subject

$y = e^{x^2 - 4} \Rightarrow \ln y = x^2 - 4$ *[1 mark]*

$\Rightarrow \ln y + 4 = x^2 \Rightarrow x = \sqrt{\ln y + 4}$ *[1 mark]*

Finally, replace x with $f^{-1}(x)$ and y with x:

$f^{-1}(x) = \sqrt{\ln x + 4}$ *[1 mark]*.

(ii) The curve would be reflected in the x-axis *[1 mark]*, stretched in the y-direction by a factor of 3 *[1 mark]* and translated 5 units in the positive y-direction *[1 mark]*.

8 **a)** **(i)** Replace h with x in the height formula:

$x = \sqrt{\frac{2}{3}}a$ *[1 mark]* $\Rightarrow a = \sqrt{\frac{3}{2}}x$ *[1 mark]*

(ii) Sub $a = \sqrt{\frac{3}{2}}x$ into the expression for volume:

$V = \frac{\sqrt{2}}{12}\left(\sqrt{\frac{3}{2}}x\right)^3 = \frac{\sqrt{2}}{12} \times \frac{3\sqrt{3}}{2\sqrt{2}}x^3 = \frac{\sqrt{3}}{8}x^3$

[3 marks available — 1 mark for correctly substituting a into the formula, 1 mark for correct expansion of $\left(\sqrt{\frac{3}{2}}\right)^3$, 1 mark for final answer.]

b) From the question, $\frac{dV}{dt} = 240$ *[1 mark]*

and differentiating the answer to part a) gives $\frac{dV}{dx} = \frac{3\sqrt{3}}{8}x^2$ *[1 mark]*

Answers

Using chain rule, $\dfrac{dx}{dt} = \dfrac{dx}{dV} \times \dfrac{dV}{dt}$ *[1 mark]*

$= \dfrac{1}{\left(\frac{dV}{dx}\right)} \times \dfrac{dV}{dt}$ *[1 mark]* $= \dfrac{8}{3\sqrt{3}\,x^2} \times 240 = \dfrac{640}{\sqrt{3}\,x^2}$ *[1 mark]*

So when $x = 8$, $\dfrac{dx}{dt} = \dfrac{640}{64\sqrt{3}} = \dfrac{10}{\sqrt{3}}$ cm min⁻¹.

[1 mark — allow decimal equivalent]

c) (i) $\dfrac{dV}{dt} = \dfrac{dV}{dx} \times \dfrac{dx}{dt}$ *[1 mark]*

$= \dfrac{3\sqrt{3}\,x^2}{8} \times \dfrac{32}{9\sqrt{3}} = \dfrac{4x^2}{3}$ *[1 mark]*

So when $x = 12$, $\dfrac{dV}{dt} = \dfrac{4 \times 144}{3}$ *[1 mark]*

$= 192$ cm³ min⁻¹ *[1 mark]*

(ii) $\dfrac{dV}{dt}$ is the overall rate of change of the volume of water in the container, i.e. the difference between the rate at which the water is being poured in (240) and the rate at which it's leaking out (r).

So $240 - r$ *[1 mark]* $= \dfrac{dV}{dt} = 192$ *[1 mark]*

$\Rightarrow r = 48$ cm³ min⁻¹ *[1 mark]*

Answers

C4 Section 1 — Algebra
Warm-up Questions

1) a) $\dfrac{4x^2 - 25}{6x - 15} = \dfrac{(2x+5)(2x-5)}{3(2x-5)} = \dfrac{2x+5}{3}$

   b) $\dfrac{2x+3}{x-2} \times \dfrac{4x-8}{2x^2-3x-9}$

   $= \dfrac{2x+3}{x-2} \times \dfrac{4(x-2)}{(2x+3)(x-3)}$

   $= \dfrac{4}{x-3}$

   c) $\dfrac{x^2-3x}{x+1} \div \dfrac{x}{2} = \dfrac{x(x-3)}{x+1} \times \dfrac{2}{x}$

   $= \dfrac{x-3}{x+1} \times 2 = \dfrac{2(x-3)}{x+1}$

2) a) $\dfrac{x}{2x+1} + \dfrac{3}{x^2} + \dfrac{1}{x} = \dfrac{x \cdot x^2}{x^2(2x+1)} + \dfrac{3(2x+1)}{x^2(2x+1)} + \dfrac{x(2x+1)}{x^2(2x+1)}$

   $= \dfrac{x^3 + 6x + 3 + 2x^2 + x}{x^2(2x+1)} = \dfrac{x^3 + 2x^2 + 7x + 3}{x^2(2x+1)}$

   b) $\dfrac{2}{x^2-1} - \dfrac{3x}{x-1} + \dfrac{x}{x+1}$

   $= \dfrac{2}{(x+1)(x-1)} - \dfrac{3x(x+1)}{(x+1)(x-1)} + \dfrac{x(x-1)}{(x+1)(x-1)}$

   $= \dfrac{2 - 3x^2 - 3x + x^2 - x}{(x+1)(x-1)} = \dfrac{2 - 2x^2 - 4x}{(x+1)(x-1)}$

   $= \dfrac{2(1 - x^2 - 2x)}{(x+1)(x-1)}$

3)
$$x + 4 \overline{\smash{\big)}\ \begin{array}{l} x^2 - 2x + 7 \quad r - 9 \\ \hline x^3 + 2x^2 - x + 19 \end{array}}$$

$\ -\ \underline{x^3 + 4x^2}$

$\ -2x^2 - x$

$\ -\ \underline{-2x^2 - 8x}$

$\ 7x + 19$

$\ -\ \underline{7x + 28}$

$\ -9$

so $(x^3 + 2x^2 - x + 19) \div (x + 4) = x^2 - 2x + 7$ remainder -9.

4) $2x^3 + 8x^2 + 7x + 8 \equiv (Ax^2 + Bx + C)(x + 3) + D$.

   Set $x = -3$: $2(-3)^3 + 8(-3)^2 + 7(-3) + 8 = 0 + D \Rightarrow D = 5$.

   Set $x = 0$: $0 + 8 = C(0 + 3) + D \Rightarrow C = 1$.

   Equating the coefficients of x^3 gives $2 = A$.

   Finally, equating the coefficients of x^2 gives $8 = 3A + B$
   $\Rightarrow 8 = (3 \times 2) + B$, so $B = 2$.

   So $2x^3 + 8x^2 + 7x + 8 = (2x^2 + 2x + 1)(x + 3) + 5$. The result
   when $2x^3 + 8x^2 + 7x + 8$ is divided by $(x + 3)$ is $2x^2 + 2x + 1$
   remainder 5.

*For these questions, you can use the substitution method or the equating
coefficients method. I've just shown one method for each.*

5) a) $\dfrac{4x+5}{(x+4)(2x-3)} \equiv \dfrac{A}{(x+4)} + \dfrac{B}{(2x-3)}$

   $4x + 5 \equiv A(2x - 3) + B(x + 4)$

   Using substitution method:

   substitute $x = -4$: $-11 = -11A \Rightarrow A = 1$

   substitute $x = 1.5$: $11 = 5.5B \Rightarrow B = 2$

   $\dfrac{4x+5}{(x+4)(2x-3)} \equiv \dfrac{1}{(x+4)} + \dfrac{2}{(2x-3)}$

   b) $\dfrac{-7x-7}{(3x+1)(x-2)} \equiv \dfrac{A}{(3x+1)} + \dfrac{B}{(x-2)}$

   $-7x - 7 \equiv A(x - 2) + B(3x + 1)$

Using equating coefficients method:

coefficients of x: $-7 = A + 3B$

constants: $-7 = -2A + B$

Solving simultaneously: $A = 2$, $B = -3$

$\dfrac{-7x-7}{(3x+1)(x-2)} \equiv \dfrac{2}{(3x+1)} - \dfrac{3}{(x-2)}$

c) $\dfrac{x-18}{(x+4)(3x-4)} \equiv \dfrac{A}{(x+4)} + \dfrac{B}{(3x-4)}$

$x - 18 \equiv A(3x - 4) + B(x + 4)$

Using substitution method:

substitute $x = -4$: $-22 = -16A \Rightarrow A = \dfrac{11}{8}$.

And using equating coefficients method:

coefficients of x: $1 = 3A + B$

Substituting $A = \dfrac{11}{8}$: $1 = 3A + B \Rightarrow B = 1 - \dfrac{33}{8} = -\dfrac{25}{8}$.

$\dfrac{x-18}{(x+4)(3x-4)} \equiv \dfrac{11}{8(x+4)} - \dfrac{25}{8(3x-4)}$

*Don't worry if you get fractions for your coefficients — just put
the numerator on the top and the denominator on the bottom.*

d) Factorise the denominator:

$\dfrac{5x}{x^2+x-6} \equiv \dfrac{5x}{(x+3)(x-2)} \equiv \dfrac{A}{(x+3)} + \dfrac{B}{(x-2)}$

$5x \equiv A(x - 2) + B(x + 3)$

Using substitution method:

substitute $x = -3$: $-15 = -5A \Rightarrow A = 3$

substitute $x = 2$: $10 = 5B \Rightarrow B = 2$

$\dfrac{5x}{x^2+x-6} \equiv \dfrac{3}{(x+3)} + \dfrac{2}{(x-2)}$

e) Factorise the denominator:

$\dfrac{6+4y}{9-y^2} \equiv \dfrac{6+4y}{(3-y)(3+y)} \equiv \dfrac{A}{(3-y)} + \dfrac{B}{(3+y)}$

$6 + 4y \equiv A(3 + y) + B(3 - y)$

Using substitution method:

substitute $y = 3$: $18 = 6A \Rightarrow A = 3$

substitute $y = -3$: $-6 = 6B \Rightarrow B = -1$

$\dfrac{6+4y}{9-y^2} \equiv \dfrac{3}{(3-y)} - \dfrac{1}{(3+y)}$

f) $\dfrac{10x^2+32x+16}{(x+3)(2x+4)(x-2)} \equiv \dfrac{A}{(x+3)} + \dfrac{B}{(2x+4)} + \dfrac{C}{(x-2)}$

$10x^2 + 32x + 16$
$\equiv A(2x+4)(x-2) + B(x+3)(x-2) + C(x+3)(2x+4)$

Using substitution method:

substitute $x = 2$: $120 = 40C \Rightarrow C = 3$

substitute $x = -3$: $10 = 10A \Rightarrow A = 1$

substitute $x = -2$: $-8 = -4B \Rightarrow B = 2$

$\dfrac{10x^2+32x+16}{(x+3)(2x+4)(x-2)} \equiv \dfrac{1}{(x+3)} + \dfrac{2}{(2x+4)} + \dfrac{3}{(x-2)}$

g) Factorise the denominator:

$\dfrac{4x^2+12x+6}{x^3+3x^2+2x} \equiv \dfrac{4x^2+12x+6}{x(x^2+3x+2)} \equiv \dfrac{4x^2+12x+6}{x(x+1)(x+2)}$

$\equiv \dfrac{A}{x} + \dfrac{B}{(x+1)} + \dfrac{C}{(x+2)}$

$4x^2 + 12x + 6 \equiv A(x+1)(x+2) + Bx(x+2) + Cx(x+1)$

Using substitution method:

substitute $x = -1$: $-2 = -B \Rightarrow B = 2$

substitute $x = 0$: $6 = 2A \Rightarrow A = 3$

substitute $x = -2$: $-2 = 2C \Rightarrow C = -1$

$$\frac{4x^2 + 12x + 6}{x^3 + 3x^2 + 2x} \equiv \frac{3}{x} + \frac{2}{(x+1)} - \frac{1}{(x+2)}$$

h) $\dfrac{-11x^2 + 6x + 11}{(2x+1)(3-x)(x+2)} \equiv \dfrac{A}{(2x+1)} + \dfrac{B}{(3-x)} + \dfrac{C}{(x+2)}$

$-11x^2 + 6x + 11$
$\quad \equiv A(3-x)(x+2) + B(2x+1)(x+2) + C(2x+1)(3-x)$

Using substitution method:

substitute $x = 3$: $-70 = 35B \Rightarrow B = -2$

substitute $x = -2$: $-45 = -15C \Rightarrow C = 3$

substitute $x = -0.5$: $5.25 = 5.25A \Rightarrow A = 1$

$$\frac{-11x^2 + 6x + 11}{(2x+1)(3-x)(x+2)} \equiv \frac{1}{(2x+1)} - \frac{2}{(3-x)} + \frac{3}{(x+2)}$$

6) a) $\dfrac{2x+2}{(x+3)^2} \equiv \dfrac{A}{(x+3)} + \dfrac{B}{(x+3)^2}$

$2x + 2 \equiv A(x+3) + B$

Using substitution method:

substitute $x = -3$: $-4 = B$

substitute $x = 0$: $2 = 3A - 4 \Rightarrow A = 2$

$$\frac{2x+2}{(x+3)^2} \equiv \frac{2}{(x+3)} - \frac{4}{(x+3)^2}$$

b) $\dfrac{6x^2 + 17x + 5}{x(x+2)^2} \equiv \dfrac{A}{x} + \dfrac{B}{(x+2)} + \dfrac{C}{(x+2)^2}$

$6x^2 + 17x + 5 \equiv A(x+2)^2 + Bx(x+2) + Cx$

substitute $x = -2$: $-5 = -2C \Rightarrow C = \frac{5}{2}$

substitute $x = 0$: $5 = 4A \Rightarrow A = \frac{5}{4}$

coefficients of x^2: $6 = A + B$

substitute $A = \frac{5}{4}$: $6 = \frac{5}{4} + B \Rightarrow B = \frac{19}{4}$

$$\frac{6x^2 + 17x + 5}{x(x+2)^2} \equiv \frac{5}{4x} + \frac{19}{4(x+2)} + \frac{5}{2(x+2)^2}$$

c) $\dfrac{-18x + 14}{(2x-1)^2(x+2)} \equiv \dfrac{A}{(2x-1)} + \dfrac{B}{(2x-1)^2} + \dfrac{C}{(x+2)}$

$-18x + 14 \equiv A(2x-1)(x+2) + B(x+2) + C(2x-1)^2$

substitute $x = -2$: $50 = 25C \Rightarrow C = 2$

substitute $x = 0.5$: $5 = 2.5B \Rightarrow B = 2$

coefficients of x^2: $0 = 2A + 4C$

substitute $C = 2$: $0 = 2A + 8 \Rightarrow A = -4$

$$\frac{-18x + 14}{(2x-1)^2(x+2)} \equiv \frac{-4}{(2x-1)} + \frac{2}{(2x-1)^2} + \frac{2}{(x+2)}$$

d) Factorise the denominator:

$\dfrac{8x^2 - x - 5}{x^3 - x^2} \equiv \dfrac{8x^2 - x - 5}{x^2(x-1)} \equiv \dfrac{A}{x} + \dfrac{B}{x^2} + \dfrac{C}{(x-1)}$

$8x^2 - x - 5 \equiv Ax(x-1) + B(x-1) + Cx^2$

coefficients of x^2: $8 = A + C$ (eq. 1)

coefficients of x: $-1 = -A + B$ (eq. 2)

constants: $-5 = -B \Rightarrow B = 5$

substitute $B = 5$ in eq. 2: $-1 = -A + 5 \Rightarrow A = 6$

substitute $A = 6$ in eq. 1: $8 = 6 + C \Rightarrow C = 2$

$$\frac{8x^2 - x - 5}{x^3 - x^2} \equiv \frac{6}{x} + \frac{5}{x^2} + \frac{2}{(x-1)}$$

7) First, find the partial fractions: If

$\dfrac{3x + 10}{(2x+3)(x-4)} \equiv \dfrac{A}{2x+3} + \dfrac{B}{x-4}$,

then $3x + 10 \equiv A(x-4) + B(2x+3)$.

From this, you get the simultaneous equations $3 = A + 2B$ and $10 = -4A + 3B$. Solving these gives $A = -1$ and $B = 2$:

$\dfrac{3x + 10}{(2x+3)(x-4)} = \dfrac{-1}{2x+3} + \dfrac{2}{x-4}$.

Now putting this into the integral gives:

$$\int \frac{-1}{2x+3} + \frac{2}{x-4} \, dx = -\frac{1}{2}\ln|2x+3| + 2\ln|x-4| + C$$

8) a) $(1 + 2x)^3 = 1 + 3(2x) + \dfrac{3 \times 2}{1 \times 2}(2x)^2 + \dfrac{3 \times 2 \times 1}{1 \times 2 \times 3}(2x)^3$

$= 1 + 6x + 12x^2 + 8x^3$

You could have used Pascal's Triangle to get the coefficients here. I've done it the long way because I like to show off.

b) $(1 - x)^4 = 1 + 4(-x) + \dfrac{4 \times 3}{1 \times 2}(-x)^2$

$\quad + \dfrac{4 \times 3 \times 2}{1 \times 2 \times 3}(-x)^3 + \dfrac{4 \times 3 \times 2 \times 1}{1 \times 2 \times 3 \times 4}(-x)^4$

$= 1 - 4x + 6x^2 - 4x^3 + x^4$

c) $(1 - 4x)^4 = 1 + 4(-4x) + \dfrac{4 \times 3}{1 \times 2}(-4x)^2$

$\quad + \dfrac{4 \times 3 \times 2}{1 \times 2 \times 3}(-4x)^3 + \dfrac{4 \times 3 \times 2 \times 1}{1 \times 2 \times 3 \times 4}(-4x)^4$

$= 1 - 16x + 96x^2 - 256x^3 + 256x^4$

Be extra careful with terms like $(-4x)^2$... remember to square <u>everything</u> in the brackets — the x, the 4 <u>and</u> the minus.

9) Positive integer values (and zero).

10) a) $(1 + x)^{-4}$

$\approx 1 + (-4)x + \dfrac{-4 \times -5}{1 \times 2}x^2 + \dfrac{-4 \times -5 \times -6}{1 \times 2 \times 3}x^3$

$= 1 - 4x + 10x^2 - 20x^3$

b) $(1 - 3x)^{-3} \approx 1 + (-3)(-3x) + \dfrac{-3 \times -4}{1 \times 2}(-3x)^2$

$\quad + \dfrac{-3 \times -4 \times -5}{1 \times 2 \times 3}(-3x)^3$

$= 1 + 9x + 54x^2 + 270x^3$

c) $(1 - 5x)^{\frac{1}{2}}$

$\approx 1 + \dfrac{1}{2}(-5x) + \dfrac{\frac{1}{2} \times -\frac{1}{2}}{1 \times 2}(-5x)^2 + \dfrac{\frac{1}{2} \times -\frac{1}{2} \times -\frac{3}{2}}{1 \times 2 \times 3}(-5x)^3$

$= 1 - \dfrac{5}{2}x - \dfrac{25}{8}x^2 - \dfrac{125}{16}x^3$

11) a) $\left|\dfrac{dx}{c}\right| < 1$ (or $|x| < |\frac{c}{d}|$)

b) 10) a): expansion valid for $|x| < 1$

10) b): expansion valid for $|-3x| < 1 \Rightarrow |-3||x| < 1 \Rightarrow |x| < \frac{1}{3}$

10) c): expansion valid for $|-5x| < 1 \Rightarrow |-5||x| < 1 \Rightarrow |x| < \frac{1}{5}$

12) a) $(3 + 2x)^{-2} = \left(3\left(1 + \frac{2}{3}x\right)\right)^{-2} = \dfrac{1}{9}\left(1 + \frac{2}{3}x\right)^{-2}$

$\approx \dfrac{1}{9}\left(1 + (-2)\left(\frac{2}{3}x\right) + \dfrac{-2 \times -3}{1 \times 2}\left(\frac{2}{3}x\right)^2\right)$

$= \dfrac{1}{9}\left(1 - \frac{4}{3}x + \frac{4}{3}x^2\right)$

$= \dfrac{1}{9} - \frac{4}{27}x + \frac{4}{27}x^2$

This expansion is valid for $\left|\frac{2x}{3}\right| < 1 \Rightarrow \frac{2}{3}|x| < 1 \Rightarrow |x| < \frac{3}{2}$.

207

C4 — Answers

Answers

b) $(8 - x)^{\frac{1}{3}} = \left(8\left(1 - \frac{1}{8}x\right)\right)^{\frac{1}{3}} = 2\left(1 - \frac{1}{8}x\right)^{\frac{1}{3}}$

$\approx 2\left(1 + \frac{1}{3}\left(-\frac{1}{8}x\right) + \frac{\frac{1}{3} \times -\frac{2}{3}}{1 \times 2}\left(-\frac{1}{8}x\right)^2\right)$

$= 2\left(1 - \frac{1}{24}x - \frac{1}{576}x^2\right)$

$= 2 - \frac{1}{12}x - \frac{1}{288}x^2$

This expansion is valid for $\left|\frac{-x}{8}\right| < 1 \Rightarrow \frac{|-1\|x|}{8} < 1$
$\Rightarrow |x| < 8$.

You know what, I can't think of anything else remotely useful, witty or interesting to say about binomials... Seriously, I'm going to have to resort to slightly weird jokes in a minute... You've been warned...

Exam Questions

1   Add the partial fractions and equate the numerators:
$5 + 9x \equiv A + B(1 + 3x)$ *[1 mark]*

Using substitution method:

substitute $x = -\frac{1}{3}$: $2 = A \Rightarrow A = 2$ *[1 mark]*

substitute $x = 0$: $5 = 2 + B \Rightarrow B = 3$ *[1 mark]*

2    $\frac{2x^2 - 9x - 35}{x^2 - 49} = \frac{(2x + 5)(x - 7)}{(x + 7)(x - 7)} = \frac{2x + 5}{x + 7}$

[3 marks available — 1 mark for factorising the numerator, 1 mark for factorising the denominator and 1 mark for correct answer (after cancelling)]

3    $(16 + 3x)^{\frac{1}{4}} = 16^{\frac{1}{4}}\left(1 + \frac{3}{16}x\right)^{\frac{1}{4}} = 2\left(1 + \frac{3}{16}x\right)^{\frac{1}{4}}$

$\approx 2\left(1 + \left(\frac{1}{4}\right)\left(\frac{3}{16}x\right) + \frac{\frac{1}{4} \times -\frac{3}{4}}{1 \times 2}\left(\frac{3}{16}x\right)^2\right)$

$= 2\left(1 + \left(\frac{1}{4}\right)\left(\frac{3}{16}x\right) + \left(-\frac{3}{32}\right)\left(\frac{9}{256}x^2\right)\right)$

$= 2\left(1 + \frac{3}{64}x - \frac{27}{8192}x^2\right)$

$= 2 + \frac{3}{32}x - \frac{27}{4096}x^2$

[5 marks available in total:

• 1 mark for factorising out $16^{\frac{1}{4}}$ or 2
• 1 mark for expansion of an expression of the form $(1 + ax)^{\frac{1}{4}}$
• 2 marks for the penultimate line of working — 1 for the first two terms in brackets correct, 1 for the 3rd term in brackets correct.
• 1 mark for the final answer correct]

Why did the binomial expansion cross the road?
Don't be silly, binomial expansions can't move independently...
...can they?

4   a) $\left(1 - \frac{4}{3}x\right)^{-\frac{1}{2}}$

$\approx 1 + \left(-\frac{1}{2}\right)\left(-\frac{4}{3}x\right) + \frac{\left(-\frac{1}{2}\right) \times \left(-\frac{3}{2}\right)}{1 \times 2}\left(-\frac{4}{3}x\right)^2$

$\qquad + \frac{\left(-\frac{1}{2}\right) \times \left(-\frac{3}{2}\right) \times \left(-\frac{5}{2}\right)}{1 \times 2 \times 3}\left(-\frac{4}{3}x\right)^3$

$= 1 + \left(-\frac{1}{2}\right)\left(-\frac{4}{3}x\right) + \frac{\left(\frac{3}{4}\right)}{2}\left(-\frac{4}{3}x\right)^2 + \frac{\left(-\frac{15}{8}\right)}{6}\left(-\frac{4}{3}x\right)^3$

$= 1 + \left(-\frac{1}{2}\right)\left(-\frac{4}{3}x\right) + \frac{3}{8}\left(\frac{16}{9}x^2\right) + \left(-\frac{15}{48}\right)\left(-\frac{64}{27}x^3\right)$

$= 1 + \frac{2}{3}x + \frac{2}{3}x^2 + \frac{20}{27}x^3$

[4 marks available in total:

• 1 mark for writing out binomial expansion formula with $n = -\frac{1}{2}$
• 1 mark for writing out binomial expansion formula substituting $-\frac{4}{3}x$ for x
• 1 mark for correct constant and x-terms in final answer
• 1 mark for correct x^2- and x^3-terms in final answer]

b) $\sqrt{\frac{27}{(3 - 4x)}} = \sqrt{\frac{27}{3\left(1 - \frac{4}{3}x\right)}} = \sqrt{\frac{9}{\left(1 - \frac{4}{3}x\right)}} = \frac{3}{\sqrt{\left(1 - \frac{4}{3}x\right)}}$

$= 3\left(1 - \frac{4}{3}x\right)^{-\frac{1}{2}}$

$\approx 3\left(1 + \frac{2}{3}x + \frac{2}{3}x^2\right)$

$= 3 + 2x + 2x^2$

So $a = 3$, $b = 2$, $c = 2$.

Expansion is valid for $\left|-\frac{4}{3}x\right| < 1 \Rightarrow \left|-\frac{4}{3}\right|\|x| < 1 \Rightarrow |x| < \frac{3}{4}$

[3 marks available in total:

• 1 mark for showing expression is equal to $3\left(1 - \frac{4}{3}x\right)^{-\frac{1}{2}}$
• 1 mark for using expansion from part a) to find the correct values of a, b and c.
• 1 mark for correct valid range]

Doctor, doctor, I keep thinking I'm a binomial expansion...
I'm sorry, I don't think I can help you, I'm a cardiologist.

5   a) $\sqrt{\frac{1 + 2x}{1 - 3x}} = \frac{\sqrt{1 + 2x}}{\sqrt{1 - 3x}} = (1 + 2x)^{\frac{1}{2}}(1 - 3x)^{-\frac{1}{2}}$ *[1 mark]*

$(1 + 2x)^{\frac{1}{2}} \approx 1 + \frac{1}{2}(2x) + \frac{\left(\frac{1}{2}\right) \times \left(-\frac{1}{2}\right)}{1 \times 2}(2x)^2$

$= 1 + x - \frac{1}{2}x^2$ *[1 mark]*

$(1 - 3x)^{-\frac{1}{2}} \approx 1 + \left(-\frac{1}{2}\right)(-3x) + \frac{\left(-\frac{1}{2}\right) \times \left(-\frac{3}{2}\right)}{1 \times 2}(-3x)^2$

$= 1 + \frac{3}{2}x + \frac{27}{8}x^2$ *[1 mark]*

$\sqrt{\frac{1 + 2x}{1 - 3x}} \approx \left(1 + x - \frac{1}{2}x^2\right)\left(1 + \frac{3}{2}x + \frac{27}{8}x^2\right)$ *[1 mark]*

$\approx 1 + \frac{3}{2}x + \frac{27}{8}x^2 + x + \frac{3}{2}x^2 - \frac{1}{2}x^2$

(ignoring any terms in x^3 or above)

$= 1 + \frac{5}{2}x + \frac{35}{8}x^2$ *[1 mark]*

b)   Expansion of $(1 + 2x)^{\frac{1}{2}}$ is valid for $|2x| < 1 \Rightarrow |x| < \frac{1}{2}$

Expansion of $(1 - 3x)^{-\frac{1}{2}}$ is valid for $|-3x| < 1$

$\Rightarrow |-3|\|x| < 1 \Rightarrow |x| < \frac{1}{3}$

The combined expansion is valid for the narrower of these two ranges.

So the expansion of $\sqrt{\frac{1 + 2x}{1 - 3x}}$ is valid for $|x| < \frac{1}{3}$.

[2 marks available in total:

• 1 mark for identifying the valid range of the expansion as being the narrower of the two valid ranges shown
• 1 mark for correct answer]

Answers

The binomial expansion walks into a bar and asks for a pint. The barman says, "I'm sorry, I can't serve alcohol in a joke that may be read by under-18s."

6 a) $36x^2 + 3x - 10 \equiv A(1 - 3x)^2 + B(4 + 3x)(1 - 3x) + C(4 + 3x)$
[1 mark]

Let $x = \frac{1}{3}$, then $4 + 1 - 10 = 5C \Rightarrow -5 = 5C \Rightarrow C = -1$
[1 mark]

Let $x = -\frac{4}{3}$, then $64 - 4 - 10 = 25A \Rightarrow 50 = 25A \Rightarrow A = 2$
[1 mark]

Equate the terms in x^2:
$36 = 9A - 9B = 18 - 9B \Rightarrow -18 = 9B \Rightarrow B = -2$ *[1 mark]*

b) $f(x) = \dfrac{2}{(4 + 3x)} - \dfrac{2}{(1 - 3x)} - \dfrac{1}{(1 - 3x)^2}$

Expand each term separately:

$2(4 + 3x)^{-1} = 2\left(4\left(1 + \frac{3}{4}x\right)\right)^{-1} = \frac{1}{2}\left(1 + \frac{3}{4}x\right)^{-1}$

$= \frac{1}{2}\left(1 + (-1)\left(\frac{3}{4}x\right) + \frac{(-1) \times (-2)}{1 \times 2}\left(\frac{3}{4}x\right)^2 + ...\right)$

$= \frac{1}{2}\left(1 - \frac{3}{4}x + \frac{9}{16}x^2 + ...\right) = \frac{1}{2} - \frac{3}{8}x + \frac{9}{32}x^2 + ...$

Now the second term: $-2(1 - 3x)^{-1} =$

$-2\left(1 + (-1)(-3x) + \frac{(-1) \times (-2)}{1 \times 2}(-3x)^2 + ...\right)$

$= -2(1 + 3x + 9x^2 + ...) = -2 - 6x - 18x^2 + ...$

And the final term: $-(1 - 3x)^{-2} =$

$-\left(1 + (-2)(-3x) + \frac{(-2) \times (-3)}{1 \times 2}(-3x)^2 + ...\right)$

$= -(1 + 6x + 27x^2 + ...) = -1 - 6x - 27x^2 + ...$

Putting it all together gives

$\frac{1}{2} - \frac{3}{8}x + \frac{9}{32}x^2 - 2 - 6x - 18x^2 - 1 - 6x - 27x^2$

$= -\frac{5}{2} - \frac{99}{8}x - \frac{1431}{32}x^2 + ...$

[6 marks available in total:
- *1 mark for rewriting f(x) in the form*
  $A(4 + 3x)^{-1} + B(1 - 3x)^{-1} + C(1 - 3x)^{-2}$
- *1 mark for correct binomial expansion of $(4 + 3x)^{-1}$*
- *1 mark for correct binomial expansion of $(1 - 3x)^{-1}$*
- *1 mark for correct binomial expansion of $(1 - 3x)^{-2}$*
- *1 mark for correct constant and x-terms in final answer*
- *1 mark for correct x^2-term in final answer]*

c) Expansion of $(4 + 3x)^{-1}$ is valid for $\left|\frac{3x}{4}\right| < 1 \Rightarrow \frac{3|x|}{4} < 1$
$\Rightarrow |x| < \frac{4}{3}$

Expansions of $(1 - 3x)^{-1}$ and $(1 - 3x)^{-2}$ are valid for
$\left|\frac{-3x}{1}\right| < 1 \Rightarrow \frac{|-3\|x|}{1} < 1 \Rightarrow |x| < \frac{1}{3}$

The combined expansion is valid for the narrower of these two ranges. So the expansion of $f(x)$ is valid for $|x| < \frac{1}{3}$.

[2 marks available in total:
- *1 mark for identifying the valid range of the expansion of f(x) as being the narrower of the two valid ranges shown*
- *1 mark for correct answer]*

7 First put $x = -6$ into both sides of the identity
$x^3 + 15x^2 + 43x - 30 \equiv (Ax^2 + Bx + C)(x + 6) + D$:
$(-6)^3 + 15(-6)^2 + 43(-6) - 30 = D \Rightarrow 36 = D$ *[1 mark]*.
Now set $x = 0$ to get $-30 = 6C + D$, so $C = -11$ *[1 mark]*.
Equating the coefficients of x^3 gives $1 = A$. Equating the coefficients of x^2 gives $15 = 6A + B$, so $B = 9$ *[1 mark]*.
So $x^3 + 15x^2 + 43x - 30 \equiv (x^2 + 9x - 11)(x + 6) + 36$.

You could also do this question by algebraic long division — you just have to use your answer to work out A, B, C and D.

8 a) $13x - 17 \equiv A(2x - 1) + B(5 - 3x)$ *[1 mark]*

Let $x = \frac{1}{2}$, then $\frac{13}{2} - 17 = B(5 - \frac{3}{2}) \Rightarrow -\frac{21}{2} = \frac{7}{2}B \Rightarrow B = -3$
[1 mark]

Let $x = \frac{5}{3}$, then $\frac{65}{3} - 17 = A(\frac{10}{3} - 1) \Rightarrow \frac{14}{3} = \frac{7}{3}A \Rightarrow A = 2$
[1 mark]

b) (i) $(2x - 1)^{-1} = -(1 - 2x)^{-1}$ *[1 mark]*

$\approx -\left(1 + (-1)(-2x) + \frac{(-1) \times (-2)}{1 \times 2}(-2x)^2\right)$

$= -(1 + 2x + 4x^2)$

$= -1 - 2x - 4x^2$ *[1 mark]*

(ii) $(5 - 3x)^{-1} = 5^{-1}\left(1 - \frac{3}{5}x\right)^{-1} = \frac{1}{5}\left(1 - \frac{3}{5}x\right)^{-1}$

$\approx \frac{1}{5}\left(1 + (-1)\left(-\frac{3}{5}x\right) + \frac{(-1) \times (-2)}{1 \times 2}\left(-\frac{3}{5}x\right)^2\right)$

$= \frac{1}{5}\left(1 + \frac{3}{5}x + \frac{9}{25}x^2\right)$

$= \frac{1}{5} + \frac{3}{25}x + \frac{9}{125}x^2$

[5 marks available in total:
- *1 mark for factorising out 5^{-1} or $\frac{1}{5}$*
- *1 mark for expansion of an expression of the form $(1 + ax)^{-1}$*
- *2 marks for the penultimate line of working — 1 mark for the first two terms in brackets correct, 1 mark for the 3rd term in brackets correct.*
- *1 mark for the final answer correct]*

c) $\dfrac{13x - 17}{(5 - 3x)(2x - 1)} = \dfrac{2}{(5 - 3x)} - \dfrac{3}{(2x - 1)}$

$= 2(5 - 3x)^{-1} - 3(2x - 1)^{-1}$ *[1 mark]*

$\approx 2\left(\frac{1}{5} + \frac{3}{25}x + \frac{9}{125}x^2\right) - 3(-1 - 2x - 4x^2)$

$= \frac{2}{5} + \frac{6}{25}x + \frac{18}{125}x^2 + 3 + 6x + 12x^2$

$= \frac{17}{5} + \frac{156}{25}x + \frac{1518}{125}x^2$
[1 mark]

9 $5x^2 + 3x + 6 \equiv A(2x - 1)^2 + B(3 - x) + C(2x - 1)(3 - x)$
[1 mark]

Using substitution method:
substitute $x = 3$: $60 = 25A \Rightarrow A = \frac{12}{5}$ *[1 mark]*

substitute $x = \frac{1}{2}$: $\frac{35}{4} = \frac{5}{2}B \Rightarrow B = \frac{7}{2}$ *[1 mark]*

coefficients of x^2: $5 = 4A - 2C$

substitute $A = \frac{12}{5}$: $5 = \frac{48}{5} - 2C$

$-\frac{23}{5} = -2C \Rightarrow C = \frac{23}{10}$ *[1 mark]*

Answers

10 a) $f(x) = (9 - 4x)^{-\frac{1}{2}} = (9)^{-\frac{1}{2}}\left(1 - \frac{4}{9}x\right)^{-\frac{1}{2}} = \frac{1}{3}\left(1 - \frac{4}{9}x\right)^{-\frac{1}{2}}$

$= \frac{1}{3}\left[1 + \left(-\frac{1}{2}\right)\left(-\frac{4}{9}x\right) + \frac{\left(-\frac{1}{2}\right) \times \left(-\frac{3}{2}\right)}{1 \times 2}\left(-\frac{4}{9}x\right)^2 \right.$
$\left. + \frac{\left(-\frac{1}{2}\right) \times \left(-\frac{3}{2}\right) \times \left(-\frac{5}{2}\right)}{1 \times 2 \times 3}\left(-\frac{4}{9}x\right)^3 + \ldots\right]$

$= \frac{1}{3}\left(1 + \left(-\frac{1}{2}\right)\left(-\frac{4}{9}x\right) + \frac{\left(\frac{3}{4}\right)}{2}\left(-\frac{4}{9}x\right)^2 + \frac{\left(-\frac{15}{8}\right)}{6}\left(-\frac{4}{9}x\right)^3 + \ldots\right)$

$= \frac{1}{3}\left(1 + \left(-\frac{1}{2}\right)\left(-\frac{4}{9}x\right) + \frac{3}{8}\left(-\frac{4}{9}x\right)^2 + \left(-\frac{5}{16}\right)\left(-\frac{4}{9}x\right)^3 + \ldots\right)$

$= \frac{1}{3}\left(1 + \frac{2}{9}x + \frac{2}{27}x^2 + \frac{20}{729}x^3 + \ldots\right)$

$= \frac{1}{3} + \frac{2}{27}x + \frac{2}{81}x^2 + \frac{20}{2187}x^3 + \ldots$

[5 marks available in total:
- *1 mark for factorising out $(9)^{-\frac{1}{2}}$ or $\frac{1}{3}$*
- *1 mark for expansion of an expression of the form $(1 + ax)^{-\frac{1}{2}}$*
- *2 marks for the penultimate line of working — 1 for the first two terms in brackets correct, 1 for the 3rd and 4th terms in brackets correct.*
- *1 mark for the final answer correct]*

Multiplying out those coefficients can be pretty tricky. Don't try to do things all in one go — you won't be penalised for writing an extra line of working, but you probably will lose marks if your final answer's wrong.

b) $(2 - x)\left(\frac{1}{3} + \frac{2}{27}x + \frac{2}{81}x^2 + \frac{20}{2187}x^3 + \ldots\right)$

You only need the first three terms of the expansion, so just write the terms up to x^2 when you multiply out the brackets:

$= \frac{2}{3} + \frac{4}{27}x + \frac{4}{81}x^2 + \ldots$
$\quad - \frac{1}{3}x - \frac{2}{27}x^2 + \ldots$

$= \frac{2}{3} - \frac{5}{27}x - \frac{2}{81}x^2 + \ldots$

[4 marks available in total:
- *1 mark for multiplying your answer to part (a) by (2 – x)*
- *1 mark for multiplying out brackets to find constant term, two x-terms and two x²-terms.*
- *1 mark for correct constant and x-terms in final answer*
- *1 mark for correct x²-term in final answer]*

C4 Section 2 — Trigonometry
Warm-up Questions

1 a) $\csc 30° = 2$ (since $\sin 30° = 0.5$)

b) $\sec 30° = \frac{2}{\sqrt{3}}$ (since $\cos 30° = \frac{\sqrt{3}}{2}$)

c) $\cot 30° = \sqrt{3}$ (since $\tan 30° = \frac{1}{\sqrt{3}}$)

2) See p.59.

3) Divide the whole identity by $\cos^2\theta$ to get:
$\frac{\cos^2\theta}{\cos^2\theta} + \frac{\sin^2\theta}{\cos^2\theta} \equiv \frac{1}{\cos^2\theta}$
$\Rightarrow 1 + \tan^2\theta \equiv \sec^2\theta$
(as sin/cos ≡ tan and 1/cos ≡ sec)

4) Using the identities $\csc^2\theta \equiv 1 + \cot^2\theta$ and $\sin^2\theta + \cos^2\theta \equiv 1$, the LHS becomes:
$(\csc^2\theta - 1) + (1 - \cos^2\theta) \equiv \csc^2\theta - \cos^2\theta$,
which is the same as the RHS.

5) $\cos 2\theta \equiv \cos^2\theta - \sin^2\theta$
$\cos 2\theta \equiv 2\cos^2\theta - 1$
$\cos 2\theta \equiv 1 - 2\sin^2\theta$

6) $\sin 2\theta = -\sqrt{3}\sin\theta \Rightarrow \sin 2\theta + \sqrt{3}\sin\theta = 0$
$2\sin\theta\cos\theta + \sqrt{3}\sin\theta = 0$
$\sin\theta(2\cos\theta + \sqrt{3}) = 0$
So either $\sin\theta = 0$, so $\theta = 0°, 180°, 360°$ or
$2\cos\theta + \sqrt{3} = 0 \Rightarrow \cos\theta = -\frac{\sqrt{3}}{2}$
so $\theta = 150°$ or $210°$. The set of values for θ is $0°, 150°, 180°, 210°, 360°$.

If you don't know where the 180°, 360°, 210° etc. came from, you need to go back over your C2 notes...

7) $\frac{\pi}{12} = \frac{\pi}{3} - \frac{\pi}{4}$, so use the addition formula for $\cos(A - B)$:
$\cos\frac{\pi}{12} = \cos\left(\frac{\pi}{3} - \frac{\pi}{4}\right) = \cos\frac{\pi}{3}\cos\frac{\pi}{4} + \sin\frac{\pi}{3}\sin\frac{\pi}{4}$
As $\cos\frac{\pi}{3} = \frac{1}{2}$, $\cos\frac{\pi}{4} = \frac{1}{\sqrt{2}}$, $\sin\frac{\pi}{3} = \frac{\sqrt{3}}{2}$ and $\sin\frac{\pi}{4} = \frac{1}{\sqrt{2}}$, putting these values into the equation gives:
$\cos\frac{\pi}{3}\cos\frac{\pi}{4} + \sin\frac{\pi}{3}\sin\frac{\pi}{4} = \left(\frac{1}{2}\cdot\frac{1}{\sqrt{2}}\right) + \left(\frac{\sqrt{3}}{2}\cdot\frac{1}{\sqrt{2}}\right)$
$= \frac{1}{2\sqrt{2}} + \frac{\sqrt{3}}{2\sqrt{2}} = \frac{1 + \sqrt{3}}{2\sqrt{2}} = \frac{\sqrt{2}(1 + \sqrt{3})}{4} = \frac{\sqrt{2} + \sqrt{6}}{4}$

You could also have used $\frac{\pi}{12} = \frac{\pi}{4} - \frac{\pi}{6}$ in your answer.

8) $\sin(A + B) = \sin A \cos B + \cos A \sin B$.
As $\sin A = \frac{4}{5}$, $\cos A = \frac{3}{5}$ (from the right-angled triangle with sides of length 3, 4 and 5) and as $\sin B = \frac{7}{25}$, $\cos B = \frac{24}{25}$ (from the right-angled triangle with sides of length 7, 24 and 25). Putting these values into the equation gives:
$\sin A \cos B + \cos A \sin B = \left(\frac{4}{5}\cdot\frac{24}{25}\right) + \left(\frac{3}{5}\cdot\frac{7}{25}\right)$
$= \frac{96}{125} + \frac{21}{125} = \frac{117}{125}$

9) $a\cos\theta + b\sin\theta \equiv R\cos(\theta - \alpha)$ or
$b\sin\theta + a\cos\theta \equiv R\sin(\theta + \alpha)$

10) $5\sin\theta - 6\cos\theta \equiv R\sin(\theta - \alpha)$
$\equiv R\sin\theta\cos\alpha - R\cos\theta\sin\alpha$ (using the addition rule for sin).
Equating coefficients of $\sin\theta$ and $\cos\theta$ gives:
i. $R\cos\alpha = 5$ and ii. $R\sin\alpha = 6$.
Dividing ii. by i. to find α: $\frac{R\sin\alpha}{R\cos\alpha} = \tan\alpha$, so $\frac{6}{5} = \tan\alpha$
Solving this gives $\alpha = 50.19°$.
To find R, square equations i. and ii., then square root:
$R = \sqrt{5^2 + 6^2} = \sqrt{25 + 36} = \sqrt{61}$, so
$5\sin\theta - 6\cos\theta \equiv \sqrt{61}\sin(\theta - 50.19°)$.

11) Use the sin addition formulas:
$\sin(x + y) \equiv \sin x \cos y + \cos x \sin y$
$\sin(x - y) \equiv \sin x \cos y - \cos x \sin y$
Take the second away from the first:
$\sin(x + y) - \sin(x - y) \equiv 2\cos x \sin y$.

Let $A = x + y$ and $B = x - y$, so that $x = \frac{1}{2}(A + B)$ and $y = \frac{1}{2}(A - B)$. Then
$$\sin A - \sin B \equiv 2\cos\left(\frac{A + B}{2}\right)\sin\left(\frac{A - B}{2}\right).$$

Hint: to get the formulas for x and y in terms of A and B, you need to treat A = x + y and B = x − y as a pair of simultaneous equations.

12) Start by putting the LHS over a common denominator:
$$\frac{\cos\theta}{\sin\theta} + \frac{\sin\theta}{\cos\theta} \equiv \frac{\cos\theta\cos\theta}{\sin\theta\cos\theta} + \frac{\sin\theta\sin\theta}{\sin\theta\cos\theta}$$
$$\equiv \frac{\cos^2\theta + \sin^2\theta}{\sin\theta\cos\theta} \equiv \frac{1}{\sin\theta\cos\theta}$$
(using the identity $\sin^2\theta + \cos^2\theta \equiv 1$).

Now, $\sin 2\theta \equiv 2\sin\theta\cos\theta$, so $\sin\theta\cos\theta = \frac{1}{2}\sin 2\theta$.
So $\frac{1}{\sin\theta\cos\theta} \equiv \frac{1}{\frac{1}{2}\sin 2\theta} \equiv 2\operatorname{cosec} 2\theta$, which is the same as the RHS.

Exam Questions

1 a)

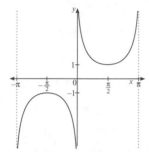

[3 marks available — 1 mark for n-shaped curve in third quadrant and u-shaped curve in first quadrant, 1 mark for asymptotes at 0 and ±π and 1 mark for max/min points of the curves at −1 and 1]

b) If $\operatorname{cosec} x = \frac{5}{4} \Rightarrow \frac{1}{\sin x} = \frac{5}{4} \Rightarrow \sin x = \frac{4}{5}$ *[1 mark]*.
Solving this for x gives $x = 0.927, 2.21$
[1 mark for each solution, lose a mark if answers aren't given to 3 s.f.].

The second solution can be found by sketching y = sin x:

You can see that there are two solutions, one at 0.927, and the other at π − 0.927 = 2.21.

c) $\operatorname{cosec} x = 3\sec x \Rightarrow \frac{1}{\sin x} = \frac{3}{\cos x} \Rightarrow \frac{\cos x}{\sin x} = 3$
$\Rightarrow \frac{1}{\tan x} = 3$ so $\tan x = \frac{1}{3}$
Solving for x gives $x = -2.82, 0.322,$ *[1 mark for appropriate rearranging, 1 mark for each solution.].*

Again, you need to sketch a graph to find the second solution:

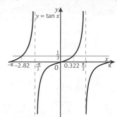

You can see that there are two solutions in the given range, one at 0.322 (this is the one you get from your calculator) and one at −π + 0.322 = −2.82.

2 a) $9\sin\theta + 12\cos\theta \equiv R\sin(\theta + \alpha)$. Using the sin addition formula, $9\sin\theta + 12\cos\theta \equiv R\sin\theta\cos\alpha + R\cos\theta\sin\alpha$. Equating coefficients of $\sin\theta$ and $\cos\theta$ gives:
$R\cos\alpha = 9$ and $R\sin\alpha = 12$ *[1 mark]*.
$\frac{R\sin\alpha}{R\cos\alpha} = \tan\alpha$, so $\tan\alpha = \frac{12}{9} = \frac{4}{3}$
Solving this gives $\alpha = 0.927$ *[1 mark — no other solutions in given range]*.
$R = \sqrt{9^2 + 12^2} = \sqrt{81 + 144} = \sqrt{225} = 15$ *[1 mark]*,
so $9\sin\theta + 12\cos\theta \equiv 15\sin(\theta + 0.927)$.

b) If $9\sin\theta + 12\cos\theta = 3$, then from part a),
$15\sin(\theta + 0.927) = 3$, so $\sin(\theta + 0.927) = 0.2$. The range for θ is $0 \le \theta \le 2\pi$, which becomes $0.927 \le \theta + 0.927 \le 7.210$. Solving the equation gives $(\theta + 0.927) = 0.201$ *[1 mark]*. As this is outside the range, use a sketch to find values that are in the range:

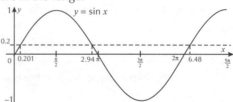

From the graph, it is clear that there are solutions at $\pi - 0.201 = 2.94$ and at $2\pi + 0.201 = 6.48$, so $(\theta + 0.927) = 2.940, 6.48$ *[1 mark for each value]*, so $\theta = 2.01, 5.56$ *[1 mark for each solution]*.

Be careful with the range — if you hadn't extended the range to 2π + 0.927, you would have missed one of the solutions.

3    $\sin 3x \equiv \sin(2x + x) \equiv \sin 2x\cos x + \cos 2x\sin x$ *[1 mark]*
$\equiv (2\sin x\cos x)\cos x + (1 - 2\sin^2 x)\sin x$ *[1 mark]*
$\equiv 2\sin x\cos^2 x + \sin x - 2\sin^3 x$
$\equiv 2\sin x(1 - \sin^2 x) + \sin x - 2\sin^3 x$ *[1 mark]*
$\equiv 2\sin x - 2\sin^3 x + \sin x - 2\sin^3 x$
$\equiv 3\sin x - 4\sin^3 x$ *[1 mark]*

4 a) $\frac{2\sin x}{1 - \cos x} - \frac{2\cos x}{\sin x} \equiv \frac{2\sin^2 x - 2\cos x + 2\cos^2 x}{\sin x(1 - \cos x)}$ *[1 mark]*
$\equiv \frac{2 - 2\cos x}{\sin x(1 - \cos x)}$ *[1 mark]*
$\equiv \frac{2(1 - \cos x)}{\sin x(1 - \cos x)}$ *[1 mark]*
$\equiv \frac{2}{\sin x} \equiv 2\operatorname{cosec} x$ *[1 mark]*

b) $2\operatorname{cosec} x = 4$
$\operatorname{cosec} x = 2$ OR $\sin x = \frac{1}{2}$ *[1 mark]*
$x = \frac{\pi}{6}$ *[1 mark]*, $x = \frac{5\pi}{6}$ *[1 mark]*.

Answers

5 a) $5\cos\theta + 12\sin\theta \equiv R\cos(\theta - \alpha)$. Using the cos addition formula, $5\cos\theta + 12\sin\theta \equiv R\cos\theta\cos\alpha + R\sin\theta\sin\alpha$. Equating coefficients gives:

$R\cos\alpha = 5$ and $R\sin\alpha = 12$ *[1 mark]*.

$\dfrac{R\sin\alpha}{R\cos\alpha} = \tan\alpha$, so $\tan\alpha = \dfrac{12}{5}$ *[1 mark]*.

Solving this gives $\alpha = 67.38°$ *[1 mark]*.

$R = \sqrt{5^2 + 12^2} = \sqrt{25 + 144} = \sqrt{169} = 13$ *[1 mark]*, so $5\cos\theta + 12\sin\theta \equiv 13\cos(\theta - 67.38°)$.

b) From part a), if $5\cos\theta + 12\sin\theta = 2$, that means $13\cos(\theta - 67.38°) = 2$, so $\cos(\theta - 67.38°) = \dfrac{2}{13}$ *[1 mark]*. The range for θ is $0 \le \theta \le 360°$, which becomes $-67.38° \le \theta - 67.38° \le 292.62°$ *[1 mark]*. Solving the equation gives $\theta - 67.38 = 81.15, 278.85$ *[1 mark]*, so $\theta = 148.53°, 346.23°$ *[1 mark for each value]*.

Look at the cos graph to get the second solution of $\theta - 67.38°$:

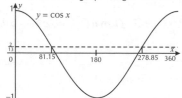

There are two solutions, one at 81.15°, and the other at 360 − 81.15 = 278.85°.

c) The minimum points of the cos curve have a value of –1, so as $5\cos\theta + 12\sin\theta \equiv 13\cos(\theta - 67.38°)$, the minimum value of $5\cos\theta + 12\sin\theta$ is –13 *[1 mark]*. Hence the minimum value of $(5\cos\theta + 12\sin\theta)^3$ is $(-13)^3 = -2197$ *[1 mark]*.

6 a) (i) Rearrange the identity $\sec^2\theta \equiv 1 + \tan^2\theta$ to get $\sec^2\theta - 1 \equiv \tan^2\theta$, then replace $\tan^2\theta$ in the equation:

$3\tan^2\theta - 2\sec\theta = 5$

$3(\sec^2\theta - 1) - 2\sec\theta - 5 = 0$ *[1 mark]*

$3\sec^2\theta - 3 - 2\sec\theta - 5 = 0$

so $3\sec^2\theta - 2\sec\theta - 8 = 0$ *[1 mark]*

(ii) To factorise this, let $y = \sec\theta$, so the equation becomes $3y^2 - 2y - 8 = 0$, so $(3y + 4)(y - 2) = 0$ *[1 mark]*. Solving for y gives $y = -\frac{4}{3}$ or $y = 2$. As $y = \sec\theta$, this means that $\sec\theta = -\frac{4}{3}$ or $\sec\theta = 2$ *[1 mark]*. $\sec\theta = \dfrac{1}{\cos\theta}$, so $\cos\theta = -\frac{3}{4}$ or $\cos\theta = \frac{1}{2}$ *[1 mark]*.

b) Let $\theta = 2x$. From above, we know that the solutions to $3\tan^2\theta - 2\sec\theta = 5$ satisfy $\cos\theta = -\frac{3}{4}$ or $\cos\theta = \frac{1}{2}$. The range for x is $0 \le x \le 180°$, so as $\theta = 2x$, the range for θ is $0 \le \theta \le 360°$ *[1 mark]*. Solving these equations for θ gives $\theta = 138.59°, 221.41°$ and $\theta = 60°, 300°$ *[1 mark]*. So, as $\theta = 2x$, $x = \frac{1}{2}\theta$, so $x = 69.30°, 110.70°, 30°, 150°$ *[1 mark]*.

Once you have the values 60° and 138.59°, you can sketch the graph to find the other values:

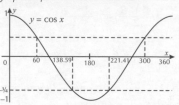

There is a solution at 360 − 60 = 300°, and another at 360 − 138.59 = 221.41°. Don't be fooled by the 2x in this question — you don't need to use the double angle formulas for this one.

C4 Section 3 — Parametric Equations
Warm-up Questions

1) a) $r = 7$, centre $= (0, 0)$.

b) $r = 5$, centre $= (2, -1)$.

2) a) Substitute the values of t into the parametric equations to find the corresponding values of x and y:

$t = 0 \Rightarrow x = \dfrac{6 - 0}{2} = 3$, $y = 2(0)^2 + 0 + 4 = 4$

$t = 1 \Rightarrow x = \dfrac{6 - 1}{2} = 2.5$, $y = 2(1)^2 + 1 + 4 = 7$

$t = 2 \Rightarrow x = \dfrac{6 - 2}{2} = 2$, $y = 2(2)^2 + 2 + 4 = 14$

$t = 3 \Rightarrow x = \dfrac{6 - 3}{2} = 1.5$, $y = 2(3)^2 + 3 + 4 = 25$

b) Use the given values in the parametric equations and solve for t:

(i) $\dfrac{6 - t}{2} = -7 \Rightarrow t = 20$

(ii) $2t^2 + t + 4 = 19$

$\Rightarrow 2t^2 + t - 15 = 0$

$\Rightarrow (2t - 5)(t + 3) = 0$

$\Rightarrow t = 2.5, t = -3$

c) Rearrange the parametric equation for x to make t the subject:

$x = \dfrac{6 - t}{2} \Rightarrow 2x = 6 - t \Rightarrow t = 6 - 2x$

Now substitute this into the parametric equation for y:

$y = 2t^2 + t + 4$

$= 2(6 - 2x)^2 + (6 - 2x) + 4$

$= 2(36 - 24x + 4x^2) + 10 - 2x$

$y = 8x^2 - 50x + 82$.

3) a) Substitute the values of θ into the parametric equations to find the corresponding values of x and y:

(i) $x = 2\sin\dfrac{\pi}{4} = \dfrac{2}{\sqrt{2}} = \sqrt{2}$

$y = \cos^2\dfrac{\pi}{4} + 4 = \left(\cos\dfrac{\pi}{4}\right)^2 + 4 = \left(\dfrac{1}{\sqrt{2}}\right)^2 + 4 = \dfrac{1}{2} + 4 = \dfrac{9}{2}$

So the coordinates are $\left(\sqrt{2}, \dfrac{9}{2}\right)$.

(ii) $x = 2\sin\dfrac{\pi}{6} = 2 \times \dfrac{1}{2} = 1$

$y = \cos^2\dfrac{\pi}{6} + 4 = \left(\cos\dfrac{\pi}{6}\right)^2 + 4 = \left(\dfrac{\sqrt{3}}{2}\right)^2 + 4 = \dfrac{3}{4} + 4 = \dfrac{19}{4}$

So the coordinates are $\left(1, \dfrac{19}{4}\right)$.

b) Use the identity $\cos^2\theta = 1 - \sin^2\theta$ in the equation for y so both equations are in terms of $\sin\theta$:

$y = \cos^2\theta + 4$

$\quad = 1 - \sin^2\theta + 4$

$\quad = 5 - \sin^2\theta$

Rearrange the equation for x to get $\sin^2\theta$ in terms of x:

$x = 2\sin\theta \;\Rightarrow\; \frac{x}{2} = \sin\theta \;\Rightarrow\; \sin^2\theta = \frac{x^2}{4}$

So $y = 5 - \sin^2\theta \;\Rightarrow\; y = 5 - \frac{x^2}{4}$

c) $x = 2\sin\theta$, and $-1 \le \sin\theta \le 1$ so $-2 \le x \le 2$.

I know what you're thinking — this answer section would be brightened up immensely by a cheery song-and-dance number. Sorry, no such luck I'm afraid. Here's the next answer instead...

4) Use the identity $\cos2\theta = 1 - 2\sin^2\theta$ in the equation for y:

$y = 3 + 2\cos2\theta$

$\quad = 3 + 2(1 - 2\sin^2\theta)$

$\quad = 5 - 4\sin^2\theta$

Rearrange the equation for x to get $\sin^2\theta$ in terms of x:

$x = \frac{\sin\theta}{3} \;\Rightarrow\; 3x = \sin\theta \;\Rightarrow\; \sin^2\theta = 9x^2$

So $y = 5 - 4\sin^2\theta$

$\Rightarrow y = 5 - 4(9x^2)$

$\Rightarrow y = 5 - 36x^2$

5) a) On the y-axis:

$x = 0 \;\Rightarrow\; t^2 - 1 = 0 \;\Rightarrow\; t = \pm1$

If $t = 1$, $y = 4 + \frac{3}{1} = 7$

If $t = -1$, $y = 4 + \frac{3}{-1} = 1$

So the curve crosses the x-axis at $(0, 1)$ and $(0, 7)$.

b) Substitute the parametric equations into the equation of the line:

$x + 2y = 14$

$\Rightarrow (t^2 - 1) + 2(4 + \frac{3}{t}) = 14$

$\Rightarrow t^2 - 1 + 8 + \frac{6}{t} = 14$

$\Rightarrow t^2 - 7 + \frac{6}{t} = 0$

$\Rightarrow t^3 - 7t + 6 = 0$

$\Rightarrow (t - 1)(t^2 + t - 6) = 0$

$\Rightarrow (t - 1)(t - 2)(t + 3) = 0$

$\Rightarrow t = 1, t = 2, t = -3$

When $t = 1$, $x = 0$, $y = 7$ (from part (i))

When $t = 2$, $x = 2^2 - 1 = 3$, $y = 4 + \frac{3}{2} = 5.5$

When $t = -3$, $x = (-3)^2 - 1 = 8$, $y = 4 + \frac{3}{-3} = 3$

So the curve crosses the line $x + 2y = 14$ at $(0, 7)$, $(3, 5.5)$ and $(8, 3)$.

6) a) $\frac{dx}{dt} = 2t$, $\frac{dy}{dt} = 9t^2 - 4$, so $\frac{dy}{dx} = \frac{dy}{dt} \div \frac{dx}{dt} = \frac{9t^2 - 4}{2t}$

b) The stationary points are when $\frac{9t^2 - 4}{2t} = 0$

$\Rightarrow 9t^2 = 4 \Rightarrow t = \pm\frac{2}{3}$

$t = \frac{2}{3} \Rightarrow x = \left(\frac{2}{3}\right)^2 = \frac{4}{9}$, $y = 3\left(\frac{2}{3}\right)^3 - 4\left(\frac{2}{3}\right) = \frac{8}{9} - \frac{8}{3} = -\frac{16}{9}$

$t = -\frac{2}{3} \Rightarrow x = \left(-\frac{2}{3}\right)^2 = \frac{4}{9}$,

$y = 3\left(-\frac{2}{3}\right)^3 - 4\left(-\frac{2}{3}\right) = -\frac{8}{9} + \frac{8}{3} = \frac{16}{9}$

So the stationary points are $\left(\frac{4}{9}, -\frac{16}{9}\right)$ and $\left(\frac{4}{9}, \frac{16}{9}\right)$.

Exam Questions

1 a) Substitute the given value of θ into the parametric equations:

$\theta = \frac{\pi}{3} \;\Rightarrow\; x = 1 - \tan\frac{\pi}{3} = 1 - \sqrt{3}$

$\qquad y = \frac{1}{2}\sin\left(\frac{2\pi}{3}\right) = \frac{1}{2}\left(\frac{\sqrt{3}}{2}\right) = \frac{\sqrt{3}}{4}$

So $P = \left(1 - \sqrt{3}, \frac{\sqrt{3}}{4}\right)$

[2 marks available — 1 mark for substituting $\theta = \frac{\pi}{3}$ into the parametric equations, 1 mark for both coordinates of P correct.]

b) Use $y = -\frac{1}{2}$ to find the value of θ:

$-\frac{1}{2} = \frac{1}{2}\sin2\theta \Rightarrow \sin2\theta = -1$

$\qquad\qquad\qquad\quad \Rightarrow 2\theta = -\frac{\pi}{2}$

$\qquad\qquad\qquad\quad \Rightarrow \theta = -\frac{\pi}{4}$

You can also find θ using the parametric equation for x, with $x = 2$.

[2 marks available — 1 mark for substituting given x- or y-value into the correct parametric equation, 1 mark for finding the correct value of θ.]

c) $x = 1 - \tan\theta \;\Rightarrow\; \tan\theta = 1 - x$

$y = \frac{1}{2}\sin2\theta$

$\quad = \frac{1}{2}\left(\frac{2\tan\theta}{1 + \tan^2\theta}\right)$

$\quad = \frac{\tan\theta}{1 + \tan^2\theta}$

$\quad = \frac{(1 - x)}{1 + (1 - x)^2}$

$\quad = \frac{1 - x}{1 + 1 - 2x + x^2}$

$\quad = \frac{1 - x}{x^2 - 2x + 2}$

[3 marks available — 1 mark for using the given identity to rearrange one of the parametric equations, 1 mark for eliminating θ from the parametric equation for y, 1 mark for correctly expanding to give the Cartesian equation given in the question.]

Just think, if you lived in the Bahamas, you could be doing this revision on the beach. (Please ignore that comment if you actually do live in the Bahamas. Or anywhere else where you can revise on the beach.)

2 The circle has a radius of 5, so the centre will have coordinates $(6 - 5, 4 - 5) = (1, -1)$.

$a = 1$ *[1 mark]*, $b = -1$ *[1 mark]*.

3 a) Substitute $y = 1$ into the parametric equation for y:

$t^2 - 2t + 2 = 1$

$\Rightarrow t^2 - 2t + 1 = 0$

$\Rightarrow (t - 1)^2 = 0$

$\Rightarrow t = 1$ *[1 mark]*

So a is the value of x when $t = 1$.

$a = t^3 + t = 1^3 + 1 = 2$ *[1 mark]*

Answers

b) Substitute the parametric equations for x and y into the equation of the line:

$8y = x + 6$

$\Rightarrow 8(t^2 - 2t + 2) = (t^3 + t) + 6$ **[1 mark]**

$\Rightarrow 8t^2 - 16t + 16 = t^3 + t + 6$

$\Rightarrow t^3 - 8t^2 + 17t - 10 = 0$

We know that this line passes through K, and from a) we know that $t = 1$ at K, so $t = 1$ is a solution of this equation, and $(t - 1)$ is a factor:

$\Rightarrow (t - 1)(t^2 - 7t + 10) = 0$ **[1 mark]**

$\Rightarrow (t - 1)(t - 2)(t - 5) = 0$

So $t = 2$ at L and $t = 5$ at M. **[1 mark]**

If you got stuck on this bit, go back and look up 'factorising cubics' in your AS notes.

Substitute $t = 2$ and $t = 5$ back into the parametric equations: **[1 mark]**

If $t = 2$, then $x = 2^3 + 2 = 10$

and $y = 2^2 - 2(2) + 2 = 2$

If $t = 5$, then $x = 5^3 + 5 = 130$

and $y = 5^2 - 2(5) + 2 = 17$

So $L = (10, 2)$ **[1 mark]**

and $M = (130, 17)$ **[1 mark]**

4 a) Start by differentiating x and y with respect to θ:

$\frac{dy}{d\theta} = 2\cos\theta$ **[1 mark]**

$\frac{dx}{d\theta} = 3 + 3\sin 3\theta$ **[1 mark]**

$\frac{dy}{dx} = \frac{dy}{d\theta} \div \frac{dx}{d\theta} = \frac{2\cos\theta}{3 + 3\sin 3\theta}$ **[1 mark]**

b) (i) We need the value of θ at $(\pi + 1, \sqrt{3})$:

$y = 2\sin\theta = \sqrt{3}$, for $-\pi \le \theta \le \pi \Rightarrow \theta = \frac{\pi}{3}$ or $\frac{2\pi}{3}$ **[1 mark]**

If $\theta = \frac{\pi}{3}$, then $x = 3\theta - \cos 3\theta = \pi - \cos\pi = \pi + 1$.

If $\theta = \frac{2\pi}{3}$, then $x = 3\theta - \cos 3\theta = 2\pi - \cos 2\pi = 2\pi - 1$.

So at $(\pi + 1, \sqrt{3})$, $\theta = \frac{\pi}{3}$ **[1 mark]**

$\theta = \frac{\pi}{3} \Rightarrow \frac{dy}{dx} = \frac{2\cos\frac{\pi}{3}}{3 + 3\sin\pi} = \frac{2\left(\frac{1}{2}\right)}{3 + 0} = \frac{1}{3}$ **[1 mark]**

(ii) $\theta = \frac{\pi}{6} \Rightarrow x = \frac{\pi}{2} - \cos\frac{\pi}{2} = \frac{\pi}{2} - 0 = \frac{\pi}{2}$

$\theta = \frac{\pi}{6} \Rightarrow y = 2\sin\frac{\pi}{6} = 2 \times \frac{1}{2} = 1$

So $\theta = \frac{\pi}{6}$ at the point $(\frac{\pi}{2}, 1)$ **[1 mark]**

$\theta = \frac{\pi}{6} \Rightarrow \frac{dy}{dx} = \frac{2\cos\frac{\pi}{6}}{3 + 3\sin\frac{\pi}{2}} = \frac{2\left(\frac{\sqrt{3}}{2}\right)}{3 + 3(1)} = \frac{\sqrt{3}}{6}$ **[1 mark]**

Gradient of normal $= -\frac{1}{\left(\frac{dy}{dx}\right)} = -\frac{6}{\sqrt{3}} = -\frac{6\sqrt{3}}{3}$

$= -2\sqrt{3}$ **[1 mark]**

So the normal is $y = -2\sqrt{3}x + c$ for some c.

$\Rightarrow 1 = -2\sqrt{3} \times \frac{\pi}{2} + c = -\pi\sqrt{3} + c$

$\Rightarrow c = 1 + \pi\sqrt{3}$

The equation of the normal is $y = -2\sqrt{3}x + 1 + \pi\sqrt{3}$ **[1 mark]**

5 a) As $x = \tan\theta$, $\frac{dx}{d\theta} = \sec^2\theta$ **[1 mark]**.

As $y = \sin\theta$, $\frac{dy}{d\theta} = \cos\theta$ **[1 mark]**.

So $\frac{dy}{dx} = \frac{dy}{d\theta} \div \frac{dx}{d\theta} = \frac{\cos\theta}{\sec^2\theta} = \cos^3\theta$. **[1 mark]**

At P, $\tan\theta = 1$ and $\sin\theta = \frac{1}{\sqrt{2}}$. The value of θ in the given range that satisfies both these equations is $\theta = \frac{\pi}{4}$ **[1 mark]**.

Putting this value into the expression for $\frac{dy}{dx}$:

$\frac{dy}{dx} = (\cos\frac{\pi}{4})^3 = (\frac{1}{\sqrt{2}})^3 = \frac{1}{2\sqrt{2}}$ **[1 mark]**.

b) At P, the gradient of the tangent is $\frac{1}{2\sqrt{2}}$, so the gradient of the normal is $-1 \div \frac{1}{2\sqrt{2}} = -2\sqrt{2}$ **[1 mark]**.

The coordinates of P are $(1, \frac{1}{\sqrt{2}})$. Putting all this into the equation of a line gives:

$y = mx + c \Rightarrow \frac{1}{\sqrt{2}} = (-2\sqrt{2} \times 1) + c$ **[1 mark]** $\Rightarrow c = \frac{5\sqrt{2}}{2}$.

So the gradient of the normal at P is $y = -2\sqrt{2}x + \frac{5\sqrt{2}}{2}$ **[1 mark]**.

6 a) First find the value of t when $y = -6$:

$y = 2 - t^3 = -6 \Rightarrow t^3 = 8 \Rightarrow t = 2$ **[1 mark]**

$\Rightarrow x = 2^2 + 2(2) - 3 = 5$

Now find the gradient of the curve:

$\frac{dy}{dt} = -3t^2$, $\frac{dx}{dt} = 2t + 2$

So $\frac{dy}{dx} = \frac{dy}{dt} \div \frac{dx}{dt} = \frac{-3t^2}{2t + 2}$ **[1 mark]**

So when $t = 2$, $\frac{dy}{dx} = \frac{-3(2)^2}{2(2) + 2} = \frac{-12}{6} = -2$ **[1 mark]**

So the tangent at $y = -6$ is $y = -2x + c \Rightarrow -6 = -2(5) + c$

$\Rightarrow c = 4$. The equation of L is $y = -2x + 4$ **[1 mark]**

b) (i) Sub $y = 2 - t^3$ and $x = t^2 + 2t - 3$ into the equation of L:

$y = -2x + 4$

$\Rightarrow 2 - t^3 = -2(t^2 + 2t - 3) + 4$ **[1 mark]**

$\Rightarrow 2 - t^3 = -2t^2 - 4t + 10$

$\Rightarrow t^3 - 2t^2 - 4t + 8 = 0$

We know from part (a) that $t = 2$ is a root, so take out $(t - 2)$ as a factor:

$\Rightarrow (t - 2)(t^2 - 4) = 0$ **[1 mark]**

$\Rightarrow (t - 2)(t + 2)(t - 2) = 0$

$\Rightarrow t = 2$ or $t = -2$ **[1 mark]**

So t must be -2 at P.

$t = -2 \Rightarrow x = (-2)^2 + 2(-2) - 3 = -3$, $y = 2 - (-2)^3 = 10$.

The coordinates of P are $(-3, 10)$. **[1 mark]**

(ii) At P, $t = -2$, so $\frac{dy}{dx} = \frac{-3(-2)^2}{2(-2) + 2} = \frac{-12}{-2} = 6$ **[1 mark]**

So the gradient of the normal at P is

$-\frac{1}{\left(\frac{dy}{dx}\right)} = -\frac{1}{6}$ **[1 mark]**

The equation of the normal at P is

$y = -\frac{1}{6}x + c \Rightarrow 10 = -\frac{(-3)}{6} + c \Rightarrow c = \frac{19}{2}$

So the normal to the curve at point P is

$y = -\frac{1}{6}x + \frac{19}{2}$ **[1 mark]**

As Shakespeare* himself might have put it "That section was a ruddy pain in the backside, but at least it's finished."

*Arnold Shakespeare (1948–)

Answers

C4 Section 4 — Calculus
Warm-up Questions

1) For the Trapezium Rule using 4 strips, $h = 1.5$ and you need to work out the values of y at $x = 0, 1.5, 3, 4.5, 6$:
$x_0 = 0, y_0 = -108, x_1 = 1.5, y_1 = -1.6875, x_2 = 3, y_2 = 0,$
$x_3 = 4.5, y_3 = 413.4375, x_4 = 6, y_4 = 5400.$
Putting these values into the formula gives:
$A \approx 0.75[-108 + 2(-1.6875 + 0 + 413.4375) + 5400]$
   $= 4586.625.$
Using 6 strips, $h = 1$ and you need the y-values for $x = 0, 1,$ 2, 3, 4, 5, 6. You already know the values for $x = 0, 3, 6.$
$(x_0 = 0, y_0 = -108), x_1 = 1, y_1 = 0, x_2 = 2, y_2 = 0, (x_3 = 3, y_3 = 0), x_4 = 4, y_4 = 108, x_5 = 5, y_5 = 1152, (x_6 = 6, y_6 = 5400).$
Putting these values into the formula gives:
$A \approx \frac{1}{2}[-108 + 2(0 + 0 + 0 + 108 + 1152) + 5400] = 3906.$
To calculate the percentage error, you must first work out the exact value of the integral:
$\int_0^6 (6x - 12)(x^2 - 4x + 3)^2 dx = [(x^2 - 4x + 3)^3]_0^6$
$= (6^2 - 4(6) + 3)^3 - (0 - 0 + 3)^3$
$= 3375 - 27 = 3348.$
This uses the formula $\int (n + 1)f'(x)[f(x)]^n dx = [f(x)]^{n+1} + C$.
Now work out the error for 4 strips:
$\frac{4586.625 - 3348}{3348} \times 100 = 37.00\% \ (4 \text{ s.f.})$
and for 6 strips: $\frac{3906 - 3348}{3348} \times 100 = 16.67\% \ (4 \text{ s.f.}).$
Neither of these estimates was particularly accurate — but the one with more strips had a lower % error (as you would expect).

2) If $y = \frac{1}{x}$ then $y^2 = \frac{1}{x^2}$. Putting this into the integral gives:
$V = \pi \int_2^4 \frac{1}{x^2} dx = \pi\left[-\frac{1}{x}\right]_2^4 = \pi\left[\left(-\frac{1}{4}\right) - \left(-\frac{1}{2}\right)\right] = \frac{\pi}{4}.$

3) First, rearrange the equation to get it in terms of x^2:
$y = x^2 + 1 \Rightarrow x^2 = y - 1.$ Putting this into the formula:
$V = \pi \int_1^3 y - 1 \, dy = \pi\left[\frac{1}{2}y^2 - y\right]_1^3$
$= \pi\left[\left(\frac{1}{2}(9) - 3\right) - \left(\frac{1}{2}(1) - 1\right)\right] = 2\pi.$

4) $\frac{dy}{dx} = \frac{1}{y}\cos x \Rightarrow y \, dy = \cos x \, dx$
so $\int y \, dy = \int \cos x \, dx \Rightarrow \frac{y^2}{2} = \sin x + C_0$
$\Rightarrow y^2 = 2\sin x + C_1 \text{ (where } C_1 = 2C_0)$

5) a) $\frac{dS}{dt} = kS$
   b) Solving the differential equation above gives:
   $\frac{dS}{dt} = kS \Rightarrow \int \frac{1}{S} \, dS = \int k \, dt$
   $\ln|S| = kt + C$
   $S = Ae^{kt} \text{ where } A = e^c$
   For the initial population, $t = 0$. Put $S = 30$ and $t = 0$ into the equation to find the value of A: $30 = Ae^0 \Rightarrow A = 30.$
   Now, use $S = 150, k = 0.2$ and $A = 30$ to find t:
   $150 = 30e^{0.2t} \Rightarrow 5 = e^{0.2t} \Rightarrow \ln 5 = 0.2t$, so $t = 8.047.$
   It will take the squirrels 8 weeks before they can take over the forest.

   Go squirrels go!

Exam Questions

1   $y = \cos x$, so $y^2 = \cos^2 x$. Putting this into the formula gives:
$V = \pi \int_{\frac{\pi}{4}}^{\frac{\pi}{3}} \cos^2 x \, dx.$

To integrate this, use the cos double angle formula to rewrite $\cos^2 x$ as $\frac{1}{2}(\cos 2x + 1)$:
$V = \frac{\pi}{2} \int_{\frac{\pi}{4}}^{\frac{\pi}{3}} \cos 2x + 1 \, dx = \frac{\pi}{2}\left[\frac{1}{2}\sin 2x + x\right]_{\frac{\pi}{4}}^{\frac{\pi}{3}}$
$= \frac{\pi}{2}\left[\left(\frac{1}{2}\sin\frac{2\pi}{3} + \frac{\pi}{3}\right) - \left(\frac{1}{2}\sin\frac{\pi}{2} + \frac{\pi}{4}\right)\right] = 0.306.$

[4 marks available — 1 mark for correct function for y^2, 1 mark for using the cos double angle formula to simplify, 1 mark for integrating, 1 mark for substituting in values of x to obtain correct answer]
Don't forget π here.

2   First, rearrange the equation to get it in terms of x^2:
$y = \frac{1}{x^2} \Rightarrow x^2 = \frac{1}{y}$. Putting this into the formula:
$V = \pi \int_1^3 \frac{1}{y} \, dy = \pi[\ln y]_1^3$
$= \pi[(\ln 3) - (\ln 1)] = \pi \ln 3.$

[5 marks available — 1 mark for rearranging equation, 1 mark for correct formula for volume, 1 mark for correct integration, 1 mark for substituting in limits, 1 mark for final answer (in terms of π and ln)]

3   a) When $x = \frac{\pi}{2}, y = \frac{\pi}{2}\sin\frac{\pi}{2} = \frac{\pi}{2} = 1.5708$ *[1 mark]*,
   and when $x = \frac{3\pi}{4}, y = \frac{3\pi}{4}\sin\frac{3\pi}{4} = 1.6661$ *[1 mark]*

   b) The width of each strip (h) is $\frac{\pi}{4}$, so the Trapezium Rule is:
   $A = \frac{1}{2}\frac{\pi}{4}[0 + 2(0.5554 + 1.5708 + 1.6661) + 0]$
   $= \frac{\pi}{8}[2(3.7923)] = 2.978 \ (3 \text{ d.p.}).$

   [4 marks available — 1 mark for correct value of h, 2 marks for correct use of formula, 1 mark for correct answer]

   You're given the Trapezium Rule on the formula sheet, but it's a good idea to learn it anyway.

   c) Let $u = x$, so $\frac{du}{dx} = 1$. Let $\frac{dv}{dx} = \sin x$, so $v = -\cos x$ *[1 mark for both parts correct]*. Using integration by parts,
   $\int_0^\pi x \sin x \, dx = [-x\cos x]_0^\pi - \int_0^\pi -\cos x \, dx$ *[1 mark]*
   $= [-x\cos x]_0^\pi + [\sin x]_0^\pi$ *[1 mark]*
   $= (\pi - 0) + (0) = \pi$ *[1 mark]*

   If you'd tried to use u = sin x, you'd have ended up with a more complicated function to integrate ($x^2\cos x$). Look back at your C3 notes for a reminder about integration by parts.

   d) To find the percentage error, divide the difference between the approximate answer and the exact answer by the exact answer and multiply by 100:
   $\frac{\pi - 2.978}{\pi} \times 100 = 5.2\% \ (2 \text{ s.f.}).$

   [2 marks available — 1 mark for appropriate method and 1 mark for correct answer]

Answers

4 a) $\dfrac{dy}{dx} = \dfrac{\cos x \cos^2 y}{\sin x} \Rightarrow \dfrac{1}{\cos^2 y}\,dy = \dfrac{\cos x}{\sin x}\,dx$

$\Rightarrow \int \sec^2 y\,dy = \int \dfrac{\cos x}{\sin x}\,dx$

$\Rightarrow \tan y = \ln|\sin x| + C$

[4 marks available — 1 mark for separating the variables into functions of x and y, 1 mark for correct integration of RHS, 1 mark for correct integration of LHS, 1 mark for general solution]

b) If $y = \pi$ when $x = \dfrac{\pi}{6}$, that means that

$\tan \pi = \ln\left|\sin \dfrac{\pi}{6}\right| + C$

$0 = \ln\left|\dfrac{1}{2}\right| + C$ *[1 mark]*

As $\ln \frac{1}{2} = \ln 1 - \ln 2 = -\ln 2$ (as $\ln 1 = 0$), it follows that $C = \ln 2$.

So $\tan y = \ln|\sin x| + \ln 2$ or $\tan y = \ln|2\sin x|$ *[1 mark]*.

This is the particular solution — you found the general solution in part a).

5 a) $\dfrac{dm}{dt} = k\sqrt{m}$, $k > 0$ *[1 mark for RHS, 1 mark for LHS]*

b) First solve the differential equation to find m:

$\dfrac{dm}{dt} = k\sqrt{m} \Rightarrow \dfrac{1}{\sqrt{m}}\,dm = k\,dt$

$\Rightarrow \int m^{-\frac{1}{2}}\,dm = \int k\,dt$ *[1 mark]*

$\Rightarrow 2m^{\frac{1}{2}} = kt + C$

$\Rightarrow m = \left(\dfrac{1}{2}(kt + C)\right)^2 = \dfrac{1}{4}(kt + C)^2$ *[1 mark]*

At the start of the campaign, $t = 0$. Putting $t = 0$ and $m = 900$ into the equation gives: $900 = \frac{1}{4}(0 + C)^2 \Rightarrow 3600 = C^2 \Rightarrow C = 60$ (C must be positive, otherwise the sales would be decreasing). *[1 mark]*. This gives the equation $m = \frac{1}{4}(kt + 60)^2$ *[1 mark]*.

c) Substituting $t = 5$ and $k = 2$ into the equation gives:
$m = \frac{1}{4}((2 \times 5) + 60)^2 = 1225$ tubs sold.

[3 marks available — 2 marks for substituting correct values of t and k, 1 mark for answer]

C4 Section 5 — Vectors

Warm-up Questions

1) Any multiples of the vectors will do:

a) e.g. **a** and 4**a**

b) e.g. $6\mathbf{i} + 8\mathbf{j} - 4\mathbf{k}$ and $9\mathbf{i} + 12\mathbf{j} - 6\mathbf{k}$

c) e.g. $\begin{pmatrix} 2 \\ 4 \\ -2 \end{pmatrix}$ and $\begin{pmatrix} 4 \\ 8 \\ -4 \end{pmatrix}$

2) a) $\mathbf{b} - \mathbf{a}$ b) $\mathbf{a} - \mathbf{b}$ c) $\mathbf{b} - \mathbf{c}$ d) $\mathbf{c} - \mathbf{a}$

3) $2\mathbf{i} - 4\mathbf{j} + 5\mathbf{k}$

4) a) $\sqrt{3^2 + 4^2 + (-2)^2} = \sqrt{29}$

b) $\sqrt{1^2 + 2^2 + (-1)^2} = \sqrt{6}$

5) a) $\sqrt{(3-1)^2 + (-1-2)^2 + (-2-3)^2} = \sqrt{38}$

b) $\sqrt{1^2 + 2^2 + 3^2} = \sqrt{14}$

c) $\sqrt{3^2 + (-1)^2 + (-2)^2} = \sqrt{14}$

6) a) $\mathbf{r} = (4\mathbf{i} + \mathbf{j} + 2\mathbf{k}) + t(3\mathbf{i} + \mathbf{j} - \mathbf{k})$ or $\mathbf{r} = \begin{pmatrix} 4 \\ 1 \\ 2 \end{pmatrix} + t\begin{pmatrix} 3 \\ 1 \\ -1 \end{pmatrix}$

b) $\mathbf{r} = (2\mathbf{i} - \mathbf{j} + \mathbf{k}) + t((2\mathbf{j} + 3\mathbf{k}) - (2\mathbf{i} - \mathbf{j} + \mathbf{k}))$
$\Rightarrow \mathbf{r} = (2\mathbf{i} - \mathbf{j} + \mathbf{k}) + t(-2\mathbf{i} + 3\mathbf{j} + 2\mathbf{k})$

or $\mathbf{r} = \begin{pmatrix} 2 \\ -1 \\ 1 \end{pmatrix} + t\begin{pmatrix} -2 \\ 3 \\ 2 \end{pmatrix}$

7) E.g. If $t = 1$, $((3 + 1(-1)), (2 + 1(3)), (4 + 1(0))) = (2, 5, 4)$

If $t = 2$, $((3 + 2(-1)), (2 + 2(3)), (4 + 2(0))) = (1, 8, 4)$

If $t = -1$, $((3 + -1(-1)), (2 + -1(3)), (4 + -1(0))) = (4, -1, 4)$

8) a) $(3\mathbf{i} + 4\mathbf{j}) \cdot (\mathbf{i} - 2\mathbf{j} + 3\mathbf{k}) = 3 - 8 + 0 = -5$

b) $\begin{pmatrix} 4 \\ 2 \\ 1 \end{pmatrix} \cdot \begin{pmatrix} 3 \\ -4 \\ -3 \end{pmatrix} = (4 \times 3) + (2 \times -4) + (1 \times -3) = 1$

9) a) $\begin{pmatrix} 2 \\ -1 \\ 2 \end{pmatrix} + t\begin{pmatrix} -4 \\ 6 \\ -2 \end{pmatrix} = \begin{pmatrix} 3 \\ 2 \\ 4 \end{pmatrix} + u\begin{pmatrix} -1 \\ 3 \\ 0 \end{pmatrix}$

Where the lines intersect, these 3 equations are true:

$2 - 4t = 3 - u$

$-1 + 6t = 2 + 3u$

$2 - 2t = 4$

Solve the third equation to give $t = -1$.

Substituting $t = -1$ in either of the other equations gives $u = -3$.

Substituting $t = -1$ and $u = -3$ in the remaining equation gives a true result, so the lines intersect.

Substituting $t = -1$ in the first vector equation gives the position vector of the intersection point:

$\begin{pmatrix} 6 \\ -7 \\ 4 \end{pmatrix}$

You'll often have to solve a pair of equations simultaneously (both variables will usually be in all three equations).

b) To find the angle between the lines, only consider the direction components of the vector equations:

$\begin{pmatrix} -4 \\ 6 \\ -2 \end{pmatrix} \cdot \begin{pmatrix} -1 \\ 3 \\ 0 \end{pmatrix} = 4 + 18 + 0 = 22$

magnitude of 1st vector: $\sqrt{(-4)^2 + 6^2 + (-2)^2} = \sqrt{56}$

magnitude of 2nd vector: $\sqrt{(-1)^2 + 3^2 + (0)^2} = \sqrt{10}$

$\cos \theta = \dfrac{22}{\sqrt{56}\sqrt{10}} = \Rightarrow \theta = 21.6°$

10) Find values for a, b and c that give a scalar product of 0 when the two vectors are multiplied together.

$(3\mathbf{i} + 4\mathbf{j} - 2\mathbf{k}) \cdot (a\mathbf{i} + b\mathbf{j} + c\mathbf{k}) = 3a + 4b - 2c = 0$

E.g. $a = 2$, $b = 1$, $c = 5$

Perpendicular vector = $(2\mathbf{i} + \mathbf{j} + 5\mathbf{k})$

Just pick values for a and b, then see what value of c is needed to make the scalar product zero.

11) The normal vector $\mathbf{n} = \begin{pmatrix} 1 \\ 3 \\ -3 \end{pmatrix}$.

Answers

Call the position vector of the given point **a**.
Then the coefficients of x, y and z in a Cartesian equation are the components of **n**, and the constant term is

$$d = -\mathbf{a \cdot n} = -\begin{pmatrix} 2 \\ 2 \\ 4 \end{pmatrix} \cdot \begin{pmatrix} 1 \\ 3 \\ -3 \end{pmatrix} = -[(2 \times 1) + (2 \times 3) + (4 \times -3)] = 4$$

So a Cartesian equation of the plane is
$$n_1 x + n_2 y + n_3 z + d = 0$$
$$\Rightarrow x + 3y - 3z + 4 = 0$$

12) Label the points: A = (1, –2, 5), B = (6, 2, –3), C = (4, 0, 2)
Then a vector equation for the plane is $\mathbf{r} = \mathbf{a} + \lambda\mathbf{b} + \mu\mathbf{c}$,

where **a** = position vector of A = $\begin{pmatrix} 1 \\ -2 \\ 5 \end{pmatrix}$,

$$\mathbf{b} = \overrightarrow{AB} = -\begin{pmatrix} 1 \\ -2 \\ 5 \end{pmatrix} + \begin{pmatrix} 6 \\ 2 \\ -3 \end{pmatrix} = \begin{pmatrix} 5 \\ 4 \\ -8 \end{pmatrix},$$

$$\mathbf{c} = \overrightarrow{AC} = -\begin{pmatrix} 1 \\ -2 \\ 5 \end{pmatrix} + \begin{pmatrix} 4 \\ 0 \\ 2 \end{pmatrix} = \begin{pmatrix} 3 \\ 2 \\ -3 \end{pmatrix}.$$

So the vector equation is $\mathbf{r} = \begin{pmatrix} 1 \\ -2 \\ 5 \end{pmatrix} + \lambda\begin{pmatrix} 5 \\ 4 \\ -8 \end{pmatrix} + \mu\begin{pmatrix} 3 \\ 2 \\ -3 \end{pmatrix}$

Exam Questions

1 a) $\overrightarrow{AB} = \mathbf{b} - \mathbf{a} = \begin{pmatrix} 3 \\ 2 \\ 1 \end{pmatrix} - \begin{pmatrix} 1 \\ 5 \\ 9 \end{pmatrix} = \begin{pmatrix} 2 \\ -3 \\ -8 \end{pmatrix}$

[2 marks available — 1 mark for attempting to subtract position vector a from position vector b, 1 mark for correct answer.]

b) l_1: $\mathbf{r} = \mathbf{c} + \mu(\mathbf{d} - \mathbf{c}) = \begin{pmatrix} -2 \\ 4 \\ 3 \end{pmatrix} + \mu\left(\begin{pmatrix} 5 \\ -1 \\ -7 \end{pmatrix} - \begin{pmatrix} -2 \\ 4 \\ 3 \end{pmatrix}\right)$ *[1 mark]*

$$\mathbf{r} = \begin{pmatrix} -2 \\ 4 \\ 3 \end{pmatrix} + \mu\begin{pmatrix} 7 \\ -5 \\ -10 \end{pmatrix}$$ *[1 mark]*

c) Equation of line through AB:

$$\overrightarrow{AB}: \mathbf{r} = \mathbf{a} + t(\mathbf{b} - \mathbf{a}) = \begin{pmatrix} 1 \\ 5 \\ 9 \end{pmatrix} + t\begin{pmatrix} 2 \\ -3 \\ -8 \end{pmatrix}$$ *[1 mark]*

At intersection of lines:

$$\begin{pmatrix} 1 \\ 5 \\ 9 \end{pmatrix} + t\begin{pmatrix} 2 \\ -3 \\ -8 \end{pmatrix} = \begin{pmatrix} -2 \\ 4 \\ 3 \end{pmatrix} + \mu\begin{pmatrix} 7 \\ -5 \\ -10 \end{pmatrix}$$ *[1 mark]*

Any two of: $1 + 2t = -2 + 7\mu$
$$5 - 3t = 4 - 5\mu$$
$$9 - 8t = 3 - 10\mu$$ *[1 mark]*

Solving any two equations simultaneously gives
$t = 2$ or $\mu = 1$ *[1 mark]*

Substituting $t = 2$ in the equation of the line through AB (or $\mu = 1$ in the equation for l_1) gives: (5, –1, –7) *[1 mark]*

d) (i) Vectors needed are $\begin{pmatrix} 2 \\ -3 \\ -8 \end{pmatrix}$ and $\begin{pmatrix} 7 \\ -5 \\ -10 \end{pmatrix}$ (direction vector of l_1).

$$\begin{pmatrix} 2 \\ -3 \\ -8 \end{pmatrix} \cdot \begin{pmatrix} 7 \\ -5 \\ -10 \end{pmatrix} = 14 + 15 + 80 = 109 \text{ [1 mark]}$$

magnitude of 1st vector: $\sqrt{2^2 + (-3)^2 + (-8)^2} = \sqrt{77}$
magnitude of 2nd vector:
$$\sqrt{7^2 + (-5)^2 + (-10)^2} = \sqrt{174} \text{ [1 mark]}$$

$$\cos\theta = \frac{109}{\sqrt{77}\sqrt{174}} \text{ [1 mark]}$$

$$\Rightarrow \theta = 19.7° \text{ [1 mark]}$$

(ii) Draw a diagram:

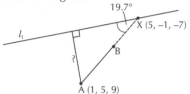

[1 mark for showing that the shortest distance is perpendicular to l_1]

X is the intersection point found in part c): (5, –1, –7).
Distance from A to X =
$$\sqrt{(5-1)^2 + (-1-5)^2 + (-7-9)^2} = \sqrt{308}$$
[1 mark]

Now you've got a right-angled triangle, so just use trig to find the side you want:
Shortest distance from A to l_1
$$= \sqrt{308} \times \sin 19.7° \text{ [1 mark]} = 5.9 \text{ units [1 mark]}$$

The tricky thing here is figuring out how to go about it. Drawing a diagram definitely helps you see what you know and what you need to work out. Often, you'll be meant to use something you worked out in a previous part of the question.

2 a) $-3(\mathbf{i} - 4\mathbf{j} + 2\mathbf{k}) = -3\mathbf{i} + 12\mathbf{j} - 6\mathbf{k}$, so lines are parallel. *[1 mark]*

b) **i** component: $3 + (\mu \times 1) = 2$ gives $\mu = -1$ *[1 mark]*
So $\mathbf{r} = (3\mathbf{i} - 3\mathbf{j} - 2\mathbf{k}) - 1(\mathbf{i} - 4\mathbf{j} + 2\mathbf{k}) = 2\mathbf{i} + \mathbf{j} - 4\mathbf{k}$ *[1 mark]*
This is the position vector of the point A(2, 1, –4)

c) B lies on l_2 so it has position vector of the form
$\mathbf{b} = (10\mathbf{i} - 21\mathbf{j} + 11\mathbf{k}) + \lambda(-3\mathbf{i} + 12\mathbf{j} - 6\mathbf{k})$ *[1 mark]*

So $\overrightarrow{AB} = \mathbf{b} - \mathbf{a}$
$= ((10\mathbf{i} - 21\mathbf{j} + 11\mathbf{k}) + \lambda(-3\mathbf{i} + 12\mathbf{j} - 6\mathbf{k})) - (2\mathbf{i} + \mathbf{j} - 4\mathbf{k})$
$= (8 - 3\lambda)\mathbf{i} + (-22 + 12\lambda)\mathbf{j} + (15 - 6\lambda)\mathbf{k}$ *[1 mark]*

You know the scalar product of the direction vector of l_1 and $\overrightarrow{AB}$ must equal zero as they're perpendicular:
$(\mathbf{i} - 4\mathbf{j} + 2\mathbf{k}).((8 - 3\lambda)\mathbf{i} + (-22 + 12\lambda)\mathbf{j} + (15 - 6\lambda)\mathbf{k})$ *[1 mark]*
$= (8 - 3\lambda) + (88 - 48\lambda) + (30 - 12\lambda)$
$= 126 - 63\lambda = 0$
$\Rightarrow \lambda = 2$ *[1 mark]*

Substitute in $\lambda = 2$ to find the position vector **b**:
$\mathbf{b} = (10\mathbf{i} - 21\mathbf{j} + 11\mathbf{k}) + 2(-3\mathbf{i} + 12\mathbf{j} - 6\mathbf{k})$ *[1 mark]*
$= 4\mathbf{i} + 3\mathbf{j} - \mathbf{k}$
Position vector of B = $4\mathbf{i} + 3\mathbf{j} - \mathbf{k}$ *[1 mark]*

You could have multiplied $\overrightarrow{AB}$ by the direction bit of the l_2 vector equation, as $\overrightarrow{AB}$ is perpendicular to both l_1 and l_2. But the numbers for the l_1 vector are smaller, making your calculations easier.

Answers

d) $\overrightarrow{AB} = \mathbf{b} - \mathbf{a}$
$= (4\mathbf{i} + 3\mathbf{j} - \mathbf{k}) - (2\mathbf{i} + \mathbf{j} - 4\mathbf{k}) = 2\mathbf{i} + 2\mathbf{j} + 3\mathbf{k}$ *[1 mark]*
$|\overrightarrow{AB}| = \sqrt{2^2 + 2^2 + 3^2} = \sqrt{17} = 4.1$ *[1 mark]*

3 a) At an intersection point: $\begin{pmatrix} 3 \\ 0 \\ -2 \end{pmatrix} + \lambda \begin{pmatrix} 1 \\ 3 \\ -2 \end{pmatrix} = \begin{pmatrix} 0 \\ 2 \\ 1 \end{pmatrix} + \mu \begin{pmatrix} 2 \\ -5 \\ -3 \end{pmatrix}$

[1 mark]

This gives equations: $3 + \lambda = 2\mu$
$3\lambda = 2 - 5\mu$
$-2 - 2\lambda = 1 - 3\mu$ *[1 mark]*

Solving the first two equations simultaneously gives:
$\lambda = -1$, $\mu = 1$ *[1 mark]*
Substituting these values in the third equation gives:
$-2 - 2(-1) = 1 - 3(1) \Rightarrow 0 \neq -2$ *[1 mark]*

So the lines don't intersect.

You could have solved any two of the equations simultaneously, then substituted the results in the remaining equation to show that they don't work and there's no intersection point.

b) (i) At the intersection point of PQ and l_1:
$\begin{pmatrix} 3 \\ 0 \\ -2 \end{pmatrix} + \lambda \begin{pmatrix} 1 \\ 3 \\ -2 \end{pmatrix} = \begin{pmatrix} 5 \\ 4 \\ -9 \end{pmatrix} + t \begin{pmatrix} 0 \\ 2 \\ 3 \end{pmatrix}$ *[1 mark]*

This gives equations: $3 + \lambda = 5$
$3\lambda = 4 + 2t$
$-2 - 2\lambda = -9 + 3t$

[1 mark for any two equations]
Solving two of these equations gives: $\lambda = 2$, $t = 1$
[1 mark]
Intersection point $= \begin{pmatrix} 5 \\ 4 \\ -9 \end{pmatrix} + 1 \begin{pmatrix} 0 \\ 2 \\ 3 \end{pmatrix} = \begin{pmatrix} 5 \\ 6 \\ -6 \end{pmatrix} = (5, 6, -6)$
[1 mark]

(ii) If perpendicular, the scalar product of direction vectors of lines will equal 0:
$\begin{pmatrix} 0 \\ 2 \\ 3 \end{pmatrix} \cdot \begin{pmatrix} 1 \\ 3 \\ -2 \end{pmatrix}$ *[1 mark]*

$= (0 \times 1) + (2 \times 3) + (3 \times -2) = 0$ *[1 mark]*

(iii) Call intersection point X.

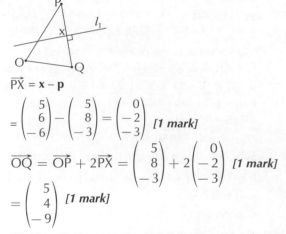

$\overrightarrow{PX} = \mathbf{x} - \mathbf{p}$

$= \begin{pmatrix} 5 \\ 6 \\ -6 \end{pmatrix} - \begin{pmatrix} 5 \\ 8 \\ -3 \end{pmatrix} = \begin{pmatrix} 0 \\ -2 \\ -3 \end{pmatrix}$ *[1 mark]*

$\overrightarrow{OQ} = \overrightarrow{OP} + 2\overrightarrow{PX} = \begin{pmatrix} 5 \\ 8 \\ -3 \end{pmatrix} + 2 \begin{pmatrix} 0 \\ -2 \\ -3 \end{pmatrix}$ *[1 mark]*

$= \begin{pmatrix} 5 \\ 4 \\ -9 \end{pmatrix}$ *[1 mark]*

The trick with this one is to realise that point Q lies the same distance from the intersection point as P does — drawing a quick sketch will definitely help.

4 a) $(\overrightarrow{OA}) \cdot (\overrightarrow{OB})$ *[1 mark]*
$= (3\mathbf{i} + 2\mathbf{j} + \mathbf{k}) \cdot (3\mathbf{i} - 4\mathbf{j} - \mathbf{k}) = 9 - 8 - 1 = 0$ *[1 mark]*
Therefore, side OA is perpendicular to side OB, and the triangle has a right angle. *[1 mark]*

You could also have found the lengths $|OA|$, $|OB|$ and $|AB|$ and shown by Pythagoras that AOB is a right-angled triangle $(|AB|^2 = |OA|^2 + |OB|^2)$.

b) $\overrightarrow{BA} = \mathbf{a} - \mathbf{b} = (3\mathbf{i} + 2\mathbf{j} + \mathbf{k}) - (3\mathbf{i} - 4\mathbf{j} - \mathbf{k}) = (6\mathbf{j} + 2\mathbf{k})$ *[1 mark]*
$\overrightarrow{BO} = -3\mathbf{i} + 4\mathbf{j} + \mathbf{k}$
$\overrightarrow{BA} \cdot \overrightarrow{BO} = 24 + 2 = 26$ *[1 mark]*
$|\overrightarrow{BA}| = \sqrt{6^2 + 2^2} = \sqrt{40}$
$|\overrightarrow{BO}| = \sqrt{(-3)^2 + 4^2 + 1^2} = \sqrt{26}$ *[1 mark]*
$\cos \angle ABO = \dfrac{\overrightarrow{BA} \cdot \overrightarrow{BO}}{|\overrightarrow{BA}| \cdot |\overrightarrow{BO}|} = \dfrac{26}{\sqrt{40}\sqrt{26}}$ *[1 mark]*
$\angle ABO = 36.3°$ *[1 mark]*

c) (i) $\overrightarrow{AC} = \mathbf{c} - \mathbf{a} = (3\mathbf{i} - \mathbf{j}) - (3\mathbf{i} + 2\mathbf{j} + \mathbf{k}) = (-3\mathbf{j} - \mathbf{k})$ *[1 mark]*
$|\overrightarrow{AC}| = \sqrt{(-3)^2 + (-1)^2} = \sqrt{10}$
$|\overrightarrow{OC}| = \sqrt{3^2 + (-1)^2} = \sqrt{10}$ *[1 mark]*
Sides AC and OC are the same length, so the triangle is isosceles. *[1 mark]*

(ii) You know side lengths AC and OC from part c)(i). Calculate length of OA:
$|\overrightarrow{OA}| = \sqrt{3^2 + 2^2 + 1^2} = \sqrt{14}$ *[1 mark]*

Now find the height of the triangle, x, using Pythagoras:
$x = \sqrt{(\sqrt{10})^2 - \left(\dfrac{\sqrt{14}}{2}\right)^2} = \sqrt{6.5}$ *[1 mark]*
Area $= \frac{1}{2}(\text{base} \times \text{height})$
$= \frac{1}{2}(\sqrt{14} \times \sqrt{6.5})$ *[1 mark]*
$= 4.77$ square units *[1 mark]*

d) (i) $\mathbf{r} = \mathbf{a} + t(\mathbf{b} - \mathbf{a})$
$\mathbf{r} = (3\mathbf{i} + 2\mathbf{j} + \mathbf{k}) + t((3\mathbf{i} - 4\mathbf{j} - \mathbf{k}) - (3\mathbf{i} + 2\mathbf{j} + \mathbf{k}))$ *[1 mark]*
$\mathbf{r} = (3\mathbf{i} + 2\mathbf{j} + \mathbf{k}) + t(-6\mathbf{j} - 2\mathbf{k})$ *[1 mark]*

(ii) $\mathbf{k}$ component: $1 - 2t = 1$, $t = 0$ *[1 mark]*
$\mathbf{r} = (3\mathbf{i} + 2\mathbf{j} + \mathbf{k}) + 0(-6\mathbf{j} - 2\mathbf{k}) = 3\mathbf{i} + 2\mathbf{j} + \mathbf{k}$
$a = 3$ *[1 mark]*, $b = 2$ *[1 mark]*

5 a) Use the coefficients of x, y and z in the equation of each plane as the components of the normal vectors.
So a normal to A is $\mathbf{n_1} = \begin{pmatrix} 3 \\ 4 \\ 2 \end{pmatrix}$, and a normal to B is $\mathbf{n_2} = \begin{pmatrix} 1 \\ -1 \\ 6 \end{pmatrix}$

[1 mark for both correct].

b) The angle between two planes is equal to the angle between their normal vectors *[1 mark]*.
So $\cos\theta = \dfrac{\mathbf{n_1} \cdot \mathbf{n_2}}{|\mathbf{n_1}||\mathbf{n_2}|} = \dfrac{(3 \times 1) + (4 \times -1) + (2 \times 6)}{\sqrt{3^2 + 4^2 + 2^2}\sqrt{1^2 + (-1)^2 + 6^2}}$
$= \dfrac{11}{\sqrt{29}\sqrt{38}}$
[1 mark for correct scalar product in numerator]
$= 0.3314$

So $\theta = \cos^{-1} 0.3314 = 70.6°$ *[1 mark]*

Answers

c) $\mathbf{r} = \begin{pmatrix} 5 \\ 1 \\ 3 \end{pmatrix} + \lambda \begin{pmatrix} -3 \\ 2 \\ 0 \end{pmatrix} = \begin{pmatrix} 5 - 3\lambda \\ 1 + 2\lambda \\ 3 \end{pmatrix}$

So at the point of intersection,
$x = 5 - 3\lambda$, $y = 1 + 2\lambda$, $z = 3$ *[1 mark]*.
Substitute these into the equation of plane A:
$3x + 4y + 2z = 1$
$\Rightarrow 3(5 - 3\lambda) + 4(1 + 2\lambda) + 2(3) = 1$ *[1 mark]*
$\Rightarrow 15 - 9\lambda + 4 + 8\lambda + 6 = 1$
$\Rightarrow 25 - \lambda = 1$
$\Rightarrow \lambda = 24$ *[1 mark]*
So at the point of intersection,
$x = 5 - 3(24) = -67$, $y = 1 + 2(24) = 49$, $z = 3$
The point of intersection is $(-67, 49, 3)$ *[1 mark]*.

C4 — Practice Exam One

1 a) When $x = 1.5$, $y = \dfrac{3 \ln 1.5}{(1.5)^2} = 0.54062$ *[1 mark]*, and when
$x = 3$, $y = \dfrac{3 \ln 3}{3^2} = 0.36620$ *[1 mark]*.

  b) $h = 0.5$. Putting h and the values from the table into the Trapezium Rule formula:
$A \approx \dfrac{0.5}{2}[0 + 2(0.54062 + 0.51986 + 0.43982) + 0.36620]$

$= \dfrac{1}{4}[2(1.5003) + 0.36620] = 0.8417$

  [3 marks available — 1 mark for putting the correct numbers into the trapezium rule formula, 1 mark for some correct working and 1 mark for correct answer]

2 a) $\dfrac{(x^2 - 9)(3x^2 - 10x - 8)}{(6x + 4)(x^2 - 7x + 12)} = \dfrac{(x + 3)(x - 3)(3x + 2)(x - 4)}{2(3x + 2)(x - 3)(x - 4)}$
$= \dfrac{x + 3}{2}$

  [2 marks available — 1 mark for correctly factorising numerator or denominator, 1 mark for correct final answer]

  b)
$$x^2 - 3x - 1 \overline{)\,2x^3 - x^2 - 16x + 3}$$
quotient $2x + 5$ remainder $x + 8$
$-\ 2x^3 - 6x^2 - 2x$
$5x^2 - 14x + 3$
$-\ 5x^2 - 15x - 5$
$x + 8$
so the quotient is $(2x + 5)$ and the remainder is $(x + 8)$.

  [4 marks available — up to 2 marks for correct working, 1 mark for quotient and 1 mark for remainder]

  If you'd tried to use the remainder theorem formula for this question, you'd have found it a bit tricky as the divisor doesn't factorise easily. Instead, you'd need to equate coefficients of x^3, x^2 and x, as well as putting in $x = 0$.

3 a) $5x^2 + 10x - 13 \equiv A(2 - x)(1 + 4x) + B(1 + 4x) + C(2 - x)^2$
  [1 mark]
Substitute values of x to make the brackets on the RHS equal to zero: *[1 mark]*
Let $x = 2$, then $5(2)^2 + 10(2) - 13 = B(1 + 4(2))$
$\Rightarrow 27 = 9B \Rightarrow B = 3$ *[1 mark]*
Let $x = -\dfrac{1}{4}$, then $5\left(-\dfrac{1}{4}\right)^2 + 10\left(-\dfrac{1}{4}\right) - 13 = C\left(2 - \left(-\dfrac{1}{4}\right)\right)^2$
$\Rightarrow \dfrac{5}{16} - \dfrac{5}{2} - 13 = C\dfrac{81}{16} \Rightarrow -\dfrac{243}{16} = \dfrac{81}{16}C \Rightarrow C = -3$ *[1 mark]*

Equate the terms in x^2:
$5 = -4A + C = -4A - 3 \Rightarrow 8 = -4A \Rightarrow A = -2$ *[1 mark]*
so $\dfrac{5x^2 + 10x - 13}{(2 - x)^2(1 + 4x)} = \dfrac{-2}{2 - x} + \dfrac{3}{(2 - x)^2} - \dfrac{3}{1 + 4x}$.

  b) $\displaystyle\int \dfrac{5x^2 + 10x - 13}{(2 - x)^2(1 + 4x)}\, dx \equiv \int \dfrac{-2}{2 - x} + \dfrac{3}{(2 - x)^2} - \dfrac{3}{1 + 4x}\, dx$

$= 2\ln|2 - x| + \dfrac{3}{2 - x} - \dfrac{3}{4}\ln|1 + 4x| + C$

  [4 marks available — 1 mark for using partial fractions from part a), 1 mark for each correct term of the answer (not including C)]

4   First, rearrange the equation to get x^2 on its own:
$e^y = x^2 - 1$, so $x^2 = e^y + 1$. Now put this into the formula for a volume of revolution:
$V = \pi \displaystyle\int_1^3 e^y + 1\, dy = \pi[e^y + y]_1^3$
$= \pi[(e^3 + 3) - (e^1 + 1)] = 60.84$

  [4 marks available — 1 mark for taking exponentials of both sides of the equation and rearranging to get x^2 on its own, 1 mark for correct formula for volume of revolution, 1 mark for correct integration and 1 mark for final answer]

5 a) $(1 - x)^{-\frac{1}{2}} \approx 1 + \left(-\dfrac{1}{2}\right)(-x) + \dfrac{\left(-\frac{1}{2}\right) \times \left(-\frac{3}{2}\right)}{1 \times 2}(-x)^2$
$+ \dfrac{\left(-\frac{1}{2}\right) \times \left(-\frac{3}{2}\right) \times \left(-\frac{5}{2}\right)}{1 \times 2 \times 3}(-x)^3$ *[1 mark]*
$= 1 + \dfrac{x}{2} + \dfrac{3}{8}x^2 + \dfrac{5}{16}x^3$ *[1 mark]*

  b) (i) $(25 - 4x)^{-\frac{1}{2}}$
$= (25)^{-\frac{1}{2}}\left(1 - \dfrac{4}{25}x\right)^{-\frac{1}{2}} = \dfrac{1}{5}\left(1 - \dfrac{4}{25}x\right)^{-\frac{1}{2}}$ *[1 mark]*
$= \dfrac{1}{5}\left(1 + \dfrac{1}{2}\left(\dfrac{4}{25}x\right) + \dfrac{3}{8}\left(\dfrac{4}{25}x\right)^2 + \dfrac{5}{16}\left(\dfrac{4}{25}x\right)^3\right)$ *[1 mark]*
$= \dfrac{1}{5}\left(1 + \dfrac{1}{2}\left(\dfrac{4}{25}x\right) + \dfrac{3}{8}\left(\dfrac{16}{625}x^2\right) + \dfrac{5}{16}\left(\dfrac{64}{15625}x^3\right)\right)$
$= \dfrac{1}{5}\left(1 + \dfrac{2}{25}x + \dfrac{6}{625}x^2 + \dfrac{4}{3125}x^3\right)$
$= \dfrac{1}{5} + \dfrac{2}{125}x$ *[1 mark]* $+ \dfrac{6}{3125}x^2 + \dfrac{4}{15625}x^3$ *[1 mark]*

   (ii) The expansion is valid for $\left|\dfrac{-4x}{25}\right| < 1 \Rightarrow \dfrac{|-4|\,\|x\|}{25} < 1$
$\Rightarrow |x| < \dfrac{25}{4}$ *[1 mark]*

6   $\sin 2\theta \equiv 2 \sin \theta \cos \theta$, so $3 \sin 2\theta \tan \theta \equiv 6 \sin \theta \cos \theta \tan \theta$
[1 mark]. As $\tan \theta \equiv \dfrac{\sin \theta}{\cos \theta}$,
$6 \sin \theta \cos \theta \tan \theta \equiv 6 \sin \theta \cos \theta \dfrac{\sin \theta}{\cos \theta} \equiv 6 \sin^2 \theta$,
so $3 \sin 2\theta \tan \theta = 5 \Rightarrow 6 \sin^2 \theta = 5$ *[1 mark]*.
Then $\sin^2 \theta = \dfrac{5}{6} \Rightarrow \sin \theta = \pm\sqrt{\dfrac{5}{6}} = \pm 0.9129$ *[1 mark]*.
Solving this for θ gives $\theta = 1.15, 1.99, 4.29, 5.13$ *[2 marks for all 4 correct answers, 1 mark for 2 correct answers]*.

Don't forget the solutions for the negative square root as well — they're easy to miss. Drawing a sketch here is really useful — you can see that there are 4 solutions you need to find:

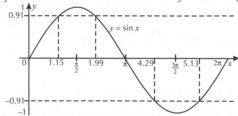

Answers

7 a) Vector equation of line through P and Q:

$$\mathbf{r} = \begin{pmatrix} -2 \\ -2 \\ -1 \end{pmatrix} + \mu\left(\begin{pmatrix} -5 \\ -4 \\ 1 \end{pmatrix} - \begin{pmatrix} -2 \\ -2 \\ -1 \end{pmatrix}\right)$$

$$\mathbf{r} = \begin{pmatrix} -2 \\ -2 \\ -1 \end{pmatrix} + \mu\begin{pmatrix} -3 \\ -2 \\ 2 \end{pmatrix} \quad \textbf{[1 mark]}$$

Where lines intersect:

$-1 + 2\lambda = -2 - 3\mu$

$2\lambda = -2 - 2\mu$

$3 + \lambda = -1 + 2\mu$ **[1 mark]**

Solving any pair of equations simultaneously gives $\lambda = -2$ and $\mu = 1$. **[1 mark]**

Substitute these values into the remaining equation to show that the lines intersect. E.g. $3 + \lambda = -1 + 2\mu$

$\Rightarrow 3 + -2 = -1 + 2(1) \Rightarrow 1 = 1$ **[1 mark]**

Intersection point:

$$\mathbf{r} = \begin{pmatrix} -2 \\ -2 \\ -1 \end{pmatrix} + \mu\begin{pmatrix} -3 \\ -2 \\ 2 \end{pmatrix} \Rightarrow \mathbf{r} = \begin{pmatrix} -2 \\ -2 \\ -1 \end{pmatrix} + 1\begin{pmatrix} -3 \\ -2 \\ 2 \end{pmatrix} = \begin{pmatrix} -5 \\ -4 \\ 1 \end{pmatrix}$$

$\Rightarrow (-5, -4, 1)$ **[1 mark]**

b) $\overrightarrow{OT} = 3\begin{pmatrix} -2 \\ -2 \\ -1 \end{pmatrix} = \begin{pmatrix} -6 \\ -6 \\ -3 \end{pmatrix}$ **[1 mark]**

$\overrightarrow{QT} = \begin{pmatrix} -6 \\ -6 \\ -3 \end{pmatrix} - \begin{pmatrix} -5 \\ -4 \\ 1 \end{pmatrix} = \begin{pmatrix} -1 \\ -2 \\ -4 \end{pmatrix}$ **[1 mark]**

$|\overrightarrow{QT}| = \sqrt{(-1)^2 + (-2)^2 + (-4)^2} = \sqrt{21}$ **[1 mark]**

c) $\overrightarrow{PV} = \begin{pmatrix} 0 \\ f \\ g \end{pmatrix} - \begin{pmatrix} -2 \\ -2 \\ -1 \end{pmatrix} = \begin{pmatrix} 2 \\ f+2 \\ g+1 \end{pmatrix}$ **[1 mark]**

The scalar product of $\overrightarrow{PV}$ and the direction vector of L_1 must be zero as they're perpendicular.

$(2 \times 2) + (2 \times (f + 2)) + (1 \times (g + 1)) = 0$ **[1 mark]**

$4 + 2f + 4 + g + 1 = 0 \Rightarrow 2f + g = -9$ **[1 mark]**

d) Find the angle between the two direction vectors,

i.e. between $\begin{pmatrix} 1 \\ 1 \\ 1 \end{pmatrix}$ and $\begin{pmatrix} 2 \\ 2 \\ 1 \end{pmatrix}$ **[1 mark]**:

$\begin{pmatrix} 1 \\ 1 \\ 1 \end{pmatrix} \cdot \begin{pmatrix} 2 \\ 2 \\ 1 \end{pmatrix} = (1 \times 2) + (1 \times 2) + (1 \times 1) = 5$ **[1 mark]**

$\sqrt{1^2 + 1^2 + 1^2} = \sqrt{3}$ and $\sqrt{2^2 + 2^2 + 1^2} = \sqrt{9} = 3$ **[1 mark]**

$\cos\alpha = \dfrac{\mathbf{a} \cdot \mathbf{b}}{|\mathbf{a}||\mathbf{b}|} = \dfrac{5}{3\sqrt{3}} = 0.962$

$\alpha = 15.739° = 15.8°$ (3 s.f.) **[1 mark]**.

e) Let R be the point $(-1, 0, 3)$. R lies on L_1, and Q lies on both L_1 and L_2 (from part a)):

Then $|\overrightarrow{QR}| = \sqrt{(-1 - -5)^2 + (0 - -4)^2 + (3 - 1)^2}$

$= \sqrt{16 + 16 + 4} = \sqrt{36} = 6$ **[1 mark]**

Shortest distance $= |\overrightarrow{QR}|\sin 15.739°$

$= 6\sin 15.739°$ **[1 mark]** $= 1.63$ **[1 mark]**

8 a) $\dfrac{dN}{dt} = k\sqrt{N}$, $k > 0$ **[1 mark for LHS, 1 mark for RHS]**

When $N = 36$, $\dfrac{dN}{dt} = 0.36$. Putting these values into the equation gives $0.36 = k\sqrt{36} = 6k \Rightarrow k = 0.06$ **[1 mark]** (the population is increasing so ignore the negative square root).

So the differential equation is $\dfrac{dN}{dt} = 0.06\sqrt{N}$ **[1 mark]**.

b) (i) $\dfrac{dN}{dt} = \dfrac{kN}{\sqrt{t}} \Rightarrow \int \dfrac{1}{N}\, dN = \int \dfrac{k}{\sqrt{t}}\, dt$

$\ln|N| = 2k\sqrt{t} + C$ **[1 mark]**

$\Rightarrow N = e^{2k\sqrt{t} + C} = Ae^{2k\sqrt{t}}$, where $A = e^C$ **[1 mark]**

For the initial population, $t = 0$, so $N = 25$ when $t = 0$. Putting these values into the equation:

$25 = Ae^0 \Rightarrow 25 = A$, so the equation for N is:

$N = 25e^{2k\sqrt{t}}$ **[1 mark]**.

(ii) When initial population has doubled, $N = 50$. Put this value and the value for k into the equation and solve for t:

$50 = 25e^{2(0.05)\sqrt{t}} \Rightarrow 2 = e^{0.1\sqrt{t}} \Rightarrow \ln 2 = 0.1\sqrt{t}$ **[1 mark]**

$10\ln 2 = \sqrt{t} \Rightarrow (10\ln 2)^2 = t \Rightarrow t = 48.045$

So it will take 48 weeks **[1 mark]** (to the nearest week) for the population to double.

c) (i) $\dfrac{dx}{dt} = 10\cos t$, $\dfrac{dy}{dt} = -600\sin 2t$ **[1 mark]**

So $\dfrac{dy}{dx} = \dfrac{dy}{dt} \times \dfrac{dt}{dx} = \dfrac{dy}{dt} \div \dfrac{dx}{dt}$

$= -600\sin 2t \div 10\cos t = \dfrac{-60\sin 2t}{\cos t}$

$= \dfrac{-60(2\sin t\cos t)}{\cos t} = -120\sin t$ **[1 mark]**

(ii) At a stationary point, $\dfrac{dy}{dx} = 0$. Putting $t = \pi$ into the expression from part (i) gives $-120\sin \pi = 0$, so this is a stationary point **[1 mark]**.

Putting $t = \pi$ into the equations for x and y gives:

$x = 10\sin \pi + 50 = 50$, $y = 300\cos 2\pi + 600 = 900$, so there are 50 ducks **[1 mark]** and 900 water boatmen **[1 mark]**.

(iii) Rewrite the equation for y using the identity $\cos 2t \equiv 1 - 2\sin^2 t$:

$y = 300\cos 2t + 600 = 300(1 - 2\sin^2 t) + 600$

$= 900 - 600\sin^2 t$ **[1 mark]**

Rearrange the equation for x to make $\sin t$ the subject:

$x = 10\sin t + 50 \Rightarrow \dfrac{x - 50}{10} = \sin t$ **[1 mark]**

Sub this into the equation for y:

$y = 900 - 600\sin^2 t = 900 - 600(\dfrac{x - 50}{10})^2$

$\Rightarrow y = 900 - 6(x^2 - 100x + 2500)$

$\Rightarrow y = -6x^2 + 600x - 14100$ **[1 mark]**

(iv) When $x = 45$, $y = -6(45)^2 + 600(45) - 14100 = 750$ **[1 mark]**

Answers

C4 — Practice Exam Two

1 a) $\dfrac{x^2 + 5x - 14}{2x^2 - 4x} = \dfrac{(x+7)(x-2)}{2x(x-2)} = \dfrac{x+7}{2x}$

   [2 marks available — 1 mark for factorising the numerator and denominator and 1 mark for correct answer]

   b) $\dfrac{x^2 + 5x - 14}{2x^2 - 4x} + \dfrac{14}{x(x-4)} = \dfrac{x+7}{2x} + \dfrac{14}{x(x-4)}$

   $= \dfrac{(x+7)(x-4)}{2x(x-4)} + \dfrac{2 \cdot 14}{2x(x-4)}$

   $= \dfrac{x^2 + 3x - 28 + 28}{2x(x-4)} = \dfrac{x^2 + 3x}{2x(x-4)}$

   $= \dfrac{x(x+3)}{2x(x-4)} = \dfrac{x+3}{2(x-4)}$

   [3 marks available — 1 mark for putting fractions over a common denominator, 1 mark for multiplying out and simplifying the numerator and 1 mark for cancelling to obtain correct answer]

2 a) $\sqrt{2}\cos\theta - 3\sin\theta \equiv R\cos(\theta + \alpha)$. Using the cos addition rule, $R\cos(\theta + \alpha) \equiv R\cos\theta\cos\alpha - R\sin\theta\sin\alpha$, so $R\cos\alpha = \sqrt{2}$ and $R\sin\alpha = 3$ **[1 mark]**.

   $\dfrac{R\sin\alpha}{R\cos\alpha} = \tan\alpha$, so $\tan\alpha = \dfrac{3}{\sqrt{2}}$

   Solving this gives $\alpha = 1.13$ (3 s.f.) **[1 mark]**.

   $R = \sqrt{(\sqrt{2})^2 + 3^2} = \sqrt{2 + 9} = \sqrt{11}$ **[1 mark]**,

   $\sqrt{2}\cos\theta - 3\sin\theta \equiv \sqrt{11}\cos(\theta + 1.13)$.

   b) If $\sqrt{2}\cos\theta - 3\sin\theta = 3$, then $\sqrt{11}\cos(\theta + 1.13) = 3$.

   So $\cos(\theta + 1.13) = \dfrac{3}{\sqrt{11}}$. Solving this gives $\theta + 1.13 = 0.441$ (3 s.f.) **[1 mark]**. $0 \le \theta \le 2\pi$, so the range of solutions is $1.13 \le \theta + 1.13 \le 7.41$ ($2\pi + 1.13$). The values of $\theta + 1.13$ within the range are $2\pi - 0.441 = 5.84$, $2\pi + 0.441 = 6.72$ **[1 mark]**. Subtracting 1.13 gives $\theta = 4.71, 5.59$ **[1 mark for both values correct]**.

   You can sketch the graph to help you find all the values of θ.

   c) $(\sqrt{2}\cos\theta - 3\sin\theta)^4 = (\sqrt{11}\cos(\theta + 1.13))^4$. The maximum values occurs when $\cos(\theta + 1.13) = \pm1$. This value is $(\sqrt{11})^4 = 121$ **[1 mark]**. Solving $\cos(\theta + 1.13) = 1$ gives the location of one maximum as $2\pi - 1.13 = 5.15$. Solving $\cos(\theta + 1.13) = -1$ gives the location of the other maximum as $2\pi - 1.13 = 2.01$. So the maximum values occur at $\theta = 2.01$ and $\theta = 5.15$. Since $(\sqrt{11}\cos(\theta + 1.13))^4 \ge 0$, the minimum value is 0 **[1 mark]** and it occurs when $\cos(\theta + 1.13) = 0$. Solving this gives the locations of the minimums at $\dfrac{\pi}{2} - 1.13 = 0.44$ and $\dfrac{3\pi}{2} - 1.13 = 3.58$ **[1 mark]**.

   This one was a bit nasty — if you didn't realise that $(\sqrt{11}\cos(\theta + 1.13))^4$ is never negative, you'd have got the minimum values wrong.

3 a) (i) The scalar product of perpendicular lines is 0.

   So $\mathbf{x} \cdot \mathbf{y} = 15p - 12 + 3q = 0$

   So $\mathbf{x} \cdot \mathbf{z} = \dfrac{3}{2}p - \dfrac{6}{5} + 4q = 0$ **[1 mark]**

   Solving simultaneously gives $p = \dfrac{4}{5}$ **[1 mark]**, $q = 0$ **[1 mark]**

   (ii) $|\mathbf{y}| = \sqrt{15^2 + (-20)^2 + 3^2} = \sqrt{634}$ **[1 mark]**

   Unit vector in the direction of $\mathbf{y}$

   $= \dfrac{1}{\sqrt{634}}(15\mathbf{i} - 20\mathbf{j} + 3\mathbf{k})$ **[1 mark]**

   Unit vectors have a magnitude of 1 — that's all there is to it.

   b) $\cos\alpha = \dfrac{\mathbf{y} \cdot \mathbf{z}}{|\mathbf{y}||\mathbf{z}|} = \dfrac{74.5}{(\sqrt{634}) \times \left(\sqrt{\left(\frac{3}{2}\right)^2 + (-2)^2 + 4^2}\right)}$ **[1 mark]**

   $= \dfrac{74.5}{118.77} = 0.627$ **[1 mark]** $\Rightarrow \alpha = 51°$ **[1 mark]**

4 a) $5x + 4 \equiv A(1 + 3x) + B(2 - x)$ **[1 mark]**

   let $x = 2$: $14 = 7A \Rightarrow A = 2$ **[1 mark]**.

   Equating coefficients of x: $5 = 3A - B \Rightarrow B = 1$ **[1 mark]**.

   b) $\dfrac{5x + 4}{(2-x)(1+3x)} \equiv \dfrac{2}{(2-x)} + \dfrac{1}{(1+3x)}$

   $\equiv 2(2-x)^{-1} + (1+3x)^{-1}$.

   Taking each term in turn, $2(2-x)^{-1} = 2\left(2\left(1 - \frac{1}{2}x\right)\right)^{-1}$

   $= 2\left(\frac{1}{2}\left(1 - \frac{1}{2}x\right)^{-1}\right) = \left(1 - \frac{1}{2}x\right)^{-1}$

   $\approx 1 + (-1)\left(-\frac{1}{2}x\right) + \dfrac{(-1)(-2)}{1 \times 2}\left(-\frac{1}{2}x\right)^2 + \dfrac{(-1)(-2)(-3)}{1 \times 2 \times 3}\left(-\frac{1}{2}x\right)^3$

   $= 1 + \frac{1}{2}x + \frac{1}{4}x^2 + \frac{1}{8}x^3$

   and $(1 + 3x)^{-1} \approx$
   $1 + (-1)(3x) + \dfrac{(-1)(-2)}{1 \times 2}(3x)^2 + \dfrac{(-1)(-2)(-3)}{1 \times 2 \times 3}(3x)^3$

   $= 1 - 3x + 9x^2 - 27x^3$

   So $2(2-x)^{-1} + (1+3x)^{-1} \approx$

   $1 + \frac{1}{2}x + \frac{1}{4}x^2 + \frac{1}{8}x^3 + 1 - 3x + 9x^2 - 27x^3$

   $= 2 - \frac{5}{2}x + \frac{37}{4}x^2 - \frac{215}{8}x^3$.

   [4 marks available in total:
   • 1 mark for correct binomial expansion of $(2-x)^{-1}$
   • 1 mark for correct binomial expansion of $(1+3x)^{-1}$
   • 1 mark for correct constant and x-terms in final answer
   • 1 mark for correct x^2- and x^3-terms in final answer]

   c) Expansion of $(1 + 3x)^{-1}$ is valid for $\left|\frac{3x}{1}\right| < 1 \Rightarrow \frac{3|x|}{1} < 1$
   $\Rightarrow |x| < \frac{1}{3}$

   Expansion of $(2 - x)^{-1}$ is valid for $\left|\frac{-x}{2}\right| < 1$
   $\Rightarrow \frac{|-1||x|}{2} < 1 \Rightarrow |x| < 2$

   The combined expansion is valid for the narrower of these two ranges. So the expansion in part b) is valid for $|x| < \frac{1}{3}$ **[1 mark]**.

5 a) The width of each strip is $(1 - 0)/4 = 0.25$. For 4 strips, the x-values are $x_0 = 0$, $x_1 = 0.25$, $x_2 = 0.5$, $x_3 = 0.75$ and $x_4 = 1$. Calculating the y-values at these points gives:
   $x_0 = 0$, $y_0 = 1$; $x_1 = 0.25$, $y_1 = 1.244$; $x_2 = 0.5$, $y_2 = 1.447$;
   $x_3 = 0.75$, $y_3 = 1.549$, $x_4 = 1$, $y_4 = 1.469$.
   [2 marks for all 5 values correct, or 1 mark for 3 or 4 values correct]. Putting these values into the formula for the Trapezium Rule gives:
   $A \approx 0.125[(1 + 1.469) + 2(1.244 + 1.447 + 1.549)]$ **[1 mark]**
   $= 1.37$ (3 s.f.) **[1 mark]**

Answers

b) To improve the approximation, increase n (i.e. use more strips) *[1 mark]*.

6 a) Use the x- or y-coordinate of H in the relevant parametric equation to find θ:

At H, $3 + 4\sin\theta = 5$

$\Rightarrow 4\sin\theta = 2$

$\Rightarrow \sin\theta = \frac{1}{2}$

$\Rightarrow \theta = \frac{\pi}{6}$

OR

At H, $\frac{1 + \cos 2\theta}{3} = \frac{1}{2}$

$\Rightarrow 1 + \cos 2\theta = \frac{3}{2}$

$\Rightarrow \cos 2\theta = \frac{1}{2}$

$\Rightarrow 2\theta = \frac{\pi}{3}$

$\Rightarrow \theta = \frac{\pi}{6}$

$\theta = -\frac{\pi}{6}$ is another solution to the equation, but this value wouldn't give $x = 5$, so you can ignore it.

[2 marks available — 1 mark for substituting one coordinate of H into the correct parametric equation, 1 mark finding the correct value of θ.]

b) Rearrange the parametric equation for x to make $\sin\theta$ the subject:

$x = 3 + 4\sin\theta \Rightarrow \sin\theta = \frac{x - 3}{4}$ *[1 mark]*

Use the identity $\cos 2\theta \equiv 1 - 2\sin^2\theta$ to rewrite the parametric equation for y in terms of $\sin\theta$:

$y = \frac{1 + \cos 2\theta}{3}$

$\equiv \frac{1 + (1 - 2\sin^2\theta)}{3}$ *[1 mark]*

$= \frac{2 - 2\sin^2\theta}{3}$

$= \frac{2}{3}(1 - \sin^2\theta)$ *[1 mark]*

$= \frac{2}{3}\left(1 - \left(\frac{x - 3}{4}\right)^2\right)$ *[1 mark]*

$= \frac{2}{3}\left(1 - \frac{(x - 3)^2}{16}\right)$

$= \frac{2}{3}\left(\frac{16 - (x^2 - 6x + 9)}{16}\right)$

$= \frac{2}{3}\left(\frac{-x^2 + 6x + 7}{16}\right)$

$= \frac{-x^2 + 6x + 7}{24}$ *[1 mark]*

c) $-\frac{\pi}{2} \leq \theta \leq \frac{\pi}{2} \Rightarrow -1 \leq \sin\theta \leq 1$ *[1 mark]*

$\Rightarrow -4 \leq 4\sin\theta \leq 4$

$\Rightarrow -1 \leq 3 + 4\sin\theta \leq 7$

$\Rightarrow -1 \leq x \leq 7$ *[1 mark]*

d) $y^2 = \left(\frac{-x^2 + 6x + 7}{24}\right)^2$

$= \frac{1}{576}(-x^2 + 6x + 7)(-x^2 + 6x + 7)$

$= \frac{1}{576}\left(\begin{array}{c}-x^2(-x^2 + 6x + 7) + 6x(-x^2 + 6x + 7) \\ + 7(-x^2 + 6x + 7)\end{array}\right)$

$= \frac{1}{576}\left(\begin{array}{c}x^4 - 6x^3 - 7x^2 - 6x^3 + 36x^2 \\ + 42x - 7x^2 + 42x + 49\end{array}\right)$

$= \frac{1}{576}(x^4 - 12x^3 + 22x^2 + 84x + 49)$

[3 marks available — 1 mark for correct expansion for y², 1 mark for simplifying expansion, 1 mark for final answer]

e) Substitute the expression for y^2 and the x-limits into the formula $V = \pi \int y^2 \, dx$:

$V = \frac{\pi}{576}\int_{-1}^{7} x^4 - 12x^3 + 22x^2 + 84x + 49 \, dx$

$= \frac{\pi}{576}\left[\frac{x^5}{5} - 3x^4 + \frac{22}{3}x^3 + 42x^2 + 49x\right]_{-1}^{7}$

$= \frac{\pi}{576}\left(\begin{array}{c}(3361.4 - 7203 + 2515.333 + 2058 + 343) \\ -(-0.2 - 3 - 7.333 + 42 - 49)\end{array}\right)$

$= \frac{\pi}{576}(1074.733 + 17.533) = \frac{\pi}{576}(1092.266)$

$= 5.957 \text{ in}^3$ (4 s.f.)

[6 marks available — 1 mark for correct formula for volume of revolution, 2 marks for correctly integrating each term, 2 marks for substituting in x-values correctly, 1 mark for final answer]

7 a) First, rearrange the equation into the form $\frac{dP}{dt} = f(t)g(P)$:

$\frac{dP}{dt} = 2P\frac{e^{2t} + t}{e^{2t} + t^2}$.

Then separate out the variables and integrate:

$\frac{1}{P} \, dP = \frac{2(e^{2t} + t)}{e^{2t} + t^2} \, dt \Rightarrow \int \frac{1}{P} \, dP = \int \frac{2(e^{2t} + t)}{e^{2t} + t^2} \, dt$

$\Rightarrow \ln|P| = \ln|e^{2t} + t^2| + C$

$\Rightarrow P = A(e^{2t} + t^2)$.

[7 marks available — 1 mark for separating variables, 1 mark for integrating LHS correctly, 1 mark for spotting that RHS is of the form f'(t)/f(t), 1 mark for integrating this correctly, 1 mark for adding C, 1 mark for simplifying to remove ln, 1 mark for rearranging to get in terms of P]

For this one, you need to spot that $2(e^{2t} + t)$ is the derivative of $e^{2t} + t^2$. A is just a constant ($= e^C$). You don't need the modulus signs around P as you're told that $P \geq 0$.

b) (i) Substitute $P = 3$ and $t = 0$ *[1 mark]* into the equation above to find the value of A:

$3 = A(e^0 + 0^2) \Rightarrow 3 = A \cdot 1 \Rightarrow A = 3$.

So the particular solution is $P = 3(e^{2t} + t^2)$. *[1 mark]*

(ii) When $t = 3$, $P = 3(e^{2\cdot3} + 3^2) = 3e^6 + 27$. *[1 mark]*

So $P = 3e^6 + 27 = 1237.28 = 1240$ puffins (to the nearest 10) *[1 mark]*.

c) $\cos 2A \equiv 2\cos^2 A - 1 \Rightarrow 1 + \cos 2A \equiv 2\cos^2 A$

$\Rightarrow \frac{1 + \cos 2A}{2} = \cos^2 A$. Replacing A with $\frac{x}{2}$ gives:

$\frac{1 + \cos x}{2} \equiv \frac{1}{2}\left(1 + \cos 2\left(\frac{x}{2}\right)\right)$ *[1 mark]*

$= \frac{1}{2}\left(1 + \left(2\cos^2\frac{x}{2} - 1\right)\right)$ *[1 mark]*

$= \frac{1}{2}\left(2\cos^2\frac{x}{2}\right) = \cos^2\frac{x}{2}$ *[1 mark]*

d) If $\cos^2\frac{x}{2} = 0.75$, then $\frac{1 + \cos x}{2} = 0.75$.

So $1 + \cos x = 1.5$

$\cos x = 0.5 \Rightarrow x = \frac{\pi}{3}, \frac{5\pi}{3}$.

So from the graph, the range of values for which $y < 0.75$ is $\frac{\pi}{3} < x < \frac{5\pi}{3}$.

[4 marks available — 1 mark for rearranging equation to get in terms of cos x, 1 mark for each correct x-limit and 1 mark for correct final range]

You should know the solutions to $\cos x = 0.5$ from the trig triangles from Section 2.

Answers

S2 Section 1 — Bivariate Data
Warm-up Questions

1) a)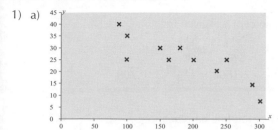

b) First you need to find these values:
$\sum x = 2060$, $\sum y = 277$, $\sum x^2 = 442\,800$,
$\sum y^2 = 7799$ and $\sum xy = 46\,000$.
Then put these values into the PMCC formula:

$$\frac{46\,000 - \dfrac{[2060][277]}{11}}{\sqrt{\left(442\,800 - \dfrac{[2060]^2}{11}\right)\left(7799 - \dfrac{[277]^2}{11}\right)}}$$

$$= \frac{46000 - \dfrac{570\,620}{11}}{\sqrt{\left(442\,800 - \dfrac{4\,243\,600}{11}\right)\left(7799 - \dfrac{76\,729}{11}\right)}}$$

$$= \frac{-5874.5455}{\sqrt{57\,018.1818 \times 823.6364}} = -0.857 \text{ (to 3 sig.fig.)}$$

c) The sample was randomly selected and the bulk of the data-points on the scatter graph look like they would fall inside an ellipse, so the hypothesis test that follows should be valid. This is a two-tailed test at a 5% significance level with $n = 11$.
H_0: $r = 0$ and H_1: $r \neq 0$.
From the table of critical values for the PMCC, the critical value is 0.6021. Since the PMCC from b) is less than –0.6021, you can reject H_0 and conclude that this data provides evidence at a 5% significance level of a correlation between the volume of alcoholic drinks and their alcohol concentration.

Don't panic about that nasty ol' PMCC equation. You need to know how to USE it, but they give you the formula in the exam, so you don't need to REMEMBER it. Hurrah.

2)

Physics	54	34	23	57	56	58	13	65	69
English	16	73	89	83	23	81	56	62	61
Physics rank	6	7	8	4	5	3	9	2	1
English rank	9	4	1	2	8	3	7	5	6
d	3	3	7	2	3	0	2	3	5
d^2	9	9	49	4	9	0	4	9	25

So $\sum d^2 = 118$, and
$$r_s = 1 - \frac{6\sum d^2}{n(n^2 - 1)} = 1 - \frac{6 \times 118}{9(9^2 - 1)}$$
$$= 1 - \frac{708}{720} = 0.0167 \text{ (to 3 sig.fig.)}$$
You need to carry out a two-tailed test at a 5% significance level with $n = 9$.
H_0: No association between the marks in Physics and English, and H_1: Some association.

From the table of critical values for the SRCC, the critical value is 0.7000. Since the SRCC here is not greater than 0.7000, you cannot reject H_0. Therefore this data does not provide evidence of an association between the marks in Physics and English exams.

3) a) **Independent**: the annual number of sunny days
Dependent: the annual number of volleyball-related injuries

b) **Independent**: the annual number of rainy days
Dependent: the annual number of Monopoly-related injuries

c) **Independent**: a person's disposable income
Dependent: a person's spending on luxuries

d) **Independent**: the number of cups of tea drunk per day
Dependent: the number of trips to the loo per day

e) **Independent**: the number of festival tickets sold
Dependent: the number of pairs of Wellington boots bought

4) a) (i) $S_{rr} = 26\,816.78 - \dfrac{517.4^2}{10} = 46.504$

(ii) $S_{rw} = 57\,045.5 - \dfrac{517.4 \times 1099}{10} = 183.24$

b) $b = \dfrac{S_{rw}}{S_{rr}} = \dfrac{183.24}{46.504} = 3.94$

c) $a = \overline{w} - b\overline{r}$, where $\overline{w} = \dfrac{\sum w}{10} = 109.9$
and $\overline{r} = \dfrac{\sum r}{10} = 51.74$
So $a = 109.9 - 3.94 \times 51.74 = -94.0$

d) The equation of the regression line is: $w = 3.94r - 94.0$

e) When $r = 60$, the regression line gives an estimate for w of:
$w = 3.94 \times 60 - 94.0 = 142.4$ g

f) This estimate might not be very reliable because it uses an r-value from outside the range of the original data.
It is extrapolation.

In the formula booklet, you'll be given the equations for finding a regression line in terms of x and y — but you might need to use them with other variables too (as in this example, where you had r and w). Practise USING these equations, otherwise the formula booklet will just be a blur of incomprehensible squiggles...

Exam Questions

1) a)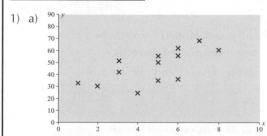

[2 marks for all points plotted correctly, or 1 mark if at least 3 points are plotted correctly.]

Aren't scatter diagrams pretty... Just make sure you're not so distracted by their artistic elegance that you forget to be accurate and lose easy marks.

Answers

b) You need to work out these sums:
$$\sum x = 61, \sum y = 606,$$
$$\sum x^2 = 335, \sum y^2 = 30\,588, \sum xy = 3070$$

Then:
$$S_{xx} = \sum x^2 - \frac{(\sum x)^2}{n} = 335 - \frac{61^2}{13} = \frac{634}{13}$$
$$S_{yy} = \sum y^2 - \frac{(\sum y)^2}{n} = 30\,588 - \frac{606^2}{13} = \frac{30\,408}{13}$$
$$S_{xy} = \sum xy - \frac{(\sum x)(\sum y)}{n}$$
$$= 3070 - \frac{61 \times 606}{13} = \frac{2944}{13}$$

[3 marks available — 1 for each correct term]

This means:
$$r = \frac{S_{xy}}{\sqrt{S_{xx}S_{yy}}} = \frac{\left(\frac{2944}{13}\right)}{\sqrt{\left(\frac{634}{13}\right)\left(\frac{30\,408}{13}\right)}}$$
$$= \frac{2944}{\sqrt{634 \times 30\,408}} = 0.671\,(\text{to 3 d.p.}).$$

[1 mark]

c) The sample was randomly selected and the bulk of the data-points on the scatter graph look like they would fall inside an ellipse, so the hypothesis test that follows should be valid *[1 mark]*. This is a two-tailed test *[1 mark]* at a 5% significance level with $n = 13$.
$H_0: r = 0$ and $H_1: r \neq 0$ *[1 mark]*.
From the table of critical values for the PMCC, the critical value is 0.5529 *[1 mark]*. Since the PMCC here is greater than the critical value, you can reject H_0 *[1 mark]* and conclude that this data provides evidence at a 5% significance level of a correlation between the number of catch-up sessions attended by a Year-7 pupil at that school during the year and their mark on the maths test *[1 mark]*.

2 a)
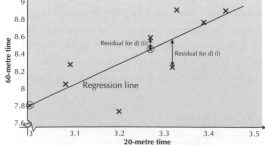

[2 marks for all points plotted correctly, or 1 mark if at least 3 points are plotted correctly.]

b) It's best to make a table like this one, first:

20-metre time, x	3.39	3.2	3.09	3.32	3.33	3.27	3.44	3.08	Totals 26.12
60-metre time, y	8.78	7.73	8.28	8.25	8.91	8.59	8.9	8.05	67.49
x^2	11.4921	10.24	9.5481	11.0224	11.0889	10.6929	11.8336	9.4864	85.4044
xy	29.7642	24.736	25.5852	27.39	29.6703	28.0893	30.616	24.794	220.645

[2 marks for at least three correct totals, or 1 mark if one total found correctly.]

Then: $S_{xy} = 220.645 - \dfrac{26.12 \times 67.49}{8} = 0.29015$

[1 mark]

$S_{xx} = 85.4044 - \dfrac{26.12^2}{8} = 0.1226$

[1 mark]

Then the gradient b is given by:
$$b = \frac{S_{xy}}{S_{xx}} = \frac{0.29015}{0.1226} = 2.3666$$
[1 mark]

And the intercept a is given by:
$$a = \bar{y} - b\bar{x} = \frac{\sum y}{n} - b\frac{\sum x}{n}$$
$$= \frac{67.49}{8} - 2.3666 \times \frac{26.12}{8} = 0.709$$

[1 mark]

So the regression line has equation: $y = 2.367x + 0.709$

[1 mark]

To plot the line, find two points that the line passes through. A regression line always passes through $(\bar{x}, \bar{y})$, which here is (3.27, 8.44). Then put $x = 3$ (say) to find that the line also passes through (3, 7.81).
Now plot these points (in circles) on your scatter diagram, and draw the regression line through them *[1 mark for plotting the line correctly]*.

Hmm, lots of fiddly things to calculate there. Remember, you get marks for method as well as correct answers, so take it step by step and show all your workings.

c) (i) $y = 2.367 \times 3.15 + 0.709 = 8.17$ (to 3 sig. fig.), (8.16 if $b = 2.3666$ used) *[1 mark]*

This should be reliable, since we are using interpolation within the range of x for which we have data *[1 mark]*.

(ii) $y = 2.367 \times 3.88 + 0.709 = 9.89$ (to 3 sig. fig.) *[1 mark]*

This could be unreliable, since we are extrapolating beyond the range of the data *[1 mark]*.

d) (i) residual = $8.25 - (2.367 \times 3.32 + 0.709)$
$= -0.317$ (3 sig. fig.), (-0.316 if $b = 2.3666$ used)

[1 mark for calculation, 1 mark for plotting residual correctly]

(ii) residual = $8.59 - (2.367 \times 3.27 + 0.709)$
$= 0.141$ (3 sig. fig.), (0.142 if $b = 2.3666$ used)

[1 mark for calculation, 1 mark for plotting residual correctly]

3 a) Put the values into the correct PMCC formula:
$$\text{PMCC} = \frac{S_{xy}}{\sqrt{S_{xx}S_{yy}}} = \frac{6333}{\sqrt{155\,440 \times 395.5}}$$
$$= \frac{6333}{\sqrt{61\,476\,520}} = 0.808\,(\text{to 3 d.p.})$$
[1 mark for correctly substituting the values into the PMCC formula, and 1 mark for the correct final answer.]

b) This is a one-tailed test *[1 mark]* at a 1% significance level with $n = 10$.
$H_0: r = 0$ and $H_1: r > 0$ *[1 mark]*.
From the table of critical values for the PMCC, the critical value is 0.7155 *[1 mark]*. Since the PMCC here is greater than the critical value, you can reject H_0 *[1 mark]* and conclude that this data provides evidence at a 1% significance level of a positive correlation between the

distance in miles cycled during a training ride and the number of calories eaten at lunch for the members of the cycling club *[1 mark]*.

c) For this test to be valid, the underlying distribution should be bivariate normal *[1 mark]*. If this is the case, the bulk of the data points should form a roughly elliptical shape on a scatter diagram *[1 mark]*.

4 a) (i) At $x = 12.5$,
   $y = 211.599 + (9.602 \times 12.5) = 331.624$ *[1 mark]*

   (ii) At $x = 14.7$,
   $y = 211.599 + (9.602 \times 14.7) = 352.748$ *[1 mark]*

b) (i) Using the equation:
   'Residual = Observed y-value – Estimated y-value':
   At $x = 12.5$: Residual = $332.5 - 331.624 = 0.876$
   [1 mark]

   (ii) At $x = 14.7$: Residual = $352.1 - 352.748 = -0.648$
   [1 mark]

   And that's the end of that — Section 1 done and dusted.

S2 Section 2 — Poisson Distribution
Warm-up Questions

1) a) $P(X = 2) = \dfrac{e^{-3.25} \times 3.25^2}{2!} = 0.2048$ (to 4 d.p.).

b) $P(X = 1) = \dfrac{e^{-3.25} \times 3.25}{1!} = 0.1260$ (to 4 d.p.).

c) $P(X = 0) = \dfrac{e^{-3.25} \times 3.25^0}{0!} = 0.0388$ (to 4 d.p.).

d) $P(X < 3) = P(X = 0) + P(X = 1) + P(X = 2)$
   $= 0.0388 + 0.1260 + 0.2048 = 0.3696$

e) $P(X \geq 3) = 1 - P(X < 3)$
   $= 1 - 0.3696 = 0.6304$

2) a) $P(X = 2) = \dfrac{e^{-8.7} \times 8.7^2}{2!} = 0.0063$ (to 4 d.p.).

b) $P(X = 1) = \dfrac{e^{-8.7} \times 8.7}{1!} = 0.0014$ (to 4 d.p.).

c) $P(X = 0) = \dfrac{e^{-8.7} \times 8.7^0}{0!} = 0.0002$ (to 4 d.p.).

d) $P(X < 3) = P(X = 0) + P(X = 1) + P(X = 2)$
   $= 0.0002 + 0.0014 + 0.0063 = 0.0079$

e) $P(X \geq 3) = 1 - P(X < 3)$
   $= 1 - 0.0079 = 0.9921$

   You could do this question using tables if you like that kind of thing.

3) a) $E(X) = Var(X) = 8$
   standard deviation $= \sigma = \sqrt{8} = 2.828$ (to 3 d.p.).

b) $E(X) = Var(X) = 12.11$
   standard deviation $= \sigma = \sqrt{12.11} = 3.480$ (to 3 d.p.).

c) $E(X) = Var(X) = 84.2227$
   standard deviation $= \sigma = \sqrt{84.2227} = 9.177$ (to 3 d.p.).

4) Using tables:
a) (i) $P(X \leq \mu) = P(X \leq 9) = 0.5874$
   (ii) $P(X \leq \mu - \sigma) = P(X \leq 6) = 0.2068$

b) (i) $P(X \leq \mu) = P(X \leq 4) = 0.6288$
   (ii) $P(X \leq \mu - \sigma) = P(X \leq 2) = 0.2381$

5) a) The defective products occur randomly, singly and (on average) at a constant rate, and the random variable represents the number of 'events' (i.e. defective products) within a fixed period, so this would follow a Poisson distribution.

b) There is a fixed number of trials in this situation, and so this situation would be modelled by a binomial distribution. (Or you could say it won't follow a Poisson distribution, as the events don't occur at a constant rate over the 25 trials.)

c) If the random variable represents the number of people joining the queue within a fixed period, and assuming that the people join the queue randomly, singly and (on average) at a constant rate, then this would follow a Poisson distribution.

   You do need to make a couple of assumptions here — the Poisson model wouldn't work if you had, say, big groups of factory workers all coming in together a couple of minutes after the lunchtime hooter sounds.

d) The mistakes occur randomly, singly and (on average) at a constant rate, and the random variable represents the number of mistakes within a fixed 'period' (i.e. the number of pages in the document), so this would follow a Poisson distribution.

6) a) The number of atoms decaying in an hour would follow the Poisson distribution Poisson(2000). So the number decaying in a minute would follow Poisson(2000 ÷ 60) = Poisson(33.3).

b) The number of atoms decaying in a day would follow Poisson(2000 × 24) = Poisson(48 000).

7) a) If X represents the number of atoms from the first sample decaying per minute, then $X \sim$ Poisson(60). And if Y represents the number of atoms from the second sample decaying per minute, then $Y \sim$ Poisson(90). So $X + Y$ (the total number of atoms decaying per minute) $\sim$ Poisson(60 + 90) = Poisson(150).

b) The total number of atoms decaying per hour would be distributed as Poisson(150 × 60) = Poisson(9000).

8) a) $P(X \leq 2) = 0.0138$
b) $P(X \leq 7) = 0.4530$
c) $P(X \leq 5) = 0.1912$
d) $P(X < 9) = P(X \leq 8) = 0.5925$
e) $P(X \geq 8) = 1 - P(X < 8) = 1 - P(X \leq 7)$
   $= 1 - 0.4530 = 0.5470$
f) $P(X > 1) = 1 - P(X \leq 1) = 1 - 0.0030 = 0.9970$
g) $P(X > 7) = 1 - P(X \leq 7) = 1 - 0.4530 = 0.5470$
h) $P(X = 6) = P(X \leq 6) - P(X \leq 5) = 0.3134 - 0.1912 = 0.1222$
i) $P(X = 4) = P(X \leq 4) - P(X \leq 3) = 0.0996 - 0.0424 = 0.0572$
j) $P(X = 3) = P(X \leq 3) - P(X \leq 2) = 0.0424 - 0.0138 = 0.0286$

Answers

9) If X represents the number of geese in a random square metre of field, then $X \sim$ Poisson(1) — since the 'rate' at which geese occur is constant, they're randomly scattered, and geese only occur singly.

a) $P(X = 0) = \dfrac{e^{-1} \times 1^0}{0!} = 0.3679$

b) $P(X = 1) = \dfrac{e^{-1} \times 1^1}{1!} = 0.3679$

c) $P(X = 2) = \dfrac{e^{-1} \times 1^2}{2!} = 0.1839$

d) $P(X > 2) = 1 - P(X \le 2) = 1 - (0.3679 + 0.3679 + 0.1839)$
$= 1 - 0.9197 = 0.0803$

This is one of those questions where you could use either your Poisson tables or the probability function.

10) a) No — n is not very large, and p is not very small.

b) Yes — n is large, and p is small, so approximate with Poisson(7).

c) Not really — n is large, but p isn't as small as you'd like.

d) Not really — n is quite small (and so you don't really need to approximate it anyway).

e) This is perfect for a Poisson approximation — n is enormous and p is tiny. It should follow Poisson(0.1) very closely.

f) If Y represents the number of 'successes' in 80 trials, then define a new random variable X representing the number of 'failures' in those 80 trials. Then $X \sim$ B(80, 0.1). Since n is quite large, and p is quite small, you could approximate X with Poisson(80 × 0.1) = Poisson(8). Then $Y = 80 - X$.

11) Mean $= \dfrac{\sum x}{n} = \dfrac{13}{15} = 0.867$ (to 3 d.p.).

Variance $= \dfrac{n}{n-1}\left[\dfrac{\sum x^2}{n} - \left(\dfrac{\sum x}{n}\right)^2\right]$
$= \dfrac{15}{14}\left[\dfrac{23}{15} - \left(\dfrac{13}{15}\right)^2\right] = 0.838$ (to 3 d.p.).

The mean and the variance are very close to each other, which suggests that the data may be taken from a population that follows a Poisson distribution.

Exam Questions

1 a) Events need to happen at a constant average rate *[1 mark]* and singly ("one at a time") *[1 mark]*.

You could also have had "events occur randomly" or "independently".

b) (i) If X represents the number of chaffinches visiting the observation spot, then $X \sim$ Poisson(7) *[1 mark]*.
Using tables, $P(X < 4) = P(X \le 3) = 0.0818$ *[1 mark]*.

(ii) $P(X \ge 7) = 1 - P(X < 7) = 1 - P(X \le 6)$ *[1 mark]*
$= 1 - 0.4497 = 0.5503$ *[1 mark]*

(iii) $P(X = 9) = P(X \le 9) - P(X \le 8)$ *[1 mark]*
$= 0.8305 - 0.7291 = 0.1014$ *[1 mark]*

Or you could work this last one out using the formula:
$P(X = 9) = \dfrac{e^{-7}7^9}{9!} = 0.1014$

— you get the same answer either way, obviously.

c) The number of birds of any species visiting per hour would follow the distribution Poisson(22 + 7) = Poisson(29) *[1 mark]*. So the total number of birds visiting in a random 15-minute period will follow Poisson(29 ÷ 4) = Poisson(7.25) *[1 mark]*.
$P(X = 3) = \dfrac{e^{-7.25} \times 7.25^3}{3!}$ *[1 mark]*
$= 0.045$ (to 3 d.p.) *[1 mark]*.

2 a) (i) If the mean is 20, then the number of calls per hour follows Poisson(20). So the number of calls in a random 30-minute period follows Poisson(20 ÷ 2) = Poisson(10) *[1 mark]*.
Using tables for $\lambda = 10$:
$P(X = 8) = P(X \le 8) - P(X \le 7)$ *[1 mark]*
$= 0.3328 - 0.2202 = 0.1126$ *[1 mark]*

Or you could work this out using the formula:
$P(X = 8) = \dfrac{e^{-10}10^8}{8!} = 0.1126$.

(ii) $P(X > 8) = 1 - P(X \le 8)$ *[1 mark]*
$= 1 - 0.3328 = 0.6672$ *[1 mark]*

b) In this context, independently means that receiving a phone call at one particular instant does not affect whether or not a call will be received at a different instant. *[1 mark]*.

3 a) The number of trials here is fixed (= 400) and the probability of the engineer being unable to fix a fault is constant (= 0.02). This means X (the total number of unsuccessful call-outs) will follow a binomial distribution *[1 mark]*. In fact, $X \sim$ B(400, 0.02) *[1 mark]*.

b) (i) To approximate a binomial distribution B(n, p) with a Poisson distribution, n should be large *[1 mark]* and p should be small *[1 mark]*.

(ii) Poisson(400 × 0.02) = Poisson(8) *[1 mark]*.

(iii) Mean = 8 and variance = 8 *[1 mark]*.

(iv) P(engineer unable to fix fewer than 10 faults)
$= P(X < 10) = P(X \le 9)$ *[1 mark]*.
Using Poisson tables for $\lambda = 8$:
$P(X \le 9) = 0.7166$ *[1 mark]*.

S2 Section 3 — Contingency Tables
Warm-up Questions

1) a) (i) 18
(ii) 21
(iii) 27
(iv) 15
(v) 136

b)

Expected frequencies		Type of car			
		Saloon	Estate	Other	Total
Number of occupants	1 person	40	24.12	15.88	80
	2 people	20.5	12.36	8.14	41
	3 or more people	7.5	4.52	2.98	15
	Total	68	41	27	136

Answers

c) The expected frequencies are reasonably close to the observed frequencies. Although there are discrepancies (e.g. the number of estates with 1 person in was slightly lower than expected), these discrepancies are typically fairly small.

2) The 1% point of $\chi^2_{(4)}$ = value of x where $P(X > x) = 0.01$ (or 1%). Using the χ^2 table, the critical value is 13.28. Since 8.3 < 13.28, there is no evidence at the 1% level of an association between the variables.

3) a) H_0: there is no association between the variables 'age' and 'marital status'.
   H_1: there is some association between the variables 'age' and 'marital status'.

b)
Expected frequencies		Marital status				
		Single	Married	Divorced	Other	**Total**
Age (years)	Less than 30	16.95	26.05	5.38	6.62	**55**
	30 or over	24.05	36.95	7.62	9.38	**78**
	Total	**41**	**63**	**13**	**16**	**133**

c)
Contribution		Marital status			
		Single	Married	Divorced	Other
Age (years)	Less than 30	5.96	3.88	0.03	0.02
	30 or over	4.20	2.73	0.02	0.02

d) $\chi^2 = 16.86$.
   This has $(2 - 1) \times (4 - 1) = 1 \times 3 = 3$ degrees of freedom.

e) Since all the expected frequencies are above 5, $X^2 \sim \chi^2_{(3)}$ (approximately). At the 5% level of significance, the critical value is 7.815. Since here, $\chi^2 = 16.86 > 7.815$, the result is significant and we can reject H_0.
   There is evidence at the 5% level that the variables 'age' and 'marital status' are associated.

4) H_0: no association between the variables 'gender' and 'likes/dislikes olives',
   H_1: there is an association.

   Make tables showing: (i) the expected frequencies, $\frac{(\text{row total}) \times (\text{column total})}{n}$; and (ii) the contributions to the test statistic $\frac{(O - E)^2}{E}$.

Expected frequencies	Likes olives	Doesn't like olives	Total
Male	20.8	19.2	40
Female	31.2	28.8	60
Total	52	48	100

Contribution	Likes olives	Doesn't like olives
Male	0.069	0.075
Female	0.046	0.050

So $\chi^2 = 0.240$ (to 3 d.p.).

Under H_0, $X^2 \sim \chi^2_{(\nu)}$ where $\nu = 1$.
So the critical value at the 5% level is 3.841.
0.240 < 3.841, so do not reject H_0.
There is no evidence at the 5% level of an association between a person's gender and whether or not they like olives.

Exam Questions

1 a) H_0: no association between age and severity of back pain *[1 mark]*.
   H_1: there is some association between age and severity of back pain *[1 mark]*.

b) Use the formula:
   Expected frequency $= \frac{(\text{Row total}) \times (\text{Column total})}{\text{Overall total } (n)}$

   [1 mark]
   The expected frequencies under H_0 are:

Expected frequencies		Severity of back pain			
		No pain	Mild	Severe	**Total**
Age (years)	30 and under	35.79	23.68	20.53	**80**
	31-50	18.34	12.14	10.52	**41**
	51 and over	13.87	9.18	7.95	**31**
	Total	**68**	**45**	**39**	**152**

[2 marks for all expected frequencies calculated correctly or 1 mark for at least three values calculated correctly.]

c) For the '30 and under' and '31-50' age groups, the observed frequencies are roughly in line with what would be expected under H_0 *[1 mark]*. The biggest discrepancy in these two groups is in the '30 and under group with no pain', where the observed frequency is higher than would be expected, but the other differences are much smaller *[1 mark]*. However, the '51 and over' observations are much further from what would be expected under H_0. There are far fewer people than predicted with 'no pain', while far more people than predicted suffered 'severe pain' *[1 mark]*.

d) (i) For each cell, use the formula:
   $$X^2 \text{ contribution} = \frac{(O_i - E_i)^2}{E_i} \text{ [1 mark]}$$

Contribution to test statistic		Severity of back pain		
		No pain	Mild	Severe
Age (years)	30 and under	1.08	0.30	0.61
	31-50	0.01	0.67	0.60
	51 and over	2.48	0.00	4.60

[2 marks for all contributions calculated correctly or 1 mark for at least three values calculated correctly.]

(ii) Add up all the individual contributions to get:
   $$X^2 = \sum \frac{(O_i - E_i)^2}{E_i} = 10.35 \text{ [1 mark]}$$

Answers

e) The data here has $(3 - 1) \times (3 - 1) = 4$ degrees of freedom and so (since all the expected frequencies are greater than 5) X^2 will approximately follow a $\chi^2_{(4)}$ distribution *[1 mark]*. Using the χ^2-table, the critical value at a 5% level of significance is 9.488 *[1 mark]*.
Since $10.35 > 9.488$ *[1 mark]*, this is a significant result, and you can reject the null hypothesis *[1 mark]*. There is evidence of an association between 'age' and 'severity of back pain' at this level of significance *[1 mark]*.

2 a) H_0: no association between age and favourite flavour of ice cream; H_1: there is an association *[1 mark]*.
The expected frequencies under H_0 are:

Expected frequencies		Age		
		0 – 40	41 +	Total
Flavour of ice cream	Vanilla	11.52	12.48	24
	Chocolate	24	26	50
	Strawberry	5.28	5.72	11
	Mint choc chip	7.2	7.8	15
	Total	48	52	100

[1 mark for using the row and column totals to calculate the expected frequencies, plus 1 mark if all expected frequencies are correct.]

The contributions to the test statistic X^2 are:

Contribution		Age	
		0 – 40	41 +
Flavour of ice cream	Vanilla	0.200...	0.185...
	Chocolate	0	0
	Strawberry	0.560...	0.517...
	Mint choc chip	0.005...	0.005...

[1 mark for calculating contributions using $(O - E)^2 / E$, plus 1 mark for all contributions correct.]
So $\chi^2 = 1.47$ *[1 mark]*
Under H_0, $X^2 \sim \chi^2_{(v)}$ where $v = (4 - 1) \times (2 - 1) = 3$ *[1 mark]*.
So the critical value at the 5% level is 7.815 *[1 mark]*.
$1.47 < 7.815$, so do not reject H_0.
There is no evidence at the 5% level of association between age and favourite flavour of ice cream *[1 mark]*.

b) The probability of selecting a shopper whose favourite flavour is strawberry from the '0-40' age group is $\frac{7}{48}$ *[1 mark]*, while the probability of selecting a shopper whose favourite flavour is strawberry from the '41+' age group is $\frac{4}{52} = \frac{1}{13}$ *[1 mark]*. Since these probabilities are independent, the probability of selecting two shoppers, one from each age group, whose favourite flavour is strawberry is: $\frac{7}{48} \times \frac{1}{13} = \frac{7}{624} = 0.0112$ (to 3 sig. fig.) *[1 mark]*.

S2 Section 4 — Normal Distribution
Warm-up Questions

1) Use the Z-tables:
   a) $P(Z < 0.84) = 0.7995$
   b) $P(Z < 2.95) = 0.9984$
   c) $P(Z > 0.68) = 1 - P(Z \leq 0.68) = 1 - 0.7517 = 0.2483$
   d) $P(Z \geq 1.55) = 1 - P(Z < 1.55) = 1 - 0.9394 = 0.0606$
   e) $P(Z < -2.10) = P(Z > 2.10) = 1 - P(Z \leq 2.10)$
      $= 1 - 0.9821 = 0.0179$
   f) $P(Z \leq -0.01) = P(Z \geq 0.01)$
      $= 1 - P(Z < 0.01) = 1 - 0.5040 = 0.4960$
   g) $P(Z > 0.10) = 1 - P(Z \leq 0.10) = 1 - 0.5398 = 0.4602$
   h) $P(Z \leq 0.64) = 0.7389$
   i) $P(Z > 0.23) = 1 - P(Z \leq 0.23) = 1 - 0.5910 = 0.4090$
   j) $P(0.10 < Z \leq 0.50) = P(Z \leq 0.50) - P(Z \leq 0.10)$
      $= 0.6915 - 0.5398 = 0.1517$
   k) $P(-0.62 \leq Z < 1.10) = P(Z < 1.10) - P(Z < -0.62)$
      $= P(Z < 1.10) - P(Z > 0.62) = P(Z < 1.10) - (1 - P(Z \leq 0.62))$
      $= 0.8643 - (1 - 0.7324) = 0.5967$
   l) $P(-0.99 < Z \leq -0.74) = P(Z \leq -0.74) - P(Z \leq -0.99)$
      $= P(Z \geq 0.74) - P(Z \geq 0.99)$
      $= (1 - P(Z < 0.74)) - (1 - P(Z < 0.99))$
      $= (1 - 0.7704) - (1 - 0.8389) = 0.0685$

   I know... these all get a bit fiddly. As always — take it nice and slow, and double-check each step as you do it.

2) a) If $P(Z < z) = 0.913$, then from the table of 'normal inverses' (i.e. the table showing $\Phi^{-1}(p)$), $z = 1.360$.
   b) If $P(Z < z) = 0.587$, then $z = 0.2198$.
   c) If $P(Z > z) = 0.035$, then $P(Z \leq z) = 0.965$.
      From the 'normal inverses' table, $z = 1.812$.
   d) If $P(Z > z) = 0.01$, then $P(Z \leq z) = 0.99$.
      From the 'normal inverses' table, $z = 2.326$.
   e) If $P(Z \leq z) = 0.401$, then z must be negative.
      But this means $P(Z < -z) = 1 - 0.401 = 0.599$. Using the 'normal inverses' table, $-z = 0.2508$, so $z = -0.2508$.

      It's getting a bit trickier here, with all the z and -z business. If you need to draw a graph here to make it a bit clearer what's going on, then draw one.

   f) If $P(Z \geq z) = 0.995$, then z must be negative.
      But if $P(Z \leq z) = 0.995$, then from the 'normal inverses' table, $z = 2.576$. This means $z = -2.576$.

      When you've answered a question like this, always ask yourself whether your answer looks 'about right'. Here, you need a number that Z is very very likely to be greater than... so your answer is going to be negative, and it's going to be pretty big.
      So $z = -2.576$ looks about right.

3) a) $P(X < 55) = P\left(Z < \frac{55 - 50}{\sqrt{16}}\right) = P(Z < 1.25) = 0.8944$

   b) $P(X < 42) = P\left(Z < \frac{42 - 50}{\sqrt{16}}\right) = P(Z < -2)$
      $= P(Z > 2) = 1 - P(Z \leq 2) = 1 - 0.9772 = 0.0228$

Answers

c) $P(X > 56) = P\left(Z > \dfrac{56 - 50}{\sqrt{16}}\right) = P(Z > 1.5)$

$= 1 - P(Z \leq 1.5) = 1 - 0.9332 = 0.0668$

d) $P(47 < X < 57) = P(X < 57) - P(X \leq 47)$

$= P\left(Z < \dfrac{57 - 50}{\sqrt{16}}\right) - P\left(Z \leq \dfrac{47 - 50}{\sqrt{16}}\right)$

$= P(Z < 1.75) - P(Z \leq -0.75)$

$= 0.9599 - P(Z \geq 0.75)$

$= 0.9599 - (1 - P(Z < 0.75))$

$= 0.9599 - (1 - 0.7734) = 0.7333$

4) $P(X < 8) = 0.892$ means $P\left(Z < \dfrac{8 - \mu}{\sqrt{10}}\right) = 0.892.$

From the inverse normal table, $\dfrac{8 - \mu}{\sqrt{10}} = 1.237.$

So $\mu = 8 - 1.237 \times \sqrt{10} = 4.09$ (to 3 sig. fig.).

5) $P(X < 13) = 0.6$ means $P\left(Z < \dfrac{13 - 11}{\sigma}\right) = 0.6.$

From the inverse normal table, $\dfrac{13 - 11}{\sigma} = 0.2533.$

So $\sigma = \dfrac{13 - 11}{0.2533} = 7.90$ (to 3 sig. fig.).

6) $P(X < 15.2) = 0.978$ means $P\left(Z < \dfrac{15.2 - \mu}{\sigma}\right) = 0.978.$

From tables, $\dfrac{15.2 - \mu}{\sigma} = 2.014,$ or $\underline{2.014\sigma + \mu = 15.2}.$

$P(X > 14.8) = 0.106$ means $P\left(Z > \dfrac{14.8 - \mu}{\sigma}\right) = 0.106,$

or $P\left(Z \leq \dfrac{14.8 - \mu}{\sigma}\right) = 1 - 0.106 = 0.894.$

From tables, $\dfrac{14.8 - \mu}{\sigma} = 1.248,$ or $\underline{1.248\sigma + \mu = 14.8}.$

Solving these simultaneous equations gives $\sigma = 0.522$

and $\mu = 14.15.$

7) Use the normal approximation $X \sim N(45, 24.75).$

a) $P(X > 50) \approx P(X > 50.5) = P\left(Z > \dfrac{50.5 - 45}{\sqrt{24.75}}\right)$

$= P(Z > 1.106)$

$= 1 - P(Z \leq 1.106)$

$= 1 - 0.8655 = 0.1345$

b) $P(X \leq 45) \approx P(X < 45.5) = P\left(Z < \dfrac{45.5 - 45}{\sqrt{24.75}}\right)$

$= P(Z < 0.101)$

$= 0.5402$

c) $P(40 < X \leq 47) \approx P(X \leq 47.5) - P(X \leq 40.5)$

$= P\left(Z \leq \dfrac{47.5 - 45}{\sqrt{24.75}}\right) - P\left(Z \leq \dfrac{40.5 - 45}{\sqrt{24.75}}\right)$

$= P(Z \leq 0.503) - P(Z \leq -0.905)$

$= P(Z \leq 0.503) - (1 - P(Z \leq 0.905))$

$= 0.6925 - 1 + 0.8172 = 0.5097$

8) Use the normal approximation $X \sim N(25, 25).$

a) $P(X \leq 20) \approx P(X \leq 20.5) = P\left(Z \leq \dfrac{20.5 - 25}{5}\right)$

$= P(Z \leq -0.9)$

$= 1 - P(Z \leq 0.9)$

$= 1 - 0.8159 = 0.1841$

b) $P(X > 15) \approx P(X > 15.5) = P\left(Z > \dfrac{15.5 - 25}{5}\right)$

$= P(Z > -1.90)$

$= P(Z < 1.90) = 0.9713$

c) $P(20 \leq X < 30) \approx P(X \leq 29.5) - P(X \leq 19.5)$

$= P\left(Z \leq \dfrac{29.5 - 25}{5}\right) - P\left(Z \leq \dfrac{19.5 - 25}{5}\right)$

$= P(Z \leq 0.90) - P(Z \leq -1.10)$

$= P(Z \leq 0.90) - (1 - P(Z \leq 1.10))$

$= 0.8159 - 1 + 0.8643 = 0.6802$

9) People join the queue (on average) at a constant rate. Assuming they join the queue randomly and singly, the total number of people joining the queue in a 15-minute period follows a Poisson distribution, Poisson(7).

a) If X represents the number of people joining the queue in a 7-hour day, then $X \sim$ Poisson(7×28) = Poisson(196). λ is large, so use the normal approximation $X \sim N(196, 196).$

$P(X > 200) \approx P(X > 200.5) = P\left(Z > \dfrac{200.5 - 196}{14}\right)$

$= P(Z > 0.321)$

$= 1 - P(Z < 0.321)$

$= 1 - 0.6259 = 0.3741$

b) Let C represent the number of people out of the 200 customers who are seen within 1 minute.
Then $C \sim B(200, 0.7).$
n is large, and $np = 200 \times 0.7 = 140$ and
$nq = 200 \times 0.3 = 60$ are both greater than 5, so use the
normal approximation, i.e. $C \sim N(140, 42).$
You need to find $P(C < 70\%$ of 200), i.e. $P(C < 140).$

$P(C < 140) \approx P(C \leq 139.5) = P\left(Z \leq \dfrac{139.5 - 140}{\sqrt{42}}\right)$

$= P(Z \leq -0.077)$

$= 1 - P(Z \leq 0.077)$

$= 1 - 0.5307 = 0.4693$

10) $X \sim N(8, 2) \Rightarrow \overline{X} \sim N\left(8, \dfrac{2}{10}\right) = N(8, 0.2)$

$P(\overline{X} < 7) = P\left(Z < \dfrac{7 - 8}{\sqrt{0.2}}\right) = P(Z < -2.236)$

$= P(Z > 2.236) = 1 - P(Z < 2.236)$

$= 1 - 0.9873 = 0.0127$

11) $H_0: \mu = 45,$ $H_1: \mu < 45,$ $\alpha = 0.05$ and $\sigma^2 = 9.$
Under $H_0,$ $\overline{X} \sim N\left(45, \dfrac{9}{16}\right)$ and $z = \dfrac{42 - 45}{\frac{3}{4}} = -4$
Critical region = $Z < -1.645.$
$-4 < -1.645,$ so there is evidence to reject H_0 at the 5% level.

12) The sample mean is given by $\overline{x} = \dfrac{1360}{100} = 13.6.$

Because the sample size is large, the population variance can be estimated by the sample variance, $s^2.$

$s^2 = \dfrac{n}{n - 1}\left[\dfrac{\sum x^2}{n} - \left(\dfrac{\sum x}{n}\right)^2\right] = \dfrac{100}{99}\left[\dfrac{19\,300}{100} - \left(\dfrac{1360}{100}\right)^2\right]$

$= 8.12$

Hypotheses are $H_0: \mu = 13.5$ and $H_1: \mu > 13.5.$

Answers

This means that under H_0,

$\overline{X} \sim N\left(13.5, \frac{8.12}{100}\right) = N(13.5, 0.0812)$.

The test statistic z is given by:

$z = \frac{\overline{x} - 13.5}{\sqrt{0.0812}} = \frac{13.6 - 13.5}{\sqrt{0.0812}} = 0.351$

This is a one-tailed test at a 1% level of significance, so the critical value is z, where $P(Z \le z) = 0.99$. From tables, this is $z = 2.326$, and so the critical region is $Z > 2.326$.

Since $0.351 < 2.326$, you cannot reject H_0.

Exam Questions

1 Assume that the lives of the batteries (X) are distributed as: $N(\mu, \sigma^2)$. Then $P(X < 20) = 0.4$ and $P(X < 30) = 0.8$. *[1 mark]*

Transform these 2 equations to get:

$P\left[Z < \frac{20 - \mu}{\sigma}\right] = 0.4$ and $P\left[Z < \frac{30 - \mu}{\sigma}\right] = 0.8$ *[1 mark]*

Now you need to use your 'inverse normal' table to get:

$\frac{20 - \mu}{\sigma} = -0.2533$ *[1 mark]* and $\frac{30 - \mu}{\sigma} = 0.8416$ *[1 mark]*

Now rewrite these as:

$20 - \mu = -0.2533\sigma$ and $30 - \mu = 0.8416\sigma$. *[1 mark]*

Subtract these two equations to get:

$10 = (0.8416 + 0.2533)\sigma$

i.e. $\sigma = \frac{10}{0.8416 + 0.2533} = 9.1333$ *[1 mark]*

Now use this value of σ in one of the equations above:

$\mu = 20 + 0.2533 \times 9.1333 = 22.31$ *[1 mark]*

2 a) (i) Need n to be large ("as large as possible") *[1 mark]* and p to be close to 0.5 *[1 mark]*.

Or you could say that you need $np > 5$ and $n(1 - p) > 5$ — that would also get you the marks. Engrave upon your heart all the conditions required for the various approximations to work. Well... actually, that might be considered to be cheating, so don't do that. But make sure you know them.

(ii) A binomial distribution is discrete, whereas a normal distribution is continuous *[1 mark]*. The continuity correction means probabilities can be calculated for the continuous normal distribution that correspond approximately to the discrete binomial probabilities *[1 mark]*.

b) (i) n is large and p is fairly close to 0.5, so use the normal approximation N(60, 24) *[1 mark]*.

$P(X \ge 65) \approx P(X > 64.5)$

$= P\left(Z > \frac{64.5 - 60}{\sqrt{24}}\right)$ *[1 mark]*

$= P(Z > 0.919)$

$= 1 - P(Z \le 0.919)$ *[1 mark]*

$= 1 - 0.8209 = 0.1791$ *[1 mark]*

(ii) $P(50 < X < 62)$

$\approx P(X < 61.5) - P(X < 50.5)$ *[1 mark]*

$= P\left(Z < \frac{61.5 - 60}{\sqrt{24}}\right) - P\left(Z < \frac{50.5 - 60}{\sqrt{24}}\right)$

$= P(Z < 0.306) - P(Z < -1.939)$ *[1 mark]*

$= P(Z < 0.306) - (1 - P(Z < 1.939))$

$= 0.6202 - (1 - 0.9737) = 0.5939$ *[1 mark]*

All the usual tricks involved there... normal approximation, continuity correction, subtracting values of $\Phi(z)$. They'll all be there on exam day too.

3 a) $\overline{x} = \frac{\sum x}{n} = \frac{490}{100} = 4.9$ m *[1 mark]*

$s^2 = \frac{n}{n - 1}\left[\frac{\sum x^2}{n} - \left(\frac{\sum x}{n}\right)^2\right]$

$= \frac{100}{99}\left[\frac{2421}{100} - 4.9^2\right]$ *[1 mark]*

$= \frac{20}{99} = 0.202$ (to 3 d.p.) *[1 mark]*

b) Let μ = mean height of trees in 2nd area.

H_0: $\mu = 5.1$ and H_1: $\mu \ne 5.1$ *[1 mark]*

Under H_0, $\overline{X} \sim N\left(5.1, \frac{20/99}{100}\right)$ *[1 mark]* $= N\left(5.1, \frac{1}{495}\right)$

$z = \frac{4.9 - 5.1}{\sqrt{1/495}}$ *[1 mark]* $= -4.45$ *[1 mark]*

This is a two-tailed test at the 1% level, so the critical values you need are z such that $P(Z < z) = 0.005$ and $P(Z > z) = 0.005$. Looking these up in the normal tables you get critical values of -2.576 and 2.576 *[1 mark]*. Since $-4.45 < -2.576$, the result is significant. There is evidence to reject H_0 and to suggest that the trees have a different mean height *[1 mark]*.

4 a) The normal approximation is: $Y \sim N(\mu, \sigma^2)$.

$P(X \le 151) \approx P(Y \le 151.5)$ *[1 mark]*

$= P\left(Z \le \frac{151.5 - \mu}{\sigma}\right) = 0.894$ *[1 mark]*.

Look up $p = 0.894$ in the 'inverse normal' table:

$\frac{151.5 - \mu}{\sigma} = 1.248$.

So $\mu + 1.248\sigma = 151.5$ *[1 mark]*.

$P(X > 127) \approx P(Y > 127.5)$ *[1 mark]*

$= P\left(Z > \frac{127.5 - \mu}{\sigma}\right) = 0.997$ *[1 mark]*.

This means $P\left(Z \le \frac{127.5 - \mu}{\sigma}\right) = 0.003$.

But this probability is less than 0.5, so $\frac{127.5 - \mu}{\sigma} < 0$.

Find $1 - 0.003 = 0.997$.

Look up $p = 0.997$ in the 'inverse normal' table:

$P(Z \le z) = 0.997$ means $z = 2.748$.

This tells you that $\frac{127.5 - \mu}{\sigma} = -2.748$,

or $\mu - 2.748\sigma = 127.5$ *[1 mark]*.

Now you can subtract the underlined equations to give $3.996\sigma = 24$, or $\sigma = 6.006... = 6.01$ (to 3 sig.fig.) *[1 mark]*. This then gives $\mu = 144.00... = 144$ (to 3 sig.fig.) *[1 mark]*.

I call this question "The Beast" — there's loads to do here. But as always in maths, when something looks hard, the best thing to do is take a deep breath, look at the information you have (here, some probabilities from a normal approximation), and write down some formulas containing that information. Then you can start piecing things together, and try to find out things you don't yet know. The worst thing you can do is panic and start thinking it's too hard. That's what Luke Skywalker did in that film before Yoda told him to chill out a bit. Something like that anyway.

b) You know $\mu = \underline{np = 144.00}$ *[1 mark]* and $\sigma^2 = \underline{np(1 - p) = 36.07}$ *[1 mark]*.
Divide the second underlined equation by the first to give $1 - p = 36.07 \div 144 = 0.2505$, or $p = 0.749...$ $= 0.75$ (to 2 d.p.). *[1 mark]*.
Then $n = 144 \div 0.749... = 192.12...$ $= 192$ (to the nearest whole number) *[1 mark]*.

Phew... made it.

5 a) Let X represent the base diameters.
Then $P(X > 13) = 0.05$ *[1 mark]*.

$P(X > 13) = P\left(Z > \dfrac{13 - 12}{\sigma}\right) = 0.05$.

This means that $P\left(Z \le \dfrac{13 - 12}{\sigma}\right) = 0.95$ *[1 mark]*.

From the 'inverse normal' table, $\dfrac{1}{\sigma} = 1.645$ *[1 mark]*.

This means $\sigma = \dfrac{1}{1.645} = 0.608$ (to 3 sig. fig.) *[1 mark]*.

b) $P(X < 10.8) = P\left(Z < \dfrac{10.8 - 12}{0.608}\right)$
$= P(Z < -1.974)$ *[1 mark]*
$= 1 - P(Z \le 1.974) = 1 - 0.9758 = 0.0242$ *[1 mark]*

So you would expect $0.0242 \times 100 \approx 2$ pizza bases to be discarded *[1 mark]*.

c) P(at least 1 base too small) = 1 – P(no bases too small).
P(base not too small) = 1 – 0.0242 = 0.9758.
P(no bases too small) = $0.9758^3 = 0.9291$ *[1 mark]*
P(at least 1 base too small) = 1 – 0.9291 *[1 mark]*
= 0.0709 (to 3 sig.fig.) *[1 mark]*.

S2 — *Practice Exam One*

1 a) $S_{xx} = \sum x^2 - \dfrac{(\sum x)^2}{n}$
$= 847 - \dfrac{79^2}{8} = 66.875 = 66.9$ (to 3 sig. fig.) *[1 mark]*

$S_{yy} = \sum y^2 - \dfrac{(\sum y)^2}{n}$
$= 45\,884 - \dfrac{600^2}{8} = 884$ *[1 mark]*

$S_{xy} = \sum xy - \dfrac{\sum x \sum y}{n}$
$= 6143 - \dfrac{79 \times 600}{8} = 218$ *[1 mark]*

b) $r = \dfrac{S_{xy}}{\sqrt{S_{xx} \times S_{yy}}} = \dfrac{218}{\sqrt{66.875 \times 884}}$ *[1 mark]*
$= 0.897$ (to 3 sig. fig.) *[1 mark]*

c) The teacher believes there is a positive correlation, so use the following null and alternative hypotheses:
$H_0: r = 0$, and $H_1: r > 0$ *[1 mark]*.
This is a one-tailed test at a 5% significance level, so from tables the critical value is 0.6215 *[1 mark]*.
The correlation coefficient from this data exceeds the critical value *[1 mark]*, and so you can reject the null hypothesis *[1 mark]*, and say that there is evidence at the 5% level that students' marks in the exam and the quantity of revision they do are positively correlated *[1 mark]*.

d) For this test to be valid, the data needs to be bivariate normal *[1 mark]*. This can be checked by examining whether the data points fall within a roughly elliptical shape on the scatter diagram (which they do in this case) *[1 mark]*.

e) All the points lie close to a straight line on the scatter diagram *[1 mark]*.

f) If the regression line is $y = a + bx$, then
$b = \dfrac{S_{xy}}{S_{xx}} = \dfrac{218}{66.875} = 3.26$ (to 3 sig. fig.) *[1 mark]*
Find a using the fact that the line passes through the point $(\overline{x}, \overline{y})$.
So $a = \overline{y} - 3.26\overline{x} = \dfrac{600}{8} - 3.26 \times \dfrac{79}{8} = 42.8$ *[1 mark]*.
This means $y = 42.8 + 3.26x$ (to 3 sig. fig.) *[1 mark]*.

g) Using the regression line to estimate the mark:
$y = 3.26 \times 8 + 42.8 = 68.88 \approx 69$ marks *[1 mark]*.

h) This should be a fairly reliable estimate, since it is an interpolation between two known values / This estimate may be unreliable, since this student may not fit the pattern generated by the others *[1 mark for any sensible comment]*.

2 a) (i) Since the average number of houses sold per week is 2, $X \sim$ Poisson(2) *[1 mark]*.
$P(X = 1) = \dfrac{e^{-2}2^1}{1!} = 2e^{-2} = 0.271$ (to 3 d.p.) *[1 mark]*
You can do this with tables, but here it's quicker just to use the formula.

(ii) $P(2 \le X \le 4) = P(X \le 4) - P(X < 2)$
$= P(X \le 4) - P(X \le 1)$ *[1 mark]*
$= 0.9473 - 0.4060$ *[1 mark]*
$= 0.5413$ *[1 mark]*.

And you could do this one by working out $P(X = 2)$, $P(X = 3)$ and $P(X = 4)$ using the formula, and then adding the results. Do it the way that seems to involve less work, that's my (obvious) advice.

b) $P(X \ge 2) = 1 - P(X < 2) = 1 - P(X \le 1)$
$= 1 - 0.4060 = 0.5940$ *[1 mark]*.
Since the sales can be modelled by a Poisson distribution, the individual events (i.e. house sales) are independent, meaning that total sales in each week are also independent. This allows you to multiply probabilities for individual weeks.

So P(qualify for "monthly bonus") = 0.5940^4 *[1 mark]*
= 0.124 (to 3 d.p.) *[1 mark]*.

c) (i) $X \sim$ Poisson(2) and $Y \sim$ Poisson(3), so $H = X + Y \sim$ Poisson(5) *[1 mark]*

Answers

(ii) Let J be the total number of houses sold between them in a two-week period. Then $J \sim$ Poisson(10) *[1 mark]*.
$P(J \geq 9) = 1 - P(J < 9) = 1 - P(J \leq 8)$ *[1 mark]*
$= 1 - 0.3328 = 0.6672$ *[1 mark]*

d) Let Q represent the total number of houses sold over the next 26 weeks. Q will follow the Poisson distribution Poisson(26×5) = Poisson(130) *[1 mark]*.
Since λ is large, this can be approximated by a normal distribution, i.e. $Q \sim$ N(130, 130) *[1 mark]*.
$P(Q < 120) = P(Q < 119.5)$ *[1 mark]*
$\qquad = P\left(Z < \dfrac{119.5 - 130}{\sqrt{130}}\right)$ *[1 mark]*
$\qquad = P(Z < -0.921)$
$\qquad = 1 - P(Z < 0.921)$ *[1 mark]*
$\qquad = 1 - 0.8215 = 0.1785$ *[1 mark]*

A neat transition from Poisson to normal there — don't be caught out.

3 a) This is one of those where you have to 'standardise' the normal variable (i.e. subtract the mean and divide by the standard deviation) and use tables for the standard normal variable Z.

(i) $P(X < 7.5) = P\left(\dfrac{X - 8}{\sqrt{1.2}} < \dfrac{7.5 - 8}{\sqrt{1.2}}\right)$
$\qquad = P(Z < -0.456)$ *[1 mark]*
$\qquad = 1 - P(Z \leq 0.456)$ *[1 mark]*
$\qquad = 1 - 0.6758 = 0.3242$ *[1 mark]*

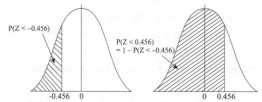

A quick sketch always helps.

(ii) You need to find the probability that the duration is less than 7 minutes or more than 9 minutes.
This is $P(X < 7) + P(X > 9)$.
By symmetry, these are equal, so:
$P(X < 7) + P(X > 9) = 2 \times P\left(Z < \dfrac{7 - 8}{\sqrt{1.2}}\right)$ *[1 mark]*
$\qquad = 2 \times P(Z < -0.913)$ *[1 mark]*
$\qquad = 2 \times (1 - P(Z \leq 0.913))$ *[1 mark]*
$\qquad = 2 \times (1 - 0.8194) = 0.3612$ *[1 mark]*

These do definitely get a bit tricky. Just have a good think about what you need to find out before you launch into a load of working out. Getting loads of practice at this kind of question is dead helpful — it gets you used to working with those tables.

(iii) You need to find d where: $P(X > d) = 0.01$.
$P(X > d) = 0.01$, so $P(X \leq d) = 0.99$,
or $P\left(Z \leq \dfrac{d - 8}{\sqrt{1.2}}\right) = 0.99$ *[1 mark]*.
Using the inverse normal table:
$\dfrac{d - 8}{\sqrt{1.2}} = 2.326$ *[1 mark]*.
So $d = \sqrt{1.2} \times 2.326 + 8$ *[1 mark]*,
i.e. $d = 10.5$ minutes (to 3 sig. fig.) *[1 mark]*

These 'standardise the normal variable' questions get everywhere. They look hard, but you soon get used to them. And once you get your head round the basic idea, you'll be able to do pretty much anything they ask you.

b) (i) A hypothesis test tests the claim made about a parameter by a null hypothesis against that made by an alternative hypothesis *[1 mark]*. In a one-tailed test, the alternative hypothesis states either that the value of the parameter is greater than the value specified by the null hypothesis or that the value of the parameter is less than the value specified by the null hypothesis *[1 mark]*.

(ii) H_0: $\mu = 8$
H_1: $\mu < 8$ *[1 mark]*

(iii) Under H_0, $X \sim$ N(8, 1.2)
This means $\overline{X} \sim$ N$\left(8, \dfrac{1.2}{20}\right)$ = N(8, 0.06) *[1 mark]*
The test statistic is $z = \dfrac{7.8 - 8}{\sqrt{0.06}} = -0.816$ *[1 mark]*.
This is a one-tail test at a significance level of 5%, and so the critical value (i.e. z with $P(Z \leq z) = 0.05$) is -1.645, meaning the critical region is $Z \leq -1.645$ *[1 mark]*. Since $z = -0.816 > -1.645$, you cannot reject H_0 *[1 mark]* — i.e. based on the evidence, you cannot conclude that the mean duration of the car wash has fallen from 8 minutes *[1 mark]*.

4 a) H_0: no association between the variables 'gender' and 'foreign language studied';
H_1: there is an association between the variables 'gender' and 'foreign language studied' *[1 mark]*.

b) Use the formula:
$\text{Expected frequency} = \dfrac{\text{(Row total)} \times \text{(Column total)}}{\text{Overall total } (n)}$
[1 mark]
The expected frequencies under H_0 are:

	French	Spanish	**Total**
Male	8.8	11.2	**20**
Female	13.2	16.8	**30**
Total	**22**	**28**	**50**

[2 marks for all expected frequencies calculated correctly or 1 mark for at least two values calculated correctly.]

Answers

c) Work out the contribution to the test statistic for each cell using the formula:

$$X^2 \text{ contribution} = \frac{(O_i - E_i)^2}{E_i}$$ *[1 mark]*

	French	Spanish
Male	3.073	2.414
Female	2.048	1.610

[2 marks for all contributions calculated correctly or 1 mark for at least two values calculated correctly.]

Add up all the individual contributions to get: $\chi^2 = 9.145$ *[1 mark]*

The data here has $(2 - 1) \times (2 - 1) = 1$ degree of freedom, so X^2 will follow a $\chi^2_{(1)}$ distribution *[1 mark]*. Using the χ^2-table, the critical value at a 1% level of significance is 6.635 *[1 mark]*.

Since 9.145 > 6.635, this is a significant result, and you can reject the null hypothesis *[1 mark]*. There is evidence of an association between 'gender' and 'foreign language studied' at the 1% level of significance *[1 mark]*.

d) For the males, the observed value for French was greater than expected, while the observed value for Spanish was much lower than expected *[1 mark]*.

For the females, the opposite was true — the observed value for French was less than expected, and the observed value for Spanish was much greater *[1 mark]*.

e) There are two possibilities, and you have to add the probabilities for each.

The first possibility is that you select a male studying French and a female studying Spanish (remembering that you can select these in two different orders).

The probability of this is:

$\left(\frac{14}{50} \times \frac{22}{49}\right) + \left(\frac{22}{50} \times \frac{14}{49}\right) = \frac{616}{2450}$ *[1 mark]*

The second possibility is that you select a male studying Spanish and a female studying French (in either order).

The probability of this is:

$\left(\frac{6}{50} \times \frac{8}{49}\right) + \left(\frac{8}{50} \times \frac{6}{49}\right) = \frac{96}{2450}$ *[1 mark]*

So the overall probability of selecting students that are of different genders and study different languages is:

$\frac{616}{2450} + \frac{96}{2450} = \frac{712}{2450} = \frac{356}{1225}$ *[1 mark]*

S2 — Practice Exam Two

1 a)

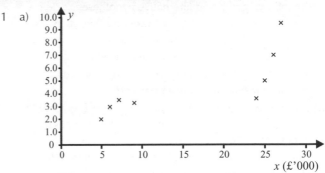

[2 marks for all points plotted correctly, or 1 mark if at least 3 points are plotted correctly]

b) First calculate S_{xx}, S_{yy} and S_{xy}.

$$S_{xx} = \sum x^2 - \frac{(\sum x)^2}{n}$$
$$= 2797 - \frac{129^2}{8} = 716.875 \text{ [1 mark]}$$

$$S_{yy} = \sum y^2 - \frac{(\sum y)^2}{n}$$
$$= 212.7 - \frac{36.8^2}{8} = 43.42 \text{ [1 mark]}$$

$$S_{xy} = \sum xy - \frac{\sum x \sum y}{n}$$
$$= 731.2 - \frac{129 \times 36.8}{8} = 137.8 \text{ [1 mark]}$$

Now you can find the correlation coefficient, r.

$$r = \frac{S_{xy}}{\sqrt{S_{xx} \times S_{yy}}} = \frac{137.8}{\sqrt{716.875 \times 43.42}} \text{ [1 mark]}$$

$= 0.781$ (to 3 sig. fig.) *[1 mark]*

c) To carry out the significance test the manager is requesting, the data needs to be bivariate normal *[1 mark]*. On a scatter diagram, this would mean the data points would fall in a roughly elliptical shape, which is not the case here *[1 mark]*.

Or you could say that the values of x here fall into two definite groups (i.e. the data for x is bimodal). This means the significance test on the product moment correlation coefficient would not be valid.

d) To find Spearman's rank correlation coefficient (SRCC), you need to find the ranks for the two sets of data points. These are shown in the table below, together with a row showing the difference (d) between the ranks in each pair.

x (£'000)	1	2	3	4	5	6	7	8
y	1	2	4	3	5	6	7	8
d	0	0	1	1	0	0	0	0

[1 mark for assigning the correct ranks for the x- and y-values, and 1 mark for correctly calculating the values of d.]

The SRCC (r_s) is then given by:

$$r_s = 1 - \frac{6\sum d^2}{n(n^2 - 1)} = 1 - \frac{6 \times 2}{8 \times 63} \text{ [1 mark]}$$

$= 0.976$ (to 3 sig. fig.) *[1 mark]*

Answers

e) The manager believes there is a positive association, so use the following null and alternative hypotheses:

H_0: there is no association between the cost of the marketing campaign (x) and public awareness (y);

H_1: there is a positive association between the cost of the marketing campaign (x) and public awareness (y).

[1 mark for both hypotheses correct]

This is a 1-tailed test with 8 pairs of values (i.e. $n = 8$) at a 1% significance level, so from tables the critical value is 0.8333 *[1 mark]*.

The value of r_s for this data exceeds the critical value *[1 mark]*, and so you can reject the null hypothesis *[1 mark]*, and say that there is evidence at the 1% level of a positive association between the cost of the marketing campaign (x) and public awareness (y) *[1 mark]*.

2 a) (i) The surviving bacteria are spread randomly, singly and are assumed to occur at a constant average rate, which would give rise to a Poisson distribution: $X \sim \text{Poisson}(6)$ *[1 mark]*.

Using tables:
$P(X < 10) = P(X \le 9) = 0.9161$ *[1 mark]*

(ii) $P(5 \le X \le 7) = P(X \le 7) - P(X < 5)$
$= P(X \le 7) - P(X \le 4)$ *[1 mark]*
$= 0.7440 - 0.2851$ *[1 mark]*
$= 0.4589$ *[1 mark]*

Careful with the step: "$P(5 \le X \le 7) = P(X \le 7) - P(X \le 4)$" — it's easy to make a mistake there, because that '5' has somehow become a '4'. Think of it as subtracting the 'values of X you want to exclude'. So $P(5 \le X \le 7)$ means X can be 5, 6 or 7 — that means you want all the values of X less than or equal to 7 ($= P(X \le 7)$), and then you want to subtract all the values of 4 or less ($= P(X \le 4)$).

b) sample mean $= \dfrac{\sum x}{n} = \dfrac{83}{15} = 5.53$ (to 2 d.p.) *[1 mark]*

sample variance $= \dfrac{n}{n-1}\left[\dfrac{\sum x^2}{n} - \left(\dfrac{\sum x}{n}\right)^2\right]$
$= \dfrac{15}{14}\left[\dfrac{538}{15} - \left(\dfrac{83}{15}\right)^2\right]$ *[1 mark]*
$= 5.62$ (to 2 d.p.) *[1 mark]*

c) The above estimates of the population mean and variance are approximately equal. This is a characteristic of a Poisson distribution *[1 mark]*.

Whenever you see a mean and a variance that are roughly equal, the little bell in your head marked 'Poisson' should start ringing.

d) If $X \sim \text{Poisson}(5.53)$, then:
$P(X = 5) = \dfrac{e^{-\lambda}\lambda^x}{x!}$
$= \dfrac{e^{-5.53} \times 5.53^5}{5!}$ *[1 mark]*
$= 0.171$ (to 3 d.p.) *[1 mark]*.

e) (i) Here, there is a fixed number of trials (100) and Y describes the total number of 'successes' in those trials (where 'success' means a tile contains no bacteria after an hour).

So this is a binomial distribution: $Y \sim \text{B}(100, 0.35)$.

[1 mark for 'binomial', and 1 mark for the correct values of n and p.]

(ii) Since n is large and p is not too far from 0.5 (and $np = 35$ and $n(1-p) = 65$ are both greater than 5), Y can be approximated using a normal distribution *[1 mark]*. In fact, $Y \sim \text{N}(35, 22.75)$ (approximately) *[1 mark]*.

Using this approximation:

$P(Y > 40) = P(Y > 40.5) = P\left(Z > \dfrac{40.5 - 35}{\sqrt{22.75}}\right)$ *[1 mark]*
$= P(Z > 1.153)$
$= 1 - P(Z \le 1.153)$
$= 1 - 0.8755$ *[1 mark]*
$= 0.1245$ *[1 mark]*

3 a) Let X represent the height of a sunflower in the second field, then $X \sim \text{N}(\mu, 20)$. The distribution is normal and the variance is known, so you can do a z-test.

Your null and alternative hypotheses are:

H_0: $\mu = 150$ and H_1: $\mu \ne 150$ *[1 mark]*.

The significance level is $\alpha = 0.01$.

Under H_0:

$\overline{X} \sim \text{N}\left(\mu, \dfrac{\sigma^2}{n}\right) = \text{N}\left(150, \dfrac{20}{6}\right) = \text{N}\left(150, \dfrac{10}{3}\right)$ *[1 mark]*.

Since $\bar{x} = \dfrac{\sum x}{n} = \dfrac{840}{6} = 140$ cm *[1 mark]*, the test statistic z is given by:

$z = \dfrac{140 - 150}{\sqrt{10/3}} = -5.48$ *[1 mark]*,

where $Z \sim \text{N}(0, 1)$.

This is a two-tailed test at the 1% level, so the critical values are $\pm z$ such that $P(Z > z) = 0.005$ *[1 mark]*. By looking up $P(Z < z) = 0.995$ in the inverse normal table, you get critical values of ± 2.576, and so the critical region is $Z < -2.576$ and $Z > 2.576$ *[1 mark]*.

Since $z = -5.48$ is in the critical region, you can reject H_0 *[1 mark]*. There is evidence at the 1% level to suggest that the average height is different *[1 mark]*.

b) The heights of the sunflowers in the third field are normally distributed, so if their heights are represented by the random variable Y, then $Y \sim N(\mu, \sigma^2)$. But the variance is unknown — this means you'll have to estimate it. An unbiased estimate of the variance is:

$$s^2 = \frac{n}{n-1}\left[\frac{\sum y^2}{n} - \left(\frac{\sum y}{n}\right)^2\right]$$
$$= \frac{40}{39}\left[\frac{884\,180}{40} - \left(\frac{5928}{40}\right)^2\right]$$
$$= 144.88 \; \textit{[1 mark]}$$

Since the sample size is large *[1 mark]*, this should be a reasonably good estimate of σ^2.

Use null and alternative hypotheses as follows:
$H_0: \mu = 150$ and $H_1: \mu < 150$ *[1 mark]*.

Since the heights are normally distributed, the sample mean $\overline{Y}$ will also follow a normal distribution.

In fact, $\overline{Y} \sim N\left(\mu, \frac{\sigma^2}{n}\right)$, and so under H_0 (and using the estimated variance) this means

$\overline{Y} \sim N\left(150, \frac{144.88}{40}\right) = N(150, 3.622)$ *[1 mark]*.

For this data, $\overline{y} = \frac{\sum y}{n} = \frac{5928}{40} = 148.2$ *[1 mark]*, and so the test statistic is $z = \frac{148.2 - 150}{\sqrt{3.622}} = -0.946$ *[1 mark]*.

This is a one-tailed test at a significance level of 5%, and so the critical value is z, where $P(Z \le z) = 0.05$ *[1 mark]*. Looking up $p = 0.95$ in the inverse normal table and using the symmetry of a normal distribution, the critical value is -1.645, and so the critical region is $Z < -1.645$ *[1 mark]*.

Since the test statistic here does not fall in the critical region $(-0.946 > -1.645)$, you cannot reject H_0 *[1 mark]*. There is no evidence at the 5% level to suggest that the average height of the sunflowers in this field isn't the same as in the first field *[1 mark]*.

4 a) Use as your null and alternative hypotheses:
H_0: no association between the variables 'height of tree' and 'presence of leaf disease';
H_1: there is an association between the variables 'height of tree' and 'presence of leaf disease' *[1 mark]*.

Under H_0, you can use the following formula to calculate the expected frequencies for each cell of the table:

Expected frequency $= \frac{(\text{Row total}) \times (\text{Column total})}{\text{Overall total } (n)}$

[1 mark]

So the expected frequencies under H_0 are:

Expected frequencies	Leaf disease	No leaf disease	Total
Height < 3m	33.13	37.87	71
3m ≤ Height < 4m	21.47	24.53	46
Height ≥ 4m	15.40	17.60	33
Total	70	80	150

[2 marks for all expected frequencies calculated correctly or 1 mark for at least two values calculated correctly.]

Work out the contribution to the test statistic for each cell using the formula:

$X^2 \text{ contribution} = \frac{(O_i - E_i)^2}{E_i}$ *[1 mark]*

Contribution	Leaf disease	No leaf disease
Height < 3m	0.039	0.034
3m ≤ Height < 4m	0.284	0.249
Height ≥ 4m	0.842	0.736

[2 marks for all contributions calculated correctly or 1 mark for at least two values calculated correctly.]

Add up all the individual contributions to get: $\chi^2 = 2.184$ *[1 mark]*

All the expected frequencies are greater than 5, and the data here has $(3-1) \times (2-1) = 2$ degrees of freedom, so X^2 will (approximately) follow a $\chi^2_{(2)}$ distribution *[1 mark]*. Using the χ^2-table, the critical value at a 5% level of significance is 5.991 *[1 mark]*.
Since $2.184 < 5.991$, this is not a significant result, and you cannot reject the null hypothesis *[1 mark]*. There is no evidence of an association between the variables 'height of tree' and 'presence of leaf disease' at the 5% level of significance *[1 mark]*.

b) The expected frequencies are all fairly close to the values actually observed. The category whose observed frequencies were furthest from those expected was the group of trees over 4 m tall, but even here the differences are not great *[1 mark]*. For the other two groups, the observed and expected frequencies are even closer *[1 mark]*.

c) The probability that a tree with the leaf disease is selected from those that are under 3 m in height is $\frac{32}{71}$ *[1 mark]*. Similarly, the probabilities that a tree with the leaf disease is selected from each of the other two height categories are $\frac{19}{46}$ *[1 mark]* and $\frac{19}{33}$ *[1 mark]*. Since all these probabilities are independent, the probability of selecting a tree with the leaf disease from each category is:
$\frac{32}{71} \times \frac{19}{46} \times \frac{19}{33} = \frac{11\,552}{107\,778} = 0.107$ (to 3 sig. fig.) *[1 mark]*.

Answers

M2 Section 1 — Centres of Mass

Warm-up Questions

1) a) Particles in a horizontal line so use $\Sigma mx = \overline{x}\Sigma m$

$m_1x_1 + m_2x_2 + m_3x_3 = \overline{x}(m_1 + m_2 + m_3)$

$\Rightarrow (1 \times 1) + (2 \times 2) + (3 \times 3) = \overline{x}(1 + 2 + 3)$

$\Rightarrow 14 = 6\overline{x} \Rightarrow \overline{x} = 14 \div 6 = 2\frac{1}{3}$.

So coordinates are $(2\frac{1}{3}, 0)$.

b) Particles in a vertical line so use $\Sigma my = \overline{y}\Sigma m$

$m_1y_1 + m_2y_2 + m_3y_3 = \overline{y}(m_1 + m_2 + m_3)$

$\Rightarrow (1 \times 3) + (2 \times 2) + (3 \times 1) = \overline{y}(1 + 2 + 3)$

$\Rightarrow 10 = 6\overline{y} \Rightarrow \overline{y} = 10 \div 6 = 1\frac{2}{3}$.

So coordinates are $(0, 1\frac{2}{3})$.

c) Particles in 2D so use $\Sigma m\mathbf{r} = \overline{\mathbf{r}}\Sigma m$

$m_1\mathbf{r}_1 + m_2\mathbf{r}_2 + m_3\mathbf{r}_3 = \overline{\mathbf{r}}(m_1 + m_2 + m_3)$

$\Rightarrow 1\binom{3}{4} + 2\binom{3}{1} + 3\binom{1}{0} = \overline{\mathbf{r}}(1 + 2 + 3)$

$\Rightarrow \binom{12}{6} = 6\overline{\mathbf{r}} \Rightarrow \overline{\mathbf{r}} = \binom{12}{6} \div 6 = \binom{2}{1}$.

So coordinates are (2, 1).

2) Use $\Sigma m\mathbf{r} = \overline{\mathbf{r}}\Sigma m$

$m\binom{0}{0} + 2m\binom{0}{4} + 3m\binom{5}{4} + 12\binom{5}{0} = (m + 2m + 3m + 12)\binom{3.5}{2}$

$\Rightarrow \binom{15m + 60}{20m} = \binom{21m + 42}{12m + 24}$

$\Rightarrow 20m = 12m + 24 \Rightarrow 8m = 24 \Rightarrow m = 24 \div 8 = 3$ kg.

3) a) Large rectangle (1) has area $2 \times 3 = 6$, so $m_1 = 6$.

$x_1 = 2$ and $y_1 = 2.5$ (symmetry).

Square (2) has area $1 \times 1 = 1$, so $m_2 = 1$.

$x_2 = 3.5$ and $y_2 = 1.5$ (symmetry).

Combined shape has:

$m_1x_1 + m_2x_2 = \overline{x}(m_1 + m_2)$

$(6 \times 2) + (1 \times 3.5) = (6 + 1)\overline{x}$

$\Rightarrow 15.5 = 7\overline{x} \Rightarrow \overline{x} = 15.5 \div 7 = 2.21$ (3 s.f.).

and:

$m_1y_1 + m_2y_2 = \overline{y}(m_1 + m_2)$

$\Rightarrow (6 \times 2.5) + (1 \times 1.5) = (6 + 1)\overline{y}$

$\Rightarrow 16.5 = 7\overline{y} \Rightarrow \overline{y} = 16.5 \div 7 = 2.36$ (3 s.f.).

So coordinates are (2.21, 2.36).

You could also have used the formula in 2D to find this, but sometimes it's nice to find each coordinate separately.

b) Semicircle (1) has area $\frac{1}{2} \times \pi \times 3^2 = 4.5\pi$, so $m_1 = 4.5\pi$.

$x_1 = 8$ (symmetry) and $y_1 = 1 + \dfrac{2 \times 3 \times \sin\frac{\pi}{2}}{\frac{3\pi}{2}} = \dfrac{4 + \pi}{\pi}$

(COM is $\dfrac{2r\sin\alpha}{3\alpha}$ up from the centre of the circle, where $2\alpha = \pi$).

Don't forget — the arc angle is 2α not α...

Triangle (2) has area $\frac{1}{2} \times 2 \times 1 = 1$, so $m_2 = 1$.

$x_2 = 8$ (symmetry) and $y_2 = \frac{2}{3} \times 1 = \frac{2}{3}$ ($\frac{2}{3}$ up the median from the bottom vertex).

Combined shape has $\overline{x} = 8$ (symmetry) and:

$m_1y_1 + m_2y_2 = \overline{y}(m_1 + m_2)$

$\Rightarrow (4.5\pi \times \dfrac{4 + \pi}{\pi}) + (1 \times \frac{2}{3}) = (4.5\pi + 1)\overline{y}$

$\Rightarrow 18\frac{2}{3} + 4.5\pi = (4.5\pi + 1)\overline{y}$

$\Rightarrow \overline{y} = (18\frac{2}{3} + 4.5\pi) \div (4.5\pi + 1) = 2.167$ (to 3 d.p.).

So coordinates are (8, 2.167).

c) Circle (1) has area $\pi \times 2^2 = 4\pi$, so $m_1 = 4\pi$.

$x_1 = 14$ and $y_1 = 2$ (symmetry).

Square (2) has area $1 \times 1 = 1$, so $m_2 = 1$.

$x_2 = 14.5$ and $y_2 = 2.5$ (symmetry).

Using the removal method:

$m_1\mathbf{r}_1 - m_2\mathbf{r}_2 = \overline{\mathbf{r}}(m_1 - m_2)$

$\Rightarrow 4\pi\binom{14}{2} - 1\binom{14.5}{2.5} = (4\pi - 1)\overline{\mathbf{r}}$

$\Rightarrow \binom{56\pi - 14.5}{8\pi - 2.5} = (4\pi - 1)\overline{\mathbf{r}}$

$\Rightarrow \overline{\mathbf{r}} = \binom{56\pi - 14.5}{8\pi - 2.5} \div (4\pi - 1) = \binom{13.957}{1.957}$ (to 3 d.p.).

So coordinates are (13.957, 1.957).

4)

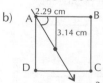

Large square (1) has area $10 \times 10 = 100$, so $m_1 = 100$.

$y_1 = 5$ cm from top edge (symmetry).

Small square (2) has area $2 \times 2 = 4$, so $m_2 = 4$.

$y_2 = 1$ cm from top edge (symmetry).

Using the removal method:

$m_1y_1 - m_2y_2 = \overline{y}(m_1 - m_2)$

$\Rightarrow (100 \times 5) - (4 \times 1) = (100 - 4)\overline{y}$

$\Rightarrow 496 = 96\overline{y} \Rightarrow \overline{y} = 496 \div 96 = 5.167$ cm from the top edge (to 3 d.p.).

You can pick any place to be the origin, but the top edge makes most sense here.

5) a) i) $m_1y_1 + m_2y_2 + m_3y_3 + m_4y_4 = \overline{y}(m_1 + m_2 + m_3 + m_4)$

$(7 \times 0) + (6 \times 0) + (10 \times 5) + (12 \times 5) = \overline{y}(7 + 6 + 10 + 12)$

$110 = 35\overline{y} \Rightarrow \overline{y} = 3.14$ cm.

The framework is 'light' so it has no mass.

ii) $m_1x_1 + m_2x_2 + m_3x_3 + m_4x_4 = \overline{x}(m_1 + m_2 + m_3 + m_4)$

$(7 \times 0) + (6 \times 5) + (10 \times 5) + (12 \times 0) = \overline{x}(7 + 6 + 10 + 12)$

$80 = 35\overline{x} \Rightarrow \overline{x} = 2.29$ cm.

b)

Angle $= \tan^{-1}\dfrac{3.14}{2.29} = 54°$ to the nearest degree.

Answers

6) P is a uniform cylinder, so the COM will be directly in the middle: on the axis of symmetry, 3 cm up from the base. When P is on the point of toppling, its COM is directly above the 'bottom edge', as shown:

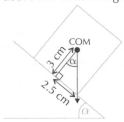

Now using trig on the right-angled triangle:
$$\alpha = \tan^{-1}\left(\frac{2.5}{3}\right) = 40° \text{ to the nearest degree.}$$

Exam Questions

1   a) Using the formula $\Sigma my = \overline{y}\Sigma m$
$$m_1y_1 + m_2y_2 + m_3y_3 = \overline{y}(m_1 + m_2 + m_3)$$
$$\Rightarrow (4 \times 3) + (3 \times 1) + (2 \times y) = 2 \times (4 + 3 + 2) \text{ [1 mark]}$$
$$\Rightarrow 15 + 2y = 18 \text{ [1 mark]}$$
$$\Rightarrow y = (18 - 15) \div 2 = 1.5 \text{ [1 mark].}$$

   b) Using the formula $\Sigma mx = \overline{x}\Sigma m$
$$m_1x_1 + m_2x_2 + m_3x_3 = \overline{x}(m_1 + m_2 + m_3)$$
$$\Rightarrow (4 \times 1) + (3 \times 5) + (2 \times 4) = \overline{x}(4 + 3 + 2) \text{ [1 mark]}$$
$$\Rightarrow 27 = 9\overline{x} \text{ [1 mark]}$$
$$\Rightarrow \overline{x} = 27 \div 9 = 3 \text{ [1 mark].}$$

   c) Centre of mass of the lamina is at (3.5, 2.5), due to the symmetry of the shape, and $m_{lamina} = 6$ kg.
Centre of mass of the group of particles is (3, 2) (from (b)) and $m_{particles} = 4 + 3 + 2 = 9$ kg. Using $\Sigma m\mathbf{r} = \overline{\mathbf{r}}\Sigma m$:
$$m_{lamina}\mathbf{r}_{lamina} + m_{particles}\mathbf{r}_{particles} = \overline{\mathbf{r}}(m_{lamina} + m_{particles})$$
$$\Rightarrow 6\binom{3.5}{2.5} + 9\binom{3}{2} = \overline{\mathbf{r}}(6 + 9)$$
$$\Rightarrow \binom{21 + 27}{15 + 18} = 15\overline{\mathbf{r}}$$
$$\Rightarrow \overline{\mathbf{r}} = \binom{48}{33} \div 15 = \binom{3.2}{2.2},$$
so the coordinates are (3.2, 2.2).

[6 marks available — 1 mark for the correct x_{lamina}, 1 mark for the correct y_{lamina}, 1 mark for correct entry of horizontal positions in the formula, 1 mark for correct entry of vertical positions in the formula, 1 mark for x coordinate of 3.2, 1 mark for y coordinate of 2.2.]

2   a) Splitting up the shape into a triangle (1), large square (2) and small square (3), where the mass of each shape is proportional to the area, gives the following masses:
$$m_1 = \frac{1}{2} \times 70 \times 30 = 1050.$$
$$m_2 = 50 \times 50 = 2500.$$
$$m_3 = 10 \times 10 = 100.$$

Taking the point A as the origin, the position vectors of the centres of mass of each shape are as follows:

Triangle:
$x_1 = 25$ (due to the symmetry of the shape) and
$y_1 = 50 + (\frac{1}{3} \times 30) = 60$ (since the COM of a triangle is $\frac{2}{3}$ down the median from the vertex, and so $\frac{1}{3}$ up from the edge). So $\mathbf{r}_1 = \binom{25}{60}$.

Large Square:
$x_2 = 25$ and $y_2 = 25$ (due to the symmetry of the shape) so $\mathbf{r}_2 = \binom{25}{25}$.

Small Square:
$x_3 = 50 + 5 = 55$ and $y_3 = 5$ (due to the symmetry of the shape) so $\mathbf{r}_3 = \binom{55}{5}$.

Using the formula $\Sigma m\mathbf{r} = \overline{\mathbf{r}}\Sigma m$
$$m_1\mathbf{r}_1 + m_2\mathbf{r}_2 + m_3\mathbf{r}_3 = \overline{\mathbf{r}}(m_1 + m_2 + m_3) \Rightarrow$$
$$1050\binom{25}{60} + 2500\binom{25}{25} + 100\binom{55}{5} = \overline{\mathbf{r}}(1050 + 2500 + 100)$$
$$\Rightarrow \binom{26250 + 62500 + 5500}{63000 + 62500 + 500} = 3650\overline{\mathbf{r}}$$
$$\Rightarrow \overline{\mathbf{r}} = \binom{94250}{126000} \div 3650 = \binom{25.8219...}{34.5205...}.$$

So, to 3 s.f., the centre of mass of the sign is 25.8 cm from AB and 34.5 cm from AI.

[6 marks available — 1 mark for masses in the correct proportion, 1 mark for each individual centre of mass entered correctly into the formula, 1 mark for correct distance from AB, 1 mark for correct distance from AI.]

   b) For the sign to hang with AI horizontal, the centre of mass of the whole system (sign + particle) must be vertically below D, i.e. $\overline{x}$ must be 25 (taking A as the origin again).

Given that $m_{sign} = 1$ kg and $x_{sign} = 25.8219...$ (from (a)), and $x_{particle} = 0$ (since it's attached at the origin):
$$m_{sign}x_{sign} + m_{particle}x_{particle} = \overline{x}(m_{sign} + m_{particle})$$
$$(1 \times 25.8219...) + 0 = 25(1 + m_{particle})$$
$$\Rightarrow 25.8219... \div 25 = 1 + m_{particle}$$
$$\Rightarrow 1.03287... - 1 = m_{particle}$$
$$\Rightarrow m_{particle} = 0.0329 \text{ kg, to 3 s.f.}$$

[3 marks available — 1 mark stating the correct required value of $\overline{x}$, 1 mark for correct entry of values into the formula, 1 mark for correct final answer.]

3   a) The stencil is a rectangle (1) with a quarter circle (2) of radius $(10 - 2) = 8$ cm removed. The lamina is uniform so mass is proportional to area, so $m_1 = 12 \times 10 = 120$, and $m_2 = \frac{1}{4} \times \pi \times 8^2 = 16\pi$.

Taking O as the origin, the position of the centre of mass of the rectangle, $\mathbf{r}_1 = \binom{6}{5}$ (from the symmetry of the shape).

The sector angle $2\alpha = \frac{\pi}{2}$, so $\alpha = \frac{\pi}{4}$, and the centre of mass of the sector is $\frac{2r\sin\alpha}{3\alpha}$ from O along the axis of symmetry
$$= \frac{2 \times 8 \times \sin\frac{\pi}{4}}{\frac{3\pi}{4}} = \frac{64}{3\pi\sqrt{2}} \text{ cm.}$$

This is on the formula sheet — you just have to know how to use it. And you'll have to use trig to find the position vector... In the right-angled triangle below, $\cos\alpha = x/hyp$, and $\sin\alpha = y/hyp$, so with a bit of rearranging you can find x and y for the position vector...

238

Answers

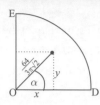

Using trig, the position vector of the centre of mass of the

sector, $r_2 = \begin{pmatrix} \frac{64}{3\pi\sqrt{2}} \times \cos\frac{\pi}{4} \\ \frac{64}{3\pi\sqrt{2}} \times \sin\frac{\pi}{4} \end{pmatrix} = \begin{pmatrix} \frac{32}{3\pi} \\ \frac{32}{3\pi} \end{pmatrix}$.

Using the removal method:

$m_1 r_1 - m_2 r_2 = \bar{r}(m_1 - m_2)$

$\Rightarrow 120\binom{6}{5} - 16\pi\begin{pmatrix} \frac{32}{3\pi} \\ \frac{32}{3\pi} \end{pmatrix} = \bar{r}(120 - 16\pi)$

$\Rightarrow \begin{pmatrix} 720 - \frac{512}{3} \\ 600 - \frac{512}{3} \end{pmatrix} = \bar{r}(120 - 16\pi)$

$\Rightarrow \begin{pmatrix} \frac{1648}{3} \\ \frac{1288}{3} \end{pmatrix} \div (120 - 16\pi) = \bar{r}$

$\Rightarrow \bar{r} = \begin{pmatrix} 7.8774... \\ 6.1566... \end{pmatrix}$.

So, to 3 s.f., the coordinates of the centre of mass of the stencil are (7.88, 6.16).

[7 marks available — 1 mark for the correct total mass, 1 mark for correct r_y, 1 mark for correct r_x, 1 mark for correct entry of horizontal positions in the formula, 1 mark for correct entry of vertical positions in the formula, 1 mark for x coordinate of 7.88, 1 mark for y coordinate of 6.16.]

(b) At the point of toppling, the centre of mass will be vertically above the point D, as shown:

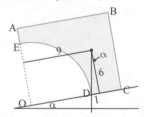

Horizontal distance from D to the centre of mass
= 9 − 8 = 1 cm *[1 mark]*.

Using trig, $\alpha = \tan^{-1}\left(\frac{1}{6}\right)$ *[1 mark]* = 0.165 rads to 3 s.f. *[1 mark]*.

4 a) (i) Setting M as the origin, the distance of the centre of mass from MP is the horizontal distance $\bar{x}$.
For each element, the masses and centres are:
Particle at A: $m_A = 3m$ and $x_A = -10$ (since A is 10 cm to the left of M).
Particle at B: $m_B = 4m$ and $x_B = 10$.
Straight rod: $m_{rod} = 2m$ and $x_{rod} = 0$ (M is the midpoint of the rod, which is the centre of its mass).
Arc: $m_{arc} = \pi m$ and $x_{arc} = 0$ (due to the symmetry of the semicircular arc).
Don't forget to include the masses of all the rods and arcs — unless you're told that they're 'light'.
Combining these elements in the formula $\Sigma mx = \bar{x}\Sigma m$
$m_A x_A + m_B x_B + m_{rod} x_{rod} + m_{arc} x_{arc} = \bar{x}(m_A + m_B + m_{rod} + m_{arc})$
$\Rightarrow (3m \times -10) + (4m \times 10) + (2m \times 0) + (\pi m \times 0)$
$= \bar{x}(3m + 4m + 2m + \pi m)$
$\Rightarrow -30m + 40m = (9 + \pi)m\bar{x}$
$\Rightarrow \bar{x} = 10 \div (9 + \pi) = 0.8236$ cm to 4 d.p.
[3 marks available — 1 mark for correct total mass of system, 1 mark for correct entry into formula, 1 mark for correct final answer.]

(ii) With M as the origin still, the distance of the centre of mass from AB is the vertical distance $\bar{y}$.
So: $y_A = y_B = y_{rod} = 0$, since all three lie on the line AB.
For the arc, use the formula $y_{arc} = \frac{r\sin\alpha}{\alpha}$, where $r = 10$, and $\alpha = \frac{\pi}{2}$ (since the angle at the centre, $2\alpha = \pi$), so
$y_{arc} = \frac{10\sin\frac{\pi}{2}}{\frac{\pi}{2}} = \frac{20}{\pi}$.
This is on the formula sheet if you can't remember in the exam...
Combining these in the formula $\Sigma my = \bar{y}\Sigma m$
$m_A y_A + m_B y_B + m_{rod} y_{rod} + m_{arc} y_{arc} = \bar{y}(m_A + m_B + m_{rod} + m_{arc})$
$\Rightarrow (\pi m \times \frac{20}{\pi}) = (9 + \pi)m\bar{y}$
$\Rightarrow \bar{y} = 20 \div (9 + \pi) = 1.6472$ cm to 4 d.p.
[3 marks available — 1 mark for correct value of y_{arc}, 1 mark for correct entry into formula, 1 mark for correct final answer.]

b) On a sketch, draw a line from P to the centre of mass to represent the vertical and label relevant lengths and angles:

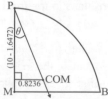

The vertical distance between P and the centre of mass =
10 − 1.6472 (from (a)(ii)) = 8.3528 cm *[1 mark]*.
Using trig:
$\theta = \tan^{-1}\left(\frac{0.8236}{8.3528}\right)$ *[1 mark]* = 0.0983 rads to 3 s.f. *[1 mark]*.

Answers

5 a) Find the centre of mass using the removal method, by subtracting the triangle (2) from the circle (1).

Since both the circle and the triangle that's removed from it are made from the same uniform material, their masses are in proportion to their areas:

Circle $m_1 = \pi r^2 = \pi \times 2^2 = 4\pi$.

Triangle $m_2 = \frac{1}{2} \times 1.5 \times 1.5 = 1.125$.

Taking the point P as the origin, the centre of mass of the circle, $\mathbf{r}_1 = \binom{0}{0}$, since P is the centre of the circle.

The centre of mass of the triangle is at the mean of the coordinates of $P(0,0)$, $Q(0, 1.5)$ and $R(1.5, 0)$, so:

$\mathbf{r}_2 = \binom{(0 + 0 + 1.5) \div 3}{(0 + 1.5 + 0) \div 3} = \binom{0.5}{0.5}$.

Using the removal method:

$m_1\mathbf{r}_1 - m_2\mathbf{r}_2 = \bar{\mathbf{r}}(m_1 - m_2)$

$\Rightarrow 4\pi\binom{0}{0} - 1.125\binom{0.5}{0.5} = \bar{\mathbf{r}}(4\pi - 1.125)$

$\Rightarrow \binom{-0.5625}{-0.5625} = 11.4413...\bar{\mathbf{r}}$

$\Rightarrow \bar{\mathbf{r}} = \binom{-0.5625 \div 11.4413...}{-0.5625 \div 11.4413...} = \binom{-0.04916...}{-0.04916...}$.

The <u>distance</u> of the COM from P is the magnitude of the position vector:

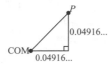

Distance $= \sqrt{0.04916...^2 + 0.04916...^2} = 0.06952...$
$= 0.070$ cm to 3 d.p.

There are other ways to find the centre of mass of this shape, because you can think of it in a different orientation, or take another point as the origin, but this way's as easy as any.

[5 marks available — 1 mark for correct masses of both shapes, 1 mark for individual centre of mass for both shapes, 1 mark for correct use of removal method formula, 1 mark for correct position vector or coordinates of centre of mass, 1 mark for correct distance from P.]

b) The shape is being hung from Q. Drawing a sketch will make it easier to see what's going on:

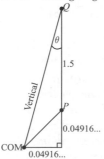

θ is the angle that PQ makes with the vertical.
Using basic trigonometry:

$\theta = \tan^{-1}\left(\dfrac{0.04916...}{1.5 + 0.04916...}\right) = 1.8177... = 1.8°$ to 1 d.p.

[3 marks available — 1 mark for correct sides of the right-angled triangle, 1 mark for correct working, 1 mark for correct final answer.]

6 a) Call the 5 × 4 rectangle 'A' and the 5 × 3 rectangle 'B'. The masses of A and B are proportional to their areas, so $m_A = 20$ and $m_B = 15$ **[1 mark]**. A and B are both uniform, so their centres of mass are at their respective centres: COM$_A$ = (0, –2, 2.5) **[1 mark]** and COM$_B$ = (1.5, 0, 2.5) **[1 mark]**. The shape has a plane of symmetry at $z = 2.5$, so $\bar{z} = 2.5$ **[1 mark]**. Use $\Sigma m\mathbf{r} = \bar{\mathbf{r}}\Sigma m$ to find the x- and y-coordinates of the COM **[1 mark]**:

$20\binom{0}{-2} + 15\binom{1.5}{0} = 35\binom{\bar{x}}{\bar{y}}$

$\Rightarrow \binom{\bar{x}}{\bar{y}} = \dfrac{1}{35}\binom{22.5}{-40} = \binom{0.643}{-1.143}$ **[1 mark]**

So the coordinates of the centre of mass of the shape are $(\bar{x}, \bar{y}, \bar{z}) = (0.643, –1.14, 2.50)$ (3 s.f.)

b) View the shape from 'side-on':

When the shape is on the point of toppling, its COM will be directly above OB:

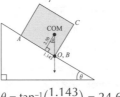

$\theta = \tan^{-1}\left(\dfrac{1.143}{2.50}\right) = 24.6°$ (3 s.f.)

[4 marks available — 1 mark for forming right-angled triangle, 1 mark for correct sides of the right-angled triangle, 1 mark for correct working, 1 mark for correct final answer.]

7   As the traffic cone is made from uniform material, the masses of the parts are proportional to their areas.
So $m_B = 0.25$. **[1 mark]**
Find the sloped length of A using Pythagoras:
$l = \sqrt{0.15^2 + 1.2^2} = 1.2093...$ m.
So $m_A = \pi \times 0.15 \times 1.2093... = 0.5698...$ **[1 mark]**
As B is a uniform square lamina, its centre of mass is at its centre, O, i.e. $y_B = 0$ m from O. **[1 mark]**
Using the formula for COM of conical shell:

$y_A = \dfrac{1}{3}(1.2) = 0.4$ m from O. **[1 mark]**

Now use $\Sigma my = \bar{y}\Sigma m$ to find the COM of C: **[1 mark]**

$m_B y_B + m_A y_A = m_C y_C$

$\Rightarrow 0.25(0) + 0.5698...(0.4) = (0.25 + 0.5698...)y_C$

$\Rightarrow y_C = 0.28$ m (2 d.p.)

So, centre of mass of the traffic cone is 0.28 m vertically above O, on a line through O and the vertex of A. **[1 mark]**

Answers

M2 Section 2 — Force

Warm-up Questions

1) Resolving perpendicular to slope, taking ↖ as +ve:

$F_{net} = ma$

$R - 1.2g\cos25° = 1.2 \times 0$

$R = 1.2g\cos25° = 10.66$ N.

Resolving parallel to slope, taking down slope as +ve:

$F_{net} = ma$

$1.2g\sin25° - F = 1.2 \times 0.3$

So, $F = 1.2g\sin25° - 1.2 \times 0.3 = 4.61$ N

Limiting friction, so:

$F = \mu R$

$4.61 = \mu \times 10.66$

$\mu = 0.43$ (to 2 d.p.)

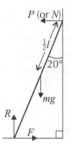

2) Moments about B: $60g \times 3 = T_2 \times 8$

So $T_2 = \dfrac{180g}{8} = 220.5$ N

Vertically balanced forces, so $T_1 + T_2 = 60g$

$T_1 = 367.5$ N

3) A rod (a long, inextensible particle) where the centre of mass is not at the central point of the rod.

M2 statics is pretty rod-heavy. Think of them as really simple sticks. They don't bend, don't stretch or compress, and have no width.

4) Where:

mg = weight of the ladder
F = friction between ground and ladder
R = normal reaction of the ground
P / N = normal reaction of the wall

As the rod is uniform the weight of the ladder acts at the centre of the rod (i.e. at half of l).

Assumptions: e.g. the ladder can be modelled as a rod, the ladder is rigid, friction is sufficient to keep the ladder in equilibrium, the ladder is perpendicular to the wall when viewed from above.

'Perpendicular' and 'normal' are both used in M2 (as are 'P' and 'N' to label the forces). No need to panic — they mean the same thing in all you'll do here.

5) a)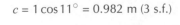

$a = 0.8\sin39.6° = 0.510$ m (3 s.f.)

b) $b = 3\sin50° = 2.30$ m (3 s.f.)

c) $c = 1\cos11° = 0.982$ m (3 s.f.)

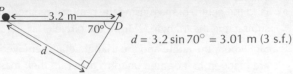

$d = 3.2\sin70° = 3.01$ m (3 s.f.)

The perpendicular distance is always the shortest distance between a point and a force's line of action. Simple.

6) a) Resolving the forces vertically:

$42 = 28\cos30° + T\cos38.3°$

so $T = \dfrac{42 - 14\sqrt{3}}{\cos38.3°} = 22.6$ N (3 s.f.)

b) Taking moments about the left-end:

$42xy = 28\cos30°(xy + y)$

$42xy - (28\cos30°)(xy) = (28\cos30°)y$

$17.75xy = 24.25y$

$x = 1.37$ (3 s.f.)

Exam Questions

1) a) Taking moments about A:

$2g \times 0.4 = 30\cos55° \times x$

so $x = \dfrac{7.84}{17.2} = 0.456$ m

[3 marks available in total]:
- **1 mark for taking moments about A**
- **1 mark for correct workings**
- **1 mark for correct value of x**

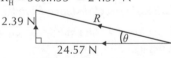

I've made an educated guess in the diagram above at which directions R_V and R_H act in. If I work out their values and they turn out to be negative then I just need to reverse their direction.

b) Resolving vertically:

$R_V = 2g - 30\cos55° = 2.39$ N

Resolving horizontally:

$R_H = 30\sin55° = 24.57$ N

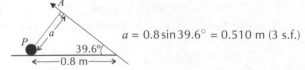

$|R| = \sqrt{2.39^2 + 24.57^2} = 24.7$ N

$\tan\theta = \dfrac{2.39}{24.57}$

so $\theta = 5.56°$ to the horizontal

[5 marks available in total]:
- **1 mark for resolving vertically**
- **1 mark for resolving horizontally**
- **1 mark for correct workings**
- **1 mark for correct magnitude of R**
- **1 mark for correct direction**

Answers

2

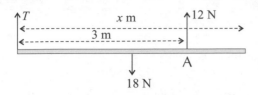

Taking moments about end string:

$12 \times 3 = 18 \times \frac{x}{2}$ so, $36 = 9x$

$x = 4$ m

[3 marks available in total]:
- *1 mark for diagram*
- *1 mark for correct workings*
- *1 mark for showing that x = 4 m*

3 a)

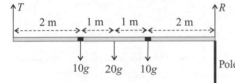

[2 marks available in total]:
- *1 mark for diagram*
- *1 mark for correct labelling*

b) Take moments about the pole:

$6T = (2 \times 10g) + (3 \times 20g) + (4 \times 10g)$

$6T = 20g + 60g + 40g = 120g$

So, $T = 20g$

[3 marks available in total]:
- *1 mark for taking moments about the pole*
- *1 mark for correct workings*
- *1 mark for correct value of T*

Why work around the pole? Because we have no idea what the magnitude of R is and working there allows us to ignore it.

c) Resolve vertically:

$T + R = 10g + 20g + 10g$

$20g + R = 40g$

So, $R = 20g$

[2 marks available in total]:
- *1 mark for resolving vertically*
- *1 mark for correct value of R*

I suppose we could have found R first and then T, but that's not the order the questions are in, so it's best just to run with it...

4 a) Resolve horizontally:

$T\cos\theta = 72.5$ N

$\tan\theta = \dfrac{0.8}{1.7}$

$\Rightarrow \theta = 25.201...°$

so $T = \dfrac{72.5}{\cos\theta}$

$\quad = 80.126... = 80.1$ N (3 s.f.)

[4 marks available in total]:
- *1 mark for resolving horizontally*
- *1 mark for calculating θ or cosθ*
- *1 mark for correct workings*
- *1 mark for correct value of T*

b) Taking moments about A:

$(1.2 \times 3g) + (2.4 \times mg) = 1.7 \times \dfrac{72.5}{\cos\theta} \times \sin\theta$

$35.28 + 23.52m = 1.7 \times 72.5 \times \tan\theta$

so $23.52m = 58 - 35.28 = 22.72$

and $m = 0.965... = 0.966$ kg (3 s.f)

[3 marks available in total]:
- *1 mark for taking moments about A*
- *1 mark for correct workings*
- *1 mark for correct value of m*

c) Resolving vertically:

$F + \dfrac{72.5}{\cos\theta}\sin\theta = 3g + 0.965... \times g$

so $F = 38.86... - 34.117... = 4.75$ N (3 s.f)

[3 marks available in total]:
- *1 mark for resolving vertically*
- *1 mark for correct workings*
- *1 mark for correct value of F*

5 a) Taking moments about A:

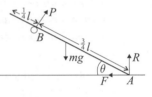

$\frac{1}{2}l \times mg\cos\theta = \frac{3}{4}l \times P$

so $P = \dfrac{\frac{1}{2}lmg\cos\theta}{\frac{3}{4}l} = \frac{2}{3}mg\cos\theta$

[3 marks available in total]:
- *1 mark for taking moments about A*
- *1 mark for correct workings*
- *1 mark for correct answer*

Mechanics is harder with algebra than with numbers, but once you've mastered it, doing it with numbers will seem trivial. I know it's not nice, but at least it's useful.

b) $\sin\theta = \frac{3}{5}$ so $\cos\theta = \frac{4}{5}$

Using the result of part a) gives $P = \frac{8}{15}mg$

Resolving horizontally:

$F = P\sin\theta = \frac{8}{15}mg \times \frac{3}{5} = \frac{8}{25}mg$

Resolving vertically:

$R + P\cos\theta = mg$

so $R = mg - \frac{4}{5}P = mg - \frac{32}{75}mg = \frac{43}{75}mg$

Non-limiting equilibrium so $F \le \mu R$

so $\frac{8}{25}mg \le \mu\frac{43}{75}mg$ and $\mu \ge \frac{24}{43} = 0.56$

[6 marks available in total]:
- *1 mark for finding P*
- *1 mark for resolving horizontally*
- *1 mark for resolving vertically*
- *1 mark for using F ≤ μR*
- *1 mark for correct workings*
- *1 mark for correct value of μ*

That wasn't much fun, but it's good to get some use out of your calculator's fraction button. Unless you did it without a calculator, in which case, congratulations, you're officially 'hardcore'.

Answers

6 a) Resolving parallel to slope,
taking up the slope as +ve:

$F_{net} = ma$

$8\cos15° + F - 7g\sin15° = 7 \times 0$

$F = 7g\sin15° - 8\cos15°$

$F = 10.03$ N

Resolving perpendicular to slope,
taking ↖ as +ve:

$F_{net} = ma$

$R - 8\sin15° - 7g\cos15° = 7 \times 0$

$R = 8\sin15° + 7g\cos15° = 68.33$ N

Limiting friction:

$F = \mu R$, i.e. $10.03 = \mu \times 68.33$,

which gives $\mu = 0.15$ (2 d.p.)

[5 marks available in total]:
- *1 mark for resolving parallel to slope*
- *1 mark for correct value of F_{net} in this direction*
- *1 mark for resolving perpendicular to slope*
- *1 mark correct value of R*
- *1 mark for correct value of μ*

b) 8 N removed:

Resolving parallel to the plane, taking down
the plane as +ve:

$7g\sin15° - F = 7a$ ①

Resolving perpendicular to slope, taking ↖ as +ve:

$R - 7g\cos15° = 7 \times 0$

$R = 7g\cos15° = 66.26$ N

$F = \mu R$

$F = 0.147 \times 66.26 = 9.74$ N

①: $7g\sin15° - 9.74 = 7a$

$a = \dfrac{8.01}{7} = 1.14$ ms⁻² (to 2 d.p.)

$s = 3;\ u = 0;\ a = 1.14;\ t = ?$ $s = ut + \frac{1}{2}at^2$

$3 = 0 + \frac{1}{2} \times 1.14 \times t^2$ $t = \sqrt{\dfrac{6}{1.14}} = 2.3$ s (to 2 s.f.)

[7 marks available in total]:
- *1 mark for resolving parallel to slope*
- *1 mark for resolving perpendicular to slope*
- *1 mark for correct value of R*
- *1 mark for correct value of F*
- *1 mark for correct value of a*
- *1 mark for appropriate calculation method for t*
- *1 mark for correct value of t*

7 a) Taking moments about B:

$(mg\cos\theta \times 1.4) + (180\cos\theta \times 2.1)$

$= (490\sin\theta \times 4.2)$

Dividing by $\cos\theta$ gives:

$1.4mg + 378 = 2058\tan\theta = 2058 \times \dfrac{8}{11}$

so, $1.4mg = 2058 \times \dfrac{8}{11} - 378$

so $m = 81.539... = 82$ kg (nearest kg)

[4 marks available in total]:
- *1 mark for taking moments about B*
- *1 mark for both sides of moments equation correct*
- *1 mark for correct workings*
- *1 mark for the correct value of m*

490 N

AB = 4.2 m
AC = 2.8 m
BC = 1.4 m

180 N

b) Resolving horizontally:

$F = 490$ N

Resolving vertically:

$R = 180 + 81.539... \times g = 979.1$ N (4 s.f.)

As equilibrium is limiting, $F = \mu R$

so $979.1\mu = 490$ N and $\mu = 0.500$ (3 s.f.)

[5 marks available in total]:
- *1 mark for resolving horizontally*
- *1 mark for resolving vertically*
- *1 mark for using F = μR*
- *1 mark for correct workings*
- *1 mark for correct value of μ*

8 a)

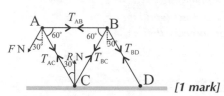

[1 mark]

b) From the diagram, all internal forces assumed to be
tensions. Resolve at the joints to find internal forces:

At A: Vertically:

$F\cos30 + T_{AC}\sin60 = 0$

$\Rightarrow T_{AC} = -F\cos30 \div \sin60 = -F$ N.

Horizontally:

$F\sin30 = T_{AC}\cos60 + T_{AB}$

$\Rightarrow T_{AB} = F\sin30 - T_{AC}\cos60$

$= 0.5F - (-0.5F) = F$ N.

At C: Horizontally:

$T_{AC}\sin30 = T_{BC}\sin30$

$\Rightarrow T_{BC} = T_{AC} = -F$ N.

Vertically:

$T_{AC}\cos30 + T_{BC}\cos30 + R = 0$

$\Rightarrow -F\cos30 - F\cos30 + R = 0$

$\Rightarrow R = 2F\cos30 = \sqrt{3}F$ N.

At B: Vertically:

$T_{BC}\cos30 + T_{BD}\cos30 = 0$

$\Rightarrow T_{BD} = -T_{BC} = F$ N.

So T_{AC} and T_{BC} are compressions of F N,
T_{AB} and T_{BD} are tensions of F N and $R = \sqrt{3}F$ N.

[7 marks available in total]:
- *1 mark for attempting to resolve and apply equilibrium conditions*
- *1 mark each for T_{AB}, T_{BC}, T_{AC}, T_{BD} correct*
- *1 mark for thrusts and tensions consistent with diagram*
- *1 mark for finding R*

Answers

9

Resolve all forces into components parallel and perpendicular to the base of the shape, as shown above.
Taking moments about A:
$4\sin30 \times 2.28 + R\cos30 \times 0 + R\sin30 \times 4 = 4\cos30 \times 2$
$2 \times 2.28 + 2R = 8\cos30$
$\Rightarrow R = (8\cos30 \div 2) - 2.28 = 1.2$ N (2 s.f.)

[4 marks available in total — 1 mark for resolving, 1 mark for attempting to take moments, 1 mark for using correct values when taking moments, 1 mark for correct answer]

10 a) The sign has a plane of symmetry at $x = 2.5$. As the horizontal force of magnitude H acts in this plane, you can ignore the x-coordinate and consider the sign as a 2D shape. Here's a diagram of what's going on, viewing the sign 'side-on':

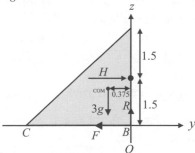

Here, F is the frictional force between the sign and the ground, $3g$ is the sign's weight, acting at the sign's COM, and R is the normal reaction of the ground on the sign, acting through B (as the sign is on the point of tipping about this point) *[1 mark]*.
Taking moments about B *[1 mark]*:
Clockwise moments: $H \times 1.5$,
Anti-clockwise moments: $3g \times 0.375$.
The sign is on the point of tipping, i.e. it is in limiting equilibrium, so:
$H \times 1.5 = 3g \times 0.375$ *[1 mark]*
$\Rightarrow H = \dfrac{0.375 \times 3 \times 9.8}{1.5} = 7.35$ N *[1 mark]*.

Taking moments about B means that you don't need to worry about F or R. You also need to remember to use the perpendicular distance to the line of action of the force when taking moments. In this case, H acts horizontally, so you want the vertical distance, 2.5, and the weight acts vertically, so you want the horizontal distance, 0.375.

b) Maximum F can be found using $F_{MAX} = \mu R$:
$F_{MAX} = 0.35mg$ *[1 mark]*
$= 0.35 \times 3 \times 9.8 = 10.29$ N *[1 mark]*.
From part a), $H = 7.35$ N.
$10.29 > 7.35$, so the frictional force is greater than the horizontal tipping force. This means that the sign will tip before it slides *[1 mark]*.

M2 Section 3 — Work, Energy and Power
Warm-up Questions

1) Work done $= F \times s$
$= 250 \times 3 = 750$ J

2) Work done against gravity $= mgh$
$34\,000 = m \times 9.8 \times 12$
$m = 289$ kg (3 s.f.)

3) Kinetic Energy $= \frac{1}{2}mv^2$
$= \frac{1}{2} \times 450 \times 13^2$
$= 38\,025$ J $= 38.0$ kJ (3 s.f.)

4) Work done $=$ Change in Kinetic Energy
$800 = \frac{1}{2}m(v^2 - u^2)$
$u = 0$ and $m = 65$, so:
$v^2 = \dfrac{1600}{65} \Rightarrow v = 4.96$ ms^{-1} (3 s.f.)

5) Increase in Potential Energy $= mg \times$ increase in height
$= 0.5 \times 9.8 \times 150$
$= 735$ J

6) "If there are no external forces doing work on an object, the total mechanical energy of the object will remain constant." You usually need to model the object as a particle, because you have to assume that the object is not acted on by any external forces such as air resistance.

7) When the hat reaches its maximum height, its velocity will be zero. Using conservation of energy:
Change in potential energy $=$ change in kinetic energy
$mgh = \frac{1}{2}m(u^2 - v^2)$
Cancel m from both sides, and substitute $u = 5$, $v = 0$ and $g = 9.8$:
$9.8h = \frac{1}{2} \times 25 \Rightarrow h = 1.28$ m (3 s.f.)

8) "The work done on an object by external forces is equal to the change in the total mechanical energy of that object." An external force is any force other than an object's weight.

9) Power of engine $=$ driving force $\times$ velocity
$350\,000 = F \times 22 \Rightarrow F = 15\,900$ N (3 s.f.)

Answers

Exam Questions

1 a) Increase in Kinetic Energy $= \frac{1}{2}m(v^2 - u^2)$ *[1 mark]*

   $= \frac{1}{2} \times 90 \times (6^2 - 4^2) = 900$ J *[1 mark]*

   Increase in Gravitational Potential Energy $= mgh$ *[1 mark]*

   $= 90 \times 9.8 \times 28\sin30° = 12\ 348$ J *[1 mark]*

   Increase in total Energy = Increase in K.E. + Increase in P.E.

   $= 900 + 12\ 348 = 13\ 248$ J $= 13.2$ kJ (3 s.f.) *[1 mark]*

 b) Using the work-energy principle:

   Work done on skier = Change in total energy *[1 mark]*

   $(L - 66) \times 28 = 13\ 248$ *[1 mark]*

   $L = \dfrac{13\ 248 + (66 \times 28)}{28} = 539$ N (3 s.f.) *[1 mark]*

2 a) K.E. $= \frac{1}{2}mv^2 = \frac{1}{2} \times 0.3 \times 20^2$ *[1 mark]*

   $= 60$ J *[1 mark]*

 b) Only force acting on the stone is its weight, so use conservation of mechanical energy:

   Change in K.E. = Change in P.E. *[1 mark]*

   $60 - 0 = 0.3 \times 9.8 \times h$ *[1 mark]*

   $h = 20.4$ m (3 s.f.) *[1 mark]*

 c) Stone's change in K.E. after hitting the water:

   $\frac{1}{2} \times 0.3 \times 1^2 - 60 = -59.85$ J *[1 mark]*

   Call the depth the stone has sunk x m.

   Change in P.E. after hitting the water:

   $-mgx = -2.94x$ *[1 mark]*

   Work done on the stone by resistive force

   $= Fs = -23x$ *[1 mark]*

   By the work-energy principle:

   Work done on the stone = Change in total energy *[1 mark]*

   $-23x = -59.85 - 2.94x$

   Rearrange to find x:

   $x = 2.98$ m (3 s.f) *[1 mark]*

3 a)

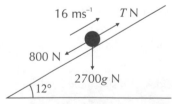

   Resolving parallel to the slope using $F = ma$ with $a = 0$:

   $T - 800 - 2700g\sin12° = 0$ *[1 mark]*

   So, $T = 6301$ N *[1 mark]*

   Power of engine = Driving Force × Velocity *[1 mark]*

   $= 6301 \times 16 = 101$ kW (3 s.f.) *[1 mark]*

 b) Work done by resistive force to stop van $= -800x$ *[1 mark]*

   Change in total energy = Change in P.E. + Change in K.E.

   $= (2700 \times g \times x\sin12°) - \left(\frac{1}{2} \times 2700 \times 16^2\right)$ *[1 mark]*

   By work-energy principle,

   $-800x = 2700gx\sin12° - 345\ 600$ *[1 mark]*

   Rearrange to find x:

   $x = \dfrac{345\ 600}{2700g\sin12° + 800} = 54.8$ m (3 s.f.) *[1 mark]*

 c) Resolve parallel to the slope using $F = ma$ to find a:

   $-800 - 2700g\sin12° = 2700a$ *[1 mark]*

   $a = -2.334$ ms⁻² *[1 mark]*

   Use $v = u + at$ to find the time taken to come to rest:

   $0 = 16 - 2.334t$ *[1 mark]*

   $t = \dfrac{16}{2.334} = 6.86$ s (3 s.f.) *[1 mark]*

4 a) Work done = Force × distance moved

   $= 800\cos40° \times 320 = 196$ kJ (3 s.f.)

   [3 marks available in total]:
   - *1 mark for using the horizontal component of the force*
   - *1 mark for correct use of formula for work done*
   - *1 mark for correct final answer.*

 b)

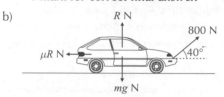

   No acceleration vertically, so:

   $R + 800\sin40° = mg$

   $R = 1500g - 800\sin40° = 14\ 186.769...$ N *[1 mark]*

   Car is moving only horizontally, so:

   Work done = change in kinetic energy *[1 mark]*

   $(800\cos40° - \mu R) \times 320 = \frac{1}{2} \times 1500 \times (16^2 - 11^2)$ *[1 mark]*

   Rearrange to find μ:

   $\mu = \dfrac{800\cos40° - 316.406...}{14\ 186.769...} = 0.0209$ (3 s.f.) *[1 mark]*

5 a) Use the work rate to find the 'driving' force, F of the cyclist:

   $250 = F \times 4$ *[1 mark]*

   $F = 62.5$ N

   Resolve parallel to the slope: *[1 mark]*

   $62.5 - 35 - 88g\sin\alpha = 0$ *[1 mark]*

   $\alpha = \sin^{-1}\dfrac{27.5}{88g} = 1.83°$ (3 s.f.) *[1 mark]*

 b) Use the new work rate to find the new 'driving' force, F':

   $370 = F' \times 4$ *[1 mark]*

   $F' = 92.5$ N

   Resolve parallel to the slope to find a: *[1 mark]*

   $92.5 - 35 - 88g\sin\alpha = 88a$ *[1 mark]*

   $a = 0.341$ ms⁻² (3 s.f.) *[1 mark]*

M2 Section 4 — Momentum and Impulse
Warm-up Questions

1) a) $(5 \times 3) + (4 \times 1) = (5 \times 2) + (4 \times v)$

   $19 = 10 + 4v$

   $v = 2\frac{1}{4}$ ms⁻¹ to the right

 b) $(5 \times 3) + (4 \times 1) = 9v$

   $19 = 9v$

   $v = 2\frac{1}{9}$ ms⁻¹ to the right

 c) $(5 \times 3) + (4 \times -2) = (5 \times -v) + (4 \times 3)$

   $7 = -5v + 12$

   $5v = 5$

   $v = 1$ ms⁻¹ to the left

Answers

d) $(m \times 6) + (8 \times 2) = (m \times 2) + (8 \times 4)$
$6m + 16 = 2m + 32$
$4m = 16$
$m = 4$ kg

Collision questions have me bouncing off the ceiling... Be careful with your directions (positive and negative) and it'll all be okay.

2) a) $m_A\mathbf{u}_A + m_B\mathbf{u}_B = m_A\mathbf{v}_A + m_B\mathbf{v}_B$, so:
$0.5(2\mathbf{i} + \mathbf{j}) + 0.4(-\mathbf{i} - 4\mathbf{j}) = 0.5(-\mathbf{i} - 2\mathbf{j}) + 0.4\mathbf{v}_B$
$\mathbf{i} + 0.5\mathbf{j} - 0.4\mathbf{i} - 1.6\mathbf{j} = -0.5\mathbf{i} - \mathbf{j} + 0.4\mathbf{v}_B$
$0.4\mathbf{v}_B = 1.1\mathbf{i} - 0.1\mathbf{j}$
$\Rightarrow \mathbf{v}_B = 2.75\mathbf{i} - 0.25\mathbf{j}$.
Speed $= |\mathbf{v}_B| = \sqrt{2.75^2 + 0.25^2} = 2.76$ ms⁻¹, to 3 s.f.

b) If they coalesce:
$0.5(2\mathbf{i} + \mathbf{j}) + 0.4(-\mathbf{i} - 4\mathbf{j}) = (0.5 + 0.4)\mathbf{v}$
$\mathbf{i} + 0.5\mathbf{j} - 0.4\mathbf{i} - 1.6\mathbf{j} = 0.9\mathbf{v}$
$0.9\mathbf{v} = 0.6\mathbf{i} - 1.1\mathbf{j} \Rightarrow \mathbf{v} = \frac{2}{3}\mathbf{i} - \frac{11}{9}\mathbf{j}$.
Speed $= |\mathbf{v}| = \sqrt{\left(\frac{2}{3}\right)^2 + \left(-\frac{11}{9}\right)^2} = 1.39$ ms⁻¹, to 3 s.f.

3) Impulse acts against motion, so $I = -2$ Ns
$I = mv - mu$
$-2 = 0.3v - (0.3 \times 5)$
$v = -1\frac{2}{3}$ ms⁻¹
Impulse has 2 different equations, I = mv − mu and I = Ft. Remember both.

4) a) $I = m\mathbf{v} - m\mathbf{u}$, so
$2\mathbf{i} + 5\mathbf{j} = 0.1\mathbf{v} - 0.1(\mathbf{i} + \mathbf{j})$
$2\mathbf{i} + 5\mathbf{j} = 0.1\mathbf{v} - 0.1\mathbf{i} - 0.1\mathbf{j}$
$0.1\mathbf{v} = 2\mathbf{i} + 5\mathbf{j} + 0.1\mathbf{i} + 0.1\mathbf{j} = 2.1\mathbf{i} + 5.1\mathbf{j}$
$\Rightarrow \mathbf{v} = 21\mathbf{i} + 51\mathbf{j}$.

b) $-3\mathbf{i} + \mathbf{j} = 0.1\mathbf{v} - 0.1\mathbf{i} - 0.1\mathbf{j}$
$0.1\mathbf{v} = -3\mathbf{i} + \mathbf{j} + 0.1\mathbf{i} + 0.1\mathbf{j} = -2.9\mathbf{i} + 1.1\mathbf{j}$
$\Rightarrow \mathbf{v} = -29\mathbf{i} + 11\mathbf{j}$.

c) $-\mathbf{i} - 6\mathbf{j} = 0.1\mathbf{v} - 0.1\mathbf{i} - 0.1\mathbf{j}$
$0.1\mathbf{v} = -\mathbf{i} - 6\mathbf{j} + 0.1\mathbf{i} + 0.1\mathbf{j} = -0.9\mathbf{i} - 5.9\mathbf{j}$
$\Rightarrow \mathbf{v} = -9\mathbf{i} - 59\mathbf{j}$.

d) $4\mathbf{i} = 0.1\mathbf{v} - 0.1\mathbf{i} - 0.1\mathbf{j}$
$0.1\mathbf{v} = 4\mathbf{i} + 0.1\mathbf{i} + 0.1\mathbf{j} = 4.1\mathbf{i} + 0.1\mathbf{j}$
$\Rightarrow \mathbf{v} = 41\mathbf{i} + \mathbf{j}$.

5) a) $I = m\mathbf{v} - m\mathbf{u}$, so
$\mathbf{Q} = 2(-2\mathbf{i} + \mathbf{j}) - 2(4\mathbf{i} - \mathbf{j}) = -4\mathbf{i} + 2\mathbf{j} - 8\mathbf{i} + 2\mathbf{j}$
$\mathbf{Q} = -12\mathbf{i} + 4\mathbf{j}$.

b)

$|\mathbf{Q}| = \sqrt{(-12)^2 + 4^2} = 12.6$ Ns, to 3 s.f.

c) $\theta = \tan^{-1}\left(\frac{4}{12}\right)$
Required angle $= 180 - \theta = 162°$ (3 s.f.)

6) Call the particles A and B. If $u_A = u$ then $u_B = -u$ (as it's going in the opposite direction at the same speed). After the collision, $v_A = 0$ and $v_B = \frac{u}{2}$ (as it's going in the opposite direction to its original motion at half the speed).
$e = \dfrac{\text{speed of separation of particles}}{\text{speed of approach of particles}} = \dfrac{v_B - v_A}{u_A - u_B}$
$\Rightarrow e = \dfrac{\frac{u}{2} - 0}{u - (-u)} = \dfrac{\frac{u}{2}}{2u} = \dfrac{u}{4u} = \dfrac{1}{4}$.

7) a) For collision with a plane surface, $e = \frac{v}{u}$, so rebound speed $v = eu \Rightarrow v = 0.4 \times 10 = 4$ ms⁻¹.

b) Call the particles A and B, so
$e = \dfrac{\text{speed of separation of particles}}{\text{speed of approach of particles}} = \dfrac{v_B - v_A}{u_A - u_B}$
$\Rightarrow 0.4 = \dfrac{v_B - v_A}{10 - (-12)} \Rightarrow v_B - v_A = 0.4 \times 22$
$\Rightarrow v_B - v_A = 8.8 \,...[1]$
Using the conservation of momentum:
$m_A u_A + m_B u_B = m_A v_A + m_B v_B$
$(1 \times 10) + (2 \times -12) = (1 \times v_A) + (2 \times v_B)$
$10 - 24 = v_A + 2v_B \Rightarrow v_A + 2v_B = -14 \,...[2]$
Equation [1] + equation [2] gives:
$3v_B = -5.2 \Rightarrow v_B = -1.7333...$ ms⁻¹.
Substituting in equation [1] gives:
$-1.7333... - v_A = 8.8$
$\Rightarrow v_A = -1.7333... - 8.8 = -10.5333...$ ms⁻¹.
So, to 3 s.f., the original particle's rebound speed is 10.5 ms⁻¹.

8) Surface is parallel to $\mathbf{i}$, so only the $\mathbf{j}$ component of velocity will change:
$\mathbf{v} = 4\mathbf{i} - e(-1)\mathbf{j} = 4\mathbf{i} + 0.5\mathbf{j}$.
Kinetic energy lost $= \frac{1}{2}m|\mathbf{v}|^2 - \frac{1}{2}m|\mathbf{u}|^2$
$= \frac{1}{2}m(4^2 + (-1)^2) - \frac{1}{2}m(4^2 + 0.5^2) = \frac{1}{2}(2)(17 - 16.25) = 0.75$ J

9) For the first collision, between A and B:
$e = \dfrac{v_B - v_A}{u_A - u_B} \Rightarrow \dfrac{1}{4} = \dfrac{v_B - v_A}{3u - 2u} \Rightarrow v_B - v_A = \dfrac{u}{4} \,...[1]$
And:
$m_A u_A + m_B u_B = m_A v_A + m_B v_B$
$(1 \times 3u) + (4 \times 2u) = (1 \times v_A) + (4 \times v_B)$
$3u + 8u = v_A + 4v_B \Rightarrow v_A + 4v_B = 11u \,...[2]$
Equation [1] + equation [2] gives:
$5v_B = 11u + \dfrac{u}{4} \Rightarrow 5v_B = \dfrac{45u}{4} \Rightarrow v_B = \dfrac{9u}{4}$.
Substituting in equation [2] gives:
$v_A + 9u = 11u \Rightarrow v_A = 11u - 9u = 2u$.
For the second collision, between B and C:
$e = \dfrac{v_C - v_B}{u_B - u_C} \Rightarrow \dfrac{1}{3} = \dfrac{v_C - v_B}{\frac{9u}{4} - u} \Rightarrow v_C - v_B = \dfrac{5u}{12} \,...[3]$
And:
$m_B u_B + m_C u_C = m_B v_B + m_C v_C$
$\left(4 \times \dfrac{9u}{4}\right) + (5 \times u) = (4 \times v_B) + (5 \times v_C)$
$\Rightarrow 4v_B + 5v_C = 14u \,...[4]$

Answers

4 × Equation *[3]* + equation *[4]* gives:

$9v_C = \frac{5u}{3} + 14u \Rightarrow 9v_C = \frac{47u}{3} \Rightarrow v_C = \frac{47u}{27}$.

Substituting in equation *[3]* gives:

$\frac{47u}{27} - v_B = \frac{5u}{12} \Rightarrow v_B = \frac{47u}{27} - \frac{5u}{12} = \frac{143u}{108}$.

So after both collisions:

A is travelling at $2u = \frac{216u}{108}$,

and B is travelling at $\frac{143u}{108}$,

which means that A is travelling faster than B and so they should collide again.

10) $e = \frac{v_2 - v_1}{u_1 - u_2} \Rightarrow 0.3 = \frac{v_2 - v_1}{3 - 0} \Rightarrow v_2 - v_1 = 0.9$ ...*[1]*

And: $m_1u_1 + m_2u_2 = m_1v_1 + m_2v_2$

$\Rightarrow (2 \times 3) + (3 \times 0) = 2v_1 + 3v_2$

$\Rightarrow 6 = 2v_1 + 3v_2 \Rightarrow v_1 + 1.5v_2 = 3$ ...*[2]*

Equation *[1]* + equation *[2]* gives:

$2.5v_2 = 3.9 \Rightarrow v_2 = 1.56$ ms⁻¹.

In equation *[1]*:

$1.56 - v_1 = 0.9 \Rightarrow v_1 = 1.56 - 0.9 = 0.66$ ms⁻¹.

Loss of K.E. $= (\frac{1}{2}m_1u_1^2 + \frac{1}{2}m_2u_2^2) - (\frac{1}{2}m_1v_1^2 + \frac{1}{2}m_2v_2^2)$

$= [(\frac{1}{2} \times 2 \times 3^2) + 0] - [(\frac{1}{2} \times 2 \times 0.66^2) + (\frac{1}{2} \times 3 \times 1.56^2)]$

$= 9 - 4.086 = 4.914$ J.

Exam Questions

1 Using the principle of conservation of momentum for the collision:

$m_1u_1 + m_2u_2 = m_1v_1 + m_2v_2$

Since marble 2 is stationary before the impact:

$(0.02 \times 2) + (0.06 \times 0) = 0.02v_1 + 0.06v_2$ *[1 mark]*

$\Rightarrow 0.02v_1 + 0.06v_2 = 0.04$

$\Rightarrow v_1 + 3v_2 = 2$ ...*[1]*

Since the collision is perfectly elastic, and so $e = 1$, the Law of Restitution gives a second equation:

$e = \frac{\text{speed of separation of particles}}{\text{speed of approach of particles}} = \frac{v_2 - v_1}{u_1 - u_2}$

$\Rightarrow 1 = \frac{v_2 - v_1}{2 - 0}$ *[1 mark]* $\Rightarrow v_2 - v_1 = 2$ ...*[2]*

Equation *[1]* + equation *[2]* gives:

$4v_2 = 4 \Rightarrow v_2 = 1$ ms⁻¹ *[1 mark]*.

Substituting in equation *[1]* gives:

$v_1 + (3 \times 1) = 2 \Rightarrow v_1 = -1$ ms⁻¹ *[1 mark]*.

So after the collision, both particles are travelling at a speed of 1 ms⁻¹ (but the first particle is going in the opposite direction to its initial path).

2 a) $I = mv - mu$, so

$3i - 8j = 0.4v - 0.4(-6i + j)$ *[1 mark]*

$3i - 8j = 0.4v + 2.4i - 0.4j$

$0.4v = 0.6i - 7.6j$ *[1 mark]*

$\Rightarrow v = 1.5i - 19j$ *[1 mark]*.

Speed is the magnitude of the velocity.

Drawing this as a right-angled triangle:

$|v| = \sqrt{1.5^2 + 19^2}$ *[1 mark]* = 19.1 ms⁻¹ to 3 s.f. *[1 mark]*.

As always, a picture makes everything make a lot more sense.

b) Using the triangle in part a), θ is the angle with the horizontal, so:

$\theta = \tan^{-1}(\frac{19}{1.5})$ *[1 mark]* = 85.5° to 3 s.f. *[1 mark]*.

3 a) Using the Law of Restitution for the collision between P and Q, where P is travelling at u and Q at $-u$ (i.e. in the opposite direction):

$e = \frac{v_Q - v_P}{u_P - u_Q} \Rightarrow \frac{3}{4} = \frac{v_Q - v_P}{u - (-u)}$ *[1 mark]* $\Rightarrow \frac{3}{4} = \frac{v_Q - v_P}{2u}$

$\Rightarrow v_Q - v_P = \frac{3u}{2}$ ...*[1]*

Using conservation of momentum:

$m_Pu_P + m_Qu_Q = m_Pv_P + m_Qv_Q$

$2mu - mu = 2mv_P + mv_Q$ *[1 mark]*

$\Rightarrow 2v_P + v_Q = u$ ...*[2]*

Equation *[2]* − equation *[1]* gives:

$3v_P = -\frac{u}{2} \Rightarrow v_P = -\frac{u}{6}$ *[1 mark]*.

Substituting in equation *[1]* gives:

$v_Q - (-\frac{u}{6}) = \frac{3u}{2} \Rightarrow v_Q = \frac{4u}{3}$ *[1 mark]*.

Since P's velocity was initially positive, and is now negative, and Q's was initially negative but is now positive, the collision has reversed the directions of both particles *[1 mark]*.

Sure about that? Yep, positive. I mean negative... erm...

$|v_Q| \div |v_P| = \frac{4u}{3} \div \frac{u}{6} = 8$,

so Q is now going 8 times faster than P *[1 mark]*.

b) For the collision with the wall, $e_{wall} = \frac{\text{speed of rebound}}{\text{speed of approach}}$.

Q approaches the wall with a speed of $\frac{4u}{3}$ (from a)), so if v_{Qwall} is its rebound speed:

$e_{wall} = \frac{v_{Qwall}}{\frac{4u}{3}} \Rightarrow v_{Qwall} = \frac{4ue_{wall}}{3}$ *[1 mark]*.

Since Q collides again with P, v_{Qwall} must be greater than v_P which is $\frac{u}{6}$ (from a)), so:

$\frac{4ue_{wall}}{3} > \frac{u}{6}$ *[1 mark]* $\Rightarrow e_{wall} > \frac{3u}{6 \times 4u} \Rightarrow e_{wall} > \frac{1}{8}$ *[1 mark]*.

c) If $e_{\text{wall}} = \frac{3}{5}$, then (from b)):

$v_{\text{Qwall}} = \frac{4ue_{\text{wall}}}{3} = \frac{4u \times 3}{3 \times 5} = \frac{4u}{5}$ *[1 mark]*.

Q is now travelling in the same direction as P, which is still travelling at a speed of $\frac{u}{6}$ (from a)), and the particles have a coefficient of restitution of $\frac{3}{4}$, so using the Law of Restitution for the second collision between P and Q:

$e = \frac{v_P - v_Q}{u_Q - u_P} \Rightarrow \frac{3}{4} = \frac{v_P - v_Q}{\left(\frac{4u}{5}\right) - \frac{u}{6}}$ *[1 mark]* $\Rightarrow \frac{3}{4} = \frac{v_P - v_Q}{\frac{19u}{30}}$

$\Rightarrow v_P - v_Q = \frac{19u}{40}$ ...[1]

Using conservation of momentum:

$m_Q u_Q + m_P u_P = m_Q v_Q + m_P v_P$

$\frac{4um}{5} + \frac{2um}{6} = mv_Q + 2mv_P$ *[1 mark]*

$\Rightarrow v_Q + 2v_P = \frac{17u}{15}$ ...[2]

Equation [2] − 2 × equation [1] gives:

$3v_Q = \frac{17u}{15} - \frac{19u}{20} = \frac{11u}{60}$ *[1 mark]*

$\Rightarrow v_Q = \frac{11u}{180}$ *[1 mark]*.

Since $v_Q = 0.22 \text{ ms}^{-1}$:

$\frac{11u}{180} = 0.22$ *[1 mark]*

$\Rightarrow u = (0.22 \times 180) \div 11 = 3.6 \text{ ms}^{-1}$ *[1 mark]*.

4 a) Using conservation of momentum:

$m\binom{8}{4} + 3m\binom{0}{0} = m\binom{v_P}{1} + 3m\binom{1}{v_Q}$. *[1 mark]* As there is a factor of m in every term, it can be cancelled:

$\binom{8}{4} = \binom{v_P}{1} + 3\binom{1}{v_Q}$.

Considering the "horizontal" and "vertical" components separately:

$8 = v_P + 3 \Rightarrow v_P = 5$ *[1 mark]*

$4 = 1 + 3v_Q \Rightarrow v_Q = 1$ *[1 mark]*

b) Now you have the velocities of P and Q as $\binom{5}{1}$ ms⁻¹ and $\binom{1}{1}$ ms⁻¹ respectively, use Pythagoras to find the speeds:

[1 mark]

Speed of $P = \sqrt{5^2 + 1^2} = \sqrt{26} = 5.10 \text{ ms}^{-1}$ (3 s.f.) *[1 mark]*

Speed of $Q = \sqrt{1^2 + 1^2} = \sqrt{2} = 1.41 \text{ ms}^{-1}$ (3 s.f.) *[1 mark]*

5 First, write down everything you're told in the question:

$m_A = 7$, $\mathbf{v}_A = 6\mathbf{i} - 4\mathbf{j}$,

$m_B = 2$, $\mathbf{u}_B = 0$, $\mathbf{v}_B = ?$

$m_C = (7 + 2) = 9$, $\mathbf{v}_C = 3\mathbf{i} + 4\mathbf{j}$

$F = |\mathbf{F}|$, $t = 5$

Now, use conservation of momentum to find $\mathbf{v}_B$:

$m_A\mathbf{v}_A + m_B\mathbf{v}_B = m_C\mathbf{v}_C$ *[1 mark]*

$7(6\mathbf{i} - 4\mathbf{j}) + 2\mathbf{v}_B = 9(3\mathbf{i} + 4\mathbf{j})$

$42\mathbf{i} - 28\mathbf{j} + 2\mathbf{v}_B = 27\mathbf{i} + 36\mathbf{j}$

$2\mathbf{v}_B = (27 - 42)\mathbf{i} + (36 + 28)\mathbf{j}$

$\mathbf{v}_B = -7.5\mathbf{i} + 32\mathbf{j}$ *[1 mark]*

Impulse given to B by force $\mathbf{F}$: $\mathbf{I} = \mathbf{F} \times t$ *[1 mark]*

But impulse is also equal to change in momentum, so:

$\mathbf{F}t = m_B\mathbf{v}_B - m_B\mathbf{u}_B$ *[1 mark]*

$\mathbf{u}_B = 0$, so $\mathbf{F}t = m_B\mathbf{v}_B = -15\mathbf{i} + 64\mathbf{j}$

$\mathbf{F} = \frac{-15\mathbf{i} + 64\mathbf{j}}{5}$

$= -3\mathbf{i} + 12.8\mathbf{j}$ *[1 mark]*

$F = |\mathbf{F}| = \sqrt{(-3)^2 + 12.8^2}$ *[1 mark]*

$F = 13.1 \text{ N}$ (3 s.f.) *[1 mark]*

When you're given loads of info in a wordy question like this, it really helps to write it all out to start with. That way you can see straight off what you know and what you don't know.

6 Using conservation of momentum:

Before | After

$(0.8 \times 4) + (1.2 \times 2) = (0.8 \times 2.5) + 1.2v$

$3.2 + 2.4 = 2.0 + 1.2v$

$v = 3 \text{ ms}^{-1}$

Before | After

$(1.2 \times 3) + (m \times -4) = (1.2 + m) \times 0$

$3.6 = 4m$

$m = 0.9 \text{ kg}$

[4 marks available in total]:
- *1 mark for using conservation of momentum*
- *1 mark for correct value of v*
- *1 mark for correct workings*
- *1 mark for correct value of m*

Diagrams are handy for collision questions too, partly because they make the question clearer for you, but they also make it easier for the examiner to see how you're going about answering the question.

7 a) For the collision between A and B, the Law of Restitution gives the following equation:

$e = \frac{v_B - v_A}{u_A - u_B} \Rightarrow e = \frac{v_B - v_A}{4u - 0}$ *[1 mark]*

$\Rightarrow v_B - v_A = 4ue$ ...[1]

Using conservation of momentum:

$m_A u_A + m_B u_B = m_A v_A + m_B v_B$

$4mu + 0 = mv_A + 2mv_B$ *[1 mark]*

$\Rightarrow v_A + 2v_B = 4u$ ...[2]

Equation [1] + equation [2] gives:

$3v_B = 4u(1 + e) \Rightarrow v_B = \frac{4u}{3}(1 + e)$ *[1 mark]*.

Substituting in equation [1] gives:

$\frac{4u}{3}(1 + e) - v_A = 4ue$

$\Rightarrow v_A = \frac{4u}{3}(1 + e) - 4ue = \frac{4u}{3}(1 - 2e)$ *[1 mark]*.

Since the coefficient of restitution must be between 0 and 1, and the coefficient of restitution between B and C is $2e$, then $0 \le 2e \le 1 \Rightarrow 1 - 2e \ge 0$ *[1 mark]*.

i.e. $v_A = \frac{4u}{3}(1 - 2e)$, where $u > 0$ and $1 - 2e \ge 0$. So:

v_A cannot be negative *[1 mark]*, so the collision does not reverse the direction of A's motion *[1 mark]*.

Answers

b) After the collision, A is travelling at $\frac{4u}{3}(1 - 2e)$ and B is travelling at $\frac{4u}{3}(1 + e)$ (from a)). In the time it takes B to travel a distance d, A has travelled $\frac{d}{4}$. So the speed of B must be 4 times the speed of A *[1 mark]* i.e.

$\frac{4u}{3}(1 - 2e) = \frac{u}{3}(1 + e)$ *[1 mark]*

$\Rightarrow 4 - 8e = 1 + e$

$\Rightarrow 9e = 3 \Rightarrow e = \frac{1}{3}$ — as required *[1 mark]*.

c) Since $e = \frac{1}{3}$ (from b)), the speed of B as it approaches C is:

$\frac{4u}{3}(1 + \frac{1}{3}) = \frac{16u}{9}$ *[1 mark]*. The coefficient of restitution between B and C is $2e = \frac{2}{3}$ *[1 mark]*. So, using the Law of Restitution: $e = \frac{v_C - v_B}{u_B - u_C} \Rightarrow \frac{2}{3} = \frac{v_C - v_B}{\frac{16u}{9} - 0}$ *[1 mark]*

$\Rightarrow v_C - v_B = \frac{32u}{27}$ ...[1]

Using conservation of momentum:

$m_B u_B + m_C u_C = m_B v_B + m_C v_C$

$(2m \times \frac{16u}{9}) + 0 = 2mv_B + 4mv_C$ *[1 mark]*

$\Rightarrow v_B + 2v_C = \frac{16u}{9}$ ...[2]

Equation [1] + equation [2] gives:

$3v_C = \frac{80u}{27} \Rightarrow v_C = \frac{80u}{81}$ *[1 mark]*.

8 a) Using the Law of Restitution for the collision between particles 1 and 2 gives:

$e = \frac{v_2 - v_1}{u_1 - u_2} \Rightarrow \frac{1}{4} = \frac{v_2 - v_1}{3u - 2u}$ *[1 mark]*

$\Rightarrow v_2 - v_1 = \frac{u}{4}$ ...[1]

Using conservation of momentum:

$m_1 u_1 + m_2 u_2 = m_1 v_1 + m_2 v_2$

$(2m \times 3u) + (3m \times 2u) = 2mv_1 + 3mv_2$ *[1 mark]*

$\Rightarrow 2v_1 + 3v_2 = 12u$ ...[2]

Equation [1] × 2 gives:

$2v_2 - 2v_1 = \frac{u}{2}$ ...[3]

Equation [2] + equation [3] gives:

$5v_2 = 12u + \frac{u}{2} \Rightarrow v_2 = \frac{25u}{2 \times 5} = \frac{5u}{2}$ *[1 mark]*.

Substituting in equation [1] gives:

$\frac{5u}{2} - v_1 = \frac{u}{4}$

$\Rightarrow v_1 = \frac{5u}{2} - \frac{u}{4} = \frac{9u}{4}$ *[1 mark]*.

b) Loss of kinetic energy =

$(\frac{1}{2}m_1 u_1^2 + \frac{1}{2}m_2 u_2^2) - (\frac{1}{2}m_1 v_1^2 + \frac{1}{2}m_2 v_2^2)$

$= [(\frac{1}{2} \times 2m \times (3u)^2) + (\frac{1}{2} \times 3m \times (2u)^2)] -$

$\quad [(\frac{1}{2} \times 2m \times (\frac{9u}{4})^2) + (\frac{1}{2} \times 3m \times (\frac{5u}{2})^2)]$

$= (9mu^2 + 6mu^2) - (\frac{81mu^2}{16} + \frac{150mu^2}{16})$

$= (15 - \frac{231}{16})mu^2 = \frac{9mu^2}{16}$ — as required.

[4 marks available — 1 mark for correct values in formula for initial kinetic energy, 1 mark for correct values in formula for final kinetic energy, 1 mark for correct calculation of initial and final energy and 1 mark for correct final answer as the difference between the two.]

9 a) Split the speed into components parallel and perpendicular to the plate *[1 mark]*. The plate is vertical, so the vertical components of the speed before and after the collision are equal,

i.e. $3\sqrt{2}\cos45 = v\cos30$ *[1 mark]* $\Rightarrow$

$v = \frac{3\sqrt{2}\cos45}{\cos30} = \frac{3}{(\sqrt{3}/2)} = 2(\frac{3}{\sqrt{3}}) = 2\sqrt{3}\,\text{ms}^{-1}$ *[1 mark]*.

b) Perpendicular to the plate, the component of the speed after the collision is:

$e \times$ (component of speed before collision) *[1 mark]*.

Notice there's no minus sign here — we're talking about speed, so only the magnitude matters, not the direction.

So, resolving horizontally, $e \times 3\sqrt{2}\sin45 = v\sin30$ *[1 mark]*

$\Rightarrow e = \frac{v\sin30}{3\sqrt{2}\sin45} = \frac{2\sqrt{3}(1/2)}{3\sqrt{2}(1/\sqrt{2})}$

So $e = \frac{\sqrt{3}}{3} = 0.577$ (3 s.f.) *[1 mark]*.

c) Initial kinetic energy $= \frac{1}{2}mu^2 = \frac{1}{2}(1)(3\sqrt{2})^2 = 9$ J.

Final kinetic energy $= \frac{1}{2}mv^2 = \frac{1}{2}(1)(2\sqrt{3})^2 = 6$ J.

Therefore, the kinetic energy lost is $(9 - 6)$ J $= 3$ J.

[2 marks available in total]:
- *1 mark for both initial and final kinetic energy correct*
- *1 mark for correct answer*

10 a) Total momentum $= m\binom{u}{1} + 5\binom{0}{-5}$ *[1 mark]*

b) (i) Using answer to part a) and conservation of momentum:

$m\binom{u}{1} + 5\binom{0}{-5} = \binom{mu}{m - 25} = (5 + m)\binom{2}{-1}$ *[1 mark]*

Considering the "vertical" component only:

$m - 25 = -5 - m$ *[1 mark]*

$\Rightarrow 2m = 20 \Rightarrow m = 10$ *[1 mark]*

(ii) First, find u using $\binom{mu}{m - 25} = (5 + m)\binom{2}{-1}$

Considering the "horizontal" component:

$mu = 2(5 + m) \Rightarrow 10u = 2(5 + 10)$ *[1 mark]*

$\Rightarrow 10u = 30 \Rightarrow u = 3$ *[1 mark]*

Find the speed using Pythagoras:

$\sqrt{3^2 + 1^2} = \sqrt{10} = 3.16\,\text{ms}^{-1}$ (3 s.f.) *[1 mark]*

And that's about your lot for Section 4, a real rollercoaster ride of mathematical wonderment. Hope you had fun...

Answers

M2 — Practice Exam One

1 a) (i) Use the Law of Restitution for the collision between A and B, where A is travelling at $5u$ which changes to $-u$ *[1 mark]* after the collision.

B has an initial velocity of 0:

$e = \dfrac{v_B - v_A}{u_A - u_B} \Rightarrow \dfrac{4}{5} = \dfrac{v_B - (-u)}{5u - 0}$ *[1 mark]* $\Rightarrow \dfrac{4}{5} = \dfrac{v_B + u}{5u}$

$\Rightarrow v_B = 4u - u = 3u$ *[1 mark]*.

With collisions questions you're usually going to have to use either the Law of Restitution, or conservation of momentum, or both. So if you're stuck, plug the numbers you have into both formulas and see what you come up with.

(ii) Use conservation of momentum to find the mass of B:

$m_A u_A + m_B u_B = m_A v_A + m_B v_B$

$(1 \times 5u) + (M \times 0) = (1 \times -u) + (M \times 3u)$ *[1 mark]*

$\Rightarrow 5u = (3M - 1)u \Rightarrow 3M - 1 = 5$ *[1 mark]*

$\Rightarrow M = (5 + 1) \div 3 = 2$ kg *[1 mark]*.

(iii) Using the Law of Restitution for the collision between B and the wall: $e = \dfrac{v}{u}$, so rebound speed $v = 3eu$ *[1 mark]*, since B is travelling towards the wall at $3u$ (from a)).

For B to collide again with A, its rebound speed v must be greater than A's speed, which is u. So:

$3eu > u$ *[1 mark]*

$3e > 1$

$e > \dfrac{1}{3}$ *[1 mark]*.

b) (i) First you need to find the speed of the ball when it hits the ground.

Resolving vertically (taking down as positive):

$s = 2; u = 0; a = 9.8; v = ?$

$v^2 = u^2 + 2as$

$v^2 = 0 + (2 \times 9.8 \times 2)$ *[1 mark]*

$v = 6.2609...$

$v = 6.26$ ms^{-1} (3 s.f.) *[1 mark]*

The ball rebounds with a vertical component of velocity of $-\left(6.2609... \times \dfrac{5}{8}\right) = -3.9131...$ ms^{-1} *[1 mark]*

The horizontal component of velocity remains at 15 ms^{-1} *[1 mark]*

Now you can use Pythagoras and trig to find the speed and angle of rebound:

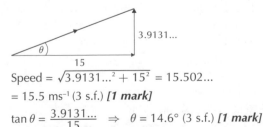

Speed $= \sqrt{3.9131...^2 + 15^2} = 15.502...$

$= 15.5$ ms^{-1} (3 s.f.) *[1 mark]*

$\tan \theta = \dfrac{3.9131...}{15} \Rightarrow \theta = 14.6°$ (3 s.f.) *[1 mark]*

Bit of a blast from the past there — don't forget that you'll probably need to use stuff you learnt in M1 (like projectiles and kinematics) to answer M2 questions.

(ii) K.E. after impact $= \dfrac{1}{2}mv^2 = \dfrac{1}{2} \times 0.06 \times (15.502...)^2$

$= 7.209...$ J *[1 mark]*

K.E. before impact $= \dfrac{1}{2}mv^2$

$= \dfrac{1}{2} \times 0.06 \times (\sqrt{(6.2609...)^2 + 15^2})^2 = 7.926$ J *[1 mark]*

K.E. loss $= 7.926 - 7.209... = 0.717$ J (3 s.f.) *[1 mark]*.

2 a) Setting point O as the origin, the distance of the centre of mass from OA is the horizontal distance $\overline{x}$.

The frame is made from a single uniform wire, so treating each side as a separate 'rod', the masses are proportional to the lengths, i.e. $m_{OA} = 3$, $m_{OB} = 4$, and $m_{AB} = 5$.

The centre of mass of each side is at its midpoint, and so $x_{OA} = 0$ (since A is vertically above O), $x_{OB} = 2$ (i.e. 4 cm $\div$ 2) and $x_{AB} = 2$ (since the triangle is right-angled, the midpoint of the hypotenuse AB is vertically above the midpoint of OB).

Combining the sides of the frame in the formula

$\Sigma mx = \overline{x}\Sigma m$

$m_{OA}x_{OA} + m_{OB}x_{OB} + m_{AB}x_{AB} = \overline{x}(m_{OA} + m_{OB} + m_{AB})$

$\Rightarrow (3 \times 0) + (4 \times 2) + (5 \times 2) = \overline{x}(3 + 4 + 5)$

$\Rightarrow 18 = 12\overline{x} \Rightarrow \overline{x} = 1.5$.

So the centre of mass of the frame is 1.5 cm from OA.

[4 marks available — 1 mark for correct individual masses of each side, 1 mark for correct centres of each side, 1 mark for correct entry into formula, 1 mark for correct final answer.]

b) With O as the origin again, the distance of the centre of mass from OB is the vertical distance $\overline{y}$. The centres of mass of each side are as follows: $y_{OA} = 1.5$ (i.e. 3 cm $\div$ 2), $y_{OB} = 0$ and $y_{AB} = 1.5$ (the midpoint of the hypotenuse AB is horizontally across from the midpoint of OA).

Combining the sides of the frame in the formula

$\Sigma my = \overline{y}\Sigma m$, using the masses found in a):

$m_{OA}y_{OA} + m_{OB}y_{OB} + m_{AB}y_{AB} = \overline{y}(m_{OA} + m_{OB} + m_{AB})$

$\Rightarrow (3 \times 1.5) + (4 \times 0) + (5 \times 1.5) = \overline{y}(3 + 4 + 5)$

$\Rightarrow 12 = 12\overline{y} \Rightarrow \overline{y} = 1$.

So the centre of mass of the frame is 1 cm from OB.

[3 marks available — 1 mark for correct centres of each side, 1 mark for correct entry into formula, 1 mark for correct final answer.]

c) You'll need to find some other angles first before you get the one asked for in the question.

They say a picture paints a thousand words, so...

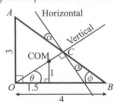

In the diagram, the angles in triangle OCB must add up to 180°, so:

$\theta + \phi + \alpha + 90 = 180 \Rightarrow \alpha = 90 - (\theta + \phi)$ *[1 mark]*,

where α is the angle that AB makes with the horizontal, as asked for in the question.

Answers

The other angles can be found using basic trigonometry. From the right-angled triangle formed between O and the centre of mass: $\theta = \tan^{-1}(\frac{1}{1.5})$ **[1 mark]** = 33.6900...° **[1 mark]**

From the right-angled triangle OBA:

$\phi = \tan^{-1}(\frac{3}{4})$ = 36.8698...° **[1 mark]**

So the angle with the horizontal, $\alpha = 90 - (\theta + \phi)$
= 90 − (33.6900... + 36.8698...) = 19.4401...°
= 19.4° to 3 s.f. **[1 mark]**

d)

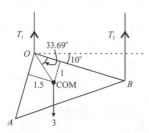

First take moments about O to find T_2.
To do this, you'll need to know the perpendicular distance between O and the line of action of the triangle's weight:
Distance between O and COM = $\sqrt{1^2 + 1.5^2}$
= 1.8027... cm **[1 mark]**

Distance between O and line of action of weight =
1.8027...$\cos(33.69 + 10)°$ = 1.3035... cm **[1 mark]**

Now, taking moments about O:
1.3035... × 3 = 4$\cos 10° × T_2$ **[1 mark]**
T_2 = 0.9927... = 0.993 N (3 s.f.) **[1 mark]**

Now you can resolve forces to find T_1:
Resolving vertically:
T_1 + 0.9927... = 3 **[1 mark]**
T_1 = 2.0072... = 2.01 N (3 s.f.) **[1 mark]**

There were some tricky bits of resolving in that last part. Remember, when you're taking moments, you need the <u>perpendicular</u> distance from the line of action of the force — so in questions like this you have to decide whether you want to resolve forces and use distances you already know, or leave the forces as they are and calculate new distances.

3 a) (i) You are given the horizontal component of the reaction, but you still need to find the vertical component.

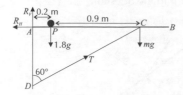

Taking moments about C:
1.1 × R_V = 0.9 × 1.8g
so, 1.1R_V = 15.876
and R_V = 14.432... N (to 3 s.f.)
Now you can use Pythagoras to find the required magnitude and direction:

Magnitude: $|R| = \sqrt{(14.432...)^2 + 35^2}$
= 37.9 N (to 3 s.f.)
Direction: $\tan \theta = \dfrac{14.432...}{35}$
$\Rightarrow \theta$ = 22.4° (to 3 s.f.) to the horizontal.
[5 marks available in total]:
• **1 mark for taking moments about C**
• **1 mark for correct value of R_V**
• **1 mark for correct working to find magnitude and direction**
• **1 mark for correct value of magnitude**
• **1 mark for correct value of direction**

It's easy to get confused by which directions R_H and R_V act in. My suggestion — make an educated guess and if you're wrong they'll just turn out to be negative. No need to panic then.

(ii) Resolving horizontally:
$T\sin 60° = R_H = 35$
so, $T = \dfrac{35}{\sin 60°}$ = 40.414... = 40.4 N (to 3 s.f.)

[3 marks available in total]:
• **1 mark for resolving horizontally**
• **1 mark for correct workings**
• **1 mark for correct value of T**

(iii) Taking moments about A:
$(0.2 × 1.8g) + (1.1 × mg) = 1.1 × T\cos 60°$
$\Rightarrow 10.78m = 22.227... - 3.528 = 18.699...$
$\Rightarrow m = 1.734... = 1.73$ kg (to 3 s.f.)

[3 marks available in total]:
• **1 mark for taking moments about A**
• **1 mark for correct workings**
• **1 mark for correct value of m**

b) Here's a diagram of the forces acting on the beam.

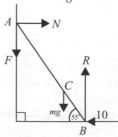

Here, R is the reaction of the ground on the beam, N is the reaction of the wall on the beam, and F is the frictional force between the wall and the beam.

Assume that the wall is rough and include F in your calculations, then if F turns out to be zero, then you know that the wall is actually smooth.

Taking moments about A:
$(mg × 1.1\cos 55°) + (10 × 1.5\sin 55°) = R × 1.5\cos 55°$ **[1 mark]**
$\Rightarrow R = \dfrac{(1.734... × 9.8 × 1.1\cos 55°) + (10 × 1.5\sin 55°)}{1.5\cos 55°}$
= 26.748... = 26.7 N (3 s.f.) **[1 mark]**

Answers

Now resolving vertically:

$F + mg = R$ *[1 mark]*

$\Rightarrow F = 26.748... - (1.734... \times 9.8) = 9.748...$

$= 9.75$ N (3 s.f.) *[1 mark]*.

So the wall is rough, and the frictional force between it and the beam is 9.75 N.

Resolving horizontally:

$N = 10$ *[1 mark]*

The beam is in limiting equilibrium, so $F = \mu N$:

$9.748... = 10\mu$ *[1 mark]* $\Rightarrow \mu = 9.748... \div 10 = 0.9748...$

So the coefficient of friction between the wall and the beam is 0.975 (3 s.f.) *[1 mark]*.

4 a)

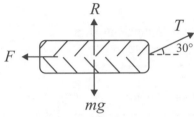

Tyre is moving only horizontally, so:

Total work done on the tyre = Change in K.E. *[1 mark]*

i.e. Work done by T + Work done by F = Change in K.E.

Using Work done = Force × Displacement:

Work done by $F = 270 \times -75 = -20\,250$ *[1 mark]*

Change in K.E. $= \frac{1}{2}m(v^2 - u^2) = \frac{1}{2} \times 160 \times (4 - 0.5625)$

$= 275$ J *[1 mark]*

So, Work done by $T - 20\,250 = 275$

$\Rightarrow$ Work done by $T = 20.5$ kJ (3 s.f.) *[1 mark]*

b) Again, using Work done = Force × Displacement:

Work done by $T = T\cos30° \times 75$ *[1 mark]*

$T\cos30° \times 75 = 20\,525$ *[1 mark]*

$T\cos30° = \dfrac{20\,525}{75}$

$T = 316$ N (3 s.f.) *[1 mark]*

c) The tension in the rope is always acting perpendicular to the motion of the tyre, so work done in the direction of motion is $T\cos90° = 0$. *[1 mark]*

d) When the tyre is at A, its kinetic energy is given by:

K.E. $= \frac{1}{2}mv^2 = \frac{1}{2} \times 160 \times 6^2 = 2880$ J *[1 mark]*

At its highest point of swing, its velocity (and therefore its K.E.) is zero. The only force working in the direction of motion is the tyre's weight, so by the conservation of mechanical energy:

K.E. lost = G.P.E. gained:

$2880 = mgh$ *[1 mark]*

$\Rightarrow h = \dfrac{2880}{160 \times 9.8} = 1.8367... = 1.84$ m (3 s.f.) *[1 mark]*.

e)

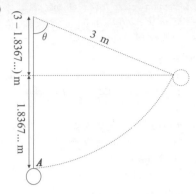

The diagram shows the tyre when at the top of its swing. θ, the angle the rope makes with the vertical at this point, can be found using trig:

$\cos\theta = \dfrac{(3 - 1.8367...)}{3} \Rightarrow \theta = 67.185...°$ *[1 mark]*

For the tyre moving back to point A, and doing work against a resistive force, F, the work-energy principle gives:

K.E. gained = G.P.E. lost – work done *[1 mark]*

i.e. work done = G.P.E. lost – K.E. gained

work done $= 2880 - \frac{1}{2}mv^2$ *[1 mark]* call this **eqn 1**

To find the work done against F, you need the distance the tyre moves in the direction of F. This is an arc with angle θ at the centre so:

distance $= r\theta = 3\theta = 3 \times \left[\dfrac{67.185...°}{360°} \times 2\pi\right]$

$= 3.5178...$ m *[1 mark]*.

Remember — you need the angle in radians.

So: work done against $F = 380 \times 3.5178...$

$= 1336.765...$ N *[1 mark]*

Substituting this value for work done into **eqn 1** gives:

$2880 - \frac{1}{2}mv^2 = 1336.765...$ *[1 mark]*

$\Rightarrow v = \sqrt{19.290...} = 4.39$ ms^{-1} (3 s.f.) *[1 mark]*

You should remember all that stuff about radians and arc length from C2. If not, it's definitely worth looking back over it — you never know when it might come in handy.

M2 — Practice Exam Two

1 a) (i)

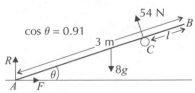

Taking moments about A:

$54(3 - l) = 1.5 \times 8g\cos\theta$

$162 - 54l = 107.02$

so, $54l = 54.98$

$\Rightarrow l = 1.02$ m (to 3 s.f.)

[3 marks available in total]:

- ***1 mark for taking moments about A***
- ***1 mark for correct workings***
- ***1 mark for correct value of l***

Now's a good time to remind you to take moments about points with unknown forces going through them (in this case about A, because you don't know R or F).

(ii) Resolving vertically:

$R + 54\cos\theta = 8g$ **[1 mark]**

so, $R = 8g - (54 \times 0.91) = 29.26$ N **[1 mark]**

Resolving horizontally:

$F = 54\sin\theta$ **[1 mark]**

Rod is in limiting equilibrium so $F = \mu R$:

$54\sin\theta = 29.26\mu$ **[1 mark]**

As $\cos\theta = 0.91$, $\theta = 24.49...°$

$29.26\mu = 54\sin 24.49...° = 22.39$

So, $\mu = 0.765$ (to 3 s.f.) **[1 mark]**

Plenty of things to calculate there on the way to the final answer (μ, not 42), but nothing that's particularly difficult at least.

b) (i)

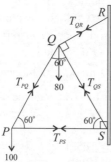

All internal forces shown as tensions.

***[1 mark for all internal forces
and loads labelled correctly]***

(ii) Resolving vertically at P:

$100 = T_{PQ}\sin 60°$ **[1 mark]**

$\Rightarrow T_{PQ} = \dfrac{100}{\sin 60°} = \dfrac{100}{(\frac{\sqrt{3}}{2})} = \dfrac{200}{\sqrt{3}}$

So T_{PQ} is a tension of magnitude $\dfrac{200}{\sqrt{3}}$ N **[1 mark]**.

Resolving horizontally at P:

$T_{PS} + T_{PQ}\cos 60° = 0$ **[1 mark]**

$\Rightarrow T_{PS} = -\dfrac{200}{\sqrt{3}}\cos 60° = -\dfrac{200}{\sqrt{3}} \times \dfrac{1}{2} = -\dfrac{100}{\sqrt{3}}$

So T_{PS} is a thrust of magnitude $\dfrac{100}{\sqrt{3}}$ N **[1 mark]**.

(iii) You need to calculate a few angles for this bit —
a diagram usually helps:

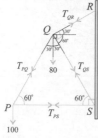

Resolving vertically at Q:

$80 + T_{PQ}\cos 30° + T_{QS}\cos 30° = T_{QR}\sin 30°$

$80 + \left(\dfrac{200}{\sqrt{3}} \times \dfrac{\sqrt{3}}{2}\right) + \dfrac{\sqrt{3}}{2}T_{QS} = \dfrac{1}{2}T_{QR}$

$180 + \dfrac{\sqrt{3}}{2}T_{QS} = \dfrac{1}{2}T_{QR}$ **[eqn 1]**

Resolving horizontally at Q:

$T_{PQ}\sin 30° = T_{QS}\sin 30° + T_{QR}\cos 30°$

$\left(\dfrac{200}{\sqrt{3}} \times \dfrac{1}{2}\right) = \dfrac{1}{2}T_{QS} + \dfrac{\sqrt{3}}{2}T_{QR}$

$\dfrac{100}{\sqrt{3}} = \dfrac{1}{2}T_{QS} + \dfrac{\sqrt{3}}{2}T_{QR}$ **[eqn 2]**

You now have a pair of simultaneous equations.
Multiplying **[eqn 2]** by $\sqrt{3}$ and rearranging:

$100 - \dfrac{\sqrt{3}}{2}T_{QS} = \dfrac{3}{2}T_{QR}$ **[eqn 3]**

Now adding **[eqn 1]** and **[eqn 3]**:

$280 = 2T_{QR}$

$\Rightarrow T_{QR} = 140$

Substitute this back into **[eqn 1]**:

$180 + \dfrac{\sqrt{3}}{2}T_{QS} = \dfrac{1}{2} \times 140$

$\Rightarrow T_{QS} = -\dfrac{220}{\sqrt{3}}$

So, T_{QR} is a tension of magnitude 140 N and
T_{QS} is a thrust of magnitude $\dfrac{220}{\sqrt{3}}$ N.

[6 marks available in total]:
* ***1 mark for resolving vertically at Q***
* ***1 mark for resolving horizontally at Q***
* ***1 mark for forming a pair of simultaneous equations***
* ***1 mark for attempting to solve simultaneous equations***
* ***1 mark for T_{QR} correct***
* ***1 mark for T_{QS} correct***

Yowza — good question eh? It's dead important that you know the exact values of cos 30°, sin 30°, cos 60°, sin 60° etc... The last thing you want is to be faffing about with massive decimals, especially in a question like this.

2 a) Using the Law of Restitution for the collision between P
and Q:

$e = \dfrac{v_Q - v_P}{u_P - u_Q} \Rightarrow 0.65 = \dfrac{v_Q - v_P}{5 - 0}$ **[1 mark]**

$\Rightarrow v_Q - v_P = 5 \times 0.65 \Rightarrow v_Q - v_P = 3.25 \,...[1]$.

Using conservation of momentum:

$m_P u_P + m_Q u_Q = m_P v_P + m_Q v_Q$

$(0.2 \times 5) + (0.6 \times 0) = (0.2 \times v_P) + (0.6 \times v_Q)$ **[1 mark]**

$\Rightarrow 1 = 0.2v_P + 0.6v_Q \Rightarrow 5 = v_P + 3v_Q \,...[2]$.

Equation [1] + equation [2]:

$4v_Q = 8.25 \Rightarrow v_Q = 2.0625 = 2.06$ ms^{-1} to 3 s.f. **[1 mark]**.

Substituting in equation [2]:

$5 = v_P + (3 \times 2.0625)$

$\Rightarrow v_P = 5 - (3 \times 2.0625) = -1.1875 = -1.19$ ms^{-1} to 3 s.f.
[1 mark].

b) The size of the impulse on Q is the change in its
momentum due to the collision, so:

$I = mv_Q - mu_Q = (0.6 \times 2.0625) - (0.6 \times 0)$ **[1 mark]**

$= 1.2375 = 1.24$ Ns to 3 s.f. **[1 mark]**.

Particles just can't help acting on impulse...

c) Loss of kinetic energy =

$(\frac{1}{2}m_P u_P^2 + \frac{1}{2}m_Q u_Q^2) - (\frac{1}{2}m_P v_P^2 + \frac{1}{2}m_Q v_Q^2)$

$= [(\frac{1}{2} \times 0.2 \times 5^2) + (\frac{1}{2} \times 0.6 \times 0^2)]$ *[1 mark]* –

$[(\frac{1}{2} \times 0.2 \times 1.1875^2) + (\frac{1}{2} \times 0.6 \times 2.0625^2)]$ *[1 mark]*

$= (2.5 + 0) - (0.14101... + 1.27617...)$

$= 1.0828... = 1.08$ J to 3 s.f. *[1 mark]*.

d) Using conservation of momentum for the collision between Q and R: $m_Q u_Q + m_R u_R = m_Q v_Q + m_R v_R$

$(0.6 \times 2.0625) + (0.7 \times 0) = (0.6 \times 0) + (0.7 \times v_R)$ *[1 mark]*

$\Rightarrow 1.2375 = 0.7v_R \Rightarrow v_R = 1.2375 \div 0.7 = 1.7678...$
[1 mark]

Using the Law of Restitution:

$e = \dfrac{v_R - v_Q}{u_Q - u_R} = \dfrac{1.7678... - 0}{2.0625 - 0}$ *[1 mark]* $= 0.8571...$

$= 0.857$ to 3 s.f. *[1 mark]*.

e) S rebounds with a velocity of $4\mathbf{i} + 3e\mathbf{j}$ *[1 mark]*

So $\tan\theta = \dfrac{3e}{4} = \dfrac{5}{12}$ *[1 mark]*

$\Rightarrow e = \dfrac{5}{12} \div \dfrac{3}{4}, \quad e = \dfrac{5}{9}$ *[1 mark]*

So the rebound velocity of S is $4\mathbf{i} + (3 \times \dfrac{5}{9})\mathbf{j}$

$= 4\mathbf{i} + \dfrac{5}{3}\mathbf{j}$ *[1 mark]*

3 a) (i) Bus is travelling at constant speed, so resolve horizontally with $F = ma$ to find the driving force of the engine, T:

$T - 4500 = 0 \Rightarrow T = 4500$ N *[1 mark]*

Power of engine = Driving force × velocity *[1 mark]*

$= 4500 \times 14 = 63$ kW *[1 mark]*

(ii) Call the new driving force of the engine T':

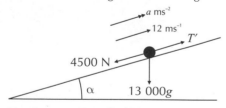

Use Power = Fv to find T':

$72\,000 = T' \times 12 \Rightarrow T' = 6000$ N

Resolve parallel to the slope with $F = ma$ to find a:

$T' - (4500 + 13\,000g\sin\alpha) = 13\,000a$

Substitute known values and rearrange:

$a = \dfrac{6000 - 4500 - 3640}{13\,000} = -0.165$ ms^{-2} (3 s.f.)

[4 marks available — 1 mark for using Power = Fv, 1 mark for finding the new driving force of the engine, 1 mark for resolving parallel to the slope and 1 mark for correct final answer.]

b) (i) Friction is the only external force doing work on the particle, so the work-energy principle gives:
W.D. by friction = change in K.E. + change in P.E.
[1 mark]

Change in K.E. = $\frac{1}{2}m(v^2 - u^2)$ *[1 mark]*

$= \frac{1}{2} \times 9 \times (0^2 - 11^2) = -544.5$ J

[1 mark]

Change in P.E. = mgh *[1 mark]*

$= 9 \times 9.8 \times 8\sin30° = 352.8$ J *[1 mark]*

So, W.D. by friction = $-544.5 + 352.8$

$= -192$ J (3 s.f.) *[1 mark]*

Don't worry, you haven't broken maths — the work done by friction is supposed to be negative, because it's being done in the opposite direction to how the particle is moving. Phew.

(ii) No motion perpendicular to the plane, so resolve in this direction with $F = ma$ to find the normal reaction force, R:

$R - mg\cos30° = 0 \Rightarrow R = mg\cos30°$ *[1 mark]*

$= 9 \times 9.8 \times \cos30°$

$= 76.38$ N *[1 mark]*

Call the frictional force F.
Particle is moving, so $F = \mu R = 76.38\mu$ *[1 mark]*
Work done = Force × Displacement, so:
Work done by $F = F \times -8 = -611.0\mu$, *[1 mark]*
So, from part a):
$-191.7 = -611.0\mu \Rightarrow \mu = \dfrac{-191.7}{-611.0} = 0.314$ (3 s.f.)
[1 mark]

4 a) Split the shape into 4 uniform laminas, P, Q, R and S:

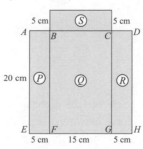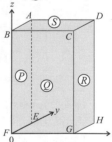

Each lamina is uniform, so the mass of each part is proportional to its area:

$m_P = 100; \ m_Q = 300; \ m_R = 100; \ m_S = 75$ *[1 mark]*

The shape has a plane of symmetry at $x = 7.5$, so $\overline{x} = 7.5$ *[1 mark]*

P, Q, R and S are uniform rectangular laminas, so by symmetry, the y- and z-coordinates of their COMs are:

$y_P = y_R = y_S = 2.5, y_Q = 0$
$z_P = z_Q = z_R = 10, z_S = 20$ *[1 mark]*

Now use the formula to find the y-coordinate:

$\Sigma my = \overline{y}\Sigma m$

$m_P y_P + m_Q y_Q + m_R y_R + m_S y_S = \overline{y}(m_P + m_Q + m_R + m_S)$

$\Rightarrow (100 \times 2.5) + (300 \times 0) + (100 \times 2.5) + (75 \times 2.5)$

$= \overline{y}(100 + 300 + 100 + 75)$ *[1 mark]*

$\Rightarrow 687.5 = 575\overline{y} \Rightarrow \overline{y} = 1.196 = 1.20$ (3 s.f.) *[1 mark]*

Answers

Now to find the z-coordinate:

$\Sigma mz = \bar{z}\Sigma m$

$m_P z_P + m_Q z_Q + m_R z_R + m_S z_S = \bar{z}(m_P + m_Q + m_R + m_S)$

$\Rightarrow (100 \times 10) + (300 \times 10) + (100 \times 10) + (75 \times 20)$

$= \bar{z}(100 + 300 + 100 + 75)$ **[1 mark]**

$\Rightarrow 6500 = 575\bar{z} \Rightarrow \bar{z} = 11.30 = 11.3$ (3 s.f.) **[1 mark]**

So the COM of the shape has coordinates:
(7.5, 1.20, 11.3).

b) As the shape has a plane of symmetry at $x = 7.5$, you can ignore the x-axis and consider the shape 'side-on':

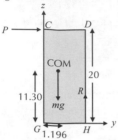

R is the reaction force of the ground on the shape, which acts along EH, as the shape is on the point of tipping about this line **[1 mark]**.

Taking moments about EH:

$0.5g \times (5 - 1.196) = P \times 20$ **[2 marks — 1 mark each for correct clockwise and anticlockwise moments]**

$\Rightarrow P = \dfrac{0.5 \times 9.8 \times (5 - 1.196)}{20} = 0.932$ N (3 s.f.).
[1 mark]

c) Again, consider the shape 'side-on':

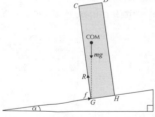

Here, f is the frictional force between the plane and the shape, and R is the reaction force between the plane and the shape, which acts through FG as the shape is about to topple about this line. **[1 mark]**

When the shape is about to topple about FG, its COM is directly above G, as shown.

You can use trig to find α:

$\tan \alpha = \dfrac{1.196}{11.30}$ **[1 mark]**

$\Rightarrow \alpha = 6.04°$ (3 s.f.) **[1 mark]**

Now consider the shape as it is about to slide down the slope:

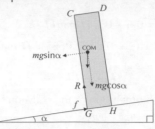

Resolving perpendicular to the plane, $R = mg\cos\alpha$ **[1 mark]**

Friction is limiting, so $f = \mu R$

Resolving parallel to the plane: $f = mg\sin\alpha$ **[1 mark]**

$\Rightarrow \mu R = mg\sin\alpha$ **[1 mark]**

$\mu mg\cos\alpha = mg\sin\alpha$

$\Rightarrow \mu = \tan\alpha$

The shape begins to slide when it is about to topple, so

$\mu = \dfrac{1.196}{11.30} = 0.106$ (3 s.f.) **[1 mark]**

Index

Index

Index

Index

Index

Index

Make sure you're not missing out on another superb CGP revision book that might just save your life...

...order your **free** catalogue today.

CGP customer service is second to none

We work very hard to despatch all orders the **same day** we receive them, and our success rate is currently 99.9%. We send all orders by **overnight courier** or **First Class** post.
If you ring us today you should get your catalogue or book tomorrow. Irresistible, surely?

- Phone: 0870 750 1252   (Mon-Fri, 8.30am to 5.30pm)
- Fax: 0870 750 1292
- e-mail: orders@cgpbooks.co.uk
- Post: CGP, Kirkby-in-Furness, Cumbria, LA17 7WZ
- Website: www.cgpbooks.co.uk

...or you can ask at any good bookshop.

MRMR61